PRAEGER LIBRARY OF U.S. GOVERNMENT
DEPARTMENTS AND AGENCIES

# The Alaska Railroad

PRAEGER LIBRARY OF U.S. GOVERNMENT DEPARTMENTS AND AGENCIES

*Consulting Editors*

ERNEST S. GRIFFITH

Former University Professor and Dean Emeritus, School of International Service, American University; former Director, Legislative Reference Service, Library of Congress; and author of *The American System of Government* and *The Modern Government in Action*

HUGH LANGDON ELSBREE

Former Chairman, Department of Political Science, Dartmouth College; former Managing Editor, *American Political Science Review;* former Director, Legislative Reference Service, Library of Congress

# The Alaska Railroad

Edwin M. Fitch

FOREWORD BY

Senator E. L. Bartlett

FREDERICK A. PRAEGER, *Publishers*
New York · Washington · London

To Paul and Evelyn Shelmerdine

FREDERICK A. PRAEGER, PUBLISHERS
111 Fourth Avenue, New York, N.Y. 10003, U.S.A.
77–79 Charlotte Street, London W.1, England

Published in the United States of America in 1967
by Frederick A. Praeger, Inc., Publishers



Library of Congress Catalog Card Number: 67–20477

Printed in the United States of America

# Foreword

The tracks extend from tidewater to 120 miles south of the Arctic Circle. They reach through great valleys and across passes leading to America's largest Far North community. They pass not far from Mt. McKinley, or, as the Indians called it, Denali, highest mountain on the North American continent. They were laid in the days when there was yet another frontier to conquer, and Americans were determined to conquer it. The frontier we know as Alaska still is not fully opened to man and his works; but if the pioneering spirit (and let us hope it still lives!) that took our forebears from the Atlantic to the Pacific and then north to what is now the forty-ninth state had not been part of the American dream, then Alaska would still be a lonely and remote and almost forbidden land.

However that may be, here is the story of The Alaska Railroad. It is a story that needed to be recorded both for its interest and so that a sure historical record would be preserved. In my opinion, no man is more qualified to do this than Edwin M. Fitch. His professional association with The Alaska Railroad has extended over a long period of time. In that capacity he has had a continuing, day-to-day involvement with this, the longest and most important government-owned-and-operated railroad under the United States flag. Further, every page of this book reveals evidence of scholarly research. Here is told in detail, and accurately, the account of the building and operation of a vital Alaska transportation artery—one that proved itself and paid for itself many times over during World War II. Since the summer day in 1923 when President Warren G. Harding drove the golden spike formally opening the railroad, it has been operated by professional railroad men and, throughout its life, has been free from political involvement.

Railroad buffs naturally will turn to Mr. Fitch's book as a valuable addition to the literature on this subject. More than that, the book has general appeal, relating as it does the epochal adventure that brought an Iron Trail into being in the distant North.

E. L. BARTLETT
*United States Senator*
*from Alaska*

nificance as a government agency. Its anecdotes tell of the adventurous men and women who helped build it, who ran it during the days of steam, and who have kept it running, despite snow, earthquake, and deficit, ever since. The author describes the opening up of the interior section known as the "Railbelt" and demonstrates the railroad's continuing importance to the state's prosperity. He also reviews the relationships of the railroad with Congress, with private business, and with the public and analyzes the unique management, labor, fiscal, and administrative problems of a government-owned railroad.

Of particular interest to railroaders and other specialists are the discussions of rates, piggybacking, containerization, palletizing, and grandfather clauses. But the book is far more general in its appeal—detailing the changes statehood has brought, and looking ahead to expansion and the problems of the future. For Dr. Fitch's book is the story of Alaska in the twentieth century as well as the story of a government operation, of value to all to whom Alaska and its career opportunities beckon.

THE AUTHOR: Edwin M. Fitch was educated at Oxford University, where he was a Rhodes Scholar, and at the University of Wisconsin. Dr. Fitch joined the U.S. Department of the Interior after serving as an executive in the transportation industry. Now Assistant to the General Manager of The Alaska Railroad, he has been concerned with the problems facing the railroad for more than two decades. He is the author of many articles in leading labor and transportation journals.

FREDERICK A. PRAEGER, *Publishers*
New York • Washington • London

t of an institution can
gnificance. He finds it
g out that the institu-
decipher its problems,
'he urge to translate a
appearances seems to
bject is the Industrial

have sought to avoid
alizations from small
and operated railroad
f the United States—
a footnote. How else
prise persistently con-
a century and produc-
noncollectivist struc-
n the student interpret
the members of the
Many of these private
n well, while not a few
r such circumstances,
ot offer any solutions
t and right, nor can it
transportation future.
ance of The Alaska

Railroad to Alaskans. There is significance here that I have tried to understand and describe. For an analysis of the railroad's economic role and organization relationships points to problems that are typical of many government activities of the kind that reach into the world of private business.

The manuscript of this book was read by several of my Alaska friends, one of whom came to work for the Alaskan Engineering Commission in 1919, and another, originally employed in the railroad's shops in Anchorage, who became its first home-grown general manager. For aid and counsel I am, therefore, particularly indebted to A. R. Sessions, retired from his position as assistant to the general manager in charge of the Seattle office, and John E. Manley, general manager, who has spent almost his entire working life with The Alaska Railroad. Senator E. L. ("Bob") Bartlett also took the time to read the entire manuscript, and was good enough to contribute a Foreword. I also owe thanks to Paul Shelmerdine, retired personnel officer, who shared with me many of the events described in Chapter VIII, and to M. W. Goding, born in Skagway, formerly with the Office of Territories of the Department of the Interior and more recently Trust Territories high commissioner. Additionally, my thanks extend to William Fravel of the Brotherhood of Railroad Trainmen, who read Chapter VIII, to Henry Whitehouse of the Interstate Commerce Commission, who read Chapter IX, and to Leland P. Draney, Alaska Railroad comptroller, who persuaded me to abandon some, though not all, of my accounting prejudices. Finally, I wish to express my appreciation to LeRoy Reeves for his knowledge and guardianship of Alaska Railroad files, which were an important part of my source material, and to my wife Charlotte, who added to her many other duties the labor of typing the manuscript.

EDWIN M. FITCH

*McLean, Virginia*
*April 1, 1967*

# Contents

# Charts



# Map



*A section of photographs follows page 84.*

# The Alaska Railroad

# I

# Introducing The Alaska Railroad

From 1923 to 1966, each newly appointed Secretary of the Interior was considerably astonished to find himself in charge of The Alaska Railroad—a 500-mile, standard-gauge railroad that operates from the warm-water ports of Seward and Whittier, on the south coast of the Kenai Peninsula, through Anchorage to Fairbanks, about 120 miles south of the Arctic Circle.

In October, 1966, the Eighty-ninth Congress, with encouragement from the President, established the Department of Transportation and added another member to the President's cabinet. Within the new department is the Federal Railroad Administration, headed by a federal railroad administrator, whose responsibilities as an operating railroad official relate almost solely to his control over The Alaska Railroad. His other duties—sponsoring high-speed passenger train experiments and promoting railroad safety—would place him on the edges of railroading rather than at its center. His supervision of The Alaska Railroad, however, makes him a bona fide railroader. He has a private car at his disposal during trips to Alaska, a profit and loss statement to disturb his sleep, and labor troubles to worry his waking hours.

Irrespective of which federal department has the duty of looking over the shoulders of its general manager, The Alaska Railroad has been a very unusual government agency. It represents a major concession to the prevailing opinion that there is little virtue in committing railroads to the rough-hewn hands of private enterprise. Yet the railroad's major boast is of its admiration for and adherence to the practices of the private railroads. In an economic climate in which various kinds of subsidies have become commonplace, The Alaska Railroad has received no congressional appropriations to meet operating expenses since 1939, and, except for the reconstruction period after the 1964 earthquake, none for capital improvement since 1956. Cash balances to the railroad's credit in the U.S. Treasury have often exceeded $10 million. Occasionally, the tabulation of its W-2 income tax forms has disclosed locomotive engineers and conductors earning more pay than all but five or six of its top officials.

A few of the surprises to federal appointees who find themselves responsible for the operation of a rail carrier have not always been pleasant. Within two years after Interior Secretary Hubert Work watched President Harding drive the golden spike at Nenana, in 1923, the secretary was urged to abandon the railroad as a disastrous financial failure. Nothing in the area between Seward and Fairbanks, insisted the critics, was worth developing. Serious labor troubles produced a strike during construction days, and there were acrimonious disputes over wages in the late 1940's and in the 1960's. Shippers have complained of excessive freight rates, and motor carriers have attacked the same rates as so unreasonably low as to constitute unfair government competition. The 1964 earthquake destroyed roadway, plant, and equipment worth, in replacement value, more than $27 million.

Particularly troublesome has been The Alaska Railroad's dual, not to say split, personality resulting from its intrusion into a field of economic activity normally reserved to private business. Even though the federal government has owned and operated the railroad for more than half a century, its officials tend to think of themselves as railroaders first and government employees second. They have a natural bias toward the kind of institutional thought that characterizes private railroads, from which most of them come. Federal agencies, on the other hand, including the Treasury, the General Accounting Office, and the Civil Service Commission, but excluding the Interstate Commerce Commission, must try to enforce on the reluctant railroad the rules and practices of the federal government. Federal and private policies are not always in opposition, but they clash often enough to produce frustration at railroad headquarters in Anchorage or exasperation in Washington, and sometimes both responses in both places. An important part of this book will be devoted to a consideration of these interesting aspects of the government's venture into railroading.

From a physical standpoint, The Alaska Railroad is not much different from railroads that operate through other parts of the United States. Its motive power is 100 per cent diesel, even though a large share of its income derives from the annual intrastate shipment of 750,000 tons of Alaska-mined coal. Its principal passenger trains are comparatively streamlined, and totally unprofitable. Its tariffs are as voluminous and as incomprehensible to laymen as the tariffs of any U.S. railroad of equal size. Many of its employees are represented by the same labor unions that speak for their occupational counterparts on private railroads. Wage and working rules are the result of collective bargaining, and settlements are usually modeled on those of the private railroads.

The Alaska Railroad is a single-track line without sufficient traffic to justify automatic block signals and centralized traffic control. It is a timetable, train-order railroad, yet modern telephone, radio, and teletype communications have supplanted Morse code. The chief dispatcher is in constant touch with road crews with respect to meeting points, change orders, and warnings of slides and washouts. Line-ups (typed records of the location and changes in location of scheduled trains, extra trains, work equipment, and motor cars) originate with the train dispatcher and are delivered at intervals around the clock to motor-car operators, station agents, and section foremen.

Rails run 115 pounds to the yard on the main line. The locally cut wooden ties of an earlier day have been largely replaced with ties pressure-treated with creosote. Ballast has been run of the pit, but in recent years crushed gravel or a dressing of crushed gravel has been used to stabilize more and more miles of track and roadway. The railroad places heavy emphasis on radio communication, and there is one fifty-mile stretch of microwave. Repair shops for locomotives, trucks, and off- and on-line line equipment are comparable to those on any railroad of equal size. (Several of The Alaska Railroad's imported general managers have regarded the railroad's repair facilities as superior to those of many of the smaller railroads in the United States.) As with other railroads, greater attention to mechanization, heavier motive power, longer trains, "piggy-backing," containerization, and automatic data processing has brought large increases in efficiency and corresponding declines in costs.

## The Truth About Winter

There are striking differences between The Alaska Railroad and railroads in the other states, which Alaskans designate as "outside" or "the lower forty-eight." There are, for example, the hard facts of railroading in Alaskan winters. The designation of the area south of Anchorage as the "banana belt" is obviously Mark Twain hyperbole. "Seward's ice box" is equally inappropriate. The southern end of the railroad is not a country of extreme cold. The mean January temperature in Seward is about 25° and in Anchorage 12°.* The average last

* Weather data is taken from the U.S. Weather Bureau's "Climatography of the United States No. 86–43—Alaska," and special supplements for Seward and Anchorage. Mean temperature and precipitation data are the "normal" averages based on the thirty years between 1931 and 1960. Where data for thirty years is not available, the quantities given are the means of the years of record. Total annual snowfall is for the years of record.

killing frost comes on May 18 in Seward and on May 25 in Anchorage. The average first killing frost comes on September 27 in Seward and on September 12 in Anchorage. Winters in Anchorage are no more severe than in Minneapolis, and temperatures in January and February in Anchorage have been higher than those in Washington, D.C., on the same day. The author of these lines, on his first February trip to Alaska, left Washington in 12° above zero, left Minneapolis in 10° below zero, and was somewhat shocked to arrive in Anchorage in 40° above zero with the sun shining and melting snow dripping from every roof.

The waters of the Pacific Ocean and the seas to the north warm the coastline of Alaska from Ketchikan to Barrow. Additionally the Japan Current System has a further moderating influence that extends from the Aleutian Islands south. That is why southeastern Alaska, sometimes called the Panhandle, has about the same average temperature as Baltimore and Philadelphia and why Seward and Whittier are ice-free ports. Finding severe cold in Alaska is often a matter of going inland rather than north. Fairbanks, the northern terminus of The Alaska Railroad, is much colder in winter and much warmer in summer than Anchorage. Point Barrow, on the Arctic Ocean, is not nearly so cold as Fairbanks in winter. On the other hand, summer can bring freezing weather to Point Barrow and temperatures between 75° and 90° to Fairbanks.

There are periods of intense cold during Fairbanks winters when the temperature may fall to 60° degrees below zero or more. Such bitter cold usually lasts only a few days or even a few hours at a time. While it lasts, diesel fuel can solidify and can be carved like a loaf of bread. A cigar smoker may find the tip of his cigar frost-hard if he waits too long between puffs. During long winter nights, tires may freeze against road or pavement, and the resulting flat spots jolt the driver on his morning trip until friction thaws the tires. Parking ramps on the hilltop front of the campus of the University of Alaska have electrical connections so that head-bolt heaters may keep turned-off motors warm. Head-bolt heaters are also standard operating equipment in most Anchorage homes.

Snow adds difficulties to railroading, yet snow and cold by themselves present no greater problem in the Alaska "Railbelt" than in the mountain areas of other northern states. Except for a narrow strip along the coast, Alaska is a land of somewhat meager precipitation. Anchorage has only about 15 inches of rain (including snow equivalent) per year, and Fairbanks has only 11. By an interesting paradox of weather, the farther north the less snow. Point Barrow, on the Arctic Ocean, has only about 4 inches of rain or snow equivalent annually and would be on the edge of a vast desert if it were located in a temperate or tropical latitude.

Precipitation in the narrow strip between the coastal mountains and the sea makes up for the comparative dryness of the interior. The Kenai Peninsula port town of Seward has about 67 inches of precipitation per year—a moderate amount compared to the Panhandle's Ketchikan, with 154 inches, or Whittier, the other ocean port, with more than 166 inches. At Whittier, the railroad pierces the coastal mountains through two long tunnels. Through the tunnels it is only 12 miles to Portage, where annual precipitation is less than 15 inches.

A great deal of Alaska's coastal precipitation in the Railbelt area descends in the form of snow. Snowfall in Seward averages 6 to 7 feet per year, in Whittier 25 feet, at McKinley Park Station 6 feet, and at Fairbanks 5 feet. In some winters, the mountain scenery from Seward to Portage is cut off by trackside snow banks higher than the cars. Fifteen-foot depths of snow in the Kenai Mountains make large spruce trees look like saplings, and snow tunnels, sloping downward, must be dug to reach the railroad's section houses. Snow in these quantities may be white, fluffy, and beautiful to those whose jobs do not require them to battle against it, but to railroaders, particularly train crews and section laborers, it means frozen switches, glaciered track, avalanches, reduced diesel tractive power, and a monotonous succession of reports about why trains are delayed.

Strangers often express surprise that The Alaska Railroad operates at all in the winter. Operations are not easy, but while snow and ice can slow down freight and passenger trains, they cannot stop them except for temporary periods. Flatcars rumble through snow cuts carrying truck trailers whose corporate owners are wryly pleased that The Alaska Railroad can make it when the trucks cannot. In fairness to the motor carriers, however, it should be said that The Alaska Railroad sometimes gets their winter business, not because trucks are unable to plow through snowy highways, but because it is cheaper to let the railroad "piggyback" the trucks.

### Wrong-way Moose

Alaska winters arouse sharply opposing viewpoints in railroaders and hunters about the value of moose. Unfortunately for railroad-employee appreciation of wildlife, moose are often worse hazards than the snow. Moose hate deep snow as much as train crews and section men hate moose. The plowed-out, snow-banked tracks make ideal moose trails. The huge animals, weighing up to 1,400 pounds, travel the hard-packed path between the rails in large numbers in January, February, and early March as they search for browse of alder, willow, and birch. In daylight, the moose, frightened by approaching trains, try to escape by jumping into the banks. If they sink in snow that is belly-deep, they will often leap back directly in front of the oncoming locomotive. A dead and mangled moose is almost certainly the result. Night kills are more numerous than day kills, partly because winter nights last sixteen to eighteen hours and partly because moose seem to be dazzled by locomotive headlights and may make no effort to escape. On the northern end of the railroad, where snowfall is lighter, there is less temptation for the moose to travel the tracks, and fatalities are less numerous. In summer, moose usually stay off the right of way, and there are relatively few kills. Almost daily in the summer, however, to the great delight of tourists, moose can be seen from the windows of the Anchorage-Fairbanks passenger trains. Conductors and brakemen, in spite of their hatred of moose, are quick to call passengers' attention to the bulls, cows, and calves that stay close enough to the tracks to be seen.

If Alaska Railroad employees had their way, moose would be banished from the Railbelt. They often make it impossible to maintain schedules in winter, and they are an utter nuisance to the section crews who, under the Alaska fish and wildlife regulations, are required to dress out salvageable meat and ship it to charitable and public institutions in Anchorage or Fairbanks. (The total may exceed 60,000 pounds annually.) Moose are a danger to life and limb for the occupants of the rail cars used on the railroad. Collision with a moose can wreck a train, and has done so. Once, at Houston (milepost 175) a pregnant moose walked onto the track from behind a freight shed just as a passenger train came by. The moose was hurled against a switch stand with such force that the stand was torn from the ties and the switch thrown. The front trucks of the first of the two locomotives stayed on the main line, but the rear trucks were diverted to the tracks of an abandoned siding. The result was the derailment of both locomotives, two baggage cars, and several coaches. Fortunately, there were only minor injuries to crew and passengers. It was 45° below zero at the time of the accident. No moose can ever again wreck an Alaska Railroad train in exactly this fashion: Special locks have been placed on all siding switches so that a switch stand, knocked from its base, cannot cause the switch to be thrown.

Because people tend to show more sympathy for moose

than for locomotives or even other people, Alaska Railroad officials dislike to discuss the number of moose killed annually. They remember with chagrin the outcry raised by the efforts of a freight-train crew to save the life of a particularly stubborn moose. The train was traveling at slow speed in daylight when the moose was sighted. The engineer slowed down still more in order to avoid the otherwise inevitable fatality. Since the moose could then keep ahead of the train, he refused to jump into the high snow banks on either side of the track. He continued to run until, completely exhausted, he lay down in front of the slowly approaching locomotive. The train was stopped, and the crew attempted to induce the moose to retreat to safety. When all efforts failed, someone thought of the fusees in the locomotive cab. (Fusees are powder flares that are ignited some distance before and behind a train making an unscheduled stop to protect against the possibility of collision.) A fusee was lighted, and the recalcitrant moose was singed sufficiently to make a successful exit. Warmly encouraged, the big animal leaped to his feet and jumped from the tracks, and the railroad's moose kill for that year was reduced by one. Somehow, this story made the newspapers. The result was a wave of criticism of the train crew for its lack of humanity in scorching the moose. There was no praise for the crew's ingenuity in saving the life of a moose so that a hunter could subsequently dispatch him with less public criticism.

A moose story of a different kind concerns a locomotive engineer noted up and down the railroad for the strength of his vocal chords and for his willingness to use them. Snow had fallen so heavily that removal required the railroad's huge rotary plow, which, with the bull-voiced engineer at the controls, rolled slowly toward a section house at Broad Pass. The whirling blades ate into masses of white flakes and threw them in long graceful arcs a hundred feet to each side of the tracks. The locomotive and the plow came to a stop at the section house, and the engineer called for the section foreman in decibels that could be heard for half a mile in all directions. The foreman appeared and was gruffly ordered to round up his men. Bewildered but intimidated, he did so and reported every man in his section gang present and accounted for. "Nobody missing?" roared the engineer, with a rising inflection that would indicate doubt. "Nobody," responded the section foreman. "Okay, then," said the Bull of the Woods, "I guess we hit a moose."

For the sake of accuracy, it must be recorded that moose kills by collision with Alaska Railroad trains have been estimated at as high as 500 in particularly bad years and, until a highway paralleling the railroad was built, rarely fell below 300. The railroad and the U.S. Fish and Wildlife Service have spent a good deal of time and money in an effort to solve the moose problem. Slowing down the trains or limiting them to daylight hours would certainly save the lives of a large number. But such procedure would add to the cost and greatly decrease the efficiency of rail operations. Since areas of highest kill are those rich in moose browse, attempts have been made to bulldoze trails as alternate routes to feeding grounds. Winter feed lots away from the railroad tracks have also been maintained. For a short time, airplanes were used in an attempt to frighten moose away from approaching trains. This experiment was a failure, both moose-wise and money-wise. The building of the highway paralleling the railroad from Anchorage to Fairbanks made the first appreciable reduction in the railroad's moose problem. The highway proved an even more attractive trail for moose than the railroad tracks. The result has been a drop in the railroad's kill of moose to less than 100 annually, but as the hazard has been decreased for the railroad, it has increased for motorists.

It is probable that the railroad's moose problem can never be eliminated, but only minimized. As long as nature provides Alaska Railroad tourists with the excitement of seeing moose from passenger-car windows, some moose must pay with their lives for choosing to live along a railroad right of way.

### Summertime Alaska

Strangers to Alaska are likely to be just as wrong about summer in the forty-ninth state as they are about winter. They are astonished at the mild temperatures that are characteristic of Fairbanks when the days are eighteen to twenty hours long. They find it hard to believe that Alaskans swim in Lake Spenard, near Anchorage; in Wasilla Lake, Nancy Lake, and Big Lake, on the edges of the Matanuska Valley; and in Harding Lake, near Fairbanks. They are surprised at the almost tropical exuberance of Alaska's summer vegetation. The grass on mountain slopes near Palmer, in the Matanuska Valley, grows taller than a man's head. The woods, almost anywhere in the Railbelt, are so thick with decayed plant material and forest undergrowth that travel over anything else but animal trails and gravel bars is extremely difficult. In the rain forests of the coastal areas, walking is almost impossible away from the trails.

Flowers, both wild and cultivated, are spectacular features of Alaska's summer scenery. Mountain meadows of the Kenai Peninsula are carpeted with blossoms of so many different kinds that the amateur can identify but a few of them. In midsummer, mountain shoulders and burned-over forest areas gleam with acres of magenta red fireweed. Sometimes, the scars of recent fires are covered with the dazzling dark blue of lupines. Many of the cultivated flowers in the gardens of Anchorage are of a size and quality difficult, perhaps impossible, to duplicate in warmer climates. They prefer a moist, cool climate and cannot thrive in temperatures above 80° or 90°.

Summer in Alaska is not only a season of flowers, it is also a time when long days permit baseball in the evenings without lights, when almost every kind of business enterprise shows bustling activity, and when The Alaska Railroad reaches peak performance in tonnage handled and maintenance accomplished as it balances out the slow months of winter. Summer is a good time to get acquainted with the railroad and the Railbelt—and a trip from Seward to Fairbanks in the cab of a diesel is the best way to make the acquaintance really count.

## From the Cab of a Locomotive

Skies are gray and rain threatens as we board the forward diesel of a freight train at a station point that is not, as might be expected, near milepost 0. The trip begins at milepost 2.9, located in the yards near the new dock and warehouse constructed after the 1964 earthquake. The old rail-water terminal located at milepost 0 was nearly 3 miles down the bay, but a post-earthquake ocean depth of more than 125 feet made the building of a replacement dock impossible. The beginning point of the railroad will remain milepost 2.9. As a result of the rebuilding program of the 1950's and the earthquake of 1964, most of the original milepost designations are wrong. They will not be changed, however, because a new survey would be tedious and costly and because the required changes in thousands of milepost references in records and documents would take many months to accomplish. For identification purposes, the slightly inaccurate milepost references serve just as well.

Our freight train has a much different complement when compared with the freight trains of fifteen years ago. Boxcars no longer predominate. Most of the cars are flats and are loaded with containers, piggyback truck trailers, or automobiles. The Alaska Steamship Company vessels that call at the port of Seward have been modified to accommodate this kind of traffic. Loose-stow cargo at Seward, except for cargo that cannot be loaded in containers or truck trailers or that cannot be palletized (made secure to a platform, often of wood, so that many items may be contained in a single load), is almost a thing of the past. Very little cargo is winched in sling loads from the holds of freighters, transferred to fork-lift trucks by thirteen-man longshore gangs, unloaded again to warehouse floors, and finally reloaded to freight cars or trucks for delivery to consignees. The efficiency of longshore operations and the hourly wages of longshoremen have been substantially increased because of the decline in this kind of freight handling.

During the night, containers and truck trailers have been craned directly from ship to waiting flatcars. Direct unloading is not always possible, however, and other cars, including boxcars and an occasional tank car, must be added to the newly loaded flatcars. Yard crews, working under the direction of a yardmaster and operating small diesels, have assembled these cars into a train. A crew caller has notified the four-man crew—engineer, conductor, and two brakemen—to report half an hour before departure time. We will ride the vacant seat of the no-longer-needed fireman.

The train dispatcher has given the crew written orders as to the time of departure, "meets" (meeting points), stops, and the location of work trains and equipment. At Portage, sixty-two miles up the line, there will be a meet with a southbound freight carrying mostly empties. Also at Portage there will be added a cut of loaded boxcars that have come through the tunnels from the port of Whittier and that have reached Whittier via train ship and car barge from Seattle and from New Westminster and Prince Rupert in British Columbia. Car-ferry operations have closed a gap between The Alaska Railroad and railroads in the other states that, were it to be closed by an overland route, would require nearly 1,500 miles of new track.

Our fifty-car freight train departs in a heavy drizzle. When skies are cloud-free at Seward, the sun shines on one of the most beautiful and largest harbors in the world. Here is a harbor that probably could accommodate all the navies of the world at the same time. The mountains on the horizon are the Kenai Mountains, high enough in this latitude to support many glaciers, yet their lower slopes are forested with spruce, birch, alder, and willow. Glacier-sheathed valleys and snow-capped mountains contrast with the dark foliage of spruce to make the snow and ice seem whiter and the woods more vividly green. The ocean waters of the huge harbor sparkle with the sky's reflected blue. In sunshine, Seward is an entrancing sample of the magnificent scenery that, changing with each mile, is one of the most noteworthy features of The Alaska Railroad. Many railroad employees feel a strong bond of sympathy with the engineer whose last wish was that his ashes be scattered from the cab of a locomotive over the part of the railroad right of way that he had loved best.

The diesels, all controlled from the lead engine, now climb 694 feet in 12 miles to Divide, at the first crossing of the Kenai Mountains. From this point, streams flow south to Resurrection Bay and north to Kenai Lake. Gray with the silt of glaciers, Kenai Lake comes into view shortly after milepost 18. We follow the shoreline to milepost 23.3, where a few log structures share the lakeshore with the railroad. This is Lawing, one of the many almost uninhabited spots that, to the uninitiated, appear as towns on strip maps of the railroad. Some of these named locations contain no more than a section house, and even some of the section houses have been abandoned, victims of technological changes that have enabled fewer section men to maintain track and roadway over longer divisions. Lawing, however, is of special interest because it commemorates a picturesque part of Alaska Railroad history that no longer has much reality except in the memories of the pioneers.

*Alaska Nellie's Lawing*

Lawing was named for her handsome husband by Nellie Neal Lawing, who was known to thousands of Alaska railroaders as "Alaska Nellie." Her death, on May 10, 1956, marked the end of an era, for growth and progress have made it almost impossible for the Railbelt to produce again the kind of authentic character that Alaska Nellie most certainly was.

Alaska Nellie was a cook during the days when the Alaskan Engineering Commission supervised the construction of The Alaska Railroad. Under contract to the Commission, she provided meals and quarters for travelers and railroad construction crews. She mushed a first-class dog team and was a crack shot. In picturesque speech, she was the equal of a good many early-day Alaskan males. Among her friends at her first Thanksgiving in Alaska—the year was 1915 and the place was Seward—were Pioneer Smith, Post-hole Pete, Malemute Kid, Wild Bill, Snaggletooth Miller, and Tin Can George. The menu included moose, mountain sheep, bear, wine, whisky, and champagne. Fifty years later there might still be an occasional nickname like "Flicker Red" in Seward, but little possibility of compiling a guest list even remotely resembling the one that included Alaska Nellie in 1915.

Alaska Nellie's last contract with the railroad covered the maintenance of meal and sleeping facilities at Curry, milepost 248.5, then known as Dead Horse Hill. When the original construction period ended in 1923 and an attractive government hotel replaced the pioneer camp at Curry, Alaska Nellie purchased a cabin at what was then called Roosevelt on Kenai Lake and made it her home. In September of that year, she married Billie Lawing of Seattle after a romance that, for more than a year, was conducted entirely by correspondence. Alaska Nellie and her husband maintained a lodge and trophy museum at Lawing, which she continued to keep open after her husband's death in 1935. During the years when passenger steamers took the inside passage to southeastern Alaska and then crossed the Gulf of Alaska to Seward, boat trains were special features of Alaska Railroad schedules. They always stopped at Lawing, and hundreds of tourists visited Alaska Nellie's wildlife museum. When encouraged, Nellie would tell and retell to guests at her lodge the story of her hair-raising escape from a ferocious brown bear; the skin of the big bear hung in her museum as proof of her prowess with a high-powered rifle. She liked to recall the time in 1923 that she was introduced to President Harding and his wife when the late President and his party stayed overnight at Dead Horse Hill.

After 1935, Alaska Nellie lived alone at Lawing entertaining guests at her lodge who arrived by train. When the passenger boats and the boat trains stopped running, the new Seward-Anchorage highway provided automobile access to Lawing. Alaska Nellie's autobiography became a best-seller with Alaskans and Alaska tourists. In 1956, just a few months before her death, an "Alaska Nellie Week" was held in Anchorage, and railroad officials, city officials, and Railbelt citizens vied to do honor to one of the most remarkable women who ever worked for The Alaska Railroad.

From Lawing, we head for Moose Pass, milepost 29.3. Here the highway, which has crossed and recrossed the railroad all the way from Seward, diverges to a separate valley but will again parallel the tracks at Portage. Not far beyond Moose Pass, the railroad meets the highway that leads to the Kenai oil fields and the peninsula towns of Kenai and Homer. The area of the first oil strike in Alaska is in the Kenai Moose Range and, although conservationists were at first fearful, moose and oil seem to have interfered little with each other. During the post-earthquake period, Moose Pass was an important transfer point for freight to the oil fields that arrived via Whittier.

Beyond Moose Pass at milepost 45 is Grandview, another station named by Alaska Nellie, where she once served meals to employees of the Alaskan Engineering Commission at 50 cents each and provided bed and bedding at $1 a night. Grandview, at an altitude of 1,060 feet, is the highest point reached by the railroad in crossing the Kenai Mountains.

*Grandview to Portage*

The route to Grandview summit and through the canyon and tunnel area to Bartlett and Spencer glaciers includes about ten miles of the railroad's most remarkable scenery. It is also dangerous country, where snow slides threaten in winter and even summer has its hazards. It was in this area that three rail-motor cars, each with a contingent of VIP's, were headed through a tunnel and across a high trestle with a dark and beautiful canyon to the left. On gaining the trestle, the operator of the lead car saw two large dogs immediately ahead. He stopped the car short, narrowly avoiding the dogs and preventing a possible derailment. The operator of the second car, a high railroad official, was pointing out the scenic features of the canyon rather than looking ahead. There was a rear-end collision, or rather two rear-end collisions, for the third car was also unable to stop. Miraculously, there were no derailments, only badly shaken operators and VIP passengers who were more interested in getting to safe ground beyond the trestle than in continuing to contemplate nature's wonders.

At another time, a freight powered by six diesels was heading south on a downgrade from Grandview in winter. Too late the engineer saw the huge slide that had thundered across the tracks at milepost 43 just moments before. The weight of the train behind the diesels derailed five of them as they hit the slide. One of the locomotives was tossed so far from the track that a 150-foot spur had to be built to get it back on the rails again. The property damage was extensive, but no one was injured in the derailment.

In another winter, there was an even more spectacular slide

between Spencer and Bartlett glaciers, at milepost 49.3. A snow fleet was stopped on a high trestle when the huge slide crashed down. The snow, ice, and debris hit the train and trestle with such force that the big rotary plow, two locomotives, two cabooses, and a mass of broken bridge timbers were hurled into the canyon. No one was hurt because the crew were eating breakfast in the buffet car of the passenger train they were assisting and were thus beyond the reach of the slide.

The loop district, or rather the former loop district, at milepost 51, was once regarded as both an engineering and a scenic marvel. Here the track, in its descent from Grandview to near sea level at Portage Flats, went through snowsheds and across wooden trestles and at one point made a complete circle on itself. The wooden trestle supporting the upper track of the loop was nearly 100 feet high. The maintenance of these wooden trestles became increasingly costly and their use increasingly dangerous. In 1951, a new location on a slightly steeper grade (3 per cent against southbound traffic) bypassed the rotting trestles of the loop altogether. The new grade curved close to the base of the snubbed and muddy nose of the Bartlett Glacier. The relocation was completed over ground that 30 years earlier had been covered with 75 to 100 feet of ice. The Bartlett Glacier had retreated nearly 1 mile in 30 years, exposing a hillside that permitted a track location that would have been impossible when the right of way was first laid out.

Past Spencer Glacier, at milepost 52.7, the train descends by easier grades 11 miles to Portage, at the head of Turnagain Arm. We watch for moose along the Portage flats, for they are often seen here in summer. As we round a slight curve, we are rewarded by the sight of three, bounding ahead between the rails and apparently afraid to jump the water-filled ditch at either side. The lead moose is a cow and, without too many seconds to spare, she leaps the ditch, followed closely by her two companions. We suddenly realize that we are watching a mother moose and two calves, each almost as large as she, but still following obediently in her footsteps.

At Portage we move to a siding to wait for a passing train and to add on a cut of cars from Whittier. Portage is hardly more than the ghost of a town after the wreckage caused by the 1964 earthquake. The railroad station was totally destroyed and will not be rebuilt. Subsidence of the land five or six feet has exposed the townsite to floods at high tide, and adequate protection would probably cost more than the land is worth. Several of the buildings that were not destroyed by the earthquake have been moved away. Railroad trackage has been raised out of reach of floodwaters, for Portage is still an important junction between the main line and the 12.4-mile cutoff to the port of Whittier.

Because of the heavy traffic it carries, the track and roadway to Whittier have been built to main-line standards. Two tunnels, one of them at 13,890 feet and among the longest railroad tunnels in the United States, carry the single track through the coastal mountains to Passage Canal, where the port town of Whittier clings to the narrow shelf of land between a glacier-covered mountain and the sea. The port facilities belong to and are operated by The Alaska Railroad. Whittier ceased to be an Army port in 1960, and federal and state officials have had no success in finding a reasonable use for the expensive military facilities, which, still standing after the earthquake, look as unreasonable in Whittier as a glacier would in Central Park.

As a seatrain and car-ferry port, however, Whittier has been an immense success. Since 1962, it has developed a lively trade based on the shipment of goods in carload lots from manufacturing and farming centers in the other states. As a result, boxcars, flatcars, tank cars, refrigerator cars, and automobile carriers bearing the marks of many U.S. railroads are now commonplace in towns of the Alaska Railbelt.

Back in Portage, our freight train now includes carloads of

steel pipe from McKeesport, Pennsylvania, house trailers from Ironwood, Michigan, beer from Milwaukee, Wisconsin, lumber from Prince George, British Columbia, bombs from Wolf Creek, Tennessee, and a refrigerator car of dressed chickens from Dardanelle, Arkansas. With 5 diesels and nearly 100 cars, we begin the 50 sea-level miles along Turnagain Arm to Anchorage.

### *Turnagain Arm to Anchorage*

The railroad and highway are parallel for most of the 50 miles between Portage and Anchorage. They occasionally cross each other, sometimes occupying a rock ledge blasted into the slopes of the Chugach Mountains, sometimes on grades raised high above the mud and water of tidal flats. To the left, the view takes in Turnagain Arm and the forests and glaciers of the Kenai Mountains. To the right are the Chugach Mountains, often ascending sharply from the track. Many streams cut through them to the sea, disclosing long glimpses of mountain slopes, green below but rocky and forbidding above, ending frequently in glaciers at the far end of steep valleys.

Six miles beyond Portage is Kern Creek, notable only as a reminder of the origin of The Alaska Railroad. Kern Creek marks the end of steel for a railroad that began, in a flurry of private promotion, at Seward in 1903 as the Alaska Central Railway. The fledgling railroad, reorganized in 1910, after bankruptcy in 1908, as the Alaska Northern Railway, was purchased by the federal government in 1915 for about $16,000 a mile.

Four miles beyond Kern Creek is Girdwood, which marks the entrance to Alyeska, a ski resort that has come into international prominence. U.S. National Ski Championship races were held there in 1963. A short mountain road and a long ski lift take ski enthusiasts and tourists to one of the most spectacular mountain recreation areas in Alaska.

At milepost 100, Turnagain Arm broadens to a width of 15 miles before joining with Cook Inlet. The railroad's headquarters at Anchorage are but 14 miles away. We pass Potter Hill on nearly 2 miles of new track, new because the old track tumbled into the ocean in a series of monstrous slides during the 1964 earthquake. Much of the previous 40 miles of railroad is also new because earthquake-caused land subsidence required a grade raise averaging more than 5 feet to keep the track out of reach of high tides.

Beyond Potter Hill, we leave the inlet shoreline and approach the suburbs, which have extended many miles from the center of the city since the mid-1930's, when the population of Anchorage was about 3,500. We pass a steel and concrete building at the head of Ship Creek valley that houses the headquarters of The Alaska Railroad and its Anchorage station. We stop in the yards along the creek where, in 1915, there was no railroad and no Anchorage but only a tent city of railroad construction workers.

With the Air Force base at Elmendorf, the Army base at Fort Richardson, and the thousands of citizens who live outside the city limits, Anchorage has a metropolitan area of more than 100,000 people. But it was born as a government railroad town, and it is interesting to speculate what the city would have been like if President Wilson had not chosen the present railroad route in 1915. He might have selected instead the route from Cordova to Fairbanks that began with the Copper River and Northwestern Railroad, then busily engaged in carrying copper ore over its 195 miles from Kennicott to Cordova. In that event, Elmendorf and Fort Richardson would have been located elsewhere, and Anchorage would probably have been little more than a small fishing village noted more for its high tides than for its enterprise.

We will leave our freight train in Anchorage, where yard crews will separate the cars that must be spotted on Anchorage sidings from those that will be made up into a new train for Fairbanks. We will ride through the rest of the Railbelt in the railroad's streamlined passenger train, the AuRoRa, which makes the twelve-hour run between Alaska's two largest cities each day during the summer season.

### *The AuRoRa to Fairbanks*

Three diesels will take the AuRoRa to Fairbanks. The name "AuRoRa" was adopted as a result of a contest sponsored by the traffic department of the railroad. The name that won seemed pleasant, and not so literary or poetic as to be unacceptable. One indignant young lady felt otherwise. She was certain that the name she had submitted had failed to receive the thoughtful consideration it truly deserved, and a good many Alaskans agreed with her. The name that seemed to her worthy of first prize was the "Moosegooser."

We board the cab of the AuRoRa's lead diesel at 8:45 A.M. for a 9:00 departure. Three seats are available, the right for the engineer, the left for the fireman (firemen have not been banished from passenger trains), and the middle seat for the head brakeman (but only when locomotives are hauling freight). The head brakeman does not ride the middle seat on passenger locomotives but assists the conductor back among the passengers.

The AuRoRa is dressed up in the railroad's colors of blue and gold. Coaches have wide picture windows to bring scenery inside as much as possible. A dining and lounge car, operated by a private concessionaire, does a thriving business. Prices are Alaskan, that is, on the high side. To make passenger trains pay, some are operated as mixed trains. The AuRoRa is a mixed train; it is pulling a dozen flatcars, each with two thirty-five-foot containers of freight consigned to Fairbanks businessmen.

We move out across Ship Creek and through the Anchorage yards. A short distance out of Anchorage we pass Elmendorf Air Force Base on our left and Fort Richardson on our right. The railroad now follows the south shore of Knik Arm, which, like Turnagain Arm, is a narrow offshoot of Cook Inlet. We are traveling toward the Matanuska Valley.

At milepost 126.6, the railroad crosses the Eagle River. On a clear day, it is possible to see the peak of Mt. McKinley, 135 miles to the north, from the highlands near the river. In spite of the attention brought to Alaska by statehood, many Americans do not know that, at 20,320 feet Mt. McKinley, or Denali, as the Indians called it, is the highest mountain in North America. For the next 120 miles, the mountain will loom larger and larger provided the weather cooperates and the summer sun is reflected on its icy summit. There are times, however, when the weather can only be described as perverse, when tourists who have waited a week or two to see this most magnificent of mountains have returned home disappointed.

A bridge over a small stream at milepost 138.7 is a reminder of one of the most tragic accidents that ever occurred on The Alaska Railroad. In the spring of 1959, the operator of a rail-motor car brought a repair crew to this bridge. After unloading the work gang, he was instructed by his foreman to drive the car backward toward a siding at Eklutna, at milepost 141.2. Coming toward the bridge was a tie tamper—a possibility of which the motor-car operator had been warned. For reasons that are still in dispute, the tie tamper and the motor car collided, though at such low speed that the motor-car operator was able to jump from his vehicle without serious injury. But the impact reversed the motor-car's gears, disengaged the brake, and opened the accelerator. The motor car rolled back from the tie tamper and rapidly gained speed, even though it was ascending a long hill that marked the approach to the bridge. The noise of its grinding wheels was drowned out by an air compressor, while a curve on the hill prevented the runaway car from being seen from the bridge. Three of the bridge crew were struck and killed instantly—men who, with even two or three seconds' warning, probably could have jumped to safety.

Back at milepost 117, an even stranger chain of events led to an accident in which cause and effect were separated, not by a few thousand feet but by more than forty miles. A motor truck, equipped with power take-off, was maneuvering near the railroad tracks at a point where they were paralleled by two pole lines, one carrying the railroad's telephone communications and the other electric power. Across the tracks from the truck was a cement silo. With winch and cable, the truck operator was attempting to remove the bucket chain from the silo. Either the chain or the cable snapped under tension, and the resulting whiplash wrapped the cable around the telephone and power lines. The contact caused a massive short circuit, which burned up telephone equipment at the railroad's headquarters in Anchorage and set telephones ringing at points many miles up the line. One railroad telephone was in an outfit car in a work train on a siding at milepost 159.8, nearly forty-three miles from the silo. A young railroad employee who happened to be passing through the car moved to the telephone to answer it and at the same time stepped on a metal plate on the floor. As he picked up the receiver, he was instantly electrocuted.

These stories have been told because they are extraordinary, not because they are typical of the day-to-day operation of the railroad. Yet truth requires the admission that there is sometimes tragedy as well as adventure about any form of transportation that involves power and moving vehicles.

For the 35 miles from Anchorage to Matanuska, milepost 150.7, the AuRoRa travels close to the shoreline of Knik Arm. On the right are Chugach Mountain peaks that seem to rise even higher than those that border Turnagain Arm. From Eagle River to Curry, a distance of nearly 125 miles, we are likely to see more moose than on any other stretch of the railroad.

### *Lake George and the Matanuska Valley*

At milepost 146.4, the AuRoRa crosses the Knik River at the head of the Matanuska Valley. The Knik, carrying a load of glacial silt, is fed from a large ice field on the north slopes of the Chugach Mountains, which also include a remarkable body of water called Lake George. There are in Alaska's mountains a few lakes formed as a result of glacial dams pressing hard and freezing tight against mountain shoulders. The melting waters of spring fill these lakes to great depths until a combination of built-up pressures and spring thaws releases their dammed-up waters. Lake George, which empties into the Knik River, is such a self-dumping lake. Its waters may reach a depth of 200 feet before spring warmth erodes the glaciated seal. The dam gives way suddenly as huge blocks of ice crash into a rapidly widening torrent. The water and ice may descend in such volume and force as to wash out a mile or two of track. Sometimes the Knik River bridge itself, which could not be replaced for less than $1 million, has been in danger. The break-up of Lake George occurs in late July or early August and has proved a bonanza to bush pilots who carry tourists to the glacier to watch the tumbling ice and churning waters. Fortunately for the railroad, the grinding of the glacier against the mountain over the years has weakened the seal and has greatly lengthened the time during which the lake empties. The excitement for the tourists has thus been lessened, but so has the danger to the tracks of The Alaska Railroad.

At milepost 150.7, at Matanuska, a branch of the railroad extends 6.5 miles to Palmer and 16 miles beyond Palmer to Jonesville and the strip mines of the Matanuska Valley. Because oil has supplanted coal for domestic heating and because the railroad has long since abandoned the use of steam engines, Matanuska coal has been used almost 100 per cent by three power plants, two of them at the military posts near Anchorage. The Kenai oil strike was accompanied by the discovery of a huge gas field, and for several years a pipeline has been bringing the gas to consumers in Anchorage. If cost-benefit ratios continue to favor natural gas over Matanuska coal, the military power plants in the Anchorage area can be expected to convert their boilers to gas. The other plant (Chugach Electric) has already done so. The railroad thus stands to lose the revenue from hauling 300,000 tons of coal each year over the branch from Jonesville through Palmer and onto the main line at Matanuska.

The AuRoRa will bypass Palmer and most of the Matanuska Valley farms. Nevertheless, some of the farms can be seen from the train during the nine-mile ride from Matanuska to Wasilla. There are occasional herds of Holsteins grazing in long and narrow pastures that seem hemmed in on the far side by a thick forest of young hardwoods. The farms bear little resemblance to those of Iowa or Illinois or Wisconsin. There are few plowed fields, and the encroaching woods seem always on the verge of taking over. Where trees have been bulldozed into long windrows in virgin fields it is easy to understand that the cost of clearing is often greater than the land is worth. Still, most of the farms look prosperous and abandonment is rare.

At milepost 159.8, we stop for a few minutes at Wasilla, one of the few stations on the railroad other than Seward, Anchorage, and Fairbanks that is large enough to be called a town. It is a trading center for a recreational as well as a farming area. Wasilla Lake is close by, and Big Lake, with its hundreds of cottages belonging to the more prosperous citizens of Anchorage, is not far away.

From just beyond Lake Nancy, milepost 180.7, to Gold Creek, near milepost 264, the railroad is never far from the banks of the wide and meandering Susitna River. The first forty miles cross a region of streams which flow into the Susitna and which once provided some of the best fishing in Alaska.

Willow and Little Willow creeks, Caswell Creek, Goose Creek, Montana Creek, and others have introduced countless fishermen to the fighting qualities of rainbow trout and silver salmon. Not many years ago, the railroad's Saturday and Sunday passenger trains were known as "Fishermen's Specials." By arrangement with the conductor, passengers could stop off at any of these streams and, on flag signal, be picked up for the return trip in the evening.

But the fisherman population has grown too great for the fish population. A highway parallel to the railroad has increased the fishing pressure, and rainbow trout become a little smaller and a little rarer with each passing summer. Silver salmon still provide good sport for a few days of each season, but fishing at its best is a solitary pastime and loses most of its fascination when fishermen must compete elbow to elbow. Good fishing means getting away from the crowd and, along the railroad and the highways of the southern portion of the Railbelt, this has become increasingly difficult to do.

Talkeetna, milepost 226.7, is a trading center for a mining and trapping area. Both enterprises, for the time being at least, seem to be on the decline. With its unpaved streets, its appearance of construction halted before its buildings were entirely finished, and its old-time bars, Talkeetna is a not unattractive example of what Hollywood imagines Alaska to be. Just before entering Talkeetna, the AuRoRa stops on the banks of the Susitna so tourists can photograph a magnificent view of Mt. McKinley and its companion peaks, Mt. Foraker and Mt. Hunter.

There is a story of the founding of Talkeetna that the late Donald MacDonald took great delight in telling. One of the most knowledgeable, colorful, and opinionated of Alaska's transportation experts, MacDonald was the central figure in a tale of deception in the public interest. Land speculators had pre-empted parts of the Talkeetna area that were strategic for the railroad's right of way. A member of the Alaskan Engineering Commission, not yet empowered by delegation of authority to select the needed lands, despaired of his ability to control the situation. MacDonald volunteered to handle the speculators if the commissioner would delegate his authority (which was nonexistent) in all matters respecting Talkeetna lands. The commissioner agreed, and an imposing "official" notice to this effect was posted. Armed with only this notice and his supreme self-confidence, MacDonald surveyed a townsite skirting that land needed by the railroad. He then issued rules for the acquisition of Talkeetna land by private persons and announced a public auction of the surveyed lots. The land boomers pulled up their stakes en masse and loudly proclaimed their right to participate in the auction of the newly plotted land. Needless to say, their rights were readily admitted. In this fashion, the town of Talkeetna was laid out and the commission's interest in land essential to the railroad's construction program was protected until the acquisition could be legalized.

Curry, at milepost 248.5, was introduced earlier in this chapter as Dead Horse Hill. For more than twenty-five years after the Alaska Railroad was built, both freight and passenger trains made overnight stops at Curry. An attractive hotel was built to accommodate passengers and crews. As we pass through the town, we look in vain for the hotel and for other indications of a bustling railroad center, but all have vanished. Today, Curry could hardly qualify even as a ghost town. The hotel declined rapidly after it was leased to an operator who became completely discouraged at his inability to make it pay. It disappeared in a tragic fire that took the lives of three persons. With the trend to lengthened divisions, Curry ceased to be a division point and thus lost its only reason for existence. To avoid the distressing appearance of decay, the railroad sent bulldozing crews to Curry to remove every idle building, leaving the townsite a neat but vacant reminder of its once exciting past. Perhaps its earlier name, Dead Horse Hill, contained prophetic significance. At Curry the mountains of the Alaska Range are closing in fast, for at

Chulitna, twenty-five miles beyond, Mt. McKinley is only forty-six miles away.

Hurricane, at milepost 284.2, is a bridge over a deep gulch and not a station. But what a bridge! Its single span is a steel arc 384 feet long. There is a drop of 296 feet from the center of the bridge to the stream below. On the left, the Chulitna River bends off in the distance. The AuRoRa, crossing the canyon at 5 miles per hour, finds all but the most blasé of passengers close to its picture windows to gain the maximum view.

At Broad Pass, between mileposts 304.3 and 310, the railroad crosses the Alaska Range. The peak altitude at milepost 310 is 2,363 feet, making this the lowest rail pass in the Rocky Mountains. This claim has been disputed on the ground that the Alaska Range should not be regarded as part of the Rocky Mountains. The protest can be dismissed as quibbling, for there is no question that Broad Pass is the lowest railroad pass in the mightiest mountain chain in all of North America.

Cantwell, milepost 319.5, has an unusual history. For a period prior to World War II, the section gang at Cantwell was composed almost entirely of Indian women. Their skill grew as their fame spread, and the railway's general manager frequently boasted that the Cantwell section was the best maintained piece of track on the entire line. After a few years, separations depleted the gang, and it finally disappeared as men replaced the Amazons. For no particular reason, this kind of experiment—if experiment it was—has not been repeated.

## *On to McKinley Park and Fairbanks*

At milepost 347.9 is the McKinley Park Hotel, built for The Alaska Railroad in part by Interior's National Park Service in the days when railroad hotels in national parks were traditional traffic promotion. The hotel was completed by

Alaska Railroad forces after General Manager Ohlson, on an inspection trip with Secretary of the Interior Harold Ickes, convinced the secretary that the original plan was too modest and that the size of the hotel should be increased. It is a pleasant but undistinguished hotel that can be seen to the left as we come to a stop at McKinley Park Station. The location of the hotel is somewhat puzzling because it is impossible to see Mt. McKinley from anywhere in the hotel area. The view is completely cut off by a high mountain. Along the 90-mile road into the park, the first good view of Mt. McKinley is at Savage River, 12 miles in from the park station. There is a particularly magnificent view 60 miles in, and a close-up view at the Wonder Lake end of the road that defeats attempts at description.

While the hotel charges were high, costs were even higher. This problem, plus an extremely short season, made the McKinley Park Hotel a much worse financial failure than the railroad itself had ever been. Years later, the railroad cut its losses on the McKinley Park Hotel by giving it to the National Park Service. A succession of concessionaires have since tried its operation with a greater degree of success, and a bonanza in the form of a road into the park from the Richardson highway has given a considerable assist. The Alaska Railroad still brings many passengers to McKinley Park, but automobiles from Anchorage and Fairbanks bring still more. With the completion of the new Anchorage-Fairbanks highway, probably in 1968, the park will become even more accessible. These developments, plus tourist interest and Alaska's booming population growth, make the outlook for the Cinderella of Alaska's hotels distinctly hopeful. McKinley Park itself, covering nearly 2 million acres, is not only the home of North America's highest mountain, but its wilderness contains a more varied and abundant wildlife that can be seen from the road than any other of the nation's great national parks.

Shortly after leaving McKinley Park Station and the much

photographed Horseshoe Lake, the AuRoRa enters the canyon of the Nenana River. For most of the distance, the track twists and turns along a right of way that seems to cling precariously to the upper slopes of the canyon. The Nenana River, flowing northward, is a rush of white water tearing at the canyon walls far below. Now a tunnel carries us through a rock buttress, and from the cab of the locomotive as we emerge around a curve, we get the dizzying impression that the track has disappeared. Farther ahead is a stretch of track where the speed of the train must not exceed five miles per hour. We are on permafrost ground, where summer thaws cause the rail and ties to slide slowly toward the river. When they slide too far, the old right of way is abandoned and a new grade constructed above it. In several places, old and deserted roadways can be seen below the present track.

We leave the canyon after trying vainly to glimpse the Dall sheep that are supposed to appear frequently on the rock wall opposite. But today the mountain sheep are nowhere to be seen. Our lookout is partly rewarded, however, as we emerge from the canyon and two large gray animals, startled by the train, bolt sharply to the right. They are timber wolves, which, unlike moose, are occasionally seen from the engine cab but never from the passenger cars. Wolves are exceedingly wary and are gone before the coaches have a chance to catch up with them.

At milepost 358.1, we pause at the coal town of Healy, where a four-mile railroad spur crosses the Nenana River to reach subbituminous coal fields. The black seams of coal outcroppings in an opposite mountain wall can be seen from the car windows. Around Suntrana, at the end of the spur, strip mining is in progress to supply coal to a military power plant at Clear (milepost 394) and to private and military power plants at Fairbanks and Eielson Air Force Base. There are enormous reserves of low-grade coal in the Healy field, and coal seams in some portions of the field are 50 feet thick.

A mine-mouth power plant, completed at Suntrana, is reducing the tonnage of coal hauled over the railroad to Clear and Fairbanks. The Gubic gas field, 400 miles north of Fairbanks, would also be sharing in the Fairbanks fuel market except that the cost of the pipeline is too great to make the natural gas competitive.

Beyond Healy, the AuRoRa leaves the mountains of the Alaska Range behind and begins to travel one of the longest stretches of straight track between Seward and Fairbanks. Along this track and bordering the Nenana River is a dot on the map called Rex. There is little at Rex, however, except some interesting history. Before World War II, the site was called Kobe. In an excess of nationalistic silliness during the war, Kobe became Rex. There was a time when Rex might have been important in its own right instead of as a mere exercise in annoyance at the Emperor of Japan. Before the building of the Alaska Highway was completed, U.S. Army Engineers surveyed the Rocky Mountain Trench across British Columbia as the location for a railroad to connect with The Alaska Railroad. Rex was the chosen junction from which the railroad would have extended for 1,500 miles across the Yukon Territory and British Columbia to Prince George on the Canadian National Railway. When victories in the Pacific pointed to an early end of the war, the railroad proposal was abandoned. In spite of subsequent Congressional efforts to revive interest in a rail connection between the states and the then Territory of Alaska, Rex never achieved the prominence that might once have been its destiny.

At milepost 394, we pass the hush-hush military base at Clear that everyone in Alaska knows about. The Army Engineers moved the tracks of The Alaska Railroad three miles to the east to give the base more land on the banks of the Nenana River and to locate it out of sight of peering passengers. The new main line is nearly ten miles long and, with its dressing of crushed gravel, is one of the best-looking sections of track on the railroad.

At milepost 411.7, we pause at Nenana before crossing the Tanana River on a 701-foot single-span steel bridge. There is a long ascending approach to the bridge, since it must be high enough to enable riverboats to pass underneath, and the grade must align with the base of the mountain on the north side of the river. It was at the north end of this bridge that President Harding drove the golden spike in 1923. The President did rather better with the golden spike than with the steel one that was quickly substituted for it. He took one swing and missed, another swing and missed, but on the third try was successful and maul and spike made contact. Nenana is also noteworthy as the take-off point for riverboat traffic down the Tanana to Yukon River towns and military installations.

Beyond Nenana, the railroad crosses sixty miles of less exciting country, sometimes flat and sometimes margined by high rolling hills. Though we are less than 200 miles from the Arctic Circle, timber is still lush though small. If the woods are protected from fire, birch and cottonwood will reach saw-timber size.

Three miles northwest of Fairbanks—for the railroad overshoots the city and must return southeast to it—we pass a high plateau that furnishes an impressive site for the University of Alaska. College, at milepost 467.1, is the station for the university, which enrolls more than 1,800 students and is widely known for its specialization in the engineering, mining, and agricultural aspects of Alaskan life.

Our journey ends on the banks of Chena Slough* at Fairbanks, milepost 470.3. Anchorage, the headquarters city, and Fairbanks, the northern terminus, have long been rivals. Fairbanks, the older of the two, was a prosperous gold-mining town before Anchorage was even an idea in the minds of the federal promoters of the government railroad. Fairbanks is less than half the size of Anchorage but, more than Anchor-

* Slough in Alaska does not mean a muddy swamp, but a clear flowing creek where grayling will jump from the water to take flies at the right time of year.

age, can lay claim to being the "real Alaska"—the last frontier.

Fairbanks, too, has changed greatly from the days when placer gold mining with enormous dredges was its principal activity. With each passing year, gold becomes of less economic importance, and service industries, the Wainwright and Eielson military bases, the University of Alaska, aviation, trucking, and The Alaska Railroad assume greater and greater meaning for Fairbanks growth and enterprise. In the midst of all these changes, however, the sourdough touch remains.

Above the Arctic Circle, there is no darkness at night in high summer and no daylight in winter. Below the Arctic Circle at Fairbanks, the sun parades the sky for twenty-three hours on June 21, then dips briefly below the horizon just before 12:00 midnight and rises again about 1:00 A.M. These solar phenomena have produced a thriving aviation business about the time of the summer solstice, when, at an altitude of 3,000 feet above Fairbanks, daylight lasts twenty-four hours. By buying an airplane ticket, passengers from the AuRoRa can prove, if they wish, that at its northern terminus, The Alaska Railroad makes a close approach to the land of the midnight sun.

# II

# Steel Rails in a Northern Wilderness

From 1914, when Congress authorized the President to construct and operate a railroad in Alaska, to 1923, when the tracks met at Nenana, the U.S. government's railroad had no name. Locomotives, passenger cars, and boxcars were simply marked "U.S." Timetables were labeled "Department of the Interior, Alaskan Engineering Commission." In a Rand McNally "Guide to Alaska and Yukon" published in 1922, the commission invited one and all to "take a trip on the people's railroad" and called it the "Government Railroad." The guidebook paid its compliments to rail transportation by devoting nearly four pages to a discussion of Alaska dog teams and less than one page to the railroad and by reporting that "The dog team will always be a part, in fact, the greatest factor in transportation in the northern country."

The "Government Railroad" had its beginning as a private railroad, not as a federal enterprise. Construction was started after the heyday of railroad enthusiasm had passed in the United States but at a time when a dozen railroads were trying for a foothold in Alaska. To these early optimists a population of only 64,900 persons in 1900, of whom 30,000 were Indians, Aleuts, and Eskimos, was no deterrent. Had not railroads transformed the West in advance of population? They would accomplish a similar miracle for Alaska by giving its long-imprisoned wealth an outlet to the sea. In the meantime, while waiting for the miracle, they would provide access by which frenzied seekers after gold might reach their promised land.

Thus, as the new century began, railroad promoters and construction engineers hurried northward, the one group full of wild hopes calculated to turn the heads of potential investors, and the other challenged by the problems of thrusting steel rail through a mountainous wilderness. One party of adventurers reached Seward early in the summer of 1903. With this little group, the predecessor of The Alaska Railroad was born, the privately constructed Alaska Central Railway.

It was more than a coincidence that railroad interest in Alaska and in Canada's Yukon Territory began in 1897 and 1898. George Carmack's discovery of gold in 1896 on the Klondike River near Dawson had started a stampede to Canada—a stampede that included thousands of Americans. It was, therefore, inevitable that the inflamed curiosity about the North that followed the Klondike gold rush should cross over to Alaska. In 1899, a year after gold was discovered on the beaches of Nome, and in 1904, two years after Felix Pedro found gold near the site on the Chena Slough that became the city of Fairbanks, Alaska experienced gold rushes of its own.

During the two years of the Klondike fever, several pleas were made to Congress for franchises and rights of way for the construction of railroads in Alaska. While the individual requests were denied, Congress responded to the gold-inspired interest in the territory by passing the Act of May 14, 1898, which granted to railroad companies duly organized under law land for rights of way and terminals and timber and stone needed for construction. Joshua Bernhardt, who wrote the only book that has ever been published (1922) on the history of the Alaskan Engineering Commission, reported that as a result of the railroad act of 1898: "In the brief period between September, 1897, and March, 1899, no less than eleven companies made filings for railroad routes totalling about 673 miles."

The governor of Alaska stated in his annual report for the year 1901 that the major deterrent to the success of those early railroaders was their inability to attract homesteaders to a country in which it was both difficult and expensive to secure clear title to land. Congress resolved this problem with a homestead law that made it relatively easy for a pioneer to obtain a patent for 320 acres.

From 1898 to the panic year of 1907, plans for railroads proliferated throughout Alaska. Railroads were proposed from Cook Inlet to Nome, from Haines Mission to Nome, from Valdez to Eagle, from the Yukon to the Kuskokwim, and from the Porcupine and Peel rivers to Mackenzie Bay. One of the most grandiose projects was the Trans-Alaska, to be built from Iliamna Bay near the mouth of Cook Inlet to Holy Cross on the Yukon River. This railroad was proposed by a group of wealthy "free-lovers" who hoped to colonize that part of Alaska which the railroad would serve.

Among the railroads constructed and in operation for a time were three near Nome—the Council City and Solomon River Railroad, the Wild Goose Railway, and the Seward Peninsula Railroad. The last was a narrow-gauge line that, after its abandonment in 1907, was used by anyone who could attach flanged wheels to an automobile. The track and roadway were maintained for this purpose by the Federal Alaska Road Commission until shortly after World War II, when the rails were taken up.

Both the Alaska Home Railroad and the Valdez-Yukon Railroad Company proposed to build a line from Valdez, on the coast, to the northern gold fields. A few miles out of Valdez is Keystone Canyon, the only practical route to the mountain pass beyond but too narrow for more than one railroad. There was a construction race to reach the canyon and a pitched battle between rival crews with casualties on both sides. The two companies counted their dead and eventually abandoned both their rivalries and their railroads. The battle of Keystone Canyon and the construction days of the Copper River and Northwestern have survived in fiction form in Rex Beach's *Iron Horse*.

One of the most interesting and profitable of the early railroads was the Copper River and Northwestern Railroad, built by the Guggenheim family from Cordova 195 miles to Kennicott to tap a field of enormously rich copper ore. The cost of the railroad was about $20 million, but the value of ore and concentrates that the railroad hauled amounted to more than $200 million. In 1938 the copper was worked out and the railroad shut down. Some of its rolling stock found its way north to Seward and spent the rest of its useful life on The Alaska Railroad. The right of way was in process of conversion to a modern highway when the earthquake of 1964 destroyed much of the construction and wrecked several of the large railroad bridges that were essential features of the new road.

Four of Alaska's pioneer railroads have survived to the present day in one form or another. One is the narrow-gauge* White Pass and Yukon Route, begun in 1898 and completed in 1901 from Skagway, Alaska, to Whitehorse in Yukon Territory. Built with Canadian and British capital, only 20 of its 110 miles are on Alaskan soil. The White Pass was a direct response to the gold rush to the Klondike. In combination with stern-wheelers on the Yukon River, it permitted easy access to Dawson, Yukon Territory, through country that took heavy toll among the thousands of gold seekers who tried to reach the promised land on foot. A second was the narrow-gauge Tanana Valley Railroad, operated from Fairbanks 46

* The gauge of a railroad track is the right-angle distance between the heads of the rails measured at points ⅝ inch below the top of the rails. Narrow-gauge is any such distance less than the standard-gauge of 4 feet, 8½ inches. This width for the White Pass and Yukon was 3 feet.

miles to the Chatanika mining district. It was purchased by the Alaskan Engineering Commission in 1917 in order to gain access to Fairbanks and to acquire the ready-made terminal facilities there. The third is the somewhat mysterious 15-mile Yakutat and Southern Railway, which, according to the "Official Guide of the Railways and Steam Navigation Lines of the United States, Puerto Rico, Canada, Mexico and Cuba," performs switching service between Situk and Lost River and the tidewater town of Yakutat. Its principal freight commodity is salmon in season. The fourth is the Alaska Central Railway, with which the story of The Alaska Railroad really begins.

## The Alaska Central Railway

There were thirty men in the survey and construction party that arrived in Seward in 1903 to begin the construction of the Alaska Central. The 1903 season was spent in surveying the route, and the first rail was not spiked down until 1904. The optimism of the Seattle financiers who backed the project was unlimited. According to the president of the Alaska Central, "The extraordinary earning powers of the road will enable it to bear all fixed charges and pay large dividends on both the preferred and common stock." The fifty miles of railroad that were built and somewhat shakily operated by the company paid nothing on its stock, and the railroad failed to survive the panic of 1907. Bankrupt in 1908, the Alaska Central operated under receivership until 1910, when it was reorganized as the Alaska Northern Railway Company. Construction was resumed but got no farther than Kern Creek, around the head of Turnagain Arm, a distance of only seventy-one miles from Seward. The goal of the Alaskan Northern, as of the Alaska Central, was to reach the coal fields of the Matanuska Valley and then the interior at Fairbanks.

Like its predecessor, the Alaska Northern was unable to recoup even its operating costs. When avalanches or blizzards shut down portions of the line, dog teams proved that, under such conditions, they were the superior form of transportation. Maintenance problems were too great for the slender finances of the company to support. Construction ceased, and only part of the line was kept in operation. Essential repairs to the dock at Seward were not made; decayed trestles were not replaced; and, when President Wilson authorized purchase of the Alaska Northern by the Alaskan Engineering Commission, it was estimated that the cost of putting the seventy-one miles of track in running order for light trains would amount to about $1 million.

A variety of reasons have been given for the collapse of almost all of the pioneer railroads in Alaska. Neither Congress nor the public was pleased with the policy of federal largesse that had made the western railroads beneficiaries of grants of millions of acres of the public domain. The Credit Mobilier was not so old a railroad scandal that it was not remembered. The Granger revolt against the railroads was still continuing. Conservationists were deeply alarmed at the alienation to private interests, whether benevolent or predatory, of the richest of the nation's natural resources. Congress turned a deaf ear to the pleas of Alaskan railroad promoters for subsidies, tax relief, guaranteed bond interest, and various exclusive rights and privileges.

Access to Alaska's coal was almost universally thought to be a guarantee of success to Territorial railroads that were linked to the coal lands. But Congress seemed to be guarding against exploitation, whether good or bad. Furthermore the navies and merchant marines of the world were converting from coal to petroleum.

There is another reason for the lack of success of these early railroads that should be touched upon. Had there been more Kennicott copper bonanzas in areas through which the pioneer Alaskan railroads were planned, the pioneering would have been justified, at least for the period of time during which the bonanzas held out. Unfortunately, mineral finds rich enough to justify rail transportation were distinguished by their rarity. Even the coal, while it existed in enormous quantities, was not high grade and to this day has not found an export market. When the *National Geographic* magazine, in December, 1915, described the route of the "Government Railroad" as one "which promises to show surprisingly quick returns in the development of mineral, agricultural and other natural resources, and to demonstrate within a very few years that this great Territory is needed a veritable 'El Dorado,'" the exaggeration was pardonable but it was, nonetheless, exaggeration.

## Toward Government Ownership

In spite of disappointment, the demand for railroads in Alaska continued strong. While Congress was unwilling to provide financial guarantees or exclusive privileges, it did feel that there was something essentially wrong in a territory twice the size of Texas having no rail transportation. Its faith in railroads, combined with lack of faith in railroad personalities and policies of the past, led Congress finally to adopt a program of government ownership and operation for a railroad in Alaska even though congressmen disbelieved profoundly in government ownership and operation. It seemed common sense to many of them that the failures of the Alaska Central and the Alaska Northern could not be counted as black marks against American business. On the other hand, federal promotion of a government railroad in far-off Alaska could hardly be considered a threat to the system of free enterprise. The desire of Alaska Northern bondholders to be bailed out was not inconsistent with these views.

Pressure by private interests for federal support for their railroad projects in Alaska was in itself partly responsible for the creation of congressional opinion in favor of a federal railroad. While the pressure failed to bring about the intended results, it did focus attention on the fact that there was a railroad problem in the Territory. In 1908 and again in 1909, the governor of Alaska urged that a commission be established to study the problem. Congress finally agreed in 1912, by including in an act creating a legislative assembly for the Territory of Alaska (Act of August 24, 1912) a section authorizing the President to appoint a commission to study the question of transportation in the Territory.

President Taft immediately formed the commission, appointing Major Jay J. Morrow of the U.S. Corps of Engineers as chairman and Alfred H. Brooks, a Department of the Interior geologist who was later to become head of the Geological Survey, as vice-chairman. In "Railway Routes in Alaska," the Morrow Commission reported in 1913 that rail connections with warm-water ports in southwestern Alaska were necessary to develop the mineral and agricultural resources of the Territory; that two railroads should be built, one using the tracks of the Copper River and Northwestern from Cordova to Chitina and extending on to Fairbanks, and the second to reach from Seward around Cook Inlet to the Iditarod River; that freight rates should not exceed 5 cents per ton per mile or passenger rates 6 cents per mile; and that the cost of the proposed railroads could be reduced if the government guaranteed both the interest and principal of bonded indebtedness or if it constructed the railroads itself.

In February, 1913, less than one month before President Wilson's inauguration, President Taft submitted the commission's report to Congress. In a statement accompanying the report, President Taft emphasized his opposition to government operation but acquiesced in government ownership. He concluded that:

> The necessary inference from the entire report is that in the judgment of the Commission its recommendations can certainly

> be carried out only if the government builds or guarantees the construction cost of the railroads recommended. If the government is to guarantee the principal and interest of the construction bonds, it seems clear that it should own the roads, the cost of which it really pays. This is true whether the government itself should operate the roads or should provide for their operation by lease or operating agreement. I am very much opposed to government operation, but I believe that government ownership with private operation under lease is the proper solution of the difficulties here presented. I urge the prompt and earnest consideration of this report and its recommendations.

Of the several bills introduced to carry out the recommendations of the commission, one became The Alaska Railroad's organic act—the Act of March 12, 1914. In extensive hearings before the House Committee on the Territories that preceded the passage of the law, no general agreement with President Taft's opposition to government operation was expressed. The President was, therefore, authorized not only to locate and construct a railroad in the Territory of Alaska, but to operate it as well. The grant of authority to the President to locate the railroad was born of a shrewd appraisal of the politics of regional interests and of such railroad feuding as had already taken place in the Territory. The Morrow Commission had made a thorough survey in its "Railway Routes in Alaska" in an amazingly short time and had indicated some preferences among routes. But Alaska delegate James Wickersham, who drafted the railroad bill, was determined that the cause should not be lost for the Territory in a war of rival railroad interests. In a speech in support of the bill, before the House of Representatives on January 14, 1914, Wickersham was frank about his reasons why the President should have authority to locate the future Alaska railroad:

> If an attempt had been made by the bill to fix a specific route, then a clamor from every other locality would have been raised. Those supporting the bill would have been accused of having

some interest in or along the line of location. If the bill, like the Pacific Railway bills, had organized a specific corporation, designated its incorporators, and given them a land grant, the clamor would have been greater. If the bill had specifically prevented the President from making any location of the road in connection with any other road, that would have brought criticism and increased lobbying. If the bill had limited the President to any particular route, it would have been open to grave criticism, upon the ground that Congress has no such information as would justify it in choosing any particular route or any particular region. The committee having charge of this bill had entire confidence in the President and believed the sanest method of securing the best results was to put the whole burden and responsibility upon his shoulders.

The Act of March 12, 1914, which still furnishes a constitution and bylaws for The Alaska Railroad, is a fascinating footnote to the economic history of the United States. It launched the government on an experiment in railroad ownership and operation that has endured for more than half a century. Yet the law had no discernible influence on relationships between the federal government and the private railroads. The officials of private railroads have treated Alaska's railroad with benevolent tolerance and have never regarded it as endangering their business interests.

The 1914 act authorized the President to locate, construct, and operate a railroad in the Territory of Alaska,

> not to exceed in the aggregate one thousand miles, to be so located as to connect one or more of the open Pacific Ocean harbors on the southern coast of Alaska with the navigable waters in the interior of Alaska, and with a coal field or fields so as best to aid in the development of the agricultural and mineral or other resources of Alaska, and the settlement of the public lands therein, and so as to provide transportation of coal for the Army and Navy, transportation of troops, arms, munitions of war, the mails, and for other governmental and public uses, and for the transportation of passengers and property.

The act gave the President such broad powers to engage in common carrier rail transportation, operation of marine terminals, and telephone and telegraph communications as to both shock and astonish most federal budget officials who have had occasion to deal with the railroad's financial and operating problems. The President was given the power to appoint officers, agents, and employees, to define their duties, and to fix their compensation; to exercise the power of eminent domain in acquiring property for the use of the railroad; to fix rates for the transportation of persons and property so long as such rates would be equal and uniform; to buy other railroads in Alaska, to make agreements for joint transportation of persons and property with any railroad, steamship company, or vessel owner; to withdraw lands from the public domain; and to lease the operation of the railroad.

Even this broad grant of authority was not enough. For Congress added that:

> It is the intent and purpose of Congress through this Act to authorize and empower the President of the United States and he is fully authorized and empowered, through such officers, agents, or agencies as he may appoint or employ *to do all necessary acts and things in addition to those specially authorized in this Act to enable him to accomplish the purpose and objects of this Act* [italics added].

There is a tendency among some government officials to justify not doing things they do not want to do by explaining that they lack specific authority. Alaska Railroad officials have little opportunity to justify failure to act in this fashion, providing the action urged or contemplated has a reasonable relation to the objectives of the law.

## The Government Railroad

President Woodrow Wilson acted swiftly to carry out the duties laid upon him by the Territory's new railroad law and, on May 2, 1914, authorized the Secretary of the Interior, Franklin K. Lane, to proceed with the location surveys. The President appointed the Alaskan Engineering Commission to supervise the location work. Members of the commission were Lieutenant Frederick Mears, who had experience as an engineer for the Great Northern Railway and in the operation and construction of the Panama Railroad; Thomas Riggs, Jr., who was thoroughly familiar with Alaska and who, as a member of the Alaska Survey Commission, had surveyed the entire Alaska-Canada boundary; and W. C. Edes, who had had many years of experience as a location and construction engineer for railroads in the western states. On May 8, Secretary Lane informed the commission that the President had authorized its members to select their assistants and purchase supplies and that they should proceed to Alaska "at the earliest practicable date."

The Alaskan Engineering Commission felt that its task was technical rather than political. Edes, Riggs, and Mears were fully aware that the question of a satisfactory route for the new railroad had been the subject of sharp debate in Congress before the act was passed. They intended to steer away from the controversy as much as possible.

The commission established offices in Seattle in May, 1914, and by June an advance party had reached the wilderness location on Ship Creek at the head of Cook Inlet that was to be the railroad town of Anchorage. Two major routes with minor alternates and branches to the coal fields were surveyed, one the present route from Seward and the other the western route from Cordova through Chitina, both terminating at Fairbanks. Among the alternate routes examined was the Whittier cutoff from Portage, where estimates were made of the tunneling necessary to avoid both mountain grades and the Portage Glacier. The results of previous surveys were carefully examined, and field trips were made to the Kuskokwim and Iditarod districts. The survey included an investigation of the condition of the Alaska Northern Railway, the Tanana Valley Railroad, and the Copper River and Northwestern. The commission submitted its findings to the President in February, 1915, but with no recommendation as to which route should be chosen.

It was left to President Wilson to make the decision, and on April 10, 1915, he selected the present location and authorized the purchase of the Alaska Northern. By letters of April 10 and April 30 to the Secretary of the Interior, the President ordered the construction to begin and made it clear that the Alaskan Engineering Commission would be subject to the control of the Secretary. The Secretary of the Interior was delegated the President's authority under the Act of March 12, 1914, "in all respects and to all intents and purposes the same as if said work had been placed by law under the jurisdiction and control of the Department of the Interior."

There must have been something about the climate of Alaska that counteracted the traditional slowness of bureaucracy. Within a few weeks after President Wilson selected the Seward–Cook Inlet route and before the month of April, 1915, was ended, Mears had landed men and supplies on the banks of Ship Creek. Edes, as chairman of the commission, made Seward his headquarters, since it had been originally selected as the site of the railroad's administrative offices. Riggs took charge of the parties that were to complete the location work, particularly in the Broad Pass–Fairbanks section, where surveys were most incomplete.

The Cook Inlet site was selected for construction headquarters because it was more centrally located and because the condition of the Alaska Northern had so deteriorated that train operation through to Turnagain Arm and Kern Creek was impossible. Anchorage, as the Cook Inlet site came to be known, did have the handicap of an ice-locked harbor for four or five months of the year, but was open to shipping for the remainder.

A tent city rose in an incredibly short time on the flats along Ship Creek as word spread of the possibilities for employment on the government railroad. Within a few weeks the tents housed nearly 2,000 people. Instead of a labor shortage, there was such a surplus that the Alaskan Engineering Commission warned in a notice of April 28, 1915: that "The Commission will not engage large numbers of men on force account basis, and those going to Ship Creek, Alaska with the idea of finding ready employment on the new work will be largely disappointed." This was at a time when the going rate for construction labor was only 37.5 cents an hour.

By June, 1915, a newspaper, the *Cook Inlet Pioneer,* was being published at the Ship Creek construction site. According to advertisements in the early issues, the town possessed a movie theater, restaurants, bakeries, general stores, meat markets, drugstores, lumberyards, transfer and storage firms, barbers, and even a jeweler. Many of these enterprises were housed in tents. Strangest of the newspaper announcements was one for the Pioneer Hotel, which advertised that it had "no bar." This was the official position in regard to alcohol, since the first town lots in Anchorage were sold with the stipulation that "If any lot or lots sold or any part thereof shall be used for the purpose of manufacturing, selling, or otherwise disposing of intoxicating liquors as a beverage, or for gambling, prostitution, or any unlawful purpose before final payment is made, and during a period of five years from the date of register's certificate of sale, the lot or lots and all payments made thereon may be declared forfeited by the Secretary of the Interior."

The tent city on the banks of Ship Creek lasted but a few weeks. The high tablelands on the south side of the Ship Creek valley provided an enormously superior townsite. Furthermore, the land along the creek was needed for railroad yards and buildings. The land at the mouth of the creek would carry the docks that were to make the new town a shipping point for

Matanuska Valley coal, which in turn was to make the railroad a profitable enterprise.

By vote of its citizens, "Anchorage" became the official name of the new town after the move to the plateau above the creek valley. There was some dissent about the name from Alaska's Governor Strong, seconded by the Alaskan Engineering Commission's Lieutenant Mears. They both would have preferred "Matanuska" because of the town's closeness to the Matanuska coal fields. By midsummer of 1915, however, the townspeople had become accustomed to "Anchorage," and the suggestions of the governor and the lieutenant were disregarded.

President Wilson, Secretary of Interior Lane, and the Alaskan Engineering Commission literally created the city of Anchorage. President Wilson's order of June 19, 1915, authorized the commission to recommend lands to be set aside for townsite purposes. The order then required the Secretary of the Interior to cause townsite reservations to be surveyed, withholding such land as would be needed for railroad use. Streets were to be laid out and lots platted and sold to the highest bidder. The survey was made, railroad engineers platted the streets and lots, and the first public sale of lots was held on July 10, 1914. Before the sale, the *Cook Inlet Pioneer* reported that fancy prices were not expected because the restrictions imposed would eliminate "the purely speculative individual." However, a headline in the next issue read: ANCHORAGE LOTS BRING BIG PRICES AT AUCTION SALE. The first lot auctioned brought $825, and the highest priced lot $1,150. Total sales for the two-hour auction amounted to about $150,000. At later sales, bargain lots in outlying sections were sold for as little as $25.

The Alaskan Engineering Commission planned, built, and operated all the facilities needed by the rapidly growing city. Water, electricity, sewers, telephone service, fire protection, sidewalks, street improvements, and a hospital were provided.

Schools were built for the children of the commission's employees. A railroad official was made townsite manager. The Department of the Interior was thus responsible for consumer charges for a variety of municipal services that were even more alien to federal operations than the building of a railroad. The modern city of Anchorage has long since taken over responsibility for all these services (except hospitals), including the ownership and operation of the local telephone system.

Seward had been established as the headquarters of the Alaskan Engineering Commission and there was every intention that it should remain so. There was consternation in Seward, therefore, when the commission decided to move its headquarters to Anchorage in 1917. The immediate occasion for the move was a flurry of land speculation caused by the knowledge that the commission would need more space in Seward. In Anchorage, there was almost no privately owned land until the commission sold lots at public auction, and the commission was careful not to put up any land for sale that might be needed for railroad purposes. Seward, as the older town, contained more land in private ownership, so some areas needed by the commission could be obtained only by purchase. Quite naturally, landowners in Seward anticipated a boom in real estate prices. They overestimated their power in holding back for higher prices, however, and the commission escaped these prices by moving its headquarters to Anchorage. Criticism on the part of Seward residents, including commission employees, was loud and vigorous but unavailing. Anchorage remained the headquarters city.

## Eight Years of Construction

The first construction of The Alaska Railroad occupied the eight years from 1915 to 1923. The year 1915 was largely one of preparation, in which an organization was created, employees were hired, supply lines established, equipment and materials assembled, and detailed surveys progressed toward completion.

The Act of March 12, 1914, made mandatory the use of any "machinery, equipment, instruments, material and other property of any sort whatsoever" no longer needed for the construction of the Panama Canal. A representative of the commission went to Panama and arranged for the shipment by chartered vessel of steam shovels, derricks, locomotives, flatcars, structural steel, shop machinery, and other construction and railroad equipment. Quantities of the Panama Canal surplus reached Anchorage in the summer of 1915, including the commission's first locomotives.* There was no reimbursement, but the Alaskan Engineering Commission paid the freight. A similar but far more extensive program brought many millions of dollars worth of military surplus property to Alaska after World War II at no cost to the railroad except freight, repairs, and modification expense.

Other supply lines were almost as long as the one from Panama. Before the rails reached Nenana, some supplies had to be shipped from Seattle to the mouth of the Yukon River, then upriver to the junction of the Yukon and Tanana rivers, then up the Tanana River to Nenana. Special rates were secured from the White Pass and Yukon Route to permit shipment by steamer to Skagway, by railroad to Whitehorse, and by riverboat down the Yukon to the junction with the Tanana and then up the Tanana River to Nenana. Seattle, as a major supply point, cemented a relationship with Alaska that was begun during the gold stampedes and that has continued to the present day. Commission offices were established in Seattle and, for a time, in Portland and San Francisco as well.

* At the time the French bought the Panama Railroad and started digging the Panama Canal, they used 5-foot gauge track and equipment. But The Alaska Railroad used the standard gauge of 4 feet 8½ inches. The 200- and 600-class locomotives acquired from the Isthmian Canal Commission were converted to standard-gauge by installing extra-wide tires on the wheels.

In terms of supply, winter was the most important part of the year, particularly during the first years of the construction period. Overland transportation was possible in winter with sleds and horses but was impossible in summer except where wagon roads could be constructed or where rivers and lakes could be navigated by small or medium-sized boats. In winter, hundreds of horses and many sleds were used to transport supplies and equipment to construction camps in advance of the summer construction season. Where conditions permitted construction at reasonable cost or where the need was so great as to justify high costs, construction was pushed on through the winter. This was particularly true of bridge-building. Structural steel could be put in place in winter, and piling could be sunk to required depths by the use of steam points.

The building of the railroad required enormous quantities of lumber of all kinds. Large-dimension and finished lumber was shipped from Seattle to Anchorage, while locally cut wood was used for crossties and piling. Orders were placed with state-side steel mills for 70-pound rail for use in the main line and 60-pound rail for sidings. The original location of the railroad bypassed Anchorage at a distance of four or five miles, and a spur was built to the town. The Ship Creek location for a rerouting of the main line was chosen after a dock and warehouse had been built at the mouth of the creek and after yards and repair facilities had been located along the stream.

The Alaska Northern Railway was taken over by the commission in the early summer of 1915, though the down payment of $500,000 was not made until August. In accordance with the requirements of the 1914 Act, the Interstate Commerce Commission had previously made a valuation of the property. Litigation over title to the Alaska Northern delayed the completion of the purchase until June, 1916, when a final payment of $650,000 was made. Accrued interest brought the total price to $1,157,339. This compares with a total cost to the original owners and builders of $5,250,000. In spite of the neglected and decrepit condition of the 71 miles of railroad thus acquired, the Alaskan Engineering Commission began rail operations in the summer of 1915 by running a motor car over 35 miles of track out of Seward on a regular schedule. Passengers were charged 12.5 cents per mile, and freight service cost $25 per ton. While this may well be a record-high ton-mile rate for a railroad, freighting a comparable distance by dog team would have cost at least three times as much.

The 45-mile Tanana Valley Railroad, a narrow-gauge line (3 feet), was purchased by the Alaskan Engineering Commission in 1917 for $300,000. It operated to the Chatanika mining area northwest of Fairbanks and earned a small annual net as long as mining continued along its line. At the time of purchase, however, mining was on the decline and the Tanana could barely meet its operating expenses. It was purchased primarily to acquire its terminal facilities in Fairbanks and its right of way from Happy to Fairbanks. The commission was unable to obtain a reasonable return from the operation of what now was the Chatanika branch of the government railroad, and abandoned it in 1930. After June, 1923, there were three rails from the junction of the two railroads, near Happy, to Fairbanks. Thus, standard-gauge trains from Seward and Anchorage and narrow-gauge trains from Chatanika could travel the last few miles on the same right of way and stop in Fairbanks at the same station. (Prior to June, 1923, a narrow-gauge track constructed by the Alaskan Engineering Commission extended from the junction with the Tanana Valley Railroad about fifty miles south to Nenana. In winter during the construction period, narrow-gauge track was laid across the ice of the Tanana River. In this manner, freight and passengers were carried from Seward to Fairbanks with a transfer to narrow-gauge equipment at Nenana.)

A good deal of the basic work of building The Alaska

Railroad was accomplished through an incentive system imported from the western states but which seems to have disappeared from the American scene. Some bright engineer must have noticed that clearing and grading the right of way for a railroad can be measured in standardized units of acres and cubic yards, while bridge and building construction and the laying of ties and rail do not lend themselves to such standardization. So a system of payments was established by which workers would be paid on a piece-work basis rather than an hourly wage for units of clearing and grading accomplished.

This system of payment based on results was adopted by the Alaskan Engineering Commission from the beginning of the construction period. Men associated themselves as partners and made contracts with the commission for clearing and grading work. They were called "station men" because the right of way was measured in units of 100 feet and contracts were awarded for work from one numbered station to another. Station men were permitted to hire laborers at hourly rates fixed by the commission. Their contracts called for payment calculated on units of work performed, but would vary with the degree of difficulty encountered. When a contract was completed, payments were made to the partners on the basis of one share each. Hardly any capital was needed to become an independent contractor in this fashion, since the commission supplied equipment at modest rentals. Station men bought their supplies and provisions from commission-maintained commissaries. Since they were working for themselves, the eight-hour work law that applied to federal workers generally did not apply to them.

On June 5, 1915, the *Cook Inlet Pioneer* reported that the first contract, for clearing right of way from station 3548 to 3689, a distance of 14,100 feet, had been issued by Commissioner Mears. There were twenty men in this particular partnership. Almost immediately the small contract system was extended to other kinds of work for which a price could be established for a project not easily divisible into standard units. Thus a contract was let to eight men for building a wagon road and crossing, to two men for laying a water line, to one man for painting, to two men for supplying 3,000 railroad ties and to two men for supplying 40 tons of hay. In later years, the Alaskan Engineering Commission received a good deal of praise for the economy with which the railroad had been constructed, and much of the credit was given to this system of contracting.

Peak employment in the summer of 1915 reached about 1,400, a little more than half of whom were independent contractors or station men. With this system, but with hourly paid men used for track-laying and bridge and building work, 13.5 miles of roadway were cleared and graded and track laid during the first construction season. In addition, 35 miles were cleared and graded and 40 more miles were cleared. In the following year, track was laid for 60 miles, and in 1917 for an additional 103 miles. Employment reached a peak of about 4,500 in 1917, but, with the outbreak of war, many Alaska railroaders, including Commissioner Mears, joined the armed forces. Employment in 1919 dropped sharply, to about 2,500. By the end of 1920, the commission had built 382 miles of track, not including the 70.7 miles of the Alaska Northern and the 31.9 miles of the Tanana Valley, which, by 1920, had been rebuilt.

Unfinished bridges at Riley Creek, milepost 347, and over the Tanana River between mileposts 411.7 and 413.7 were all that prevented steel rail from meeting between Seward and Fairbanks in 1921. The Riley Creek bridge was finished by the commission in February, 1922. But the bridge over the Tanana River at Nenana was another matter. This was the most formidable bridge crossing along the entire railroad and would require a 701-foot single span, at that time the longest such bridge span in the United States. Contract was let to the

American Bridge Company in May, 1922, and the bridge was finished in February, 1923. This company also built the Hurricane Gulch and the Susitna River bridges. The building of these large steel bridges constituted the major exception to the practice of the Alaskan Engineering Commission of building the railroad with its own employees or with station men.

When the Riley Creek bridge was completed, in February, 1922, there was almost continuous steel between Seward and Fairbanks. The commission originally planned the opening ceremony for that month. While there was no bridge over the Tanana River, there was narrow-gauge rail over the ice that continued for the 57 miles to Fairbanks. Second and wiser thoughts prevailed, and the celebration was postponed until the Tanana River bridge was finished and the 57 miles north to Fairbanks was converted to standard-gauge. The conversion was completed in June, 1923, and the driving of the golden spike was held in the following month.

It should be noted in passing that, from 1919 to the completion of The Alaska Railroad in 1923, the Alaskan Engineering Commission was kept as a name even though its sole member was Colonel Mears, who had returned to the railroad as a colonel after a year of war duty. Riggs had left the commission in 1918 to become the governor of the Territory of Alaska, while Edes became a consulting engineer to the commission, with headquarters in Washington, D.C.

During the construction period, the commission hauled thousands of tons of supplies, materials and equipment and hundreds of thousands of tons of gravel and fill on its own rails. As fast as track was laid, it was placed in operation for supply and work trains. At the end of 1916, 80 miles of railroad could be used for company freight; at the end of 1917, 121 miles; and at the end of 1918, 294 miles. Miles operated increased to 414 in 1919 and to 456 in 1920.

Commercial freight and passengers were accepted, but they were incidental to the hauling of company freight. While

Anchorage was the first main construction base and Nenana, on the banks of the Tanana River, the second, Seward and Fairbanks were also supply and construction bases. Many intermediate camps were established and abandoned to suit the changing construction needs as increasing miles of track permitted train operations.

On October 24, 1917, the first train reached the coal mines at Chickaloon, seventy-four miles from Anchorage, and on October 30 the first shipment of coal arrived in Anchorage. This shipment was a milestone, since access to coal had provided one of the strongest drives behind the building of the railroad. In 1918, trains were operated between Anchorage and Montana, Anchorage and Bird, and Seward and Kern.

Snow and snowslides often made these early operations precarious. Thus the *Alaska Railroad Record,* official publication of the Alaskan Engineering Commission, reported in January, 1919, that conditions on the Seward-Anchorage line had considerably improved because trains could get through for most of the distance, and transfer by dog team or horse sled was necessary only for the 15 miles between mileposts 47 and 62 and for the 6.5 miles between Kern and mile 77. In 1920, trains operated from Seward to mile 236 above Talkeetna and from Fairbanks to Healy at mile 358. With the Tanana River bridge not yet built, this meant a transfer across the ice or by ferry at Nenana. Between the ends of track, mail was carried by horse sled. Railroad supplies were taken from mile 236 to Hurricane Gulch by horse sled in winter and by a combination of boat and horse sled or caterpillar tractor in summer.

In November and December, 1921, train operation was possible over the entire line with transfers at the unfinished Riley Creek bridge and to narrow-gauge track at Nenana. The first through train from Seward reached Nenana on February 5, 1922. On July 7, 1923, a special passenger train was operated from Seward to Fairbanks. The trip took four days, with night stopovers at Anchorage, Curry, and McKinley

Park. On June 15, 1923, the line from Nenana to Fairbanks had been converted to standard-gauge, and trains were operating over the entire railroad shortly thereafter. Riverboat service from Nenana down the Tanana River to points on the Yukon was begun at about this time.

With full allowance for wilderness conditions, winter hardships, and long and difficult supply lines, it should not have required eight years to build the railroad. The principal reason for delay was the outbreak of war, which caused a drop in employment from about 4,500 in 1917 to about 2,500 in 1918, and an inflationary increase in wages and prices aggravated an appropriation problem that would have existed in any case. In 1917, 103 miles of main-line track and roadway were completed. This dropped to 54 in 1918 and to 68 in 1919. Even when the war was over, the exhaustion of the original appropriation and the uncertainties as to when money would be available from subsequent appropriations kept the commission from going ahead as fast as possible.

The economic consequences of World War I included an upward spiral in costs that brought commission expenditures for one mile of track from $9,860 in 1915 to $14,691 in 1918 to $15,600 in 1920. By June, 1919, the original appropriation of $35 million was exhausted and Congress was requested to appropriate an additional $17 million. The request was granted in October, 1919, to be paid in three installments in the years 1919, 1920, and 1921. In recommending passage of the bill, the House Committee on Territories declared that: "The construction of The Alaska Railroad by the Alaskan Engineering Commission has been prosecuted under most adverse conditions, due in large part to the war, and the work has been done at the lowest cost consistent with the permanent character of the work performed."

During the next four years, additional appropriations to meet construction work brought the total cost of constructing The Alaska Railroad to about $65 million.

In addition to inflation and war-caused shortages of manpower, the commission had to contend with the many problems resulting from fiscal-year appropriations that did not coincide with the pace of construction. Work was slowed or stopped at crucial times because money was not available to meet payrolls or to buy supplies in advance of the summer work season. In 1919, the commission was nearly four months in arrears in paying wages to employees and contract amounts to station men. The deficit occurred because the money needed for the 1919 work season was not appropriated until July. Although Colonel Mears and Interior Secretary Lane made strong protest against the inefficiencies caused by annual fiscal-year appropriations for long-term projects, exactly the same mistake was made when The Alaska Railroad was rebuilt after the war.

## Driving the Golden Spike

As he steamed northwest to Seward in June, 1923, and on the special train that would take him to Nenana, President Harding was surrounded by distinguished members of his cabinet, high military officers, federal and territorial officials, and reporters. They included Secretary of Interior Hubert Work, Secretary of Commerce Herbert Hoover, Secretary of Agriculture Henry Wallace, Speaker of the House Frederick Gillette, Admiral Hugh Rodman, Governor Scott Bone of Alaska, Colonel W. J. Greeley, chief of the Forest Service, and Ike Taylor of the Alaska Road Commission. But the man who more than any other individual was responsible for the successful construction of The Alaska Railroad was unable to be with the President and his party. This was Colonel Frederick Mears, who had returned to the Army for a short stay before becoming an official of the Great Northern. His place was taken by Colonel James G. Steese, who was called temporarily from the Alaska Road Commission to head the Alaskan Engineering Commission.

President Harding and his party reached Anchorage from Seward on July 13, the same day that his ship had docked. The next day, the Presidential special made a side trip to the coal fields at Chickaloon and, back on the main line, put up at Curry for the night. On July 15, the party reached North Nenana, across the river from Nenana proper. Here President Harding was to drive the golden spike.

Charles Ross, who had been present at the ceremony and who was later President Truman's press secretary, described the events of July 15, 1923, for an Anchorage weekly newspaper, *The Forty Ninth Star,* on the occasion of the twenty-fifth anniversary of the symbolic joining of steel. Ross recalled that, no matter how tremendously impressed he had been with Alaska's scenery, his most vivid memory was of his extreme discomfort on July 15 and 16. It seems that Admiral Rodman, as an expert on Alaska's climate, had advised the reporters to outfit themselves in heavy shirts, heavy underwear, sweaters, galoshes, and leggings. The heavy clothes were obviously intended to protect against the cold and the leggings against Alaskan mosquitoes. Nenana proved both hot and mosquitoless. But worse was to come. The temperature was 94° the next day at Fairbanks when President Harding made a speech at the local baseball park. Three members of his audience collapsed from heat prostration. Ross's diary carried the notation that the wearers of heavy underwear threatened reprisals against Admiral Rodman.

At the Nenana ceremony, President Harding made a short and gracious speech. He paid tribute to the pioneers of Alaska and to the builders of the railroad whose genius and confidence had made it possible. Then,

> I do not suppose any individual or set of individuals would have undertaken the construction of such a railway, that it had to be left to the government itself.
>
> I am glad a generous government understood and carried to completion the construction of The Alaska Railroad. It is not

> possible to liken a railway to a magician's wand, but the effect to me is the same. For the whole problem of civilization, the development of resources and the awakening of communities lies in transportation.

With a few additional words and several swings of his maul, the President drove the golden spike and The Alaska Railroad was ceremonially complete.

# III

# Rags to Riches

It could hardly be expected that The Alaska Railroad would earn more than a fraction of its operating costs during the construction years and for some time thereafter. But there were Congressmen who felt that, when the golden spike was driven, the Alaskan Engineering Commission abolished, and The Alaska Railroad launched officially, the deficits should cease. At long last, the coal mines of the Matanuska Valley and the Healy River fields were accessible by rail. Homesteads were within easy reach. It was high time that El Dorado became self-supporting.

These expectations were not realized for 15 years. Deficit succeeded deficit, and the more vociferous of the railroad's critics insisted that it be abandoned altogether. During the 25 years from 1916 to 1940, gross revenues, including non-operating income from hotels, riverboats, and other ventures, amounted to $27,348,593. Expenditures, excluding capital costs and without charges to depreciation, climbed to $44,-086,430. The 25-year deficit totaled $16,737,837—a figure so large that arguments about the depreciation that should have been charged seem academic.

The difficulty with celebrating the completion of a railroad comes with attempts to avoid the conclusion that the railroad is complete. But the joining of steel did not mean that construction was finished. Many bridges were temporary wooden trestles, banks needed widening, and ballasting was woefully inadequate. Unless these deficiencies were corrected, high maintenance costs almost guaranteed annual losses except as unusual events should bring large increases in tonnage handled.

Colonel Steese, the last chairman of the Alaskan Engineering Commission, presented this problem to the House Appropriations Committee at hearings for fiscal year 1925. He said:

> While the formal completion of the railroad was announced last summer . . . and standard-gauge trains are actually operating between the coast at Seward and the inner terminal at Fairbanks, a great deal of additional work is still required to bring the entire line up to standard. Furthermore, The Alaska Railroad as a growing concern will never be complete in the sense that capital investment may cease. As revenues increase and more business is presented, additional sums will be required for extensions and betterments.

Colonel Steese added that he thought at least $5 million was necessary to bring the railroad to reasonable standards of efficient and economical operation.

Noel W. Smith, a veteran of the Pennsylvania Railroad, became general manager of The Alaska Railroad on December 19, 1924, succeeding Lee Landis, who had served for an interim period of about a year. At hearings before the House Appropriations Committee on the fiscal 1926 budget, Noel Smith presented the same argument as Colonel Steese, but with considerably greater force. He told the committee that, in his judgment, more than $1,000 in maintenance costs per mile could be saved annually and serious hazards eliminated by a judicious investment in improving the condition of the road. He estimated that the amount of investment should be about $11 million. He concluded that:

> The outstanding facts of The Alaska Railroad are that maintenance and operation costs can be reduced by the intelligent

> expenditure of funds for completion of road and equipment; that the savings effected by such expenditure will exceed the interest on the money expended; that by so reducing maintenance and operation costs, the time will be shortened for appropriation for deficits, which must be made if the road is to continue in operation.

The Bureau of the Budget and the House and Senate appropriations committees had been sympathetic and even generous to the railroad during the construction period. The several times that the Alaskan Engineering Commission was without funds was the result of the perversity of a system of annual financing. No one expected a railroad under construction to show profits, and there was no criticism even when operating costs in some construction years were more than ten times the operating income. After 1923, the standards of judgment changed. The period of heavy capital investment was supposed to be over and the period of reasonable return was supposed to have begun.

Even if the financial prospects of the railroad had been good, Congress would have been reluctant to advance large sums for capital improvement. Whatever attitudes congressmen may have toward their own business affairs, they are not attuned to a situation that calls for the federal government to invest money to make money. This, after all, is the province of private business rather than of government. So when by some accident of history the federal government comes into possession of an enterprise that is supposed to balance income against expenses, Congress and the Bureau of the Budget tend to apply to it not business canons but the financial canons appropriate to most other federal agencies. The ordinary government bureau is not in the business of making money by providing a service for a price. Failure to appropriate more funds to such a bureau may decrease its effectiveness but cannot produce deficits, since measurements of profit and loss are not applicable to its operations. The cost-benefit ratios of an allegedly more enlightened age are unlikely to change the direction of this kind of generalizing.

It is highly probable, therefore, that The Alaska Railroad would have had trouble convincing Congress of the need for appropriations for capital improvements even if there had been no deficits. The argument that the use of taxpayers' money for plant investment in the present would eliminate the need for taxpayer money to meet deficits in the future struck no responsive chord. The climate of opinion might well have made congressmen more suspicious of a successful government enterprise than of an unsuccessful one. Financially, however, the railroad was a conspicuous failure. The operating deficit for both rail and riverboat operations was $1,813,862 in 1924, $1,673,997 in 1925, and $1,169,204 in 1926.

## Demands for Abandonment

While Congressional opposition to more appropriations may not have been surprising, it was surprising that demands for abandonment began as early as 1925. In that year, Congressman A. M. Free of California visited Alaska and made an inspection trip over the railroad. On his return, he announced that The Alaska Railroad, far from deserving capital appropriations, was not worth the expenditure of federal money for its operation and maintenance. He suggested that the rails be torn up and the remaining grade used for a highway.

General Manager Noel Smith took Free's suggestion seriously. In a letter of September 25, 1925, to Interior Secretary Hubert Work, he included an elaborate analysis of alternate ways of dealing with the railroad's problems, including abandonment. He ended his report on the following discouraged note:

> It would appear to us, however, that if it would be desired to abandon the road, that it would be better policy to simply

abandon the road, not attempt to tear it up, and then if some future administration of the Government might be more liberally disposed to the development of the Territory and would be willing to rehabilitate the line abandoned, the present administration would be spared a great deal of adverse criticism which it would, no doubt, receive if it had been instrumental in practically destroying an investment of over $60,000,000.

The suggestion to abandon caused great concern in Alaska. James Wickersham, former delegate to Congress from the Territory, denounced it in caustic terms. Alaskans who had made commitments based on an expectation that the railroad would continue to operate complained to the secretary. Officials of the railroad vigorously defended attacks upon it. Nevertheless, the agitation to abandon all or part of the railroad continued for several years. The annual deficits immediately responsible for this agitation also continued. Expenditures for operations, including nonrailroad items, exceeded income by $900,174 in fiscal year 1927, by $840,890 in 1928, and by $954,294 in 1929.

Though starved for funds, officials of the railroad tried to make do with what they had and spent some money for capital items in each year. A few of the longer wooden trestles were replaced with steel bridges. New shop machinery was purchased. Gas cars were acquired and, by the middle of 1926, officials could boast that only about one-third of the section foremen still had to depend on hand-pumped locomotion to get them over the tracks. A second-hand river steamer was bought for operations on the Tanana and Yukon rivers. Several new locomotives and a Brill car were placed in service. Additional work on track and roadway barely kept up with losses from floods, frost heaves, and snow and rock slides.

Tourist traffic was vigorously pursued, and early tourist leaflets had four-color covers and forty pages of pictures and text extolling the romance and beauty of Alaska, the magnificence of Mt. McKinley National Park, and the virtues of combination tours that included riverboats, steamships in the Inside Passage, and the White Pass and Yukon Route. An immigration officer was appointed, with headquarters first in Washington, D.C., and later in Chicago, Illinois. His duties were to encourage both homesteading and tourist traffic.

Some efforts were made toward encouraging small business in the Territory. Thus, the railroad operated a creamery for making butter and ice cream and an experimental plant for making concrete culverts. Homesteaders were introduced to the mysteries of canning fruits and vegetables by means of a portable cannery operated in a rebuilt outfit car.

Bright hopes for an Alaskan coal industry seemed to have faded soon after the coal mines in the Matanuska Valley and in the Healy River field were opened. To reach the Matanuska coal, the railroad had built a 19-mile branch from the main line at Matanuska to Sutton and 18 miles farther to mines at Chickaloon. From Sutton, a branch line less than 3 miles long led to coal at Jonesville and Eska. A 4.4-mile branch from Healy reached the coal fields at Suntrana north of the Alaska Range.

A good deal of coal was required for the railroad's locomotives. Fairly large quantities were used for domestic heating, and a market would eventually develop for coal as fuel for power plants. For several years, small tonnages were brought to the docks at Anchorage for transhipment by steam vessel. They never exceeded 7,000 tons a year and did not mean an export trade for Alaska, for the coal was consigned to towns along the Alaskan coast. Eventually, even this small market dwindled away. The expected use of coal for the U.S. Navy was thwarted because the navies of the world were turning to oil. Furthermore, Alaska coal was not high grade and proved difficult to ship. The hope that huge tonnages would be sold in the states or abroad failed to materialize in the 1920's and has never materialized since.

## A New General Manager Takes Over

The story of the transformation of The Alaska Railroad from the rags of the 1930's to the riches of the 1940's is the story of Colonel Otto F. Ohlson, aided and abetted by his employees and by World War II. Colonel Ohlson became general manager of The Alaska Railroad on August 1, 1928. He was a veteran railroader with twenty-seven years' experience with the Northern Pacific Railway. He was also a veteran of World War I, having served with a railroad battalion in France. His employees and his officials agreed that he was tough but fair. If his temper and speech sometimes got out of hand, he was quick to make up for his explosiveness. If he fired an employee in anger one day he was apt to hire him back the next. Above all, he was a competent railroader and placed his imprint upon more than seventeen years of the history of The Alaska Railroad.

Six months before Colonel Ohlson was sworn in as general manager, a senator from Nebraska was questioning Department of Interior officials about a $400,000 appropriation for capital improvements to be included in the department's Appropriations Act for fiscal 1929. This was Senator Robert B. Howell of Nebraska, whose dislike of The Alaska Railroad seems to have been acquired early in his Congressional life. The senator was interested in (but not concerned about) the possible abandonment of the Chatanika branch and of the trackage between Seward and Anchorage and between Nenana and Fairbanks. He wanted to know how much of the $400,000, which he apparently regarded as an overgenerous amount, would be spent on those three sections of the railroad. In a letter to the general manager of February 6, 1928, from B. H. Barndollar, examiner of accounts for The Alaska Railroad, there is the following reference to Senator Howell: "In the course of the conversation, Senator Howell expressed his opinion that certain parts of the railroad should be abandoned, claiming that the people of the country could import all their supplies during nine months of the year and that if the Fairbanks Exploration Company needed service for their operations, they should pay for it and not expect the U.S. Government to stand the expenses."*

Unfortunately for The Alaska Railroad, Senator Howell continued his interest in the railroad and decided that an investigation was necessary. In 1930, impelled by a congressional joint resolution, he set off for the Railbelt with members of a Senate committee of which he was chairman. According to Benjamin Thoron, former director of Interior's Division of Territories and the author of a report based upon the most thorough investigation ever made of The Alaska Railroad, Senator Howell's trip was hasty and his report superficial. The senator filed his committee's recommendations:

1. That the operation of the Railroad be continued but that train miles be decreased by 100,000 annually;
2. That, contrary to existing practice, business efficiency and economy be strictly enforced;
3. That passenger fares be increased to 10 cents per mile and freight rates be increased so as to yield at least 50 per cent more revenue;
4. That only $250,000 in the pending appropriations bill be used for capital expenditures.

No report could have better illustrated the low estate to which the railroad had fallen in its relationship with Congress.

* The Fairbanks Exploration Company had built a steam-generating plant in the Fairbanks area to supply electricity to its gold dredges. The plant depended on Alaska Railroad–hauled coal and it is quite possible that the company received a rate on coal that might be regarded as promotional. After more than forty years, the company ceased operating its huge dredges in the placer gold gravels of the Fairbanks area. The "pay dirt" no longer pays enough.

The recommendation for a capital program of $250,000 and for increased freight and passenger rates meant that the committee and any congressman who agreed with its analysis had, to all practical purposes, abandoned the railroad.

The Department of the Interior and the general manager of the railroad tried in good faith to follow the Howell Committee recommendations. The Chatanika branch was closed down, maintenance was reduced to a bare minimum on the rest of the railroad, freight and passenger rates were increased, and winter operations were curtailed. The rate proposals proved to be so lacking in common sense that they had to be discarded within two years. Their apparently intended result was to increase revenues. Their real effect was, of course, exactly the opposite.

The only gain that the railroad derived from this series of events was an announcement from the Department of the Interior that The Alaska Railroad would not be abandoned. An Anchorage publisher, C. J. Link of the Midnight Sun Publishing Company, wired President Hoover on August 16, 1930: "Owing to rumors of approaching discontinuance Alaska Railroad, this portion of Alaska almost in panic of uncertainty with many preparing remove elsewhere. Can you authorize statement calculated to allay fears and re-establish confidence?"

The telegram was referred to the Secretary of the Interior, who replied on August 21: "Your telegram of sixteenth has been referred to Interior Department for answer. Interior Department knows of no plan to discontinue The Alaska Railroad."

## Declining Deficits

It may be that Colonel Ohlson went too far in appeasing the Howell Committee. If he retreated, however, he never surrendered, and within two years he gained back the ground he had lost. Appropriations were as niggardly as ever, but small-scale capital expenditures continued. The railroad's annual report for fiscal year 1932 was written in a spirit of optimism. In spite of ten years of poverty and congressional neglect, Colonel Ohlson stated: "In view of the improved physical condition of the entire property, the lowering of the deficit from year to year, and the fact that further reduction of operating and maintenance costs can be attained through the rehabilitation program, which if carried on can be completed within a period of five years, and regardless of opinions to the contrary stated by certain individuals, it can safely be predicted that the railroad will be on a self-sustaining basis by the end of that time."

The colonel was granted only the shadow of his rehabilitation program. Yet astonishingly enough, he came within one year of being right. For in fiscal year 1938, The Alaska Railroad, for the first time in its history, could boast a net return—$76,703.* From that time, there was no year in which The Alaska Railroad had to beg an appropriation from Congress to meet operation and maintenance expenses. The general manager accomplished this apparent miracle by a persistent attention to the details of economizing as well as to the rules of good railroading. It was said that he ran a one-man railroad. It was said that he took maximum advantage of the fact that Washington, D.C., was 3,000 air miles away. It was said that his rule was arbitrary and sometimes tyrannical. Yet the colonel's accomplishment in reducing annual deficits was sufficiently remarkable that a matter of depreciation ought not to be allowed to deprive him of his triumph. Even his critics admired his success in accomplishing his goals.

There were occasions in the years before Pearl Harbor that Fortune smiled, faintly at least, upon The Alaska Railroad. One occasion, inspired by the general manager and taken up by Harry Hopkins and the Federal Emergency Relief Administration, brought 900 agricultural colonists from Michigan, Minnesota, and Wisconsin to the Matanuska Valley. They

* Depreciation was not at that time a charge against operating expenses.

came in May, 1935, after Colonel Ohlson had worked out the details for their transportation by ship from staging points in San Francisco and Seattle. Arriving at Seward, the settlers were transferred to Alaska Railroad trains that carried them 157 miles to Palmer and the farm lands of the valley.

The Alaska Rural Rehabilitation Administration was formed to manage the colony, which was also managed by experts in Washington, by more experts in California, and even by a few in Juneau. A chronicler of the Matanuska experiment described this welter of administrative direction: "Each [agency] issued orders, occasionally contradictory, to the man in charge at Palmer; the result was an intolerable situation." With unwitting understatement, he added that "In planning for additional settlements in Alaska, it is advisable to prevent the recurrence of multiple agency responsibility."

A kind of regimentation succeeded the initial wild confusion. This was later attacked and modified by a secret organization of colonists who called themselves the "Ice Worms" and who made life difficult for the paternalists. Some of the Matanuska immigrants were poorly adapted to agricultural life in an isolated mountain valley and left soon after they arrived. Over the years, two-thirds of the original settlers gave up and abandoned the valley, although not all of them left Alaska. Replacements filled the gaps and both administrators and farmers learned a great deal the hard way. To the amazement of almost everyone, including many of the colonists, the great Matanuska experiment finally resulted in a reasonably prosperous farming community.

Earlier, The Alaska Railroad had worked hard to induce homesteaders to take up land in the valley and for several years had employed an agricultural development agent for this kind of promotion. By 1935, there were 500 people in 117 families who were farming valley land, many of them on a part-time basis. By 1948, however, the 500 had increased to about 2,500, largely because the federal effort had succeeded in spite of itself. Both Palmer and Wasilla became thriving trading communities, and the railroad benefited in number of passengers carried and in the amount of freight hauled. The principal driving force behind these developments was Colonel Ohlson.

The year 1936 added a steamship operation to the railroad's activities, bringing benefits to the Territory but pain to the general manager, who was thereby prevented from boasting of the first profit in the railroad's history. In the fall of 1936, ships in the Alaska trade were idled by a maritime strike that lasted until February, 1937. The Territory, so largely dependent on imports, was soon faced with a supply crisis, particularly in food. Colonel Ohlson took direct action. Armed with a Presidential order, he chartered two salmon cannery ships and refurbished two additional vessels owned by Interior's Bureau of Indian Affairs. With this fleet, he set out to supply Alaska, including the Panhandle, Kodiak Island, and the Aleutian Islands. Since he had hired cannery ships, he paid cannery seamen's wages, which were higher than the wages of the seamen on strike. Because of the higher wages, the cost of repairs that the owners would otherwise have had to make for themselves, very little southbound tonnage, and the inexperience of railroaders with steamships, the railroad's ship line lost about $175,000. Colonel Ohlson was careful to point out in his annual report to the department that, had it not been for his maritime losses, the railroad would have earned a profit of $2,500 in fiscal year 1937. With due allowances for these losses, there was no doubt that the railroad had come a long way from the time when it was a matter of jubilation that the annual deficit had finally dropped to less than $1 million.

In addition to the Matanuska venture, the Public Works Administration and the Federal Emergency Relief Administration brought other New Deal programs to The Alaska Railroad. In 1937, PWA made a $730,000 allotment for buildings and improvements, including funds for a hotel at the railroad entrance to McKinley Park. In May, 1938, there was an emergency relief allotment of $210,000 to permit the hiring of workers from Alaska's unemployed for maintenance-of-way operations. In June, 1938, a grant of $168,400 was made for a similar purpose. In 1939, another small grant marked the end of the use of New Deal recovery and relief funds by the railroad.

In general, neither Colonel Ohlson nor the Department of the Interior was aggressive in trying to obtain Depression-born funds for badly needed rehabilitation. It was said that Interior's failure to seek recovery money for the railroad was hard to understand at a time when, according to the Thoron Committee Report, "The Administration was beating the bushes for orders for the steel mills." When it is remembered that private railroads were loaned nearly $250 million during the depression for the purchase of rails and equipment, understanding becomes even more difficult.

Since the retreat from the increased freight rates put into effect after the Howell report, there had been little resort to tariff changes to increase revenues. The year 1937 seemed propitious, however, for a general review of freight-rate policies. Deficits had declined rapidly after 1932, and freight tonnage was increasing. A judicious adjustment of tariffs might give the railroad its first experience with operations in the black. It is quite true that, even with tariff increases, apparent net income would not indicate real net income if no charges were made to depreciation. But this was an accounting subtlety which few people understood and in which, as far as The Alaska Railroad was concerned, no one at that time seemed interested.

In the spring of 1937, Colonel Ohlson ordered a study of the railroad's freight-rate structure which resulted in a general increase in tariffs. The rate changes were described in the annual report for fiscal year 1937 as follows:

> Coal rates were increased on May 20, 1937, in amounts varying from 25 to 30 cents per ton on local shipments; and the low

> export rates were increased 60 cents per ton. Petroleum and petroleum products were increased on the same date 15 cents per 100 pounds, being equivalent to 1 cent per gallon. The through rate applying from Seattle and Tacoma, Washington, to Railroad points were revised on May 30, 1937, to provide for a 3 per cent increase on the Railroad proportion of the through rates and a Seward terminal charge of $2 per ton. Local class and commodity rates were increased 3 per cent.
>
> A competitive tariff was issued on April 12, 1937, naming carload rates on beer, groceries and items of iron and steel from Seattle to Anchorage, at an increase over similar rates in effect last year during the period of navigation on Cook Inlet.

It was estimated that The Alaska Railroad portion of the through rates from Seattle and Tacoma to points in the Railbelt was increased by these changes by 7 per cent. This included both the increase in the line-haul rate and in the Seward terminal charge.

This rather dull summary of what happened to Alaska Railroad freight rates in 1937 has a dramatic significance for subsequent rate history and accounts for its inclusion here. Since these 1937 increases, and in spite of the tremendous price inflation that has occurred since, there has been no general increase in freight rates on The Alaska Railroad. There have been selective increases up and down, including competitive changes frankly made to meet the charges of water or motor carrier competitors. On the over-all, and with some qualifications with respect to individual rates, it is probable that The Alaska Railroad is the only rail common carrier in the world that has continued to charge 1937 prices for its transportation services. Some freight rates are in fact lower than they were in 1937. Passenger fares, at 6 cents per mile and basic fare plus one-third for round trips, are identical to those charged in 1937.

One more event in the history of The Alaska Railroad in the 1930's, should be noted. In 1938, at the insistence of

General H. H. ("Hap") Arnold, the construction of Ladd Air Force Base near Fairbanks had begun. General Arnold was in the great tradition established by General Billy Mitchell, who long before had called attention to the strategic importance of Alaska. General Mitchell was building telegraph lines in the Territory in 1901 and had sponsored the Black Wolf Squadron flight from New York to Nome in 1920. Each of these airmen played his part in initiating the series of decisions that eventually resulted in the building of a huge defense establishment in Alaska. As these defenses grew, so did the railroad. Of the major military Army and Air Force bases in Alaska, all were built along the tracks of The Alaska Railroad except Fort Greely, at the junction of the Richardson and Alaska highways.

## The Railroad in Wartime

In 1938, both Europe and Asia were wracked with the violence of fascist regimes—violence that led them, together with the United States, to the tragedies and triumphs of World War II. Many leaders in the democratic world did not foresee an inevitable conflict. Japan, it was hoped, would confine itself to forays against the Chinese that began with the invasion of Manchuria in 1931 and the invasion of China in 1937. Hitler, dictator of Germany in 1933, had forcefully annexed the Rhineland in 1936 and occupied Austria in 1938. In return for the Sudetenland, he had promised both England and France that he would not resort to aggressive war.

The promise, quickly made, was quickly broken. In 1939, Hitler's armies marched into Czechoslovakia and Mussolini's into Albania. There followed, in rapid succession, the formation of the Rome-Berlin Axis, the promise by Germany and Russia that they would not attack each other, Hitler's invasion of Poland, and the September declarations of war against Germany and Italy by England and France. In his quarantine speech in 1937, President Roosevelt moved beyond the neutrality acts, to which he had been sharply opposed, and moved, perhaps, ahead of the country. When England and France were confronted with the mechanized might of Germany, majority opinion in the United States favored aid to England and France, but with means short of actual war.

In November, 1940, President Roosevelt was elected to a third term. Hitler had already overrun all of Europe, and only England stood in the way of the total defeat of the Allied powers. Congress voted $13 billion for preparedness in the summer of 1940, President Roosevelt made his "four freedoms" speech in January, 1941, and Congress passed lend-lease in March of the same year. Charles Lindbergh, two months before Hitler attacked Russia in June, 1941, opposed the United States' entry into the war on the pragmatic grounds that Hitler could not possibly be defeated. Then came the attack of the Japanese air fleet on Pearl Harbor, on December 7, 1941, an attack so unexpected and so incredible that American isolationists charged that the Japanese bombing was part of a Roosevelt plot. The Axis powers declared war a few days later, and once again the United States was in a crisis struggle that extended over half the world.

After Pearl Harbor, with the Berlin-Moscow pact in shreds, our Communist enemy became our Communist ally. There was a possibility that Russia would pin down, temporarily at least, a very large number of German troops. With help from her allies, Russia might even hold out a little longer. The United States supplied a great deal of the needed help with military supplies and airplanes flown over the Great Circle route for transfer to the Russians at Fairbanks. (The Russians took delivery of the planes in Fairbanks and refused to allow U.S. pilots to fly to Siberia.)

In his annual report for fiscal year 1942, the Secretary of the Interior said of Alaska: "Close to the top of the world, where airline distances telescope amazingly, the Alaskans were keenly aware of their distance to the enemy. They were awake, also, to the assiduity with which the Japanese had studied and charted Alaskan waters, explored the coastline, and penetrated the Aleutian Islands. It was no surprise to them, therefore, when bombs fell on Dutch Harbor. They had expected them earlier." The bombs fell in June, 1942, and the Japanese occupied the three westernmost Aleutian Islands—Attu, Agattu, and Kiska—shortly thereafter.

The Alaska Railroad was needed for two major war purposes, to carry construction materials, supplies, and soldiers on the last leg of the journey to the Army and Air Force bases at Anchorage and Fairbanks and to keep military storage tanks replenished with aviation gasoline for U.S. airmen on the ferry route to Russia. As a part of these supply lines, the Army Transport Service began operations to Seward, and a five-mile spur was built to connect Ladd Field with the main line of The Alaska Railroad at Fairbanks.

As a result of these catastrophic events, The Alaska Railroad more than doubled the freight tonnage in fiscal year 1941 over 1939, and almost doubled it again in fiscal year 1944 over 1941. Gross revenue jumped from $3,058,055 in fiscal year 1940 to $11,289,637 in 1944. Net income in 1944 reached the astonishing total of $5,242,924. Even with an allowance for depreciation, which could hardly have amounted to more than $1,250,000 in 1944, The Alaska Railroad in that year was probably the most profitable railroad in the entire United States. It is small wonder that the military made gestures toward recapturing some of the railroad's net income on the grounds that this income included a large fraction of excess profits. The military were not successful in winning back some of The Alaska Railroad's wartime profits, but the following record indicates that they were on good ground in making the attempt.*

* Data taken from Alaska Railroad annual reports to the Secretary of the Interior. It is somewhat disconcerting to find differences in the totals for the same fiscal year in successive annual reports. Many of these apparent discrepancies are unavoidable because of adjustments made after a given fiscal year report has been issued. The latest figure for a given year is, therefore, the most accurate.

| *Year* | *Tons of Freight* | *Operating Revenue* | *Net Income* |
|---|---|---|---|
| 1938 | 155,833 | $ 2,212,845 | 76,704 |
| 1939 | 157,904 | 2,553,927 | −19,831 |
| 1940 | 194,467 | 3,058,055 | 341,663 |
| 1941 | 361,295 | 5,518,624 | 2,521,898 |
| 1942 | 419,867 | 5,951,590 | 2,416,187 |
| 1943 | 461,383 | 8,464,386 | 4,532,950 |
| 1944 | 627,847 | 11,289,637 | 5,242,924 |
| 1945 | 549,248 | 8,603,546 | 1,936,841 |

In retrospect, it is not easy to explain how The Alaska Railroad, with low-standard track and roadway, with worn-out, second-hand motive power and rolling stock, and with a painful problem of recruiting sufficient manpower, could have survived the war without complete breakdown. In 1941, before Pearl Harbor, Colonel Ohlson described the condition of the railroad to a subcommittee of the House Appropriations Committee. Among other things he said that:

> Economical and safe operation of the railroad requires that ballast be applied to roadbed at many places that were not ballasted when the railroad was constructed. . . . Many temporary wooden culverts and bridges erected during construction of the railroad are now badly deteriorated by decay and dry rot, and they must be replaced by new structures. . . . To take care of the increased business, new locomotives are required to replace worn-out and obsolete locomotives transferred from the Panama Canal 25 years ago.

The equipment problem was handled by buying as much as possible second-hand. During the first years of the military buildup, the railroad had insufficient money to do otherwise. When several millions of net income became available, wartime shortages made new equipment extremely difficult to obtain. A large quantity of second-hand material—boxcars, flatcars, refrigerator cars, hopper cars, cabooses, cranes, gas cars, and a few items of work equipment—from the shutdown Copper River and Northwestern Railroad and from other railroads was brought to the Railbelt in 1940. Each of the railroad's annual reports for the war period contains a record of more rolling stock and work equipment obtained second-hand. For fiscal year 1943, the second-hand list contained 1 Mikado 2-8-2-type locomotive, 10 steel hopper cars, 10 flat-cars, and 32 boxcars. For fiscal 1944, the second-hand list included 70 boxcars, 50 gondolas, 18 flatcars, 11 automatic dump cars, 3 locomotive cranes, 1 locomotive steam shovel, and 1 Jordan spreader.

In his 1944 annual report, Colonel Ohlson apologized for the second-hand purchases: "Although it is not economical to purchase second-hand rolling stock owing to high maintenance cost, the immediate necessity for equipment would not permit delays incident to the securing of new equipment. It is anticipated that future requirements will be met through the purchase of new equipment whenever possible."

In spite of shortages, some important items of new equipment were purchased. For example, acquisitions in 1941 included twenty 50-ton boxcars and 1 Pacific 4-6-2 locomotive; in 1943, 1 mountain-type 4-8-2 locomotive; in 1944, 6 military-type locomotives from the War Department, one rail-mobile, one locomotive crane, and two diesel-electric locomotives. Two 1,000-horsepower diesels were purchased for operation through the tunnels to Whittier and marked the beginning of the railroad's diesel fleet.

## Manpower Problems

The war quickly changed the manpower situation in Alaska from one of general balance with occasional shortages to one in which the shortages were both chronic and acute. By the summer of 1941, it was becoming difficult to recruit common labor. A year later, after many of the railroad's employees had been drafted or had enlisted, new recruits had to be brought under contract from the states. By the fall of 1942, even the most intensive recruiting by railroad recruiters and the U.S.

Employment Service failed to locate sufficient workers. The problem was temporarily met by the loan of a number of servicemen from Alaskan defense bases. By the spring of 1943, however, with railroads throughout the United States suffering manpower shortages, The Alaska Railroad could not take care of the volume of wartime freight being offered to it with the employees it was able to recruit.

The general manager appealed to the military and, as a result, the War Department assigned the 714th Railway Operating Battalion to the railroad. On April 3, 1943, the battalion arrived in Anchorage with a strength of nearly 1,150 men. The men of the 714th worked under the control of the civilian officials of the railroad, and, after July 1, 1943, the War Department was reimbursed for their services. The railroad paid an amount equal to army pay of officers and enlisted men plus the cost of subsistence and 10 per cent for overhead. For fiscal year 1944, these totaled $1,329,390. The addition of the soldier railroaders more than doubled the working force. Even with this enlarged personnel, the manpower shortage was not solved. The number of skilled locomotive machinists, boilermakers, blacksmiths, and car repairmen in the railway battalion was not sufficient to meet the railroad's needs. Recruiting for shopmen in the states was continued, but with only partial success.

There was a similar problem in the Eska coal mine, which the railroad had operated intermittently since construction days. In this early period, there had been numerous occasions when private mines were unable to meet the demand for coal, including that needed by the railroad. The Eska mine was purchased and maintained by the railroad for such situations and had produced as much as 70,000 tons in a single year. In the early stages of the war and despite production in the railroad-owned-and-operated mine, some coal was imported from the states. Worker shortage at the Eska mine was met by men transferred from the Enlisted Reserve Corps. At the end of June, 1944, nearly 70 per cent of the Eska coal miners were Reserve Corpsmen.

By January, 1945, the war with Germany and Italy had been won but was not yet over. The successful African and Italian campaigns were far behind. The Allies opened a second front in June, 1944, and Paris was freed from Nazi rule in August. The last German counteroffensive, in the Battle of the Bulge, had been thrown back by soldiers under General Patton. The Russians were preparing the offensive that would take them to Berlin. In January, 1945, the first withdrawals of the men of the 714th Battalion were ordered. By May 1, 1945, the number in the Railbelt had been reduced to 97. On May 8, 1945, Berlin fell, Hitler's armies surrendered, and the war in Europe was over.

On December 25, 1944, the last Christmas before the 714th was ordered to leave Alaska, its soldier railroaders contrived a good-will gesture toward the civilian employees of the railroad and their families—a gesture typical of American G.I.'s far from home. By arrangement with officials of the railroad, they made up a special train that brought Christmas gifts and cheer to station and section stops from Seward to Fairbanks. The train said more than "Merry Christmas"—it was also saying "good-by."

In 1944 and 1945, before the war ended, the railroad had continued to hire new employees, first to supplement and then to replace the 714th. In January, 1945, coincident with the beginning of the withdrawal of the railway battalion, the War Manpower Commission took over the task of recruiting. The results were not entirely satisfactory, for the quality of many of the imported workers left much to be desired. More than one-third of the 1,716 employees, hired under contract by the commission either failed to report for duty, resigned, or were discharged a short time after arriving in Alaska.

The war in the Pacific continued a few months longer. In August, 1945, the bombs that changed the world's history were dropped on Hiroshima and Nagasaki. On September 1, 1945, Japan surrendered. With both wars over, returning soldiers became an additional source of recruits but did not solve the railroad's manpower problems. High turnover, perhaps a product of postwar restlessness, was made worse by a bitter wage dispute, which was finally settled by a secretarial fiat but which left employee ill-feeling that took several years to dissipate. This and other wage disputes, however, are another story.

## The Whittier Cutoff

It is possible that the most enduring memorial to the energy and persistence of Colonel Ohlson as general manager of The Alaska Railroad will be the two long tunnels of the Whittier cutoff. It will be remembered that these tunnels pierce the coastal range to give The Alaska Railroad a 12.4-mile sea level route to its second port on Passage Canal, formerly known as Portage Bay. The tunnels suffered little damage in the great earthquake of 1964, and it is entirely possible that they will endure for centuries.

In 1913, the Alaska Railroad Commission (in "Railway Routes in Alaska," previously cited) considered and rejected this shorter railroad route to a warm-water port. The commission reported to President Taft that: "Another suggestion has been made to carry the road over the Kenai Mountains to Port Welles in Portage Bay, on the west side of Prince William Sound. This is a shorter route to tidewater, but the difficulties of construction through the pass occupied by the Portage Glacier probably remove it from consideration, and information at hand indicates that Port Welles is an inferior harbor." It did not occur to the members of this commission, as it did to the Alaskan Engineering Commission, that tunnels would provide a feasible way to bypass the Portage Glacier. As for economy, there was more money spent on the Seward-Portage line by the private builders and the Alaskan Engineering Commission between 1903 and 1919 than was spent in 1941–43 on the Whittier cutoff, including the tunnels.

Colonel Ohlson undoubtedly knew that his predecessor, Noel Smith, had considered the route to Passage Canal in 1925 as part of his search for operating-cost savings that would silence congressional critics who wanted to abandon the railroad. The National Archives contains pictures of Passage Canal that Noel Smith snapped from an airplane to prove that the bay was ice-free in winter. The project got no further than these pictures. Colonel Ohlson revived the proposal to transfer the railroad's port activities from Resurrection Bay to Passage Canal. He could not get effective support from his superiors in the Department of the Interior and none from officials in the Bureau of the Budget. He reacted in the manner of a man not accustomed to being second-guessed from 3,000 miles away. When congressional committees were considering appropriations for fiscal year 1941, Colonel Ohlson set out for Washington and appeared as a witness before a House committee considering appropriations for the military rather than for the Interior. As a railroad man testifying about a railroad construction project in an area with which he was intimately familiar, his testimony was undoubtedly effective. The military construction bill for 1941 was passed and contained $5 million to the Corps of Engineers for the construction of a branch line from Portage to Whittier.

Construction began in the fall of 1941. About a year later, a "holing through" ceremony was held in the longer of the two tunnels, where, after a final blast, General Simon Bolivar Buckner and Colonel Ohlson shook hands in a gesture of success and cooperation.

The Whittier cutoff was completed in the spring of 1943, and train operations through the tunnels to the unfinished port began on June 1. When the port facilities were constructed in

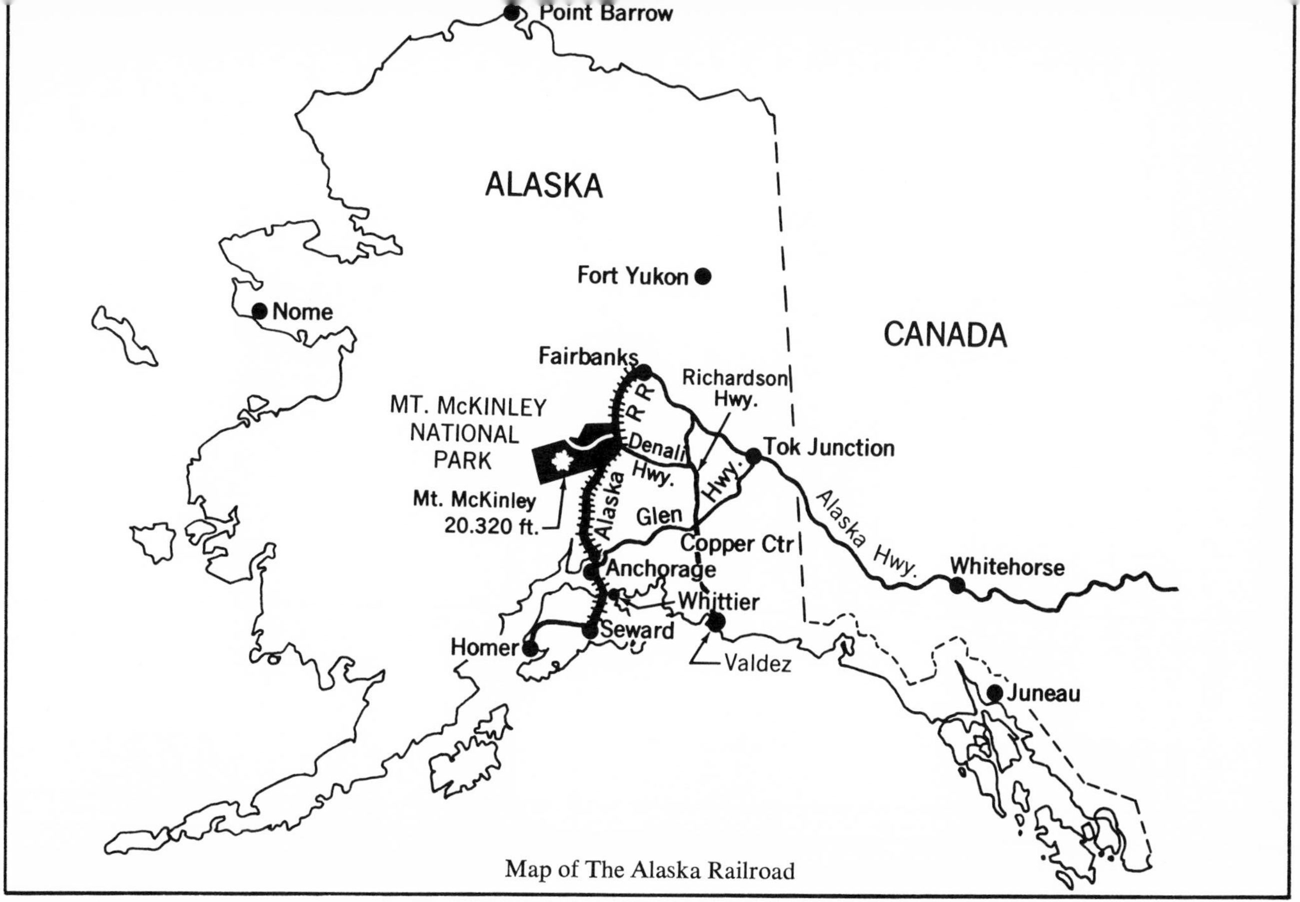


Map of The Alaska Railroad

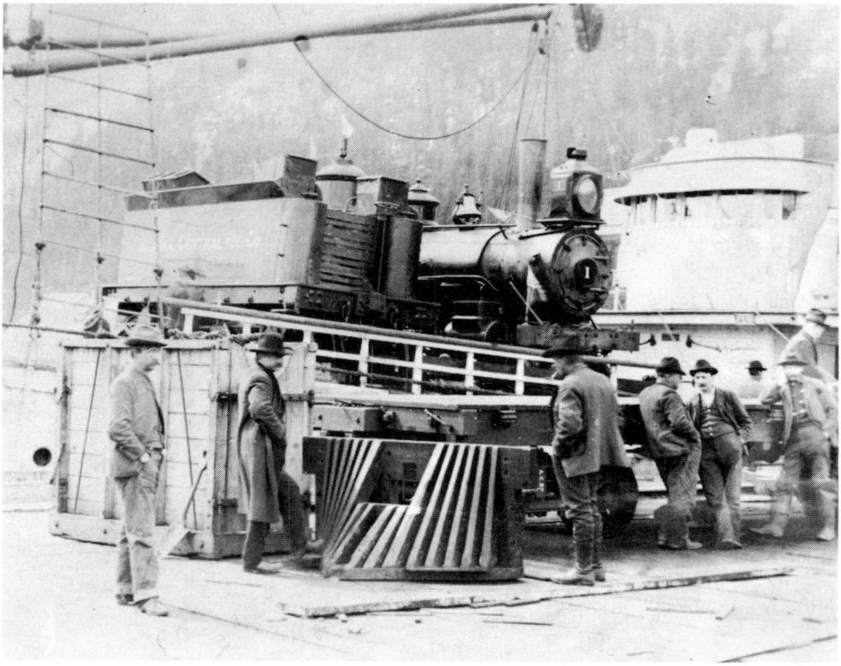

Unloading first locomotive at Seward for the Alaska Central Railway in 1914.

Narrow-gauge dinkey from the Tenana Valley Railroad on display in Fairbanks.

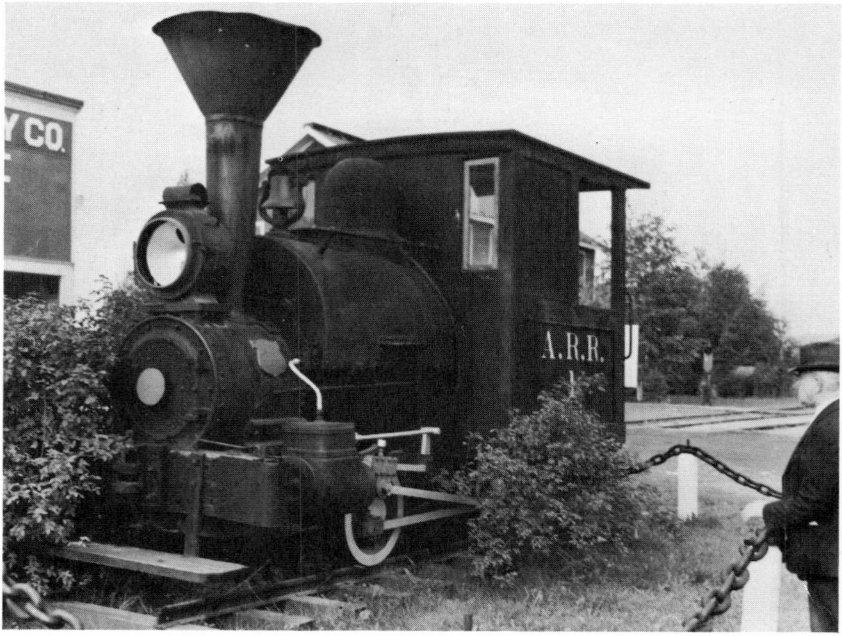

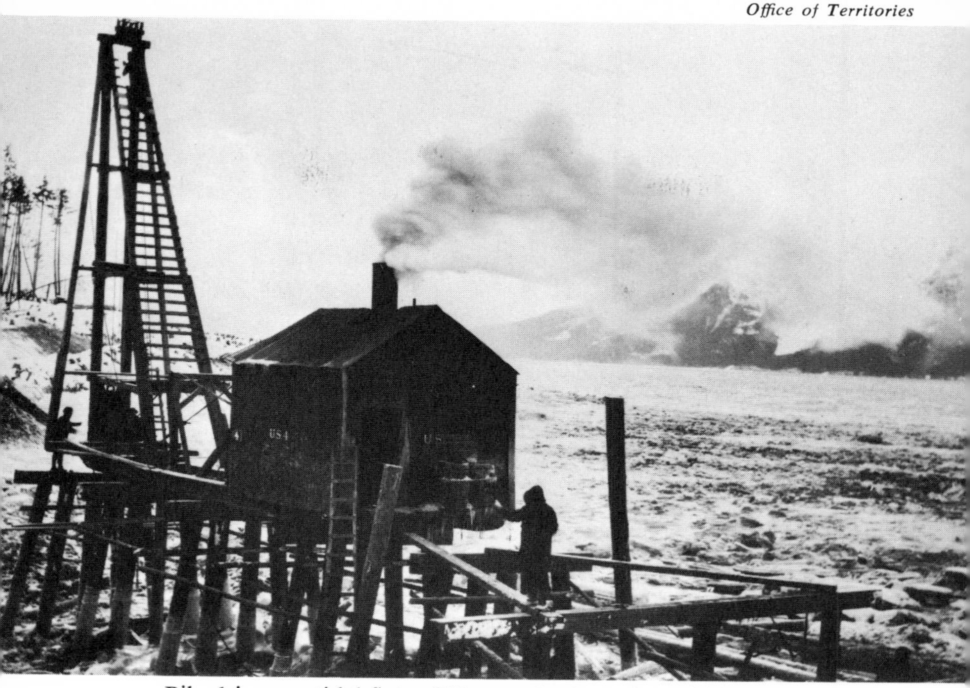

Pile driver on tidal flats of Turnagain Arm about 1917.

Station men working a rock cut north of the Alaska Range in 1917.

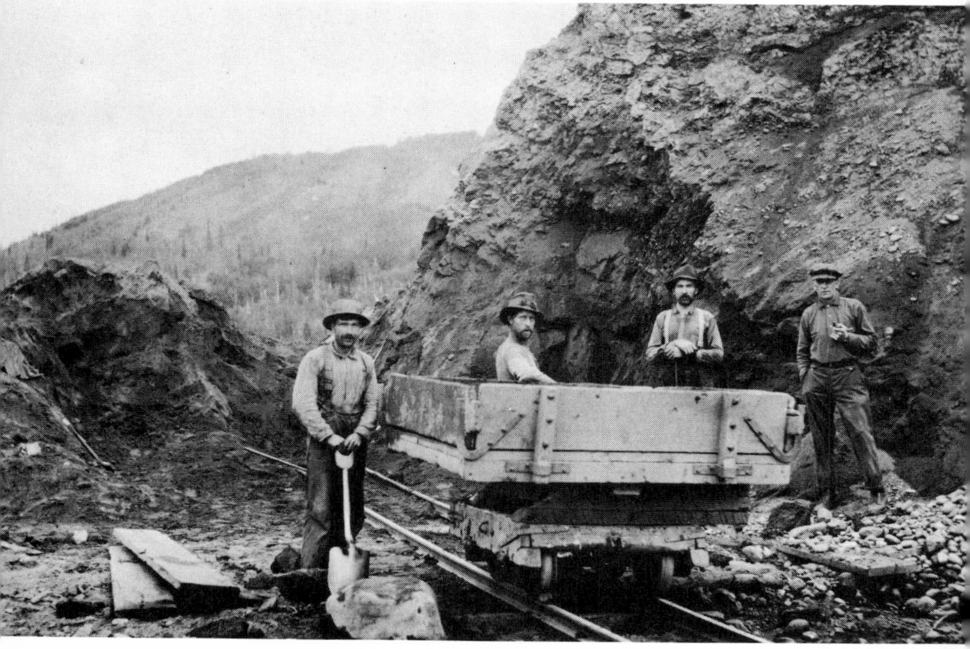

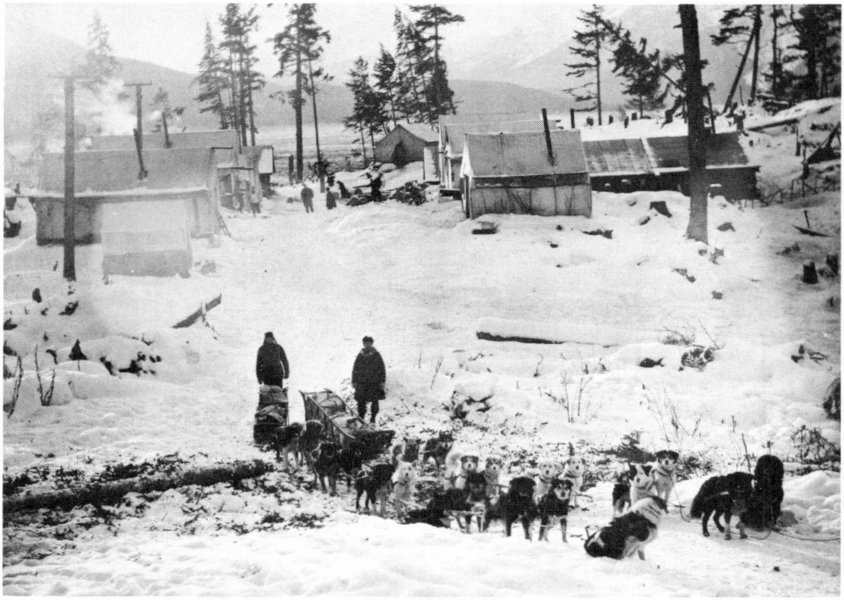

Mail for railroad construction camp arrives by dog team.

Healy River coal mine about 1922.

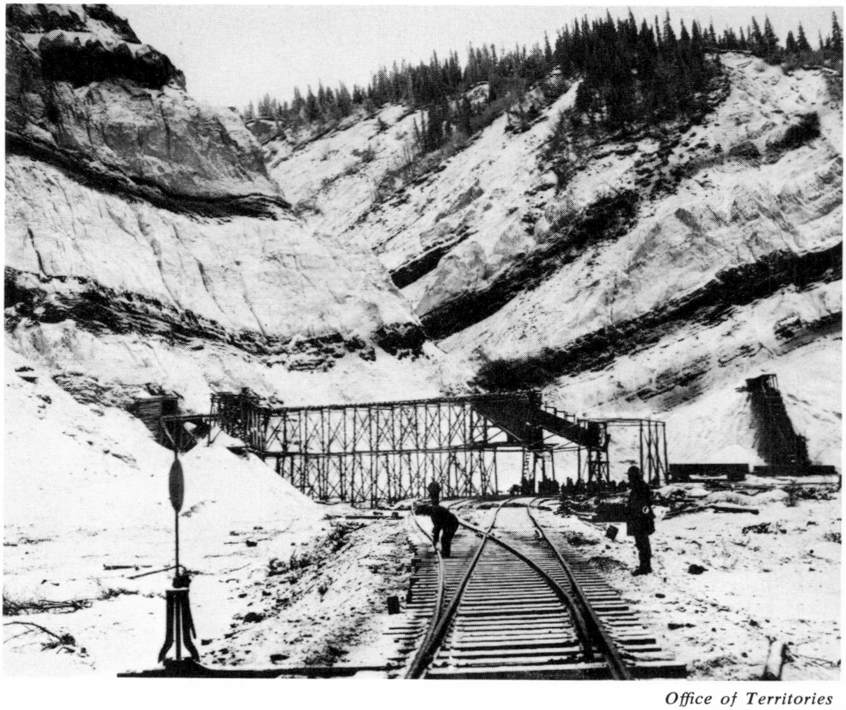

*Office of Territories*

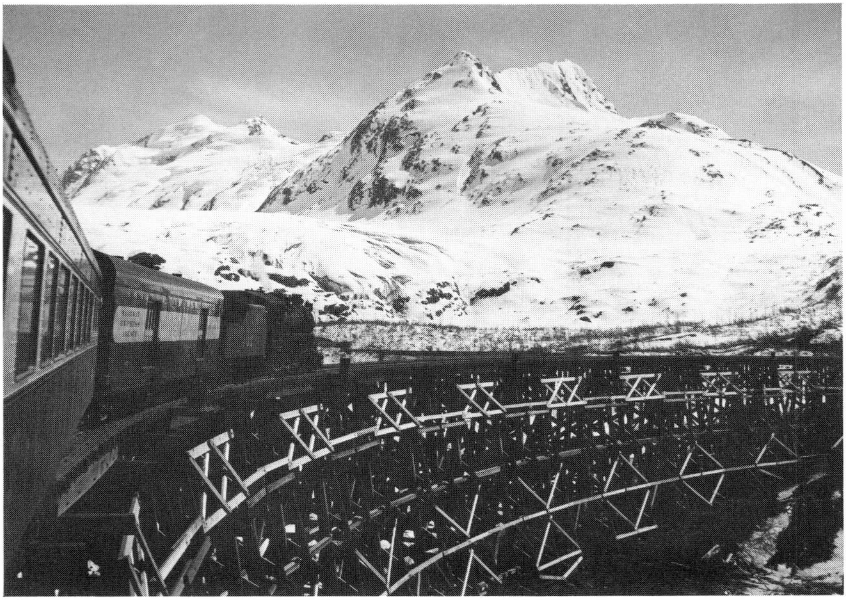

With steam gone and Loop bypassed, there can be no more pictures like this.

Interior Secretary Harold Ickes and his wife on a Railbelt honeymoon, 1938.

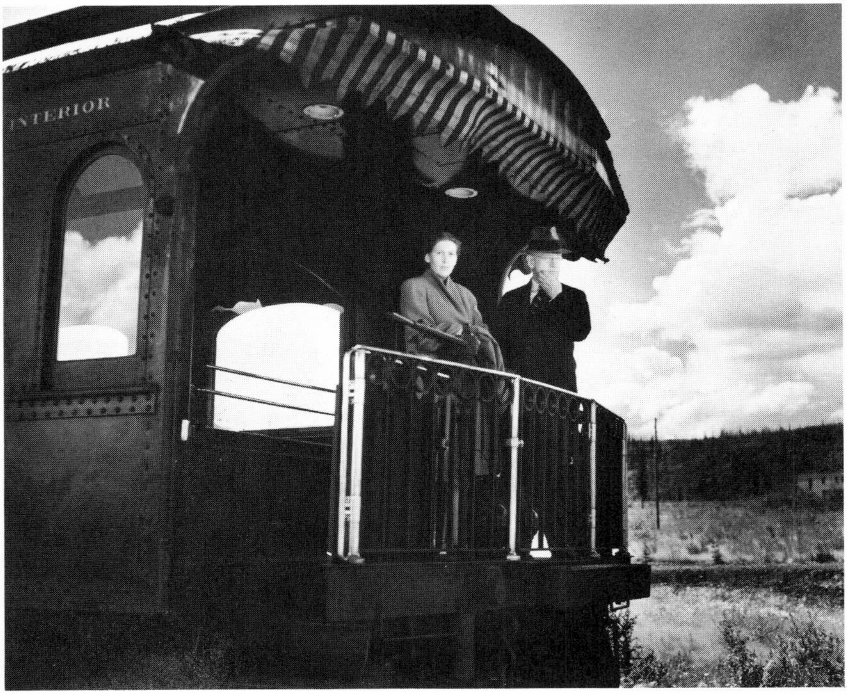

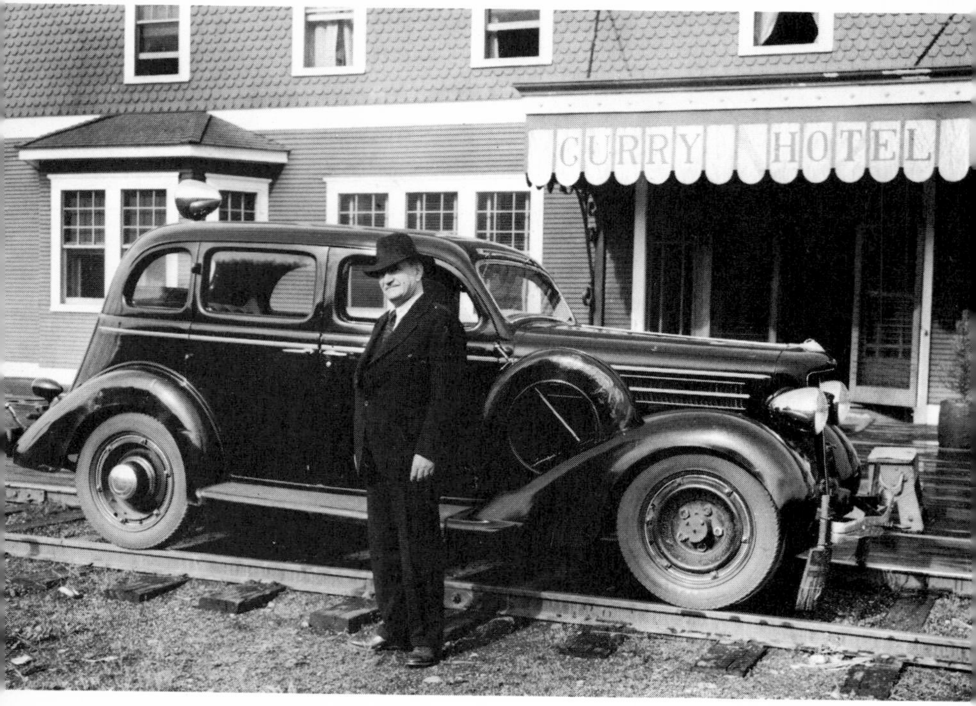


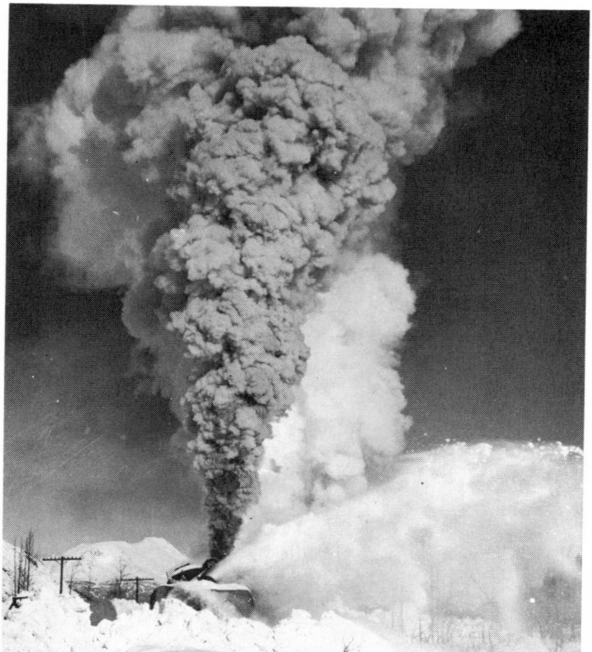

Colonel Otto F. Ohlson, the Railroad's general manager, 1928–45, on a rail car inspection trip.

Snow fleet in action in the days of steam.

A bewildered moose finds himself a passenger aboard The Alaska Railroad.

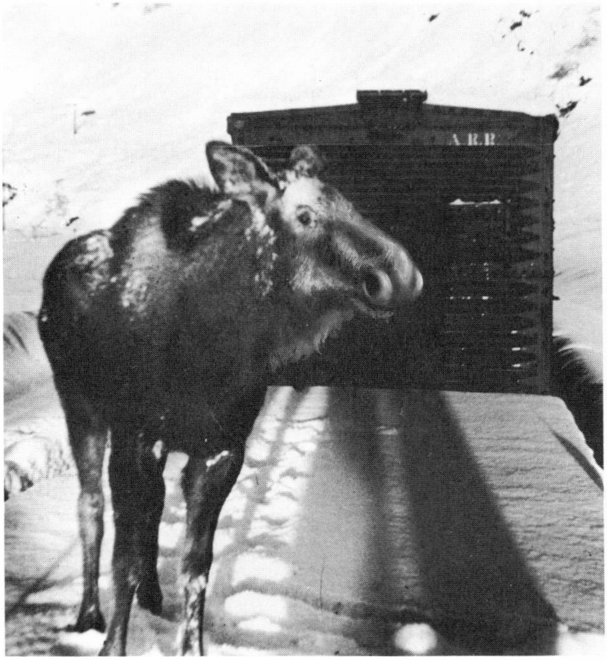


One of The Alaska Railroad's finest—2,250-horsepower diesel.

*The Alaska Railroad*

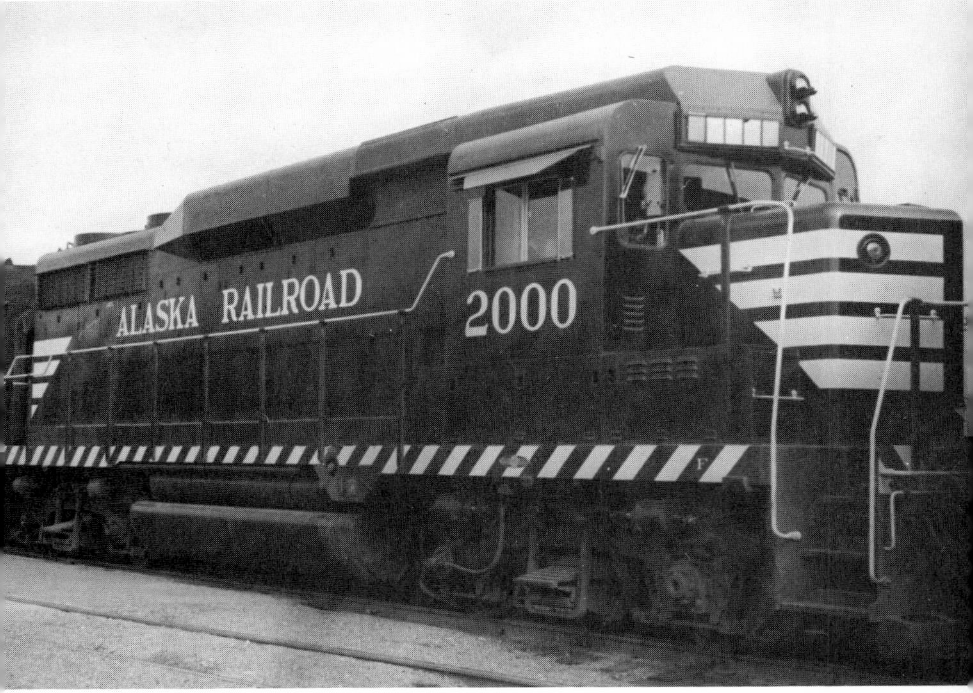

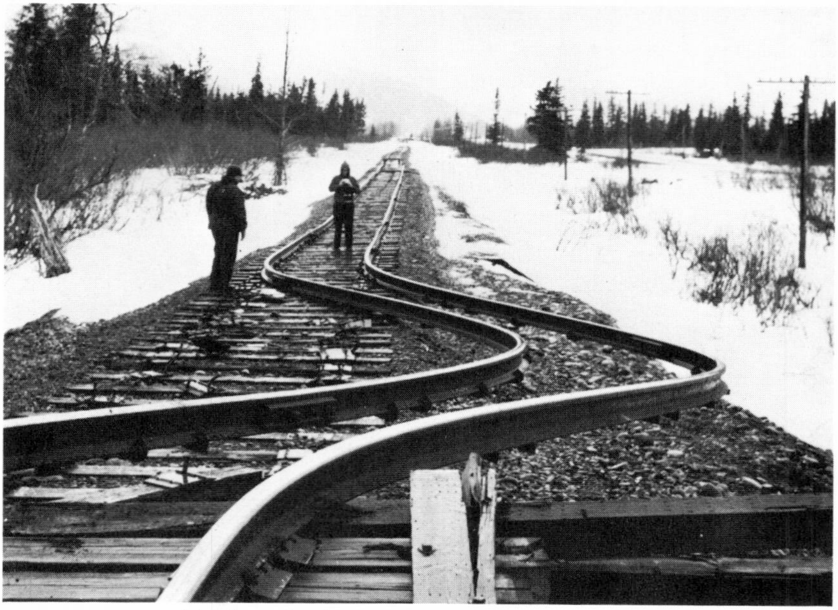

Earthquake damage to track and roadway.

A modern four-unit diesel long freight on Turnagain Arm.

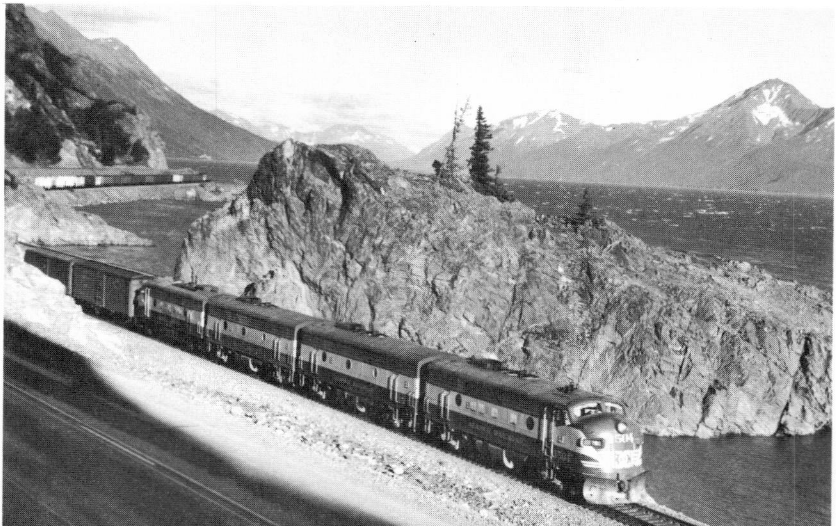

*Mac's Foto Service, Anchorage*

the following year, they were turned over to the railroad for operation. Soldier longshoremen handled loading and unloading operations at Whittier, which was operated as an Army port. Commercial freight continued to move through Seward.

The Whittier cutoff has been the subject of a good deal of controversy and the object of a good deal of abuse. The cutoff made it possible, however, for a run-down, inadequately equipped railroad to handle military traffic that, for a short time during the war, increased with geometric progression. In his annual report to Interior for fiscal year 1944, Colonel Ohlson said: "It is estimated that with the Whittier cut-off in operation, the Railroad has been able to handle approximately 75 per cent more freight traffic with existing equipment than would have been possible through the Seward gateway."

The wartime head of the Division of Territories and Island Possessions, Benjamin Thoron, confirmed this judgment. In his 1947 study of the railroad (the Thoron Committee report), he wrote: "The addition of this new terminal and short line was a life saver to Alaska. Without it, it is hard to see how the tremendous volume of traffic which the Railroad was called upon to handle for the Army could have been moved without serious restriction of civilian supplies."

# IV

# The Alaska Railroad Grows Up

That the Alaska Railroad survived the wear and tear of World War II did not mean that, henceforth, it would be treated with respect. To many Alaskans, it was a kind of Toonerville Trolley operation, useful but not to be taken too seriously. The breezier citizens of Seward were inclined to describe the incoming passenger train from Anchorage as "the good old Alaska Railroad, on time—to the day." The railroad was frequently an object of amused contempt. After all, it was a government operation and what could one expect from the government? To change a metaphor in midstream, the performance of the railroad was like the dog that had learned, after a fashion, to walk on his two front legs. The wonder was not that the dog did it badly, but that he was able to do it at all.

The records showed, nevertheless, remarkable wartime accomplishment. After Pearl Harbor, the railroad handled more freight each month than it had in the peak months of the prewar years—more than Army experts had thought possible considering the state of roadway, track, and equipment. The price paid for this performance was the inevitable postponement of all but absolutely essential maintenance, repairs, and replacements. After the war, the Department of the Interior, the Bureau of the Budget, Congress, and the President had to decide whether to approve multimillion dollar expenditures for capital improvements or to allow the railroad to lapse into ineffectiveness.

Under the circumstances, Colonel Ohlson's last annual report to the Department of the Interior before his retirement on December 31, 1945, comes as a surprise. It did not touch on the enormity of the problems of rehabilitation that lay ahead—problems of which the colonel, more than any man, was thoroughly aware. In the report, he duly recorded that because of the changed war situation, ton-miles of freight were 21.5 per cent less than in the previous fiscal year, gross revenues were 23.7 per cent less, and net income had dropped 63 per cent. Of future needs, he wrote:

> Postwar plans include the continued renovation and modernization of the properties to provide better service and to reduce costs. The plans also include building an addition to the Mount McKinley Park Hotel, and a new lodge building and cabins at Wonder Lake, 89 miles within Mount McKinley National Park, as an attraction for park visitors. The development of the tourist traffic will be of major importance, and five new buses will be required to transport guests from McKinley Park Station to the interior of the park. Two new modern passenger trains will be needed to furnish the standards of comfort expected by the tourist and traveling public.

With years of deferred maintenance to be made up, with new shops to be built, with locomotives, rolling stock, and work equipment worn out and requiring replacement, it was strange that the general manager would write casually of an addition to the McKinley Park Hotel and of five new buses to take tourists to Wonder Lake. Even the two passenger trains hardly deserved a priority. It was equally curious that Interior's annual report for fiscal 1945 ignored the railroad's postwar needs. It was as though the department and the general manager were as war-weary as the locomotives from the Isthmus of Panama, some of which were still being used in work-train, yard, and road service.

The explanation of this apparent indifference to the rehabilitation problems of the future is contained in the ambiguities of the world situation in 1945. It was not then certain that our relationship with Soviet Russia would change from military partner to cold-war adversary, and it was therefore uncertain that the big military bases in Alaska would continue operations. If they were maintained, more than a minimum rebuilding of The Alaska Railroad would be required. During the war, Russia's deep suspicion of the United States had been indicated by its insistence that American war planes be delivered in Fairbanks and not in Siberia. The suspicion quickly changed to hostility, and this ensured that Alaska would remain an essential link in the nation's chain of defense and preparedness. On the other hand, it is doubtful whether the American public would have accepted its wartime ally as a friendly nation even if the Soviet Union had made a strong bid for friendship. Thus the long period of cold war began, and one of its results was a reconstruction program for The Alaska Railroad that would eventually cost nearly $100 million.

It would have been entirely appropriate had General Manager Ohlson been able to round out his long years of accomplishment for The Alaska Railroad with a successfully completed program for its rehabilitation. His World War II profits gave him the funds with which to start, and both his knowledge and his vigor, in spite of his seventy years, should have been equal to the task. However appropriate, this was not to be. The general manager was long past the railroad's special, compulsory retirement age of sixty-two, and the future would bring a new Alaska Railroad that would require the substitution of team management for one-man rule. Reluctantly, in December, 1945, Colonel Ohlson retired, embittered to an extent by the realization that he could not remain general manager forever.

The job of rebuilding The Alaska Railroad became the province of a new general manager, Colonel J. P. Johnson, who like Colonel Ohlson, was a veteran of both civilian and military railroading. Johnson came from the mechanical department of the Atchison, Topeka, and Santa Fe. He was called to service as a reserve officer in World War II and, after a variety of military duties in the Middle East and Far East, finished his military career in charge of railroads in the Philippines. With the coming of peace, he was not satisfied to return to an unexciting job on his home railroad. With some of the officers who had served with him, he decided to go to Alaska for the larger opportunity that The Alaska Railroad offered. His first interest was in the position of superintendent of motive power and equipment, but when he learned that the number one job was open, he successfully changed direction and was appointed general manager effective January 1, 1946.

## Postwar Blueprint

A blueprint for the postwar future of The Alaska Railroad was prepared in Anchorage during the early months of 1946 by a committee headed by Benjamin Thoron, who had just completed a term as director of the Office of Territories. The other members were George Sundborg, later administrative assistant to Alaska's Senator Gruening, and Edward Margolin, later head of the Bureau of Economics of the Interstate Commerce Commission. The new general manager, Colonel Johnson, together with officials of long experience on his staff, was an integral part of the committee. In December, 1945, J. A. Krug, who had just succeeded Harold Ickes as Secretary of the Interior, had concurred with a suggestion of Edwin Arnold, director of the Office of Territories, that such a committee should review the rate structure of The Alaska Railroad and make recommendations for future policy. General Manager Johnson not only welcomed the proposal but urged that its scope be broadened to include operating and management policies.

The result of this collaboration was a 220-page report,

issued by the Department of the Interior in 1947, in which the committee thus described its work:

> At Anchorage, conferences were held with the General Manager and other officials of the Railroad in regard to operations, physical conditions, organization, accounting practices, etc. Many of the recommendations in regard to operating matters emanated from these discussions, and the Committee wishes to give full credit to the General Manager for his initiative in regard to them. Operating data and accounts were studied and analyzed and a detailed analysis of the freight traffic of the Railroad for a sample period was undertaken. The Committee traveled the length of the Railroad in below-zero weather and observed operating difficulties at first hand. Shop and yard facilities at Anchorage were inspected. Public meetings were held in Anchorage, Fairbanks, Palmer and Seward at which all interested persons were invited to present data and suggestions that would be useful to the Committee in reaching a conclusion. Conferences were also held with the Directors of the Anchorage Chamber of Commerce and with other interested persons, including Office of Price Administration representatives, the Manager of the Alaska Development Board and the principal representative of the Civil Aeronautics Board in Alaska.

After a study thus detailed and meticulous, the committee recommended:

1. A complete program of physical rehabilitation of the railroad;

2. That freight rates be reduced except on coal, that through rates should not be favored over local rates,* and that inequities between rates be eliminated;

3. That port operations be abandoned at Seward and transferred to Whittier;

4. That passenger service be improved by eliminating the overnight stop at Curry and by providing a three-times-a-week schedule between Anchorage and Fairbanks;

* This recommendation is not generally good tariff policy and has not been followed by The Alaska Railroad.

5. That riverboat passenger service be eliminated;

6. That the management organization include an assistant general manager, a comptroller, a traffic and development department, and a personnel department;

7. That accounting and statistical reports be thoroughly revised;

8. That operation of the Curry and McKinley Park hotels be discontinued;

9. That meal and boarding-house operations be put on a paying basis;

10. That a firm wage policy be adopted, that private railroad personnel practices be followed and exemptions obtained from government regulations in conflict with these practices;

11. That an advisory committee of railroad experts should review annually the operations and activities of the railroad.

The Thoron report showed a breadth of viewpoint and a comprehensiveness of specifics that are remarkable in a government document, and much of the railroad's subsequent history reflects the extent to which its recommendations have been carried out.

It was not enough, however, merely to have a program. Congress and the Bureau of the Budget would have to be persuaded to provide the funds, initially estimated at between $35 and $50 million. When general managers Noel Smith and Otto Ohlson had tried in the 1920's to convince these guardians of the treasury of the need for much smaller sums, they had been met with indifference, occasionally varied with hostility, and always with a refusal to appropriate more than was needed to cover operating deficits.

In 1945 and 1946, the climate of opinion was much more favorable to investment in Alaska. World War II had called attention to the Territory in a way that gold rushes had been unable to do. As thousands of soldiers returned home, they retained a much more inviting memory of Alaska than was possible for the grizzled adventurers who had prospected the graveled streams near Fairbanks or had panned the beach sands of Nome.

On August 12, 1944, just eight months before his death, President Roosevelt made a speech at Bremerton, Washington, in which he said: "I am going to set up a study of Alaska and the Aleutian Islands as a place to which many veterans of this war, especially those who do not have strong roots, can go to become pioneers. Alaska is a land with a very small population . . . I am convinced that it has great opportunities to those who are willing to work and to help build up all kinds of new things in new lands."

Soldiers who had been to the Aleutians would give short shrift to the Aleutian part of the proposal, but many who had been stationed at Elmendorf Air Base or Fort Richardson, near Anchorage, or at Ladd or Eielson fields, near Fairbanks, would be encouraged to return. After the President's speech, letters from returning soldiers inquiring about opportunities in Alaska came to the Department of the Interior at the rate of about 600 a month. One such veteran was W. C. Davidson, whose first service with The Alaska Railroad was as a member of the 714th Railroad Operating Battalion and who is now superintendent of transportation. There were many others who followed his example.

Even more important to the railroad than enthusiasm for the Territory was the need of the Army and Air Force for continued rail service to the military bases of the Railbelt. High-ranking officers supported Interior requests for appropriations for the railroad with force and persistence. In 1948, Major General Howard A. Craig, then commanding general in Alaska, told a subcommittee of the House Committee on Appropriations that "We consider the rapid accomplishment of the rehabilitation program and re-equipping of The Alaska Railroad as essential to the progress of the military development program and as primary requisites for the security of Alaska."

The growth of interest in the Territory of Alaska was also manifest by Secretary Ickes' declaration for statehood in 1945 and, in 1946, by the adoption for the first time by a President of a policy favoring Alaskan statehood. President Truman's 1946 State of the Union message contained this endorsement (in addition to approval of statehood for Hawaii) but made it subject to the acceptance of the majority of Alaskans. It was natural that some of this interest in the Territory should rub off on The Alaska Railroad.

### Rebuilding Begins

Thanks to the nest egg left over from the tremendous wartime profits of the last years of Colonel Ohlson's tenure, his successor, Colonel Johnson, did not have to wait for congressional appropriations to begin the work of reconstruction. In his annual report for fiscal year 1946, it was thus possible for the director of the Division of Territories and Island Possessions, to whom the railroad was administratively responsible, to state that: "By the end of the fiscal year, a complete rehabilitation program for The Alaska Railroad was already under way."

In September, 1946, a maritime strike brought a supply crisis to the railroad that was alleviated to an extent by a dramatic motor-truck relief convoy that made the distance from Seattle to Anchorage in twenty-five days in the dead of winter. The convoy was organized by the railroad and manned by railroad employees. Of the eighteen trucks that started the trek from Seattle, the seventeen that got through were needed for railroad construction purposes almost as badly as the supplies they carried.

In 1947 and 1948, almost all of the reorganization recommendations of the Thoron Committee were adopted. The railroad was growing up, and the intensely personal management of Colonel Ohlson was no longer possible. Johnson was fortunate in both the old and new officials whom he selected. Among the long-time Alaska railroaders were J. T. Cunningham, who became assistant general manager in fact as well as in title; John E. Manley, ex-machinist and ex-locomotive fireman and engineer who became superintendent of transportation; George Benedict, superintendent of motive power and equipment; A. R. Sessions, chief clerk to the general manager (later placed in charge of the Seattle office); J. J. Delaney, general auditor and later real estate and contract agent; Anton Anderson, assistant chief engineer; and C. L. Griffith, assistant chief engineer. Among the new appointees were Robert Sharood, chief engineer; Paul Shelmerdine, who became the railroad's first director of personnel; and Larry Moore, the first head of the traffic and public relations department. Shelmerdine and Moore had been officers with Colonel Johnson in the Philippine theater. A former China hand, Delmas Nucker, became budget officer.

The result of this reorganization and of the new appointments was the substitution of a team effort for Colonel Ohlson's one-man railroad.

While some reconstruction contracts were issued and some additional equipment purchased in 1946 and 1947, the big job waited on the millions in congressional appropriations that the program would require. President Truman gave a boost with his State of the Union message to Congress on January 7, 1948, by again proposing statehood for Alaska and Hawaii, and, in his annual budget message a few days later, he stated his approval of the budget item for the improvement of The Alaska Railroad. On May 21, 1948, the President sent a special message to Congress in which he called attention to the five-year program for the rehabilitation of the railroad and said that its urgency was such that it should "be accelerated in order to accomplish most of the work within three years."

Under these auspicious circumstances, Congress gave its blessing to the rebuilding of The Alaska Railroad. An outright

$4 million was appropriated for fiscal year 1948 together with $15 million in contract authorization.* Successive Congresses appropriated many millions more. The original cost estimates were based on the assumption that the Seward-Portage line of the railroad would be abandoned and that Seward port activities would be transferred to Whittier. Subsequent events, triggered by the Korean War, changed this assumption, and funds were eventually appropriated to include the Seward line and the Seward terminal. With this change, and with added funds from the railroad's earnings, the total cost of the rehabilitation program eventually reached about $100 million.

In celebration of the railroad's new style, new direction, and its first appropriations for the rehabilitation program, a streamlined passenger train, gleaming impressively in blue and gold, was placed in service in October, 1948. This was the AuRoRa, alias the Moosegooser, which, after a shakedown trip to Palmer with a load of school children, made its official maiden run from Anchorage to McKinley Park and Fairbanks.

## A Modern Railroad

Most of the rebuilding of The Alaska Railroad was accomplished between 1948 and 1952. The biggest jobs of reconstruction were performed under contract rather than by force account, and multimillion dollar contracts became almost commonplace. However, this brought problems of differential

* The grant of contract authority to The Alaska Railroad proved an expensive luxury because it precluded the possibility of doing rehabilitation work with railroad employees (force account). Since a great deal of rail hauling of supplies, rock, and gravel was a part of many projects, the railroad was in the strange position of, in effect, renting out its cars and locomotives to contractors and paying in the contract price not only the "rent" but the administrative overhead on the use of its own equipment. When direct appropriations were substituted for contract authority, the cost of many projects was materially reduced even though they were completed by contract rather than by force account. The possibility of force-account work proved to be a substantial factor in securing low bids.

pay for the railroad's workers, sometimes working side by side with the more highly paid construction company workers. These wage difficulties contributed to astoundingly high labor turnover rates. In fiscal year 1948 for example, it required the recruiting of 3,585 employees to achieve a net addition of 679.

A major source of supplies and equipment was found in the stores of military surplus property that was made available at the end of the war without exchange of funds. Interior's Appropriation Act for 1947 had authorized the acquisition of such property by the railroad upon a certification by the Department of the Interior that federal surplus items were necessary to operation and maintenance. A temporary surplus-property office was established in Washington, D.C., and, during the rehabilitation program, more than $10 million worth was selected and shipped to Alaska. However, the very substantial freight charges were paid by the railroad.

The list of property items obtained as surplus from the War Assets Administration is impressive. In fiscal year 1948, for example, it included 18 locomotives (of which 14 were diesels), 500 gondolas, 175 boxcars, 45 refrigerator cars, 31 kitchen cars, 16 flatcars, 6 hospital cars, and 15 locomotive cranes. The hospital cars were modified in Seattle into baggage cars, parlor cars, and passenger coaches. Many other items of rolling stock were rebuilt in the shops at Anchorage.

Among the more unusual items of government surplus was a shell-forging plant built in Denver and completed just as the war was over. It was dismantled, shipped to Anchorage in pieces, and re-erected as the railroad's diesel shop. A power plant in Carlsbad, New Mexico, was similarly shipped to Alaska and became the Knik Arm power plant on Ship Creek in Anchorage. It was jointly financed by the railroad and an electric cooperative, the Chugach Electric Association. After a long and harrowing period of negotiation, the railroad share of the plant was eventually sold to Chugach and is still an important part of the Anchorage power system.

The Knik Arm power plant was not the first instance of the railroad's resorting to unusual measures to meet power shortages in Anchorage. An even more unique venture in electricity was fathered by the railroad's Anton Anderson, who learned of a wrecked steamer, split in two over rocky shoals, with a complete power plant intact in one-half of the vessel. Under his auspices, the power-plant half of the ship was towed to Anchorage, beached, and placed in operation. For several years, it fed additional current to Anchorage power lines.

There was waste as well as gain from the use of government surplus. Some lots were obtained on the gamble that they might prove useful, and some without exact knowledge of what the contents would be. This was because the railroad often could not obtain merely the item it needed but was required to accept the entire lot of which the item was a part. Some items became surplus twice over, either because they were not needed in the first place or because the quantity was greater than could be used within a reasonable time. Warehouse space to store all the property received was impossible to obtain in Anchorage, and portions were shipped to a storage yard at Eklutna. Where goods were stored in the open, there were not enough tarpaulins to protect them from weather damage. The railroad's special agent force was insufficient to protect property from pilferage, and small hardware items particularly were lost to the light-fingered.

Eventually a Republican administration, determined to manage a socialist enterprise better than the Democrats had done, sold the leftovers to the highest bidder and made a tidy sum for the railroad's revolving fund. All things considered, and with the advantages of the program summed up and the minuses subtracted, the railroad obtained several million dollars' worth of useful property and equipment at a fraction of what it would have cost on the open market. While the Thoron Committee had been sharply critical of the continued acquisition and use of second-hand equipment by the railroad, it must be remembered that many of the items obtained from federal surplus were new.

Government surplus was by no means the entire source of plant, equipment, and supplies. Newly manufactured cars, particularly hoppers and flats built in the East and Middle West, were also obtained. Sometimes cars purchased were in short supply among railroads near the plants in which they were manufactured. They were then loaned to such railroads and were carried free to Seattle in return for permission to use them under load. There was the time when the Washington, D.C., office of the railroad received a telephone call from a puzzled official of the Association of American Railroads who wanted to know what an Alaska Railroad flatcar was doing in Texas. The mystery was explained when it was found that the car was being legitimately used by a Texas railroad on a rather roundabout routing to Seattle and Anchorage. Years later, The Alaska Railroad tried a similar arrangement to get a new General Motors locomotive transported to Prince Rupert without charge. The Canadian National Railway agreed to the free transport in return for permission to work the locomotive across Canada. For a time, the plan was delayed by literal-minded Canadian customs officials who insisted that if the Canadian National used the locomotive it then became an import and the Canadian National would be required to pay the duty imposed by Canada on imported locomotives.

Nearly two-thirds of the railroad's reconstruction funds was spent for track and roadway. Cuts were widened, curves daylighted, and some track relocated to better terrain. Many wooden bridges were replaced by steel, and hundreds of trestles and culverts were torn out and rebuilt with creosoted timbers. Enormous quantities of pit run and crushed gravel base were applied, and tens of thousands of creosoted ties were inserted. Crushed-rock dressing would have improved the track still more, but its high cost precluded its use at a time when there were more urgent needs. More recently, and as additional funds from earnings became available, crushed-rock ballast has become more common.

While roadway improvements were highly necessary, they would have counted for little if the old 60- and 70-pound rail had been retained. For nearly 500 miles, from Whittier to Portage and from Seward to Fairbanks, the old rail was taken up and new 115-pound rail substituted for it. Because money ran out in the later stages of the rehabilitation program, more than 150 miles of the new rail was laid on roadbed that had not been reballasted and before all worn ties had been replaced. It required several more seasons of work to make up the deficiency.

By 1952, almost all of the main shop buildings in the yards at Anchorage had been replaced, including two totally destroyed by fire in the winter of 1951. Congress promptly appropriated $4 million to replace the burned-out buildings. When both rehabilitation and fire-damage construction was completed, the railroad had a new $2 million diesel machine shop that was once a Kaiser shell plant in Denver, a new general repair shop, a new coach shed, a new freight shed, and new warehouses. Most of the new construction was of concrete and steel, which will resist the fire demons that have destroyed so many wooden buildings in the towns and cities of Alaska.

The railroad was now almost an all-diesel operation. The music of the steam whistle at grade-crossings, the billowing smoke, the firemen struggling to keep a good head of steam for a steep grade—all were disappearing from the Railbelt as from railroads everywhere. Diesels had proved their worth on The Alaska Railroad in 1944 when it was found that their use made it unnecessary to install forced-draft ventilation in the Whittier tunnels. Diesels have eliminated the frustrating experience of watering a steam locomotive at 50° below zero. They are economical, too, for in the clean cool air of Alaska the railroad's diesels require less maintenance than those on almost any other railroad in the United States. Even the whistle problem was partly solved with a sound that echoed the more adventurous days of steam. Years later, when Alaska Railroad officials complained of the loss of revenue that would follow the conversion of Anchorage military power plants to natural gas, they were not allowed to forget their own substitution of diesel fuel for coal.

The Alaska Railroad retains several of its old steam locomotives in the Railbelt as reminders of an era whose passing even the young among railroad buffs regret. One small dinkey tops a monument in front of the Anchorage headquarters that commemorates the rehabilitation program completed in 1952. Another is a narrow-gauge locomotive inherited from the Tanana Valley Railroad that is still being used as a monument in Fairbanks. A third locomotive, more modern and more respectably sized, has become a playground for children in a downtown park in Anchorage. A fourth—another relic of pioneer railroading in Alaska—rests on a siding in the Matanuska Valley town of Palmer. There is a possibility that a few of The Alaska Railroad's ancient steamers may still be operating. In January, 1958, a Norwegian ship cleared Whittier with fourteen of these locomotives bound for Spain.

The last of The Alaska Railroad's steam locomotives was number 557. It was retained because it could haul a train through high water when diesels were unable to do so. With the purchase of GP30 and GP35 road diesels, which are capable of high-water operations, old 557 was sold for scrap, at least so railroad officials thought. However, in 1966, the *Railbelt Reporter* carried a story of the purchase of 557 by Monte Holm of Moses Lake, Washington, who had the locomotive repaired and placed on a 900-foot siding at his place of business. Coupled to a caboose obtained from the Great Northern, it is operated on the 900-foot track strictly for pleasure—no doubt the biggest toy in the state of Washington.

Rehabilitation also brought changes in communications.

Radio and telephone gradually replaced Morse code until the last of the railroad's Morse circuits was deactivated in 1959. For most of the fifty miles between Anchorage and Portage, pole lines were exposed to crashing slides from the steep slopes of the Chugach Mountains. Microwave towers, built several years after most reconstruction work had been completed, now transmit railroad, military, and commercial messages. Radio has become standard equipment on trains and in the yards.

The rehabilitation program was accompanied by a change in accounting and statistical methods. The Thoron Committee had recommended that they be revised in the interest of providing accurate information and that the statistical data required of Class I railroads be filed with the Interstate Commerce Commission. The general manager thereupon hired two accountants trained in Interstate Commerce Commission procedure to revise the railroad's accounting system to conform with that required by law and regulation of private railroads. One of these accountants, Elroy Hinman, later became assistant to the general manager for accounts and audits. Machine methods, advanced for the time, were introduced into the accounting department. The writing of checks, for example, would proceed from a manual system to a machine system and eventually to electronic data-processing equipment.

None of these changes was more significant than the introduction of depreciation accounting in 1947. Before World War II, the railroad could not possibly have earned depreciation charges, while during the war they were earned several times over. On instruction from the House Appropriations Committee, an amount to measure depreciation prior to June 30, 1947, was entered on the books as of July 1, 1947, and depreciation has been a part of the railroad's operating costs ever since.

Depreciation represents a concept somewhat unusual in the business of government. It is not surprising, therefore, that officials of the railroad and of the General Accounting Office have been at odds at various times since 1947 about its interpretation. The General Accounting Office has been right in recognizing that depreciation accounting has its dangers for government administrators. It is not impossible that they, like their counterparts in private business, may be tempted to make adjustments that do not alter the amount of available cash, but are capable, nevertheless, of turning a net loss into a net profit.

Time has demonstrated that depreciation accounting is of great value to Alaska Railroad general managers, hard pressed by congressional insistence that the railroad's expenses must not exceed its income. It is granted that depreciation charges represent the cost of used-up capital and are not properly treated as reserves from an accounting standpoint. At the same time, these charges have encouraged railroad officials to safeguard cash accumulations in sufficient amounts that requests to Congress for appropriations for capital improvements are unnecessary.

The completion of individual projects in the railroad's rehabilitation program produced an epidemic of dedications between 1948 and 1952. Ceremonies marking the inaugural run of the streamlined AuRoRa have been mentioned earlier. In 1949, there were dedication ceremonies to celebrate the completion of the new yard at Fairbanks and the big diesel shop at Anchorage. The 1950 dedications were somewhat miscellaneous—a new bridge across Ship Creek, a new freight warehouse in Anchorage, and the realignment of 12.2 miles of track south of Anchorage between Potter and Indian. In 1951, the driving of another golden spike marked the completion of the bypass around the trestles of the Loop. In 1952 came the biggest show of all, the dedication on November 17 of the monument in front of the headquarters and station building at Anchorage, to commemorate the completion of The Alaska Railroad rehabilitation program.

A few months before the dedication ceremony in Anchorage, the man in charge of spending nearly three-quarters of the $100 million cost of the program was honored by the Department of the Interior with its Award for Distinguished Service. In June, 1952, Secretary of the Interior Oscar Chapman made the formal presentation to General Manager Johnson for "outstanding accomplishment in the successful administration of a $70,000,000 program for the rehabilitation of The Alaska Railroad."

A warning of tariff troubles ahead was given by the Interstate Commerce Commission in 1953. It was well understood that the commission's jurisdiction did not extend to The Alaska Railroad, yet the commission had allowed the railroad to place ICC numbers on its joint rail-water tariffs over a period of many years. Beginning in 1941, the Federal Maritime Commission had objected to this arrangement, but it was not until 1953 that the ICC instructed the railroad to remove the identifying numbers, which had led some shippers to believe that the railroad was subject to the commission's authority. Eventually the ICC numbers would appear again on the railroad's tariff schedules, but not without a struggle that would involve the Bureau of the Budget, the Department of the Interior, Congress, and two Presidents.

The revenue picture during Colonel Johnson's tenure, shown below, is not easy to evaluate.

| *Fiscal year* | *Revenue tons* | *Revenue* | *Expenditures* | *Net income* |
|---|---|---|---|---|
| 1946 | $ 419,686 | $ 5,646,982 | $ 7,916,280 | $ −2,269,298 |
| 1947 | 641,841 | 9,617,482 | 8,487,491 | 1,129,991 |
| 1948 | 900,355 | 15,364,148 | 13,748,287 | 1,615,861 |
| 1949 | 763,267 | 11,760,015 | 11,449,189 | 310,826 |
| 1950 | 875,561 | 11,562,524 | 11,558,755 | 3,769 |
| 1951 | 1,093,726 | 15,353,426 | 15,253,550 | 99,876 |
| 1952 | 1,355,080 | 18,609,941 | 19,407,587 | −797,646 |

The handsome net incomes of fiscal years 1947 and 1948 took a sharp drop in 1949 and almost disappeared in 1950. As a result, in 1950 the railroad proposed a 10 per cent increase in freight rates. As there had been no hearings and little discussion in the press, the people of Alaska were not prepared for this increase. Protest to the Secretary of the Interior was immediate and vigorous, and the general manager was required by the department to rescind the 10 per cent. Search for an alternative resulted in a new tariff that equalized the rates from Whittier and from Seward by increasing the former and decreasing the latter. The railroad argued that since the military would not permit civilian use of the twelve-mile haul from Whittier, thereby forcing civilians to use the sixty-four-mile mountain haul from Seward, it would be unfair to burden the civilians with the higher costs of the Seward route. Rate equalization between Seward and Whittier at least shared the costs.

### Side Trip to Seward

Ever since the completion of the Whittier cutoff in 1943, the Seward-Portage line of the railroad had been under sentence of abandonment, yet imposing of the sentence was constantly postponed. It will be remembered that General Manager Ohlson had successfully urged the inclusion of funds for the Whittier line and tunnels in a Supplemental Defense Appropriations Bill for fiscal 1941. In his testimony he had stated, without qualification, that the Seward line would be abandoned once the short cut to a warm-water port became operational. This testimony was given to the House Defense Appropriations Subcommittee early in March, 1941. A few days later, Colonel Ohlson appeared before an Interior appropriations subcommittee that was considering appropriations for fiscal 1942. He was sharply taken to task for bypassing the Interior in favor of the House committee and for condemning Seward to what appeared to be possible ghost-town status. He then suggested that Anchorage be connected with the existing Hope-Sunrise highway to Seward either by construction around the head of Turnagain Arm or via a causeway across it. World War II gave Seward a reprieve and made academic for the time the questions of the abandonment of the rail line between Portage and Seward and of the highway connection between Seward and Anchorage.

After the war, and with some difficulty, Interior obtained support from the military for the building of a highway along Turnagain Arm from the Anchorage-Potter road to Portage. There was, of course, the expectation of eventual connection with the existing highway linking Seward, Hope, and Sunrise. Meanwhile, the wooden structures of the Loop were becoming increasingly unsafe and, with no highway from Anchorage to Seward, Interior officials were forced to ask Congress for money for their repair. There was explosive response in the House Appropriations Subcommittee as to why the Seward rail line was still being operated. The explanation was the obvious one that, without a first-class highway from Anchorage to Seward, abandonment of the Seward rail line was not feasible.

As one result of these events, funds were appropriated to rehabilitate the highway linking Hope, Sunrise, and Seward and to complete the new construction between Potter and Portage. The latter construction was begun in 1949 after an agreement between the railroad, Interior's Alaska Road Commission, and the Bureau of Public Roads that the highway was to use the railroad line along Turnagain Arm in return for a new railroad right of way, which would generally stay between the old location and the sea. With new construction completed and the Kenai Peninsula road rehabilitated, the Seward-Anchorage highway was opened to traffic on October 19, 1951.

Congress appropriated money for fiscal year 1951 to repair the picturesque but dangerous trestles of the Loop. But, as Anton Anderson, the railroad's brilliant location engineer was quick to point out, there was a better way. The Bartlett

Glacier, which once filled the valley above the Loop, had receded so far since 1923 as to permit bypassing the old wooden trestles altogether. In 1951, the line relocation was completed and one of the most eye-catching features of the entire railroad was left to continue its slow decay.

The Korean War convinced the military that the plan to abandon Seward was not strategically sound. In June, 1951, Secretary of the Army Frank Pace, Jr., wrote the Secretary of the Interior that Whittier "will be required indefinitely for the exclusive movement of increased military loads" and that "it will be necessary that the Port of Seward handle all civilian rail requirements for an indefinite period of time." He added that the Department of the Army would support a Department of Interior request for the funds to rebuild the Seward line and port facilities, including the dock, the transit sheds, and the railroad yards.

In 1952, Interior requested these additional funds. Secretary of War Karl Bendetsen told a subcommittee of the House Appropriations Committee that the continued operation to Seward was "a military necessity and a prudent investment in national security." General William Kepner reinforced the point by telling the committee that there was "no practical alternative to rehabilitation of The Alaska Railroad between Seward and Portage and the providing of adequate dock facilities at Seward that can meet the strategic requirements imposed by the magnitude of the Alaskan defense effort."

Sensitive to changing military appraisals of the defense importance of Seward, Congress deferred the necessary appropriations, but not for long. Interior's Appropriation Act, approved July 31, 1953, contained $1.5 million to begin construction of a new dock at Seward. Six weeks previously, the dock at Whittier as well as three freight sheds and the largest stiff-legged crane in Alaska were destroyed by fire. Seward's happier days were revived for an extended period as military traffic was transferred from Whittier until a new dock could be built at that port. The fire dramatically illustrated the value to Alaska of two southwestern ports as well as the necessity for rehabilitating the Seward-Portage rail line. A supplemental appropriation act, approved May 11, 1954, provided $4.6 million for the Seward line, and Interior's 1955 appropriations act granted $2.9 million to complete the dock and transit sheds at Seward. The work of reconstruction was spread over several years and was completed in 1959.

Accounting is an exacting but not an exact science. In the case of the Seward line, this circumstance may prove fortunate, for it provides an excuse for not attempting to determine precisely the line's original cost less depreciation. The accounting factors are complicated because, between 1903 and 1966, the Seward line was built and rebuilt four times. The first building was by the Alaska Central and the Alaska Northern between 1903 and 1910, the second by the Alaskan Engineering Commission between 1915 and 1919, and the third by The Alaska Railroad under circumstances just described. But the fates were not finished with Seward. In the early spring of 1964, by what the law calls an act of God, long stretches of track, docks, warehouses, and yards at Seward, all still showing their comparative newness, were destroyed in a great earthquake. The fourth rebuilding, which is part of another story, was completed in June, 1966.

## A Republican Adminstration Takes Over

The year 1953 brought to Washington the first Republican administration since the days of Herbert Hoover. General Dwight Eisenhower became President and Douglas McKay of Oregon his Secretary of the Interior. Some of Interior's new Republican officials were not aware that The Alaska Railroad was a federal institution. When told, their immediate reaction was to conclude that this was an inappropriate, not to say unwholesome, situation—the railroad should be disposed of forthwith.

The record is not clear as to what modified their viewpoint unless it was the complete absence of private interest in buying. Department files show that, under the Democratic administrations, there had been several letters from private parties asking whether the railroad was for sale. Polite replies were sent to the effect that Interior was not committed to keeping the railroad, that all bona fide offers would be seriously considered, and that it should be borne in mind that, at original cost less depreciation, the property was valued at about $125 million. This usually ended the correspondence, and no offer, bona fide or otherwise, was ever received.

Like many other government officials at the time of transition to a new administration, Colonel Johnson was pressured by Democratic officials into submitting his resignation as general manager before the change-over. Political appointees usually need no pressure to resign under these circumstances, but in Johnson's case there was no clear precedent because his job had escaped political coloration. Reluctantly, and with frequently expressed afterthoughts that he had made a mistake, Johnson submitted his resignation. He continued as general manager until June 20, 1953, and accumulated annual leave kept him on the payroll for some time thereafter. Johnson made considerable effort to find another railroad position. He finally found it in Colombia, South America, where he would be in charge of the construction of a government railroad. In the fall of 1953, he left for his new assignment.

A Republican appointed by a Democratic Secretary of the Interior, Johnson was second only to Colonel Ohlson in length of service as general manager. He presided over the fortunes of The Alaska Railroad during one of its most critical periods. A man of tremendous drive and with the aid of as capable a set of officials as The Alaska Railroad ever had, he was responsible for the creation in Alaska of a modern, well-equipped, and efficient rail carrier. Every general manager since has owed at least a part of his success to the work and foresight of Colonel Johnson.*

## Recruiting General Managers

With the inauguration of President Eisenhower and the appointment of Douglas McKay as his Secretary of the Interior, a novel and interesting plan was adopted for the selection of Alaska Railroad general managers. Presidents of U.S. railroads and officials of the Association of American Railroads were asked to suggest names of highly competent railroad officials who might be persuaded to accept the job. Clearly enough, a railroad president would be reluctant to release a subordinate who was in line for advancement. To overcome this reluctance, it was suggested that the official selected to direct The Alaska Railroad be given a leave of absence limited to two years. At the end of the leave, the official could choose separation or return to his home road. Under this recruiting program, five general managers, each of whom had had extensive experience in responsible positions with private railroads, were appointed. The presidents of their home railroads regarded the two years on The Alaska Railroad as a kind of apprenticeship in preparation for bigger things ahead.

In general, the eight-year experiment worked well for The Alaska Railroad as well as for the private railroads that used Alaska as a training ground for their officials. Without occasional infiltration from outside, any business, including gov-

* After Colonel Johnson left for his new position in South America, indictments were brought against him and one of his assistants for alleged violations of federal conflict-of-interest laws. Convinced that the indictments were politically motivated, Johnson refused to return to the United States for trial. His assistant remained in Alaska but was never brought to trial. The indictments against both men were subsequently dismissed.

ernment business, is in danger of developing a provincial outlook. The Alaska Railroad needed managers, for a while at least, who would not be influenced by the railroad's localisms and who would bring fresh solutions to its problems. It was inevitable that some of the new general managers (and none stayed long enough to be called old) would occasionally bring customs of their own that did not fit conditions in the Railbelt. Furthermore, changing loyalties every two years or less was not always an easy task for the new general manager's subordinates. However, adjustments were usually quick and reflected credit on both sides.

Some of these general managers avoided disagreeable problems, particularly those concerned with personnel, on the ground that tenure for a year or two did not warrant taking on a long-standing difficulty. Each manager naturally wanted to add to his record of accomplishment, but, as manager succeeded manager, new ways and new ideas to make The Alaska Railroad better decreased both in number and in importance, and the temptation to make change for change's sake became difficult to avoid.

Once the initial acquaintance was made, there were hopes that one of the new appointees would continue as general manager. Several, enthusiastic about both the railroad and about Alaska, seemed to want to remain. When decision time came, however, skepticism as to the tenure of a government job or the attraction of the home railroad (or the persuasiveness of its president), proved influences too strong to resist.

General Manager Frank Kalbaugh, first of the outside five, believed his principal mission was to bring a taste of austerity to the railroad. There is no doubt that the combination of millions in rehabilitation money and traffic that far exceeded the biggest years of World War II did not foster conservative expenditure. David P. Morgan, editor of *Trains,* has visited the Railbelt and knows a good deal about The Alaska Railroad. He called it "The Railroad That Had It Too Good" in his magazine in 1955. In May, 1963, in an article, "*Trains* Goes to Alaska," he wrote of the Republican new deal for the railroad: "Under Kalbaugh and his successors The Alaska Railroad got a new image. It had begun life as a proud baby, rapidly had sunk to pauper status, had been drafted as a soldier, then had made up for its abused past in what amounted to profligacy. Since 1953 it has acted, for the first time in its life, like a business. Insofar as its ownership and the economics of the state permit, the Alaska operates like any other U.S. railroad."

There was truth in these observations, but there was also exaggeration. The problem of separating fact from fiction was caused by an excess of publicity.

Kalbaugh was a good railroader and knew what had to be done to trim expenses down to size. He also knew when the wind was blowing his way. Thus he came to the railroad in the fall, when work forces are reduced to fit the winter slowdown. In earlier years, cessation of recruiting did the trick. The general manager cut forces more than was customary, and the newspapers gave him credit for all the layoffs, not just the extras. Employees in the shops reacted sharply toward the publicity about layoffs. For example, a writer for the *Saturday Evening Post* complained that the railroad was retaining and even hiring boilermakers although it had ceased to operate steam locomotives. Railroad shopmen, emphasizing that there were other uses for boilermakers, posted a sign on a shop bulletin board that proclaimed that blacksmiths were still hired although there had been no horses on the railroad in thirty years.

In the fall of 1953, survey teams from the Department of the Interior appraised the operations of various agencies of the department and recommended changes in organization and activities to Secretary McKay. Shortly after General Manager Kalbaugh arrived in Anchorage, such a survey was made of

The Alaska Railroad. A four-man team headed by Thomas Balmer, vice-president and general counsel of the Great Northern Railway, spent a little more than two weeks in the Railbelt and filed its report on November 23, 1953. In comparison with the Thoron report of 1947 and the carefully drawn report of Kalbaugh's successor, R. N. Whitman, in 1956, the Balmer report cannot be given high marks. It recommended, appropriately enough, a large increase in the ballasting program, but concluded that the number of men used in maintenance of way was excessive. It recommended acceleration of the diesel program and concluded that the railroad had too much shop equipment and too many shop employees. The report placed a needed spotlight on an excessive accumulation of surplus property, and this was its most effective point. It failed to mention the great changes that were then in the offing—piggybacking, containerization, and the inauguration of seatrain service to Alaska.

Kalbaugh was quite capable of coming to sound conclusions on the items covered by the Balmer Committee, including the obvious ones, without the committee's help, and his managerial decisions soon took him beyond its recommendations. He abolished the commissary at Anchorage, which, at the height of its operations, had sold more than $1 million annually in goods and groceries to railroad employees. He cooperated with the Alaska Steamship Company in the beginning of a container program. He called for bids on the railroad's riverboat operations on the Tanana and Yukon rivers and awarded a contract to conduct them with railroad equipment to the B. & R. Tug and Barge Company, later known as Yutana Barge Lines. He initiated requests to several steamship companies to explore with the railroad the possibility of seatrain service to Alaska. In April, 1955, Frank Kalbaugh returned to the Southern Pacific, and on April 16, 1955, R. N. Whitman of the Great Northern became general manager.

The ten years following Whitman's swearing in as general

manager saw a startling decline in the number of employees used on the railroad to produce the same number of ton-miles of work. Two thousand employees became 1,800, the 1,800 became 1,400, and the 1,400 became 850. There were many causes for this change—the rehabilitation program itself, great strides in the use of labor-saving machinery, the growth of piggyback and containerization, and, through all these changes, a consistently high level of management.

One post-rehabilitation problem, however, required more men rather than less. This was the enormous amount of track work that the rebuilding program had left undone. Here was an almost classic example of the conflict between economies now versus economies in the future, of short-run gains taken at the risk of long-run losses. General Manager Whitman in the 1956 "Review of Alaska Railroad Problems," to which brief reference has been made, posed alternatives with a clarity of language that more recent analysts of cost-benefit ratios would do well to emulate. Whitman first pointed out that 112 miles of the railroad's main line had not been reballasted, that 60 miles had been reballasted with crushed gravel, and that the rest of the reballasting had been done with pit run. He estimated that pit-run ballast would last about 5 years, crushed gravel about 10 years, and crushed granite about 25 years. He then wrote:

> Keeping in mind that it costs the same to put good ballast under the track as it does pit run material, the only difference in cost lies in the expense of crushing. Considering that the crushed granite should last some 25 years, it will be much more economical in the long run to use the crushed rock for ballast even though the initial cost of the product is higher. Crushed gravel will cost us approximately $2.00 per yard for crushing, whereas we hope to be able to get the granite crushed for about $2.50 per yard if bid in large enough quantities. It is my idea that we should bid this crushing on the basis of ballasting with crushed rock for a 20 mile stretch each year at 2,500 yards per mile or 50,000 yards per year. The program should be spread over a

> 10 year period, making a total ballast need for 10 years of 500,000 yards of crushed rock. This would then be put under the track on the basis of at least 20 miles per year and as much more as revenue will allow.

This recommendation, along with a dozen others, was approved by Anthony T. Lausi, director of the Office of Territories, and submitted to Interior's administrative assistant secretary for comment on July 26, 1956. The reply, dated October 3, 1956, contained not a single complimentary phrase about one of the most thorough analyses of The Alaska Railroad's problems that has ever been submitted by any of its general managers.

Whitman's review of the activities of the railroad was written toward the end of his term as general manager. It was based on a maximum of practical experience and a minimum of bureaucratic timidity. His recommendations on track ballasting followed the 1955 and partial 1956 work season, in which he had administered a huge program of track and roadway rebuilding. Whitman called his review a "turnover report," since it was written just before he relinquished his job to a new general manager and went back to the Great Northern. He emphasized long-range planning for every major phase of the railroad's operations. He outlined a ten-year program for tie renewal, for maintenance and new construction of buildings, bridges, trestles, and culverts. He submitted five-year programs for the purchase of automobiles, trucks, and off-track maintenance equipment. His rolling stock program contemplated the purchase of fifty cars a year. He made suggestions as to how the railroad could fulfill its historic role in aiding the development of industry and agriculture. He regarded these long-range plans as minimum goals to be achieved as fast as earnings could pay for them.

Whitman's formula for financing capital expenditures—a formula that has become established railroad policy—added each *prior* year's depreciation to *prior* year's net earnings, the sum of which fixed the maximum amount to be spent for improvements in the current year. There have been interesting attempts on the part of Bureau of the Budget to upset this formula by attempting to reduce the railroad's balances in cash and require it to "bet on the future" in determining the capital improvement budget. Interior officials have successfully resisted such a change in investment policy. The railroad continues to obligate money for capital expenditure only after it has been earned in the form of depreciation charges and net income.

Like the Thoron report, General Manager Whitman's review of Alaska Railroad problems was primarily concerned with planning for the future. It included four additional topics, each of which anticipated a major development in the railroad's recent history. The first of these related to a vigorous but unsuccessful attempt to obtain legislation to incorporate the railroad. The second dealt with the financial crisis that would result from the operation of a military pipeline from Haines to Fairbanks, with a loss to the railroad of $3 to $4 million in annual gross revenue. The third forecast the advantages of a containerization system that would make The Alaska Railroad a leader among railroads in this method of freight handling. The fourth pointed to additional economies and to improved service that would follow the establishment of seatrain and car-barge service to the port of Whittier.

On August 14, 1956, Whitman resigned as general manager. He was succeeded on August 16 by John H. Lloyd, an up-and-coming executive on leave from the Rock Island. Lloyd's term of office began in an atmosphere of financial gloom, for he was to bear the full brunt of the loss of millions in freight revenue to the military pipeline. As a result, there was tension during his administration, which did not exist during the incumbency of his predecessors and which would not appear again until after the great earthquake of 1964.

# V

# Pipelines, Containers, and Piggyback

Prior to 1956, it was possible to watch from the windows of the general manager's office in the headquarters building at Anchorage as trainloads of petroleum left the yards for Fairbanks. In these long freights, powered by four or five diesels in tandem, were car after car of automobile gasoline, aviation gasoline, diesel fuel, and heating oil for commercial consumption in Fairbanks and for the Air Force bases at Ladd and Eielson fields. Officials of The Alaska Railroad, anxious to demonstrate that they could operate without congressional appropriations, called these trains the "mortgage lifters." Even more than the coal cars from Suntrana and Jonesville, they made the difference between a comfortable margin of net income and worried attempts to keep the operating ratios—operating expenses divided by operating income—from going over 100. These ratios were of great concern to the men in charge of The Alaska Railroad. By the same kind of alchemy that has accompanied the divorce of ownership from management in American business, the profit motive of the general manager of the government railroad seems to work as strongly as it would if he were guiding the destiny of the Great Northern or the Northern Pacific.

Coal as well as oil has exercised large influence on Alaska Railroad financial statements. Annual shipments from the

Healy River field to Fairbanks and the Matanuska field to Anchorage have amounted to between 600,000 and 800,000 tons out of total annual tonnages of between 1.3 and 1.5 million. Coal was responsible for the longest train in the history of the railroad—164 cars powered by 6 diesels on a run from Healy to Fairbanks. Unfortunately for financial stability, considerably more than half the coal and petroleum tonnage has been for the military. As a result, Army and Air Force decisions on these commodities can see-saw the railroad from high prosperity to deep depression and back again.

### The Haines-Fairbanks Pipeline

In 1955, General Manager Whitman was faced with the prospect of a huge loss in gross revenue from the operation of a military petroleum pipeline built from the southeastern Alaska port of Haines to Fairbanks. Construction of the pipeline was begun in 1954 and completed in the following year. It spelled the end of the railroad's lucrative tank-car shipments of military petroleum (POL as Defense officials called it) to points "north of the Range," that is, from Whittier or Anchorage to Ladd or Eielson Field near Fairbanks.

Due to an unfortunate error, which Alaska Railroad officials could not be expected to appraise objectively, operation of the pipeline was delayed for a time after its completion. Many miles were laid on top of the ground over an inland route where winter temperatures sometimes drop to 60° below zero. The line was first tested with water on the assumption that the water would be forced out when the oil was pumped through. However, the water froze in the pipeline at the bottom of each dip or "Y" where the line crossed a gully or narrow valley and blocked the movement of petroleum. It is said that it was possible to read a newspaper for half the distance to Fairbanks by the light of the fires used to induce thawing.

The freeze-up postponed an otherwise inevitable income crisis for the railroad. General Manager Whitman had previously secured a temporary agreement that the military would ship 225 cars of petroleum products per month by rail to Fairbanks even with the pipeline in operation. The freeze-up made this agreement superfluous, and it was not renewed after the pipeline was cured of its subarctic disabilities and operation began.

From fiscal 1956 to fiscal 1957, gross income fell $2,680,000, from $17,905,000 to $15,225,000. In fiscal 1958, there was an additional decline of $1,873,000 so that the 2-year total showed a catastrophic drop of about $4.5 million. Not all of the decline was due to diversion to the pipeline, nor is it possible to state accurately how many tons of petroleum products the military would have shipped by rail if the line had not been built. For all practical purposes, it is accurate enough to say that the Haines-Fairbanks pipeline reduced annual gross revenues by $3 or $4 million. With a financial blow of this magnitude, it matters little whether the income loss is estimated at a few hundred thousand dollars more or less.

If 1955 and 1956 had not been years of extraordinarily large net income, the railroad's profit and loss statement for fiscal 1957 would have been written in deepest red. As it was, net income shrank from $2.6 million in 1955 and $2.1 million in 1956 to $181,000 in 1957. A major effort of every general manager from John Lloyd on has been devoted to finding a way to prevent the Haines-Fairbanks pipeline from forcing the railroad into a deficit operation.

Lloyd renewed with emphasis his predecessor's case for extra consideration from the military because of the pipeline and took up the argument that he was forced to maintain an expensive sixty-four miles of mountain railroad between Seward and Portage solely because of military insistence that two southwestern ports were necessary to the defense of

Alaska. He maintained that the pipelines should be regarded as a stand-by installation and that the railroad should be used for the shipment of military oil and gasoline except in emergencies.

As an alternative, the general manager suggested that the railroad take charge of the operation of the pipeline. Commercial as well as military oil could then be shipped through the line and the economies of close-to-capacity use be realized. As the railroad would be able to balance loss of tank-car revenue against the gains from pipeline revenue, petroleum shipment costs to the military could actually be decreased. The economics of capacity operation of a pipeline suggested another idea: Both Anchorage and Fairbanks military gasoline and oil could be shipped through the line and that destined for Anchorage could be back-hauled by the railroad. It seemed fantastic, but it was nevertheless true, that most of the additional cost of rail shipment could be met from the savings accruing from capacity operation of the pipeline.

None of these proposals found favor with the military, and the railroad turned to other means of making up petroleum revenue losses. With tankers bringing oil and gasoline to the port of Anchorage, petroleum shipments to Elmendorf Air Base and Fort Richardson by rail from Whittier dried up as well. The military tank farm at Whittier was then used for storage only, and Army transportation personnel almost forgot it existed. The railroad's commercial oil business continued to be important and profitable even though rates on petroleum products were lowered. There was a threat of additional loss of revenue when Fairbanks businessmen made a strong case to the military for the shipment of commercial oil through the Haines-Fairbanks pipeline. The Department of Defense refused to go along, however, partly because losses would result for the railroad and partly because of the complications that would accompany the commercial use of the part of the pipeline crossing Canadian territory.

## Containerization and Piggyback

In November, 1966, an industry-government conference on containerized transportation was sponsored by the National Defense Transportation Association in Washington, D.C. A folder distributed to the conferees contained a table showing the number of shipping containers (known as boxes in the trade) owned by U.S. railroads. In first place was the New York Central Railroad. The Southern Railway was second, and The Alaska Railroad third. A short-haul, train-order railroad in a pioneer land found itself among the leading carriers in this advanced method of cargo handling.

Avoiding multiple handling of individual pieces of freight by shipping them in containers is not a new concept in transportation but had its beginnings in the canalboat era. It was the subject of elaborate research on the part of Joseph P. Eastman when he was Federal Coordinator of Transportation in the early 1930's. Containerization has been widely adopted by water carriers and has become an important factor in military transportation. U.S. railroads, however, have been far more interested in a companion form of freight handling—the piggybacking of truck vans on railroad flatcars. The Alaska Railroad has been an enthusiastic proponent of both containerization and piggybacking.

A container is a metal or plywood box, that can be tied down to a railroad car, a flat-bed truck, the hold or deck of a ship, and sometimes the cargo compartment of an airplane. It makes possible the intermodal handling of freight without the tedious and costly loading and unloading of individual pieces. A container may be as small as the 8′ by 8′ by 10′ military Conex boxes or it may be a huge 40-footer. Alaska Railroad containers are 8′ by 8′6½″ by 24′ and hold about 20 tons of average-density freight. The American Standards Association has made a determined but not too successful attempt to secure industry acceptance of standardization based on a container cross section of 8′ by 8′ with lengths in multiples of 10 feet.

Before containerization (and before seatrain) days, a carload of freight en route from Chicago to Anchorage would start as a number of boxes or pieces in a manufacturer's plant or warehouse. The carload would begin its journey by being hand-loaded, perhaps with the aid of forklifts, to a truck and hauled to a railroad freight house. The boxes or pieces might be loaded directly to a waiting boxcar, but usually they would stay in a railroad freight house until an empty car was available. Switched into a train, the loaded boxcar would be hauled to Seattle. There the freight might be warehoused again or unloaded to a truck and carried across town to the docks. If no ship was immediately available (and this was usually the case), the boxcar of freight would be stacked in a dock-side freight shed to await sailing time. When a ship came in, longshoremen would take the pieces of freight, perhaps by forklift truck, to a spot on the dock apron where they could be placed in the ship's sling. Each slingload would be winched into the ship's hold, after which the pieces would be taken from the sling and stacked for the voyage. The trip to Seward would take five to seven days and, in Seward, the longshoring process would be repeated in reverse. Each piece of freight would be taken from the ship's hold, placed in a sling, winched to the dock, and removed from the sling. Sometimes the freight could be loaded directly to a boxcar, but ordinarily it would have to be warehoused until a train was made up for Anchorage. In Anchorage, it would be again unloaded and warehoused. Occasionally, direct unloading to a waiting truck would be possible. If the consignee maintained a warehouse on land leased from the railroad and served by a rail spur, the freight might be handled direct from the boxcar to his warehouse. If not, it would be loaded on a truck and hauled to the consignee's place of business, where it would get a last unloading to complete the long process.

It should be clear to anyone but a tradition-blinded railroader or trucker or longshoreman that this is a slightly insane way of handling freight. On The Alaska Railroad it meant astronomical costs, not only because of its inherent inefficiencies but because of the peculiar conditions prevailing at the port of Seward. Ship arrivals from Seattle could not be accurately predicted long in advance. Because of the high costs to a ship of remaining at dock-side, a great deal of the unloading had to be done on overtime, since the job could not be completed within the longshoremen's six-hour, straight-time day. The railroad ceased to do its own longshoring in 1946 and, in subsequent contracts with stevedoring firms, was required to assume overtime expense. Longshore gangs were large and relatively inflexible, and stevedoring bids were based on the size of gang, which, in turn, was based on union agreement. Claims for damage and loss, particularly from pilferage, were large. Finally, Seward longshore wage rates for straight time, which were paid indirectly by the railroad, contained an allowance for the higher living costs prevailing in Alaska. Prior to the adoption of container and piggyback methods of freight handling, the railroad's bill from the stevedoring company holding the longshore contract often exceeded $1.5 million a year.

It has already been noted that, in General Manager Kalbaugh's time, experiments in containerization were begun in cooperation with the Alaska Steamship Company. That company was, in fact, the real pioneer in bringing this method of cargo handling to Alaska. Small metal cargo boxes were used for high-value freight in 1949 and wooden cargo cribs, collapsible for the return journey, in 1952. The railroad's 1953 experiment with the Alaska Steamship Company in the use of temperature-controlled van service was so successful that General Manager Whitman purchased nine temperature-controlled containers in 1955. These not only provided a superior refrigerated service but so reduced longshore costs that it was estimated the boxes would pay for themselves in three or four years. Shortly thereafter, the railroad purchased seventy-four 24-foot containers.

In fiscal year 1958, containerization received a setback because Alaska Steamship vessels had not been modified for containers and had insufficient deck space to permit the handling of all that were offered. The possibilities of containerized transportation had, however, attracted a barge line to the trade—Puget Sound–Alaska Van Lines. Containers could be stacked four high on the company's barges, built especially for the Alaska run. Alaska Steam responded to the competition by modifying a Liberty ship to accommodate containers, and the problem was solved. Robert Anderson was general manager at the time and contributed a great deal to these developments.

Containerization continued to gain, assisted by the purchase of containers by the water carriers as well as by the railroad. In 1959, the railroad purchased an additional $1 million worth. Containers were handled on a pooled basis, and contracts between the water carriers and the railroad covered rental charges, the return of empties, maintenance costs, and loss and damage claims. A 40-ton Gantry crane was purchased for quick handling of containers at Anchorage, while a crawler tractor was used for this purpose at Fairbanks. There was no problem at Seward since the big stiff-leg crane on the railroad dock was capable of lifting up to 100 tons. Huge forklifts and straddle trucks were later added to Seward's box-handling equipment.

Containerization was an immediate success with customers of the railroad and ship lines. Loss and damage dropped spectacularly, parts of the same shipment were more easily kept together, and spoilage of refrigerated products was reduced. Some shippers insisted that containerization was all that kept them from going to another form of transportation. Over the years, the savings to The Alaska Railroad have been measured, not in thousands of dollars, but in hundreds of thousands. Savings at the Seward dock alone amounted to between $3 and $4 per ton. In general, the savings were not passed on in the form of lower freight rates. They made it possible, however, to avoid increases in freight rates since they played a significant part in the railroad's recovery from the losses caused by the Haines-Fairbanks pipeline.

It is to the credit of the International Longshoremen and Warehousemen's Union that its members did not resist these labor-saving developments. In the balance of short-run advantage and long-run gains, they chose the long-range point of view.

There was one occasion when the use of freight containers added to, rather than subtracted from, intermodal competitive misgivings. Alaska Railroad traffic tends to be one way, from south to north, so that it is expected that cargo containers will go north loaded and come back empty. One of these southbound containers, in use by a motor carrier and labeled empty, was involved in an accident. To the amazement of officials inspecting the damaged car, the "empty" container was found to be partially filled with the motor carrier's freight. Had it not been for this accidental discovery, the freight would have had free billing to Seattle. The trucker alleged employee carelessness and promptly paid the freight bill.

Alaska Railroad experiments with piggybacking of truck trailers began a few months after the first container shipments in 1955. The business of piggybacking grew rapidly as highway carriers found that they could often make more money with a "trailer on flat car" operation than by hauling trailers themselves. In Alaska, this is true for all motor carriers during the spring thaw, when highway weight limits are drastically reduced, and during heavy weather conditions throughout the winter. For some motor truckers, it paid year-round. Garrison Fast Freight, a motor carrier associate of Alaska Steam and later a division of Consolidated Freightways, became the largest of the railroad's piggyback customers.

These developments inevitably brought a change in viewpoint about tariffs on the part of trucking firms using the railroad. Before piggybacking, motor carriers in Alaska criticized the railroad's freight rates as much too low. They argued that the rates were not remunerative and therefore constituted unfair competition. After piggybacking, the rate interests of piggyback motor carriers were completely reversed because they were then paying Alaska Railroad tariff rates rather than competing with them. Their complaints against the railroad declined because intermodal carriage of freight made partners of competitors and reduced their traditional suspicion of each other.

But bitterness remained among the smaller truckers. They resented the fact that the railroad controlled the charges for handling freight over its dock at Seward, including freight routed beyond Seward by truck. They resented the Whittier tunnels because they gave the railroad a monopoly of traffic through Whittier. Above all, they resented the existence of a government enterprise that, without paying taxes or interest on its investment, competed with them.

The following is a record of carloads and revenue of Alaska Railroad piggyback and container traffic from fiscal year 1955 to the earthquake year of 1964.

| *Fiscal Year* | *Number of Carloads* | *Freight Revenue* |
|---|---|---|
| 1955 | 142 | $ 58,748 |
| 1956 | 831 | 207,422 |
| 1957 | 2,456 | 593,306 |
| 1958 | 2,356 | 521,526 |
| 1959 | 2,747 | 713,987 |
| 1960 | 3,541 | 939,326 |
| 1961 | 3,878 | 1,144,481 |
| 1962 | 5,215 | 1,547,052 |
| 1963 | 5,340 | 1,602,212 |
| 1964 | 5,898 | 1,791,516 |

These are not large figures, for we are dealing with a small railroad, but they demonstrated intermodal cooperation that General Paul F. Yount, former head of the U.S. Army Transportation Corps, described in a 1959 speech as "the best example of integrated transportation in the United States." In an article in the September-October, 1960, issue of the *National Defense Transportation Journal,* an Alaska Railroad general manager, R. H. Anderson, and this author set down their conclusions as to the railroad's experience with piggyback and containerization:

> No matter which way the transportation ball bounces, the result of containerization with either vans or boxes is good for the suppliers and the users of transportation. Containers and piggyback give the carriers a chance to forget about competitive infighting and join in a common interest in a common cause. They produce satisfied customers to an extent which loose-stow cargo, in a great many instances, cannot equal. They attack the cost problems of transportation at the points where these costs have been most excessive. They bring about that rare and welcome economic situation in which, in spite of a rising price level, transportation agencies can make more money supplying better service at lower shipper costs.

## Trans-Canadian Railroad to Alaska

A railroad connecting Alaska with the rest of the United States has been a kind of pipe dream that has appeared in several guises over many years. For a short time during World War II, it was more than a dream as U.S. Army engineers surveyed the Trench route across British Columbia for a rail line to connect with The Alaska Railroad about eighty miles south of Fairbanks. The location survey included plans for bridges, yards, shops, communications, motive power and equipment. While the proposed railroad was never built, U.S. interest remained.

In 1949, at the urging of Senator Warren Magnuson of Washington, Congress passed a law authorizing the President to negotiate with the Canadian government for location and economic surveys for such a railroad. Officials of the two countries met for preliminary talks in 1950, but the project was killed, first by an American-Canadian military decision that even a study of such a railroad had no military justification and, second, by a tremendous lack of interest on the part of Ottawa.

The railroad study proposal was revived in 1957, again at the urging of Senator Magnuson, in a law that created the Alaska International Rail and Highway Commission. The law gave the commission the authority and responsibility for making "a thorough and complete study of the economic and military advantages of additional highway and rail transportation facilities connecting Continental United States with Central Alaska." This time the law avoided the possibility of a Canadian veto by making the study wholly American and by providing that the commission might "cooperate with officials of the Dominion of Canada and of the province of British Columbia" rather than be required to secure their assent for a joint project.

With Senator Magnuson as chairman, the International Rail and Highway Commission issued a call for proposals for undertaking the research and finally negotiated a contract with a respected firm of economic and engineering consultants, the Battelle Memorial Institute of Columbus, Ohio. The Battelle report was published by the commission in May, 1961. It contained a wealth of data on the resources of "Northwest North America"—defined as including most of Alaska, British Columbia north of the line of the Canadian National Railway, and adjacent parts of Alberta and Northwest territories. In drawing their conclusions, Battelle researchers reacted sharply to overly optimistic appraisals of natural resources in the area and endorsed the negative views, more popular in 1959 than now, of the ability of railroads to compete successfully with other forms of transportation.

The Battelle report concluded, therefore, that the future of the Pacific Northwest depended on highway transportation.

The growth of tourism was predicted as "the only major economic-development potential in the Area that would benefit substantially from major new or improved land-transport linkages between Alaska and the southern 48 states."

The "land-transport linkages" referred to did not include railroads. Based on an estimate of railroad costs (which were promptly deflated by the general manager of The Alaska Railroad) and on an economic stance that placed the Battelle researchers somewhat to the right of President Taft, the report concluded that a rail link with Alaska was not feasible and that its annual losses would have to be covered by huge government subsidies. In rejecting such a rail connection, the report stated:

> For pioneering purposes in "opening up" a country with resources yet unproved, Battelle feels that economics favors the use of a moderately good highway served by efficient motor transport, which also serves the automobile tourist traffic. Railroads can be appropriately considered when large tonnages of resources requiring rail transportation are proved through developments sparked by transport via highways.

To forestall an obvious retort that this would have been a strange prescription for the pioneer days of the American West, it was argued, with more truth than relevancy, that transportation technology had greatly changed from the days when railroads proved superior to covered wagons.

In its summary, the Battelle report recognized the improvements in rail transportation brought about by containerization and piggyback and the possibility of further improvement by the development of an Alaskan car-ferry system. But in the rest of the report, these developments were consistently downgraded and there was no attempt to appraise their significance to Alaska.

Alaska Railroad officials were quick to seize upon what they regarded as the weaknesses of the Battelle conclusions.

Donald J. Smith, who became general manager in the fall of 1960, addressed a memorandum to the International Rail and Highway Commission on the Battelle findings while the commission was preparing its own report and recommendations. Smith pointed out that:

1. The Battelle report ignored the significance of transcontinental rate equalization to Pacific Coast ports, which make the rail rates from points east of the Missouri River to Seattle and to Prince Rupert equal even though Prince Rupert is 600 miles closer to Seward.

2. The report ignored the significance of northbound tonnage from midwestern and eastern U.S. points that would probably move by an all-rail route to Alaska if transcontinental rail rates were applicable.

3. It grossly overestimated the operating costs for the part of a proposed trans-Canadian railroad to Alaska that would extend from Whitehorse in Yukon Territory to a connection with The Alaska Railroad at Rex.

4. It ignored the potential savings for such a railroad that would result from the elimination of several of the rehandlings necessary to the present rail-water-rail route to the Alaskan Railbelt.

5. It tended to ignore the economic value that a railroad creates for the owners of property along its right of way and did not analyze the possibility that interest and amortization costs may be less meaningful if the builder and operator of the railroad is also the owner of the land along the route.

6. It did not treat interest and amortization the same way for the highways it proposed as for the railroad it rejected.

7. Because of fewer rehandlings, the movement of explosives and sophisticated weapons would be easier and safer via rail to Alaska than via the present rail-water-rail route.

Smith's report was given by the commission to W. B. Saunders & Company, transportation consultants in Washington, D.C., for appraisal. With some qualifications, Smith's findings were confirmed and a recommendation made that if additional transportation facilities to Alaska were being considered, a rail link should have priority over highways.

The Battelle report and the criticisms made of it have been treated here at somewhat unusual length because the intervention of Alaska Railroad officials persuaded the Alaska International Rail and Highway Commission to oppose the Battelle recommendation. Instead, the commission requested Congress to authorize negotiations with Canada in regard to transportation, including "establishment of all-rail service between The Alaska Railroad and the Canadian-U.S. continental rail network, by the extension of The Alaska Railroad from Rex to the Yukon border, to connect with Canadian railways through British Columbia and the Yukon."

The Battelle report is also of interest because its major conclusion—the irrelevancy of any new or improved land transport linkages with Alaska except to tourism—was demonstrated false as far as railroads were concerned within one year of its publication. And the report contained an odd mistake in the maps of the Pacific Northwest that were included in it. The maps showed a highway between Whittier and Portage that does not exist (but which motor truck operators in Alaska would very much like to see built). There was an errata in regard to this highway. There was no similar note in regard to the quoted Battelle conclusion about land transportation to Alaska.

### *Car Ferries and Seatrains*

A car-ferry and seatrain operation became the new and improved land transport linkage to Alaska. It would bring loaded rail cars in common carrier transport from the railroads in the southern forty-eight states to Alaska for the first time in history. It would also counter the upward trend in through-freight rates by making possible savings to shippers that, for some commodities, amounted to almost $1,000 per car.

A shipping innovation of this sort, in which Colonel Johnson and each of the five Republican-appointed general managers played a part, had been considered for many years. Johnson tried to interest steamship companies in carrying loaded rail cars to the Territory during the rehabilitation program after World War II. General Manager Kalbaugh queried several ocean carriers about undertaking a seatrain operation to Alaska. Companies not in the Alaska trade were the first to show real interest. They became disenchanted, however, as soon as Alaska Railroad officials refused to make an interchange agreement that would shut out other vessel operators.

The Alaska Steamship Company, the veteran operator over Alaskan ocean routes, was the first to come up with actual plans. With an emotional aversion to barges, the company began the study of a train-ship operation from Seattle to the port of Whittier. Agreements were drawn up between Alaska Steam and the railroad but did not provide for exclusive rights. There was sharp disagreement over wharfage and handling charges at Whittier and over the financing of the necessary car slip. The railroad insisted that the docking facility at Whittier for the seatrain be paid for by the steamship company.

With its studies completed, Alaska Steam called for bids on a specially designed roll-on, roll-off vessel. The lowest bid for building such a vessel, and two were called for by the plan, was $10 million. Alaska Steam decided that such a heavy investment was not justified and reluctantly turned to a search for other means of providing seatrain service. These events occurred not long before the Battelle Memorial Institute submitted its report to the Alaska International Rail and Highway Commission and may account for Battelle's pessimism in regard to the feasibility of such a service to the Alaskan Railbelt.

Not long thereafter, The Alaska Railroad discovered that the Canadian National Railway was interested in a car-barge service to Whittier. The data on carload movements, from what the railroads call U.S. Transcontinental Territory, in Smith's presentation to the Alaska International Rail and Highway Commission was gathered by Canadian National officials for the purpose of determining whether a car-barge operation from Prince Rupert to Whittier was worthwhile. The Canadian National was impressed by the advantage that equalized transcontinental rates to Pacific Coast ports would give to a Prince Rupert interchange operation. But the project would depend almost wholly on the amount of carload traffic to Alaska having midwestern and eastern U.S. cities as points of origin. All traffic that could be persuaded to take the new route to Alaska would be long-haul traffic for the Canadian National.

Its studies convinced the Canadian National that the service was economically feasible. Consultations with Alaska Railroad officials resulted in an agreement that The Alaska Railroad would build the car slip at Whittier and that the Canadian National would pay an indemnity if the project should fail. The next step was to secure Interstate Commerce Commission acceptance of a through route from points served by U.S. railroads across Canada to Prince Rupert. If the Interstate Commerce Commission would permit the filing of tariffs for such a route, the third proviso of the Jones Act would come into operation and a Canadian vessel could be used to transport rail cars between Prince Rupert and Whittier.

The Jones Act generally forbids the use of foreign-built vessels in the U.S. coastwise service. For many years, the law contained a provision, infuriating to Alaskans, that allowed Canadian and other foreign vessels to participate in the transportation of merchandise between points in the United States, except Alaska, over through routes recognized by the Interstate Commerce Commission when such routes were in part over Canadian railroads and for which tariffs had been filed with the commission.

Alaskans had always felt that the monopolistic desires of Seattle businessmen had excluded them from the benefits of the Jones Act proviso. It is doubtful that the Alaska exception helped Seattle-based water carriers as much as they liked to think it did or that it harmed Alaska as much as its citizens feared. Nevertheless, there was a successful push to eliminate the exclusion when Alaska became a state in 1958. With the Alaska exclusion eliminated, the Canadian National was able (or so its officials thought) to file tariffs with the U.S. Interstate Commerce Commission from Prince Rupert to Whittier as part of a through movement from rail points in the United States.

Unfortunately for the Canadian National, the Interstate Commerce Commission decided that a through route could not be established in this manner, that a local rate only from Prince Rupert to Whittier had been filed, and that the commission had no jurisdiction over this rate. The commission maintained that a through route from U.S. rail points could not be established under the Jones Act proviso without the concurrence of U.S. carriers. This the Canadian National was unable to obtain since four western railroads were working with the Alaska Steamship Company to begin a seatrain service through Seattle and the eastern railroads held aloof in the interest of helping out their western brethren. The Grand Trunk, a Canadian National subsidiary, would, of course, have granted the concurrence, and perhaps one or two other railroads. Such an arrangement, however, would not give the Canadian National enough U.S. origin points and would, therefore, have severely reduced the amount of potential carferry traffic.

Alaska Steam felt no unhappiness at this result. The Canadian National solved the problem, however, by turning to an

American tug and barge company to ferry freight cars between Prince Rupert and Whittier. The Jones Act proviso thus became irrelevant. Active solicitation of carload freight in the United States began, and plans were completed for a twice monthly car-barge service. The Alaska Railroad rushed the construction of a car slip at Whittier and completed it just a few days before the arrival, on May 18, 1962, of the first loaded freight cars ever to enter the Railbelt, in a common carrier movement from the forty-eight states to the south. It did not detract from the significance of this event that, of the fifteen rail cars on the first barge, only two were of U.S. origin.

In the meantime, four northwestern railroads (Great Northern, Northern Pacific, Union Pacific, and the Milwaukee) planned with the Alaska Steamship Company for a rival operation. Alaska Steam had an option on a Japanese roll-on, roll-off vessel that had been used in trade with Cuba prior to the Castro take-over. As a foreign-built ship, it could not be used in the Alaska trade except as it met the conditions of the Jones Act proviso. The railroads and the steamship company joined forces in an unsuccessful attempt to secure an amendment to the Jones Act that would grant an exception for this ship, then called the *City of New Orleans.* There was a hard-fought Senate hearing in which Puget Sound–Alaska Van Lines provided formidable opposition to the railroad-steamship plans. The company was building its own car barges in American shipyards and saw no reason why it should be subjected to the kind of competition from foreign-built ships that the Jones Act was designed to prevent.

As a result of this setback to Alaska Steam's proposed train-ship operation, Puget Sound–Alaska Van Lines established the second car-ferry operation in history to reach Whittier and the first to operate out of Seattle. Its initial barge load was tied up at Whittier on August 10, 1963, and the company continued building car barges until it had six on its Alaska car-ferry run in 1967. The largest of these accommodated forty freight cars.

The Canadian National had found a way out of its difficulties by forgetting about the Jones Act proviso. In an interesting twist of history, Alaska Steam solved its problem by using the proviso it had so strongly opposed. The Great Northern owned trackage to New Westminster, near Vancouver, and here, at Delta–Alaska Junction, a car slip was built to accommodate Alaska Steam's roll-on, roll-off vessel. Conditions that satisfied the Jones Act proviso were met, and the train-ship, *City of New Orleans*—its name now changed to *Alaska*—made its inaugural run to Whittier on June 16, 1964, only three months after the Good Friday earthquake.

There was clearly a rate problem for both the Alaska Steamship Company's train-ship subsidiary and for Puget Sound–Alaska Van Lines. Rail freight tariffs, plus rates from Seattle or New Westminster to Whittier, had to be decreased to compete with Canadian National's car-barge operation. It will be remembered that the latter was based on the equalization of transcontinental rates at the ports so that the Chicago–Prince Rupert freight rate on a given item was identical with the Chicago-Seattle freight rate. The railroads concerned filed arbitraries lowering the previously existing rates through Seattle or New Westminster to Whittier in an amount sufficient to meet Canadian National freight charges.

The change in methods that brought foreign freight cars into the Railbelt continued a transportation revolution for Alaska that had begun with The Alaska Railroad's successful use of containerization and piggyback. In one sense, the revolution was almost too successful, for it resulted in an overcapacity, which made it difficult for competing water carriers to show reasonable profits. The new use of the port of Whittier had one consequence of the kind that always defies the tabulators of trends and the forecasters of the economic future: It provided Alaska with a port that, along with its arch rival, the port of Anchorage, made possible an astonishingly rapid recovery from the devastation caused by the great earthquake of 1964.

# VI

# After Statehood

On August 15, 1958, John Lloyd's term as general manager came to an end. Before his resignation, he was witness to one of the wildest celebrations ever staged in Alaska. On June 30, 1958, the Senate voted 64 to 20 to make Alaska the forty-ninth state.* This decided the issue, for the House had passed the statehood bill and President Eisenhower was sure to sign it. There were reservations, of course, particularly on the part of those whose concern about Alaska was more financial than political, but most Alaskans were jubilant that, at long last, they were no longer Territorials, whether or not spelled with a capital "T." They were full-fledged citizens with a right to vote for two senators and a representative. As delegate from Alaska, E. L. Bartlett had been given respectful attention in the House but had no vote to reinforce his persuasion. As Senator Bartlett, he would share the realities of power. Here was a Democrat who had won Alaska elections with 80 per cent majorities even when other election victories went to Republicans. As much as any other one man he deserves to be called the father of Alaskan statehood.

As the bonfires flared in daylight skies in Anchorage and Fairbanks, the editor of the Fairbanks *News-Miner,* C. W. Snedden, prepared a special edition containing the story of congressional approval of statehood. With Washington, D.C.,

* The act was approved by President Eisenhower on July 7, 1958, and the citizens of Alaska voted to accept statehood on August 26. Upon proclamation of the President, Alaska formally became the forty-ninth state on January 3, 1959.

on daylight saving time, there was a six-hour difference between the capital and Fairbanks—it was afternoon when the Senate voted, but morning in Fairbanks. Snedden's special edition was printed, hurried to a waiting Air Force plane, and flown to Washington. On the morning of July 1, every senator and representative was startled to find the Fairbanks *News-Miner* on his desk. At the bottom of page one they read:

> This newspaper was printed in Fairbanks, Alaska, after passage of the Alaska Statehood Bill by the United States Senate the afternoon of Monday, June 30, 1958.
>
> A token shipment is being made to Washington, D.C., for delivery to every member of Congress and for sale on the newsstands, as a demonstration of the nearness, under modern transportation conditions, of the nation's capital to the heart of Alaska, the 49th state.

Statehood had many consequences for The Alaska Railroad, some of them difficult to appraise. At first there was a barrage of questions as to whether the state would take over the railroad. As the state showed no interest in shouldering such a responsibility, this line of questioning gradually ceased. At the Department of the Interior, the Alaska branch of the Office of Territories, which included The Alaska Railroad, no longer had reason for existence. It would have been as logical to include a California or South Dakota branch as to retain an Alaska one. The Alaska branch lingered on but finally disappeared, and The Alaska Railroad was left with an uncertain organization attachment. The problem was resolved with a secretarial order of December 16, 1959, which made the railroad a full bureau of the Interior, responsible to the assistant secretary for Public Land Management. For some unaccountable reason, a news release of the event was scrapped and no general announcement of the change was made. For months and even years afterward, various units of the department failed to get the message. The record, however, goes to an obscure claims section in the General Accounting Office that in the fall of 1966, was still addressing Alaska Railroad mail to the Office of Territories.

The Alaska Railroad shared in the vastly increased consideration that the press, industry, investment firms, and banks gave to Alaska after statehood. Tourists also gave Alaska added attention, with a substantial increase in their number coming to the forty-ninth state. While it is still as difficult to analyze economic consequences as it was before econometricians discovered computers, there was a noticeable increase in the tempo of business in the Railbelt. A rather long-time decline in Alaska Railroad freight income was halted in 1959, so that, in this respect, statehood seems to have been on the side of management.

In August, 1958, one Rock Island official replaced another on The Alaska Railroad as John H. Lloyd left Anchorage and Robert H. Anderson was sworn in as general manager. Anderson had been superintendent of transportation for the Rock Island and, like many of his predecessors, had been a member of a railway battalion in World War II. His war service covered three and a half years in the African and European theaters. In Anchorage he showed unusual sensitivity to problems of subordinate officials who had experienced the uncertainties of four changes in management since 1953.

During Anderson's regime as general manager, the cloud over the railroad's financial condition caused by the drop in petroleum revenue still hovered but showed signs of lifting. Annual revenues had declined from the nearly $21 million peak in fiscal year 1953 to low points of $13,351,000 in fiscal 1958 and $13,483,000 in fiscal 1959. In fiscal 1960, however, revenues increased more than $1 million.

## Figures Don't Lie

From the accounting record of net income in fiscal years 1958 and 1959, as interpreted by auditors of the General

Accounting Office, it would be impossible for a layman (or a congressman) to be sure whether the railroad's financial situation was getting better or worse. The original income and expense data for these two years showed a net income of $109,000 for 1958 and $344,000 for 1959. When an audit for fiscal years 1958 and 1959 was completed by the General Accounting Office, Anderson and Interior officials were shocked to discover that they were accused of horrendous bookkeeping errors. The combined net income of $453,000 should, according to GAO, have been reported as a two-year loss of $1,808,000. To the uninitiated, this certainly appeared as though someone had been playing fast and loose with more than $2,250,000.

With accounting differences of this order, an acrimonious dispute was inevitable. When the dispute reached the newspapers, it was indicative of the nonpartisan character of the railroad's activities that both its Republican administrators and its Democratic friends rallied to oppose the General Accounting Office. When the smoke finally cleared away, the net income for fiscal year 1958 remained the same, but the net for fiscal 1959 was changed to a loss of $151,000.

Some of the GAO criticisms were accepted as reasonable by Alaska Railroad officials. Among these was a comment that certain depreciation rates had been set too low in prior years and should be increased, that annual leave accrual should be modified, and that the accounting for the payment of retroactive wage increases should be charged against current expenses rather than to retained earnings. Two questions raised by GAO auditors involving alleged money discrepancies seemed to arise from awkward accounting, with some application to private firms trying to decrease their income tax liabilities but with little application to a government railroad. One question concerned the retirement of nondepreciable property and the other the premature retirement of depreciables. On the surface, these are dull subjects for historical analysis. There are, however, some interesting angles to them that are best disclosed by illustration rather than by too deep a plunge into the mathematics of accounting.

In The Alaska Railroad accounting system, track and roadway represent nondepreciable assets. The amount of their capital costs used up in any one year are covered not by charges to depreciation but by direct charges to current expense accounts. As long as the purchase of additional ties, rail, and ballast is regular and recurring and no basic upgrading of track and roadway is undertaken, the direct charges to expense serve the same purpose as depreciation.

Let us suppose that The Alaska Railroad has decided to abandon a rail spur because annual maintenance costs far exceed the revenue derived from its use. Suppose further that the asset value of this spur is $500,000. On the assumption that salvage value would be about equal to the cost of abandonment, the retirement of the spur would mean that the capital account should be reduced by $500,000. Under accounting procedures approved by the General Accounting Office prior to the 1959 audit, this $500,000 would have been charged against retained earnings and would not have been counted as an expense during the year in which the spur was retired. After the 1959 audit, the GAO recommended a changed rule to the Secretary of the Interior that was derived from private railroad accounting practices. This new rule required that: "Unusual, nonrecurring retirements of nondepreciable property be recorded in a separate account and separately identified as unusual charges on the *statement of income and expense for the year in which the property is retired* [italics added]."

Under the above rule, a general manager of The Alaska Railroad, just breaking even in expense and income for a given fiscal year, could not abandon the $500,000 spur, however beneficial this might be to future profit and loss statements, without showing a $500,000 loss for the year of abandonment.

A somewhat similar result obtains when depreciable assets, such as locomotives, are retired and replaced before their capital value has been fully depreciated. They are said to have been "prematurely retired." According to the GAO audit for 1958 and 1959, "Such retirements should be separately identified and reported as unusual charges in the *statement of income and expense for the year in which the property is retired* [italics added]."

In correspondence with the Comptroller General, Interior Department officials took exception to both recommendations. They argued that charging such asset "losses" to the year in which the premature retirement of either depreciable or non-depreciable assets occurred would seriously distort the accounts for that year. The general manager maintained that he ought not to be deterred from making desirable improvements through the premature retirement of capital items by being required to show accounting losses in the years in which such retirements were accomplished. He pointed out that few people would be able to make the distinction between the "beneficial" losses associated with premature retirements and the obviously damaging losses such as would result from a derailment. These fears were soon amply demonstrated when the legislature of the state of Alaska, on March 29, 1960, referred to the GAO audit here under examination and then memorialized the President, the Secretary of the Interior, and the Alaska delegation in Congress for a congressional investigation of the finances and operation of The Alaska Railroad. Fortunately, Alaska's congressmen understood the realities of the GAO accounting criticisms, and the request for an investigation was ignored.

For a time, officials of the Department of the Interior and The Alaska Railroad held out against the changed accounting rules recommended by the Comptroller General for premature retirements. Finally, an exchange of views by letter resulted in increased emphasis by the GAO on the "separate identification and accounting" for unusual asset retirements. The Alaska Railroad and the Interior Department then accepted the new rules, hoping, perhaps, that the future would provide little occasion for applying them. Here is an accounting problem that goes beyond the immediate affairs of a government railroad. It has its application and its lessons for any government enterprise, in business to provide a service for a price, that includes nondepreciable items among its assets and depreciation among its costs.

Other events of the Anderson period provide better indications of his influence on the affairs of the railroad than a controversy over accounting procedures. The renewed growth of the containerization program, already described, owes a great deal to Anderson's foresight and initiative. He was also responsible for one of the largest single acquisitions of diesel locomotives in the history of the railroad.

### The Army to the Rescue

A road-service locomotive is an extremely expensive item of railroad equipment, and the railroad's need to upgrade its motive power was almost desperate. The potential savings through the use of bigger engines was obvious, but the margin of income over expense made large purchases out of the question. Appropriations were not the answer, since the House Appropriations Committee had made it clear that the railroad must support capital improvements as well as operating costs out of its own funds.

Anderson decided that his only reasonable alternative was to turn to the Department of Defense. The Army had rescued the railroad from an impossible manpower shortage situation during World War II; perhaps it might help remedy a shortage of adequately powered diesels. The general manager therefore approached General Frank Besson, the personable and highly competent head of the Army Transportation Corps, and requested the loan of diesel locomotives that had been mothballed for future use in a military emergency. His request was denied on the ground that the diesels would not be in defense readiness if they were being worked in Alaska.

Anderson then discovered that, scattered over the West and Southwest, there were 1,500-horsepower diesels that were being used as switch engines in military yards. He also found that smaller locomotives, perfectly capable of performing yard switching tasks, were held in military storage. He thereupon offered to pay for the transfer of these switch engines from storage areas to military yards if twelve of the 1,500-horsepower diesels in use in these yards could be loaned to The Alaska Railroad. In one of the many gestures in which the Department of Defense has shown its friendship for The Alaska Railroad, the proposed arrangement was approved. The railroad paid about $110,000 for demothballing the stored military switch engines, for distributing them to the Army bases where they would be substituted for the GP 7's, and for shipping the twelve GP 7's from these bases to Alaska. The loan of the twelve diesels saved the railroad about $3 million.

Several years later, when the borrowed locomotives needed overhauling and upgrading at a substantial cost per diesel, the Department of Defense canceled the loan and gave the railroad outright ownership. In this fashion, one branch of the U.S. Army made partial recompense for the loss of income that another branch had caused through its building of petroleum pipelines.

The marriage of The Alaska Railroad and the military establishment was decreed by the 1914 law with which the railroad began. It was cemented by the transportation needs of World War II. When a Railbelt location was selected for five of the largest Army and Air Force bases in Alaska, it became as permanent as any marriage can be. There have been times when more than 60 per cent of the railroad's peacetime tonnage has been for the account of the armed forces. This situation has sometimes resulted in suggestions that the railroad be operated by a military agency. At no time, however, have military authorities favored removing the railroad from civilian control.

The gift of the twelve GP 7's is but one of many manifestations of military concern that the railroad continue in a healthy condition. The story of the 714th Railway Operating Battalion, already recounted, is another. The Whittier tunnels were built by the Corps of Engineers and paid for with money appropriated to the military. The same is true of the twenty-six-mile branch line that connects Fairbanks with the Eielson Air Force Base and that includes the five-mile branch from Fairbanks to what was once Ladd Air Force Base and is now Fort Wainwright. While the railroad has sometimes reciprocated with rate concessions, the Whittier-Seward rate equalization represented a rate decision by which shipments from the military port of Whittier carried the same rates to points up the line as similar shipments from Seward. Yet Whittier is fifty miles closer than Seward to Anchorage and Fairbanks.

The principal *quid pro quo* the railroad has given the military has been its effort to provide Alaskan defense agencies with the most efficient and fastest transportation that the state of equipment and track will permit. The railroad has also demonstrated its friendship for the military in minor ways. The name change of the railroad's business car to "Caribou Creek," commemorating a military maneuver in the Railbelt area, is one example. With military freight covering a large portion of the railroad's expenses, it is significant that the cooperative relationship with the Alaska Command has survived the strenuous endeavor of railroad officials to keep their revenues above their costs.

As with any marriage, the relationship between the railroad and the military has had its times of tension. Railroad officials have sometimes thought that military eagerness to promote trucking in Alaska may have exceeded the bounds of fair competition. They remember that genius of Alaska trucking, Al Ghezzi, who operated the Alaska Freight Lines, and who was not always treated—or so railroaders thought—with military objectivity. Wage rates, both of the construction firms hired by the Army and Air Force and of the civilian workers employed at the bases, have created conflicts. The only real evil genii in the railroad-military partnership, however, seem to have lived in military pipelines. While there will be more to the pipeline story, many years of Railbelt history indicate that the pipeline controversy will eventually disappear and that the statutory obligation to provide transportation service for the military installations in Alaska will continue to provide strong bonds between the railroad and the Department of Defense.

## The Last of the Five

On September 20, 1960, Robert H. Anderson resigned as general manager. His place was taken on the following day by the third Rock Island official to head The Alaska Railroad—Donald J. Smith, who came to Anchorage from a position as division superintendent on his home road. His World War II experience covered three years with the Army Transportation Corps in England, France, Germany, and the Far East. He was the youngest and last in the series of five Republican-appointed general managers.

Smith, at forty-one, was old for a baseball player but young for a railroad president. As general manager of The Alaska Railroad, his youthfulness brought a light touch to management decisions that was appreciated by subordinates who were feeling the uncertainties of too frequent change. His term of office, not quite a year and a half, marked the end of a Republican experiment that had served the railroad well, that had brought related benefits to a few private railroads, but that could not be expected to last forever.

Two months after Smith became general manager, the election returns were in and a young man, marked for tragedy, became President. The new President appointed Stewart Udall, a three-term member of the House of Representatives, as his Secretary of the Interior. Unlike his predecessor, Fred Seaton, the new secretary was more intrigued by rather than concerned about The Alaska Railroad.

One reason for the secretary's apparent lack of concern may have been the intense interest in the railroad shown by his assistant secretary for Public Land Management, John H. Carver, Jr. Carver took an active part in its management decisions in a way that was almost without precedent within Interior. He was quick to grasp the railroad's problems and regarded his responsibility for it (and for the Office of Territories) as the brightest aspect of his career with the department. Smith, as a Republican appointee, was naturally concerned about the attitude toward him of the new Democratic administration. He was shortly to find out, and Carver would be the means of his enlightenment.

Before the Kennedy Administration took office there began in the Interior Department the same kind of solicitation for resignations that had occurred before President Eisenhower's inauguration. General Manager Smith at first fended off the approaches. After considerable thought, he decided to refuse to submit his resignation. He had little to lose. Since he was on leave of absence from the Rock Island, there was no question about his returning to railroad service. If the Alaska Railroad position proved to be political, he would last but a few months in any event. Smith saw no point in making it easy for the Democrats to get rid of him.

There was the possibility that the pressure on the general manager to resign would become even stronger after Udall became Secretary of Interior and Carver assistant secretary. However, it developed that the pressure did not originate with the secretary or his assistant but from career employees initially appointed under Democratic administrations. When Smith learned of this, he requested Carver's advice on whether he should submit his resignation. He was promptly told that if the assistant secretary wanted his resignation the assistant secretary would ask for it. The request was never made, and Smith continued in office until his voluntary resignation a year later.

The story is important because it relates to the question as to whether The Alaska Railroad has been politically orientated under either Democratic or Republican administrations. For the time being at least, Carver averted a danger to the railroad's traditional nonpartisan character.

Smith's contribution to railroading in successfully challenging a research report arguing against a rail connection with Alaska has already been described. In persuading the Alaska International Rail and Highway Commission to recommend such a railroad, he was countering a trend toward a railroad defeatism that has been harmful to railroading and has meant a kind of pendulum reaction to the success of competing forms of transportation.

## Another Pipeline

The Alaska Railroad's entanglement with pipelines continued, this time with a natural gas pipeline that had its origin in the 1957 oil strike on the Kenai Peninsula. The Swanson River field, brought in with the Richfield discovery well in 1957, represented the first major oil strike in Alaska's history. The hope for such a strike had been disappointed for many years. Early in the 1900's oil seepages were known in many parts of Alaska. One of the earliest discoveries was in the Katalla field, about fifty miles to the east and south of Cordova. A few producing wells were drilled and a small refinery built. The field was abandoned after fire destroyed the refinery, but there have been sporadic revivals of commercial interest.

The Navy spent many millions exploring for oil in a petroleum reserve south of Point Barrow bordering on the Arctic Ocean. Both oil and gas fields were found, one of which, the Gubic gas field, has spawned unsuccessful attempts to bring natural gas into Fairbanks. There has been no commercial production of oil in this Arctic area as yet. Most of it has been thrown open to commercial drilling, and there are high hopes that it may eventually be found to contain the largest producing oil fields in Alaska.

To the Swanson River field has been added the nearby Soldotna Creek field and, recently, wells have been successfully drilled under the waters of Cook Inlet. Oil drilling on the Kenai Peninsula has also disclosed tremendous reserves of natural gas. In 1961, a natural gas pipeline was completed to Anchorage after encountering engineering problems in the laying of a twin line for an 8.5 mile crossing of Turnagain Arm. Officials of Matanuska Valley coal mines knew of these difficulties, photographed some of them, and hoped for the worst. The crossing was successful, and the twin pipeline withstood the violence of the 1964 earthquake. A market for gas was developed in the Anchorage area, and the city of Anchorage is now producing electricity from small gas-fired turbines.

The gas pipeline from the Kenai meant troublesome problems for The Alaska Railroad, for it jeopardized the coal industry of the Matanuska Valley. About 300,000 tons per year were produced from the strip mines at Jonesville, almost all of it consumed in power plants at Elmendorf Air Base, Fort Richardson, and in the Knik Arm plant at Anchorage. If the power plants were converted to natural gas, the Matanuska mines would close and the railroad's gross income would shrink by about $700,000 per year. The gas pipeline company was of course eager for the conversion, and military authorities were convinced that very large savings would result.

This was the danger that General Manager Smith pointed out to congressional appropriations committees in 1961. Smith insisted that he did not wish to stand in the way of progress but urged both the military and the Congress to consider all the costs of conversion, including the net loss to the railroad, the social cost of shutting down the coal mines, and the business setback to Palmer that abandonment of the Matanuska coal industry would occasion. The Alaska delegation in Congress took up the cudgels for the coal mines, and, initially at least, the necessary authorization and appropriations were refused. The conflict of interest between Alaska coal and Alaska natural gas continued until 1966, when Congress granted the authorization but failed to follow through with a grant of funds.

The controversy produced a claim of loss by the railroad, should the Matanuska mines be closed, which was rejected by the gas industry but which was accepted by military officials even though they regarded it with skepticism. The answer to the railroad's cost and savings problem was to be found in the difference between fully distributed and out-of-pocket costs. If the railroad lost the coal haul from Jonesville to Anchorage, its gross income would fall by a sum equal to the freight rate times the number of tons ordinarily brought to Fairbanks. But expenses would not drop by an equal amount even if the fully distributed costs were roughly equal to the gross income. Expenses would fall by the amount of the out-of-pocket costs involved, that is, the costs that would be eliminated when the coal trains no longer rolled. These costs would be measured by the wages of the men who would be laid off—trainmen and enginemen, maintenance men and repairmen—and the costs of fuel, maintenance supplies, and repair parts that are related directly to the coal trains. After careful calculation, these out-of-pocket costs were estimated by the railroad at a little less than $200,000 annually. Assuming freight revenue for Matanuska coal of $700,000 per year, the net loss to the railroad if the coal were no longer shipped would amount to $700,000 minus $200,000, or $500,000. The conversion of the two military power plants would save the military much more than this. But if all costs and savings to the federal government are calculated, the railroad loss would have to be subtracted from the military gain.

The Interstate Commerce Commission is thoroughly familiar with these concepts of out-of-pocket and fully distributed costs, although its members might disagree with Alaska Railroad officials in some instances as to the measurement and significance of each. Natural gas interests did not understand, however, and insisted that if out-of-pocket costs were so low, the profits to the railroad for shipping coal must be enormous. Military proponents of conversion maintained that, even with the railroad's net losses accounted for, the savings justified the change. The possible social costs of closing the Matanuska mines were another matter. Such costs were difficult to equate with money values, and some were too intangible for appraisal. There was one certain conclusion from all these uncertainties—efforts to convert the Anchorage power plants from coal to natural gas would continue.

## The Ports of Whittier and Anchorage

In 1961, under the compulsion of economy programs, the Army abandoned the port of Whittier. Army installations were declared surplus, and the General Services Administration attempted to dispose of them. The military retained the right to return to Whittier if a war or defense emergency required it.

The Alaska Railroad in late 1961 was about to make Whittier a flourishing car-ferry and seatrain port. For this purpose, only a car slip plus the Army dock, the power plant, and the yard installations, which had never been given up to the military, were needed. The Army freight shed and loading and unloading facilities were requested and obtained by the railroad on the ground that an interference with the Seward terminal might require loose stow and container cargo to be diverted to Whittier. The huge multipurpose building and the twelve-story apartment house at Whittier remained vacant, although they were maintained for a fee by railroad employees. In spite of a good deal of soul searching, no one in Alaska has been able to come up with a reasonable use for them.

If the port of Whittier was, temporarily at least, on the

decline, the port of Anchorage was not. Construction of an $8.2 million municipally owned dock was completed at Anchorage in April, 1961. It was a one-berth dock built to accommodate the Cook Inlet tidal range of more than 40 feet.* It was financed by a $2 million bond issue, voted by the citizens of Anchorage, and a $6.2 million bond issue sold by Ira Haupt and Company of New York. The economics of the new dock, as analyzed by an engineering consulting firm, were based on the alleged lower costs of water transportation to Anchorage as compared with the expense of the 114-mile rail haul from Seward and on the efficiency of the new port operation itself. It was obvious to both railroad and Anchorage city officials that the new dock could not be financially successful unless a great deal of inbound freight could be diverted from Seward. The engineering firm's analysis was frankly based on this expectation.

The general manager and officials of the Interior Department tried to stay neutral about the operation of the new dock. The employees of the railroad generally were not neutral. They looked on the Anchorage city dock as a threat to the railroad. They assumed that the flow of ice in Cook Inlet for four or five months out of each year would prevent the use of the dock during the winter months. They also assumed that the line from Seward to Anchorage would have to be maintained for winter use when the Anchorage dock would be unable to function. Thus, railroad employees concluded that both the railroad and the port of Anchorage would be forced to operate at a loss.

The future would demonstrate that Anchorage optimism and Alaska Railroad pessimism about the new dock would both be subject to modification. The financial problems of the dock were real enough. On occasion, the city would have to pay the interest on the bonds that were in private hands to avoid default.

* The mean tidal range is about 30 feet, but the range from the lowest point of low tide to the highest point of high tide is approximately 44 feet.

By a strange twist of fate, the earthquake completely altered the Anchorage port situation by causing a total diversion of freight from the port of Seward, some of which went to Anchorage and some to Whittier. A newcomer to Alaskan shipping, Sea-Land, Inc., a large, well-financed, and well-managed company entered the trade and began scheduled operations to Anchorage. Sea-Land used Alaska Railroad service for its vans to Fairbanks but competed vigorously with the railroad and with the water carriers that interchanged with the railroad at Whittier for the much greater traffic to Anchorage. Sea-Land also demonstrated that it was possible to tie up at the Anchorage dock despite winter ice. Only time would tell whether Anchorage's dream that it would some day become a major port city would come true.

## New Policy for General Managers

On January 12, 1962, Donald J. Smith resigned to take a position with the Missouri Pacific Railroad. John Manley, who had been assistant general manager from July 1, 1949, was named acting general manager, a title that he had held many times for temporary periods. The "acting" was not removed from his title for nearly three months. Donald Smith had continued in office for a year after the Kennedy Administration began. Except for his wish to accept a position with the Missouri Pacific, it is probable that he could have remained as general manager indefinitely. When he resigned, it was necessary for Secretary Udall to decide whether to continue the appointment policy of the Republicans or frame one of his own. For a short period, there were indications that he was inclined to place a nonrailroader in charge of The Alaska Railroad.

Secretary Udall was fully aware of rising criticism against the policy of appointing short-term general managers. A kind of diminishing returns had been eroding the Republican appointment formula, not because it did not produce highly competent men but because it was unreasonable that the department continue forever to appoint general managers who would serve on the average for less than two years.

The obvious candidate to succeed Smith was John Manley, who had come to Alaska in 1937 and had worked for The Alaska Railroad for more than twenty-five years. Manley was a tool and die maker and machinist who took a job as shop laborer for lack of a more suitable vacancy. He then chose train and engine service, working as fireman and engineer, and served for a period as general chairman for the trade unions representing the operating crafts. He was promoted to road foreman of engines in 1945 and to superintendent of operations in 1948. In this capacity he served under Assistant General Manager J. T. Cunningham, a man to whom a whole generation of Alaska railroaders have paid unanimous tribute. Manley was a craftsman with a pride of craft that comes naturally to old-timers but that does not seem to be able to withstand the pressures of a machine civilization. As assistant general manager, he provided the continuity of policy and practice that made it possible for the railroad to avoid many of the disadvantages of the Republican policy of short-term appointments.

Secretary Udall and Assistant Secretary Carver favored Manley's appointment. They did not act immediately, however, because of a political situation in Alaska that needed time to work itself out. There were some Alaskan Democrats, connected with or a part of the Democratic State Committee, who wanted a general manager who would be beholden to them for his position. If their plans succeeded, the railroad might become enmeshed in partisan politics for the first time in its history. The plan failed because of inability to discover an available candidate, because it found no favor with Udall or Carver, and because it did not get support from the senators from Alaska, E. L. "Bob" Bartlett and Ernest Gruening. So it was that on March 1, 1962, John Manley became The Alaska Railroad's first home-grown general manager.

## The Calm Before the Storm

During the two years following the Manley appointment and before the great earthquake of 1964, the history of The Alaska Railroad was one of eventful and rapid progress. The story of car ferries and train-ships, already told, extended into this period, including the first tie-up at Whittier of a Canadian National aquatrain barge from Prince Rupert, the first Puget Sound–Alaska Van Lines hydrotrain barge from Seattle, and the planning for the Alaska Steamship Company's train-ship operation.

Technological improvements continued to reduce the number of employees. In 1963, the general manager thus described the advances made in automation: "Track maintenance was accelerated materially through the use of an electromatic tamper. This machine, with a 4- or 5-man team, is capable of performing work that with older machines required 20-man teams. Four other machines, each capable of extracting and inserting ties, were placed in service. Assigned in pairs, one machine extracting and the other inserting ties, to 15-man gangs, work is now accomplished that formerly required 30-man gangs."

Until 1963 the largest locomotives in use were the 1,500-horsepower GP 7's that had been obtained from the Army Transportation Corps. In May, 1963, the first 2,250-horsepower diesel electric locomotive was placed in service. A few more have been purchased since, plus one locomotive of 2,500 horsepower. The railroad's fleet of these higher-powered engines will be increased as fast as money is available to buy them.

In the opposite direction, the railroad lost a valuable Post Office contract to the trucking industry. Truck transport, via the Alaska Highway to Fairbanks and to Anchorage, was more expensive than the rail-water-rail route, but the highway carriers could provide a frequency of service with which the ocean carriers could not compete.

The city of Anchorage continued a claim to Cook Inlet tidelands that infringed on property that the railroad, under what seemed to be appropriate land orders and legislative requirements, had long regarded as its own. One map purporting to support the city's claim showed a line, alleged to divide railroad from city property, drawn straight through the headquarters building and the Anchorage station.

The story of Alaska Railroad labor relationships, from the time of the first trade union agreement in the early 1920's to the required adoption of competitive Civil Service rules effective January 1, 1967, are described in Chapter VIII. It should be noted here, however, that labor difficulties seemed to accumulate in the two years before the earthquake. Labor agreement rules were being invalidated or changed by the application of veterans' preference procedures. Some of the nonoperating crafts, dissatisfied with the wage policies that had guided most of the wage negotiations of previous years, were unable to agree with the railroad or with each other on the kind of wage policy they would like to see adopted. Except for train and engine service employees, the confidence of men in management and of management in men seemed to have reached a new low.

Turning to a very different kind of difficulty, the railroad made an approach toward a solution of the problem of regulating its tariffs in 1963. From the beginnings of the railroad, the Secretary of the Interior had been both executive and judge in his relation to the policy decisions of Alaska Railroad officials. With statehood, the motor carriers became subject to Interstate Commerce regulation and were convinced that a reasonable balance of competitive fairness required the government railroad to be under the same jurisdiction. Most Alaska Railroad general managers brought their hostility to ICC regulation with them from their home railroads. Anderson and Smith, however, shared little of this hostility. Manley, encouraged by a friendly ICC commissioner, Laurence Walrath, who was fascinated both with Alaska and with the railroad, favored regulation. Thus it was that the stage was set for an order, which President Kennedy signed just a few months before his death, that brought to the railroad a measure of economic supervision by the Interstate Commerce Commission. (The regulation story is told in Chapter IX.)

From a revenue standpoint, fiscal years 1962 and 1963 were particularly satisfactory. The long struggle to overcome losses to the Haines-Fairbanks pipeline seemed won at last. Net income in fiscal 1962 amounted to $253,100 and in fiscal 1963 to $285,406. At the same time, there were clouds on the horizon in the form of renewed military efforts to convert the Anchorage military power plants from coal to natural gas. Another pipeline, yet a few years away, would bring strain to the partnership of the railroad with the Alaska Command. For strategic reasons, the military proposed a petroleum pipeline from Whittier to Anchorage and brought great pressure on railroad and Interior officials to allow the line to be run through the long Whittier tunnels. For safety reasons, the request was denied, and a new tunnel was constructed for the pipeline alongside of the old line which, years before, had been built with money appropriated to the military.

The winter of 1963 closed one era for The Alaska Railroad and the spring of 1964 ushered in another, both caused by an earthquake of such terrible power as had not been seen in North America since the New Madrid earthquake in Missouri in 1811–12.* Before the story of Good Friday, 1964, is told, we shall turn to aspects of the railroad's activities and growth, which, touched upon lightly thus far, can be described more clearly when separated from the rest of its history.

* In a news release on November 13, 1966, the Geological Survey of the Department of the Interior called the New Madrid earthquake "perhaps the greatest earthquake known to have occurred in the United States."

# VII

# The Management of a Government Railroad

There is nothing outwardly glamorous about the organization structure of a government agency, even though that agency operates a railroad that touches the land of the midnight sun. Yet there may be drama concealed beneath the paper work. A struggle for power sometimes ruffles the calm of many a government office, with victory to him who draws the definitive lines and boxes on a management organization chart or supplies the final wording to a delegation of authority. There is drama also when a federal official mixes courage with caution and refuses to be deterred by the literal language of a procedures manual.

The Alaska Railroad has had two reasons for concern with such problems. The first relates to its location—about 3,000 airline miles from Washington, D.C.—and the second to its preference for many of the business practices of corporation enterprise. The distance factor has placed a premium on the railroad's ability to avoid a second guessing in Washington of decisions made in Anchorage and a penalty on failure to keep decision-making in the Railbelt. Kinship with private business separates the railroad from those federal agencies in which spending accelerates before the close of the fiscal year in order that appropriation cuts in the next year may be discouraged. It also emphasizes a precept, difficult of government application, that correct decisions may lose most of their value if they are not made on time.

In the early days of containerization, when The Alaska Railroad was among the few rail carriers that used this method of freight handling, a company called Ocean Van Lines was associated with the railroad in a container enterprise. Unfortunate mistakes in the company's management brought threat of bankruptcy at a time when payments due the railroad for the carriage of freight in the company's containers had accumulated to about $300,000. Any delay in finding protection against loss would only ensure that losses would occur. And any attempt to secure procedural guidance from Washington would almost guarantee such a delay. So, without the sanction of his superiors and within a twelve-hour period from the time the danger was first recognized, the then acting general manager, John E. Manley, quietly attached every piece of property of substantial value that the company had in Alaska. The railroad thus acquired an enforceable lien against the company's assets far in excess of the freight charges due. In addition, offsets were placed with the Army Finance Center against monies owed Ocean Van Lines for transportation provided for the military. The firm's bankers in Seattle were furious but impotent. When the alarms and excursions had died away, the railroad was able to collect every penny of the $300,000 debt. In the face of accomplished fact, no one in Washington, D.C., attempted to determine whether the railroad's actions were or were not authorized by the appropriate rule and regulation.

## Organization Lines and Boxes

A description of the organization of The Alaska Railroad must inevitably be on the dull side. Chart 1 is a draftsman's view of how the various organization units fit together. The general manager directs the staff in the Railbelt, a small office

## Chart 1
## ORGANIZATION OF THE ALASKA RAILROAD

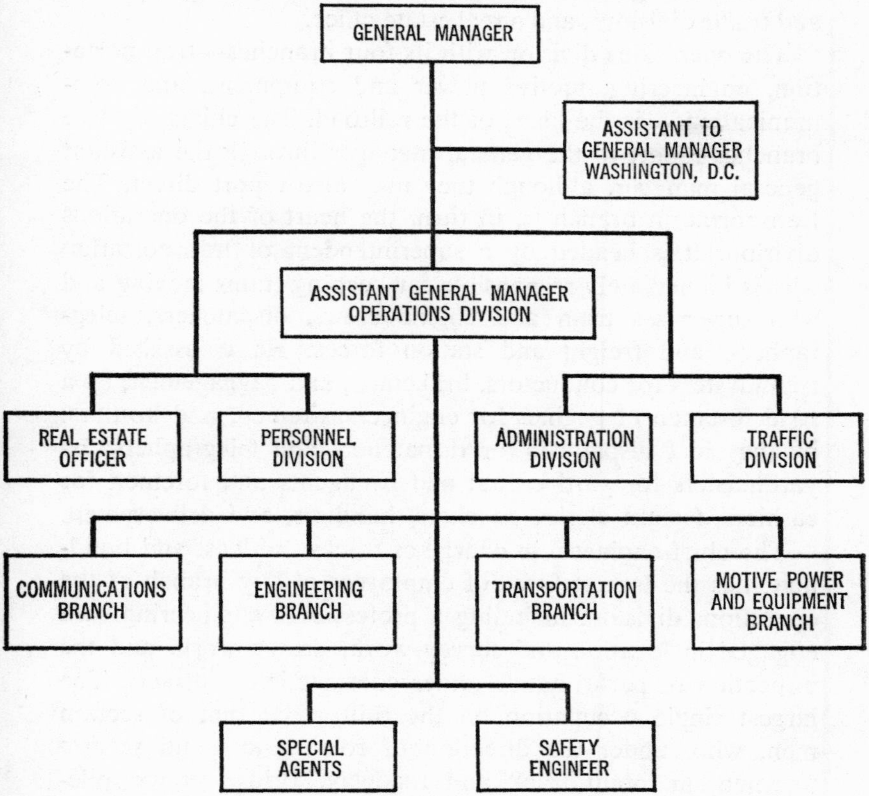

in Seattle that is part of the traffic division, and a still smaller office in Washington, D.C. Responsible to the general manager is an assistant general manager, the administration, personnel, and traffic divisions, and a real estate office.

The operations division with its four branches—transportation, engineering, motive power and equipment, and communications—is the heart of the railroad. The chiefs of these branches report to the general manager through the assistant general manager, although they may also report direct. The transportation branch is, in turn, the heart of the operations division. It is headed by a superintendent of transportation who is immediately responsible for keeping trains moving and who supervises train and engine crews, dispatchers, telegraphers, and freight and station forces. He is assisted by trainmasters for conductors, brakemen, and baggagemen; by a road foreman of engines for engineers, firemen, and hostlers; by the chief dispatcher for dispatchers and telegraphers; by yardmasters for yard crews; and by agents and foremen for cashiers, freight clerks, checkers, handlers, and deliverymen.

The chief engineer, in charge of tracks, bridges, and buildings, has the largest force of employees of any branch of the operations division, including a professional engineering staff engaged in location and survey work, design work, and the inspection of performance under construction contracts. The largest single occupation on the railroad is that of section men, who, under the direction of roadmasters and section foremen, maintain track and roadway. Bridge crews, pile-driver engineers and firemen, erectors, carpenters, painters, electricians, plumbers, and truck drivers look after the maintenance and repair of bridges, culverts, and of all buildings from the headquarters building down to the smallest tool shed.

The motive power and equipment branch is run by a chief mechanical officer who oversees the work of maintaining and repairing locomotives, freight and passenger cars, work equipment, and all off-line equipment, including trucks, bulldozers, and machines used for freight handling. Most of his personnel are journeyman shopcraft employees, including machinists, electricians, carmen, blacksmiths, automotive and heavy-duty mechanics, boilermakers, and steamfitters. Others are helpers, apprentices, coach cleaners, and laborers. His subordinate supervisors are the master mechanic, the supervisor of work equipment, and shop, roundhouse, and gang foremen. His duties do not include the repair of communications equipment.

The communications branch, under a chief communications officer, is a small but vital part of the railroad. The branch is responsible for pole lines and microwave and for telephone, radio, and electronic equipment. Its employees are construction and repair crews for communication installations along the line and radio technicians, telephone and teletype repairmen, and supervisors who man the "frame room," which monitors the whole system. The latter direct repair operations up to 350 miles distant by dictating instructions to technicians at a repeating station.

The administration division is the largest of the railroad's staff divisions and has authority over budgeting, accounting and statistics, property and supply management, systems and procedures, records management, internal auditing, and office services. It is headed by a comptroller who, with an assistant comptroller, supervises cashiers, accountants and auditors, statisticians, clerks, parts and supply men, and programers and specialists for data-processing equipment. The comptroller's accounting and data-processing forces are headed by a chief, branch of accounting, his purchasing and inventory forces by a superintendent of procurement and supply, and his file clerks and messengers by a chief of office services. Line functions formerly attached to the comptroller's office have gradually disappeared. Commissary and hotel employees formerly reported to him, but the hotels have been sold or leased (or destroyed by fire) and commissary supplies are provided only at line points far removed from stores and restaurants.

Unlike most other government agencies, the personnel function is not included in the administration division. The personnel division is headed by a personnel officer who reports to the general manager and is in charge of recruiting and training of new employees, labor relations (including the negotiation of collective-bargaining agreements), medical care programs, and personnel records. In contrast, personnel directors in most other government agencies place low in the official hierarchy. This downgrading of the personnel function is completely out of step with the practices of most large corporate businesses. It has become so embedded in the federal management structure, however, that its inadequacies often go unrecognized.

The traffic division is a small unit, but a good deal of the railroad's financial success depends on it. The division undertakes as much traffic solicitation as custom permits to a government agency in competition with private enterprise. Most important are its tariff research and tariff publication functions. The division employs traffic experts to calculate and analyze the thousands of freight rates and the dozens of tariff schedules in force even on a small railroad. Financial solvency or financial failure often rides on these tariff judgments. It is sad but true that the problems of tariff-making for railroads and, to a lesser extent, for other transportation agencies, have become so involved that only a professional can find his way through the maze. The Seattle office of the railroad is part of the traffic division and is the headquarters of the general traffic manager.

All railroads try to induce merchants and manufacturers to locate on land served by spur tracks. This decreases their transportation costs and makes the railroad less vulnerable to competition from motor carriers. Leases for such land are managed by the real estate office, whereas other types of contracts are handled by the division or branch to which the contract is related.

The Washington office is the smallest of the railroad's organization units. It has miscellaneous functions within the Department of Transportation and handles relationships with other agencies of the federal government and with private organizations (including trade unions) that are concerned with the railroad's activities.

The legal function is not included in the railroad's organization chart. At one time, the railroad employed its own legal counsel, who was professionally responsible to the Interior Department's solicitor. Republican-sponsored changes in 1953 took the lawyers out of individual divisions and branches of the Interior and concentrated them in the solicitor's office. The railroad's attorney continued to work full time for the general manager but became administratively as well as professionally responsible to the solicitor. His salary and expenses were reimbursed by the railroad. The arrangement was designed to fit an organization situation in which the Interior Department's solicitor and his attorneys would be located within reasonable proximity to each other, but for the railroad, with its headquarters in Anchorage, 3,000 miles away, it continued to present problems. The same unwieldy arrangement exists today under the Department of Transportation.

## Organization Roots and Branches

The organization relationships of The Alaska Railroad, first to the Department of the Interior and now to the Department of Transportation, are the direct product of the Act of March 12, 1914, and of the amendments and executive orders that have applied and modified it. The 1914 act did not place the railroad in any existing federal agency but gave the President the authority to locate, build, and construct it. The railroad is not a government corporation, although its founding act gives it identity and authority much the same as that of an incorporated enterprise.

It will be recalled that, in 1914, President Wilson appointed the Alaskan Engineering Commission and placed it under the control of the Secretary of the Interior. When the commission completed its surveys without recommending a route, President Wilson in 1915 selected the location, again placed the commission under the supervision of the Secretary of the Interior, and directed it to proceed with construction. In June, 1923, a few weeks before his trip to Alaska, President Harding issued an executive order placing the operation of the railroad, constructed in accordance with the authority of the 1914 act, under the Secretary of the Interior. The order was issued because President Wilson's 1915 directives had referred to construction only. At the July, 1923, golden-spike ceremony, President Harding spoke of the "Alaska Railroad" but it was not until after the President's death that his Secretary of the Interior, on August 15, 1923, issued a directive officially giving the railroad its present name and eliminating the designation "Alaskan Engineering Commission."

The choice of Interior as the home department of The Alaska Railroad may have hinged on the large stake that Interior had in the Territory through ownership of more than 95 per cent of the land area and on its conservation responsibility for the coal, fisheries, and other natural resources of Alaska. Railroads were not, after all, unknown to the department. The first annual report of the Interstate Commerce Commission, created by Congress in 1887, was made to the Secretary of the Interior.

On January 11, 1929, Secretary of the Interior Roy West issued detailed instructions spelling out the relation of the department to the railroad. The directive required that the general manager submit for the secretary's approval changes in policy, high official appointments, increases or decreases in wage rates (unless minor), and modifications of employee working rules. The general manager was also required to secure the secretary's consent before making capital improvements valued at more than $10,000, constructing new spurs or sidings, opening new stations, making important changes in tariff rates, or altering pass regulations. Finally, the general manager was obliged to submit comprehensive reports to the secretary on items of special significance and monthly reports in any event.

At a distance of more than 3,000 miles and before airlines were running scheduled flights between Seattle and Anchorage, directives of this sort were hardly possible of enforcement. General Manager Johnson registered his objections to it in 1946. Interior Secretary Chapman thereupon relaxed the 1929 instructions and permitted the general manager to act in an emergency without prior approval but with the understanding that he would report immediately what he had done. Successive delegations of authority increased the freedom of the general manager until, except for the ambiguous area of housekeeping functions, he was free to act on his own responsibility on matters other than major changes in policy or tariff rates.

Interior's over-all management of its relations with The Alaska Railroad tended to be on the casual side. In the days of the Alaskan Engineering Commission, a senior clerk, at a salary of $2,340 per year, and two other clerks, at annual salaries of $1,500 and $1,320 per year, took care of Interior's interest in the railroad location and construction work that was going on in Alaska. Later, the position of chief clerk, first attached to the railroad and subsequently to the department, was established. (The occupational designation of "chief clerk," abandoned by the Department of the Interior and The Alaska Railroad in the 1950's, is one of high honor in the railroad industry. It is the name for executive assistants who are the administrative alter egos of top railroad officials and who have been the instruments by which a great deal of railroad business has been accomplished.)

The casual relationship of the railroad to the office of the secretary and chief clerk of the Interior continued until February 13, 1936, when a secretarial order made The Alaska Railroad a part of the Division of Territories and Island Possessions, probably because of Alaska's territorial status and because it was difficult to find any other logical place among Interior's organization units. The director of the division also supervised the affairs of the Alaska Road Commission, which was responsible for most highway construction and maintenance in Alaska. Both the railroad and the road commission were made part of the division's Alaska branch.

It was hardly to be expected that either the Secretary of the Interior, the director of the Division of Territories and Island Possessions (now the Office of Territories), or the chief of the Alaska branch of that office would be experienced railroad men. Direction of the railroad by the Division of Territories was, therefore, neither technical nor close, and depended to a large extent upon the integrity of the general manager and cooperation of Interior's administrative officials. The latter, with a few significant exceptions, interpreted their role as one of providing maximum assistance to the general manager in attaining his objectives rather than in directing him on how this should be done. One of the exceptions produced the Thoron report, to which elaborate reference has been made. It represented a decisive department interference with the management of The Alaska Railroad and brought its organization into consonance with the scope of its activities by helping to create a more modern and more efficient enterprise.

The Secretary of the Interior exercised his control over The Alaska Railroad through the Division of (later Office of) Territories for the twenty-three years from 1936 to 1959. Territories reported to the secretary through the assistant secretary for Public Land Management, who, if he chose to exercise the authority that the secretary gave to him, was provided an opportunity to play an influential role in the activities of the railroad.

On December 16, 1959, Secretary Fred Seaton signed a

release transferring The Alaska Railroad from the Office of Territories and making it a full bureau of the department. The general manager thus became a bureau head with headquarters in the field office at Anchorage. His line of authority to the secretary continued to be through the assistant secretary for Public Land Management. The change gave the railroad added prestige in the federal hierarchy. It increased the railroad responsibilities of the assistant secretary for Public Land Management, and it accentuated the problem of relation between line and staff authority that has been inherent in the organization of the Department of the Interior.

Most federal agencies, including the Department of the Interior, have attempted to differentiate line responsibility for policy and performance in carrying out government functions from the housekeeping duties of budgeting, finance and accounting, property management, personnel management, management improvement, and internal audit and inspection. In Interior, responsibility for these functions has been given to an administrative assistant secretary who, in theory, furnishes advice and counsel to line officials, including all other assistant secretaries. In Interior, and possibly in some other government agencies, theory and practice are poles apart. The program assistant secretaries and bureau heads who work in politically sensitive areas are political appointees. This is as it should be, for it would make little sense to keep high officials in office who were out of sympathy with the policies of an incoming administration. The administrative assistant secretary, on the other hand, is usually regarded as a career official whose personal political views do not affect his function. His long tenure, however, brings knowledge and position advantages that sometimes make political policy-makers dependent upon him. Thus, it often happens that staff agencies assume line authority and policy-making prerogatives—a management situation that, in theory, the differentiation between staff and line is supposed to prevent.

When either custom or the obscure wording of delegations

of authority give line control to staff officials, the possibility of conflict and confusion is always present. A few examples will illustrate the point. On one occasion, the railroad, in need of a new barge for Tanana and Yukon river operations, could have obtained a free tow for such a barge from a West Coast port to the Yukon River if a decision to purchase had been made before the fall freeze-up. A veto by an Interior staff official made the consummation of the arrangement impossible. The free tow would have been worth about $50,000. In another instance, a wage dispute with trade unions representing certain nonoperating crafts resulted in an agreement to arbitrate. Against the wishes of The Alaska Railroad, an Interior staff official dictated the wording of the arbitration question in such a way that he greatly increased the problems of presenting the railroad's case to the arbitration board.

The difficulties caused by attempts of Interior housekeeping officials to make line decisions can be exaggerated, and there are many occasions when differences of opinion do not arise. The problems that the conflict does produce for Alaska Railroad general managers, however, are too great to ignore and are stressed here because they are important to the future of any economic enterprise conducted by the government. In such undertakings it is administratively wrong to give staff officials equal authority with line officials. For example, the line officer who is responsible for the financial results of the activity he heads, should have the benefit of the advice of the appropriate staff officer. But the staff officer, who does not share the financial responsibility, should never be given the power to overrule a line decision by adding to or subtracting from an agency's income and expenditure schedule.

## Management and Money

The budgetary process by which a government agency secures its annual appropriations is almost a never-ending one. It begins nearly two years before the fiscal year for which funds are requested. It ends only after the request has successfully completed an obstacle course that includes departmental review, hearings before the Bureau of the Budget, House and Senate appropriations committee hearings and reports, conference committee meetings in which the views of House and Senate must be reconciled, votes by the Senate and House, and, finally, approval by the President.

Because federal budgeting takes a good deal of time and must be repeated each year, long-range planning of government projects is often exceedingly difficult. Although Congress may indicate approval of a given program, legislation may lag many months behind. Most government agencies cannot borrow and have no unexpended funds from previous appropriations to fall back on. They cannot pay out money in a given fiscal year until their appropriation bills become law or until special and limited authorization, pending appropriation, is granted. An authorization is not a blank check, nor is it, in fact, a check of any description.

Appropriations procedures are less difficult for The Alaska Railroad than for the average federal agency or bureau so long as its income equals or exceeds expenditures for operations and capital improvements. Money received by the railroad from earnings or other sources is deposited in a revolving fund in the U.S. Treasury. While the railroad was with the Department of the Interior, this fund received an annual sanction in Interior appropriations acts reading as follows:

> The Alaska Railroad Revolving Fund shall continue available until expended for the work authorized by law, including operation and maintenance of ocean-going or coastwise vessels by ownership, charter, or arrangement with other branches of the Government service . . .

This language resulted in a near-automatic appropriation to the railroad of its own money. It also saved the railroad from the provision of its founding act of March 12, 1914, that required it to pay into the Treasury as miscellaneous receipts the amount by which earnings exceeded maintenance and operation costs. So long as income, including prior earnings, exceeded expenditure, the railroad could plan for the future because it could spend money for current operations without waiting for annual appropriations legislation. With some qualifications, this has also been true for capital expenditure. Both Senate and House appropriations committees require the railroad to present plans for such expenditure to them for approval before funds are committed. But this approval could be informally obtained and, except where appropriations were requested, it was never included in the language of appropriations acts.

The more or less automatic annual appropriation of the railroad's own income has a great deal of influence on its relationship with Congress but by no means makes it independent of Congress. The railroad is the creation of Congress and is subject to the will of its creator. The act of March 12, 1914, can be amended, as it has been on several occasions, notably by the Transportation Act of 1966. If Congress wished, it could eliminate the railroad from the roster of federal agencies. Amendment is a long process, however, and Congress exercises more direct control by requiring the railroad to take part in the budgetary process. Congress also exercises an indirect, admonitory control by making the railroad subject to periodic audits by the General Accounting Office. The "GAO," as it is almost always called, cannot order the railroad to do anything, but it can point a warning finger to which a general manager is entitled to make a defensive response. But neither the general manager nor department officials can afford to ignore the warning. Even though the railroad can be quite independent so long as no appropriations are necessary, its officials are required to present statements of income and expenditure to the appropriations committees and to Congress for each budget year.

Let us assume that we are starting on the railroad's budget

cycle for fiscal year 1969. The preliminary budget must be assembled in the summer of 1967 and presented to the department in about August. About two months later, with the changes required by the department, the budget is submitted to the Bureau of the Budget. It is the subject of hearings by a specially assigned staff of the bureau that suggest changes that might or should be made. When agreement is reached with the bureau, hearings before appropriations subcommittees of both the House and Senate are the next steps in the process. The House hearing will probably take place in early February, 1968, and the Senate hearing early in March. The subcommittee hearings are referred to the full appropriations committees, which will, if they approve, issue favorable reports. Senate and House votes and Presidential consideration follows. A department appropriations bill is finally passed, hopefully before June 30, 1968, since July 1, 1968, is the first day of fiscal year 1969. Again, so long as the railroad is self-supporting, it is not affected by any delay in the passage of appropriations bills. It can spend its available funds, and these are continually being added to from current receipts.

There can be no absolute guarantee that Congress will not sometime require the railroad to release some of its accumulated funds. The odds are very great against such action, however. Congress has never made such a requirement and it is difficult to imagine that, in the absence of a period of enormous net income, it would ever do so. A general manager can, therefore, make plans for maintenance and operating expense in the future with reasonable confidence that the money he plans to spend will be available in the Treasury.

The situation is somewhat different for the budgeting of capital items. Reference has already been made to the railroad's policy of determining a fiscal year's capital program from the total of depreciation charges and net income for the previous fiscal year. The general manager can know the amount available for improvements at the beginning of each fiscal year and is not required to refrain from spending for capital programs until appropriations bills become law. A custom has been established, however, that no general manager would be foolish enough to disregard—submission of major items of capital improvement to the House and Senate appropriations subcommittees for the department before the expenditure is actually made. Railroad budget presentations therefore include a tabulation of planned improvements for the next fiscal year. Even though the railroad has available money for the items of improvements and betterments that have been presented and justified, money will not be spent for those items of which the subcommittee disapproves.

Even here the House and Senate appropriations subcommittees allow a good deal of flexibility. Each of the railroad's capital-improvement programs contains a "nonprogramed reserve" of between $300,000 and $500,000 to cover unanticipated capital expenditures. If a bridge should be destroyed in a washout, the general manager can use nonprogramed reserve funds to replace it without subcommittee approval. It is also possible to add new planned projects to the capital program that, for one reason or another, had not been included in applicable budget requests, although custom requires that subcommittee approval be obtained before money is committed. Both House and Senate appropriations subcommittees have always given prompt and serious consideration to such requests without waiting for final action on the budget as a whole.

The Alaska Railroad has a great psychological advantage in being able to present to Congress a spending program that may total $15 to $20 million but does not call for any appropriation. The House Appropriations Committee has been particularly emphatic in urging The Alaska Railroad to keep its expenditures within its income. Each time the railroad demonstrates that it has complied with this injunction, committee members are pleased, the hearings are friendly, and the period of questioning is short. This does not mean that sharp questioning does not occur at times, but committee members realize that the general manager has no motive to submit an inflated budget for bargaining purposes. They know that the amount of money available to him for expenditure is exactly the same whether he follows this widely prevalent practice or not.

There is little evidence that political considerations have influenced relations between the appropriations committees and the railroad. The investigations of the Howell Committee may have had some political overtones (see page 71). If so, they have long since been forgotten. In general, appropriations committee members whether Republican or Democrat have been critical when millions of dollars of appropriated money were being spent for rehabilitation. Relationships improved immediately after the need for outside money disappeared.

The need for friendly appropriations committees during the 1947–52 rehabilitation period tempted the railroad into one of its few lapses from its nonpolitical posture. Manpower shortages in the early part of this period resulted in unusual recruiting programs. On one occasion, Eskimos were brought from their Arctic villages to work as section laborers. They performed well, but there were odd confrontations, as when some of them, for the first time in their lives, encountered locomotives and automobiles, and bacon and eggs. Another time, an engaging promoter, temporarily hired by the railroad to investigate industrial possibilities in the Railbelt, turned his mind to the problem of recruiting. With the general manager's sanction, he suggested to various congressmen that they recommend deserving students for summer employment as section laborers in Alaska. The response was tremendous, and a special plane was chartered to take the young men to Anchorage. The experiment was successful for the railroad and won the praise of the students and their congressional sponsors.

It is possible, though unlikely, that the general manager was not aware that a high percentage of these summer workers had been recommended by members of the Senate and House appropriations committees. The percentage increased as several summers went by until the department was faced by the embarrassing facts that a labor shortage no longer existed and special recruiting was no longer necessary. The habit of recruiting the constituents of congressmen was hard to break, particularly because most congressmen were convinced that they were doing the department and The Alaska Railroad a favor by supplying difficult to get employees. Office of Territories officials were reluctant to disabuse them of this notion, and it required several years of tapering off before the calls for summer vacancies stopped.

The most interesting thing about this recruiting was its bipartisan character. During the Truman Administration, most (but not all) of the congressional sponsors of the summer laborers were Democrats. During the Eisenhower Administration, many were Republicans. Those Democratic congressmen who had developed a habit of recommending students for summer employment in Alaska continued to do so. They paid no attention to the fact that the politics of the administration had changed. Republican Interior officials, again with an eye to appropriations committees, responded by being reasonably nonpartisan and recruited about as many students for the railroad with Democratic sponsors as with Republican.

Somewhat belatedly, congressmen were told that unemployment among laborers in Alaska was so great that recruiting in other states was unnecessary. With one melancholy exception, who happened to be a Democrat, the congressmen responded with understanding and did not insist that their constituents be hired irrespective of the need in Alaska.

### The General Accounting Office

The General Accounting Office exercises surveillance over the financial affairs of The Alaska Railroad less frequently but with greater intensity than either the Bureau of the Budget or the appropriations committees of Congress. Furthermore, the GAO, both by law and custom, has greatly increased the scope of its audits over the past twenty years. Originally the accuracy and reasonableness of agency accounting and statistical records were GAO's prime concern. Now its accountants range a much wider field. They regard business practices and policies, methods of wage payment, adequacy of tariffs, and purposes and objectives as appropriate for investigation. Their recommendations are often correspondingly broad. The GAO does not try to examine the railroad from desks in Washington but sends a team of five or six men to Anchorage to go over accounts and other records, interview officials, and otherwise get a first-hand look at the railroad's operations.

Although there is no rigid requirement that a draft of GAO reports be given to railroad officials for review, it is almost always done. The officials then have a chance to correct any errors and to disagree with conclusions that they believe unwarranted or inapplicable. The final report, with recommendations, is submitted both to the agency and to Congress. Some recommendations may seem to be so inherently sound (and there have been many of these) that the railroad adopts them immediately. Some may be difficult of application and their adoption may be postponed. Others may be rejected, only to be offered again in the next audit report. There have been some important recommendations that the GAO has itself abandoned, notably its suggestions to increase Alaska Railroad freight rates.

The General Accounting Office has no power to enforce its recommendations, but no federal agency takes them lightly. The railroad has not only given them a great deal of consideration, but regards the decreasing number of GAO criticisms over the years as cause for pride.

One of the early investigations of the railroad by the GAO applied to the month of December, 1951, and was published on April 7, 1952, under the title "Report of Survey and Review of the Operations of The Alaska Railroad." The report contained recommendations to Congress and to the Interior. It was suggested to Congress that the railroad operate under a business-type budget to be submitted annually to Congress for approval, that future advances of Treasury funds for capital improvements be returned with interest, and that tariffs be fixed at a level that would return all costs including depreciation and a fair rate of return on the government's investment.

To the Interior and the railroad, the report recommended that the McKinley Park Hotel be turned over to Interior's National Park Service, that the railroad's interest in the Knik Arm power plant be sold, that a "manual of orders" covering administrative and operating policies be prepared, and that commissary and meal prices to employees be increased to cover costs. The report suggested the adoption of activity accounting, better accounting control over inventories, tighter handling of long-standing accounts receivable, and the preparation of statistics for administrative control on a more current basis.

Many of these recommendations were adopted, including the disposition of the McKinley Park Hotel and the Knik Arm Power plant. As a result of the accounting recommendations and supplementary comments in later GAO reports, there was eventually developed a complete revision of the railroad's accounting system. The new accounting manual, painstakingly authored by the railroad's comptroller, Leland P. Draney, received the approval of the General Accounting Office in September, 1957.

The railroad adopted a business-type budget in 1954 that enabled accountants to make more accurate cost appraisals. Capital expenditure programs have been submitted annually since 1952 for appropriations committee approval. Both Senate and House committees agreed that the railroad should be self-sustaining, but not on GAO terms. Depreciation had been included as part of the cost of doing business for several years.

But Congress has not required that the railroad return to the Treasury with interest money appropriated for capital improvements. Nor has Congress directed the railroad to fix its tariffs so as to cover a fair return on the government's investment. For all but a few years of the railroad's history, this would have been an empty gesture since no conceivable adjustment of freight and passenger rates would have been successful in accomplishing this result.

The story of the controversy over the accounting for nondepreciable assets and the premature retirement of depreciables has already been told. In subsequent audits, the General Accounting Office has repeated the depreciation criticisms made in its report for fiscal years 1958 and 1959 and the railroad has acceded to them. It should be pointed out that the statistics of net income and net loss used in the chapters of this book follow customary Alaska Railroad accounting practices except where the railroad has yielded to GAO wishes for change. Whatever the final outcome, this dispute has had a large degree of unreality about it. Under the GAO view, more of the railroad's cash earnings are labeled "depreciation" and less "net income." If the railroad accounting philosophy should again prevail, the railroad's net income will be increased and its depreciation charges lessened. In either case, the sum of the two amounts would be exactly the same.

The GAO has audited the railroad's books and operations every two years from 1951 to 1965. Recently, however, it has been determined that such audits need not be made more than once every three years. As audit succeeded audit, the trend has continued toward placing greater emphasis upon management, rather than accounting, review. A 1966 survey of the history and business practices of Yutana Barge Lines, a lessee of the railroad, suggests that the GAO may sometimes regard business policy evaluation as even more important than operating economies.

## Should the Railroad Be Incorporated?

The rise and fall of a plan to incorporate The Alaska Railroad forms an interlude in its organization history that may be gone but is not forgotten. The plan began in 1952 with the submission to the Department of the Interior by the Bureau of the Budget of a draft report on federal activities in Alaska. The report concluded with a recommendation that the railroad be incorporated. The reaction of the department was cautiously negative. Director James Davis of the Office of Territories felt that incorporation was unnecessary. General Manager Johnson, about to be succeeded by Frank Kalbaugh, approved the plan provided that incorporation would not add to the railroad's expenses. Kalbaugh, noting the broad grant of powers in the railroad's organic act, concluded that the railroad already had many of the benefits that might be gained by incorporation and none of its disadvantages. He opposed the plan, basically because he could not see how the railroad could meet the financial obligations of incorporation. The department's reply to the Budget Bureau's request for comments, as finally prepared, was both a "yes" and a "no": The recommendation to incorporate was accepted provided the railroad's existing powers were retained and due regard was paid to its financial situation.

R. N. Whitman, who succeeded Kalbaugh as general manager in April, 1955, decided on a more positive approach. The Budget Bureau's report recommending incorporation for The Alaska Railroad had been transmitted to the House Appropriations Committee in January, 1954, and in May, 1955, a Hoover Commission report, "Business Enterprises," recommended incorporation. Whitman decided to prepare his own incorporation bill, which would fit the railroad's financial situation and would also resolve personnel problems that were serious enough but hardly related to incorporation.

Whitman's bill deftly avoided the impossible interest burden that other incorporation plans would have imposed on the railroad. He suggested that the railroad not be required to pay interest except on funds borrowed from the Treasury after the effective date of incorporation. If deficits from operations required congressional appropriations, such funds should not be regarded as investment capital and should not bear interest. In lieu of other interest requirements, he proposed that the railroad pay the Treasury at the end of each fiscal year 30 per cent of its net income for that year. Labor provisions of the bill related to veterans' preference, the eight-hour work law, official overtime, efficiency ratings, and rights of employees to collective bargaining.

Whitman's bill was submitted to Director Lausi of the Office of Territories, who was not at all hopeful that the 30 per cent of net income proposal would meet with ready acceptance. The Bureau of the Budget objected, of course, but not so vehemently as staff officers of the Interior objected to provisions that would have made it almost impossible for them to translate staff assistance into line authority. Officials of Interior's Management Research Division and Budget and Finance Division were particularly insistent that The Alaska Railroad Company be established "within the Department of the Interior" with the understanding that the department's staff divisions would exercise the same functions with respect to the railroad as they had been exercising for almost all bureaus of the department, including the railroad.

By this time, more than a year had passed, and John Lloyd had succeeded Whitman as general manager. Lloyd's response to the suggestion that the corporation be established within the Department of the Interior to meet the wishes of quasi staff divisions was quick and direct. In a letter of October 1, 1956, he wrote: "I am personally opposed to any bill whether it is an incorporation bill or any other that would further increase the bureaucratic work now connected with the Railroad."

Lloyd won his point, but delays in reaching agreement on the language of the incorporation bill had become a habit. Objection was raised to some of the personnel provisions of the law on the ground that even a cautious approach to restricting the application of veterans' preference laws was politically dangerous. The Bureau of the Budget's reaction to the interest provisions of the proposed bill was interestingly mild. The bureau proposed that interest be paid only on that part of federal investment made after the effective date of incorporation and that appropriations to meet deficits not bear interest. The department accepted these changes, and the 30 per cent of net income proposal was dropped.

After Robert Anderson had become general manager in 1958, the Department of the Interior submitted to the Speaker of the House on June 5, 1959, a bill "to repeal the Act of March 12, 1914, authorizing the construction and operation of a railroad in Alaska, to incorporate The Alaska Railroad Company, and for other purposes." The bill was introduced by Senator Bartlett "for himself and Mr. Gruening by request" on August 11, 1959, and was referred to the Committee on Interstate and Foreign Commerce. There was no action in the committee, and the bill died with the adjournment of the 86th Congress.

In the fall of 1960, Anderson was succeeded by Donald Smith. Smith asked that the incorporation bill be included in the 1961 legislation program of the Department of the Interior. It was not reintroduced and was promptly displaced by bills seeking to make The Alaska Railroad subject to the regulatory authority of the Interstate Commerce Commission.

## The Department of Transportation

The last change in the organization lines of The Alaska Railroad came in October, 1966, when President Johnson signed the Department of Transportation Act and more than fifty years of association with the Department of the Interior were brought to an end. Secretary Udall did not oppose the change, and there were mixed feelings among railroad officials. They had built up loyalties to Interior in spite of the clash between the customs of the railroad industry and government practice. Some Interior officials were secretly envious of the relative independence of the railroad and aided its rebellion against the more bureaucratic of Interior traditions. Others were relieved to see the railroad go. Most railroad officials looked on the transfer to the new department in the same light as they viewed the accession of a new general manager. They would be apprehensive at first but later pleased that things had turned out so much better than they had thought possible.

The new Department of Transportation was the culmination of years of study directed toward consolidating federal transportation functions at Cabinet level. There were many such agencies—the Bureau of Public Roads in the Department of Commerce, the Federal Aviation Administration, the Coast Guard, to name a few. The regulatory agencies were not included in the new department, on the experience-demonstrated grounds that judicial and administrative functions should be the beneficiaries of a decent separation. But the Maritime Administration and the military transport agencies were also excluded on less logical grounds that may not be accepted in the future. Even with these exclusions, the new Department of Transportation, with more than 90,000 employees, became the fourth largest in the executive branch.

The effective date for the establishment of the new department was set at ninety days after the appointment of a secretary of Transportation or on such earlier date after the appointment as the President should prescribe by publication in the *Federal Register*. Prior to the convening of his second Congress, President Johnson announced that he was naming Allan Boyd, undersecretary for Transportation in the Department of Commerce, as the newest member of his Cabinet. On January 12, 1967, Boyd's appointment was confirmed by the

Senate and on January 16 he was sworn in at a special ceremony at the White House. President Johnson did not wait out the ninety days but brought the Department of Transportation into existence as of April 1, 1967.

The Alaska Railroad was transferred to the new department by Section 6(1) of the law as follows:

> The Administration of The Alaska Railroad, established pursuant to the Act of March 12, 1914, as amended (38 Stat. 308), and all of the functions authorized to be carried out by the Secretary of the Interior pursuant to Executive Order Numbered 11107, April 25, 1963 (28 F.R. 4225), relative to the operation of said Railroad, are hereby transferred to and vested in the Secretary of Transportation who shall exercise the same authority with respect thereto as is now exercised by the Secretary of the Interior pursuant to said Executive Order.

It was no surprise to anyone that the railroad became an agency of the Department of Transportation. It was a surprise, however, to find that the transfer was made by statute. Prior to final congressional action on the transportation bill, it was the plan of the President and his advisers to accomplish the transfer of the railroad by executive order, thus leaving intact the provisions of the railroad's organic act which gave the President the authority to locate, construct, and operate a railroad in Alaska. For more than half a century, the Secretary of the Interior had controlled the railroad under a delegation of authority from the President and not by congressional direction. President Harding's executive order of 1923, which was the instrument of this delegation, was superseded in 1963 by President Kennedy's executive order which confirmed the Secretary of the Interior's responsibility for the railroad but delegated the task of regulating tariff rates to the Interstate Commerce Commission. Herein is the explanation of the language of the statute quoted above. The Alaska Railroad is in the Department of Transportation by a legislative fiat that can be changed only by amendment. The power to regulate is

Chart 2
THE ALASKA RAILROAD WITHIN THE DEPARTMENT OF TRANSPORTATION

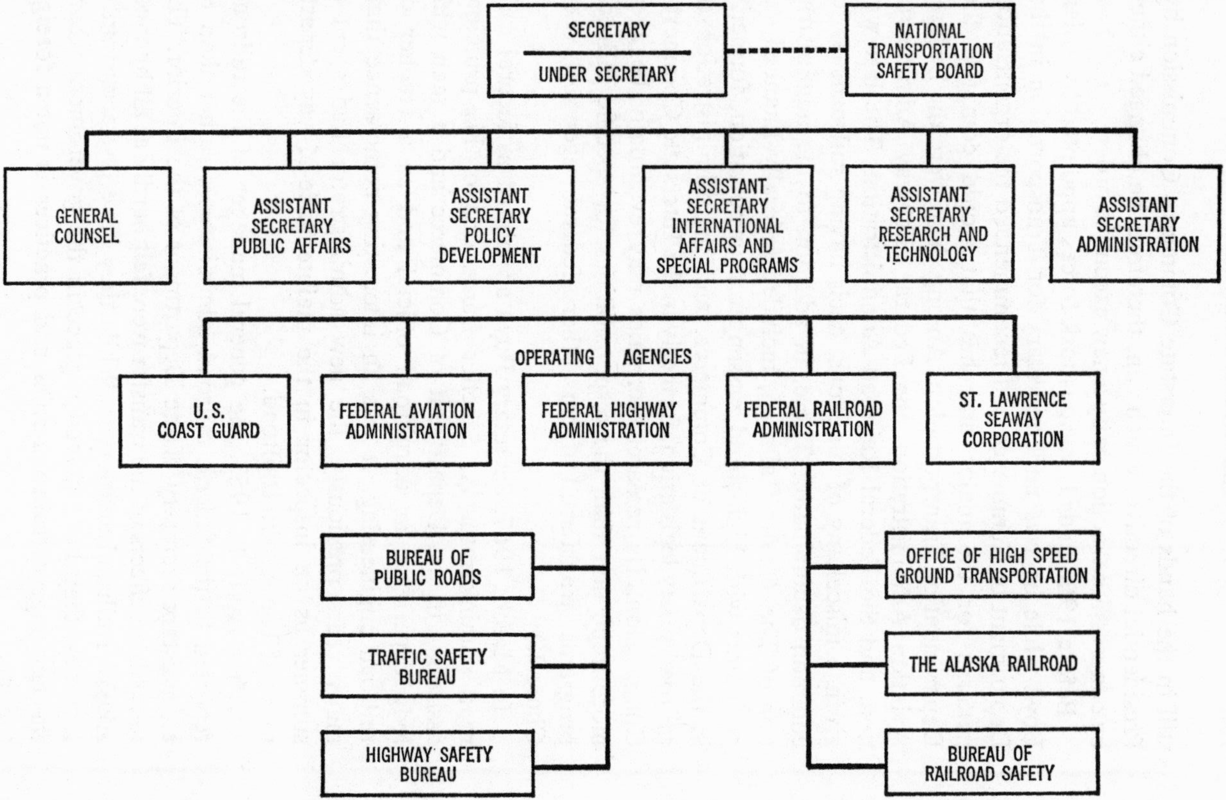

still in the hands of the Interstate Commerce Commission by Presidential directive, which can, therefore, be changed either by congressional action or by a new executive order.

Before 1966 ended, various task forces appointed by Allan Boyd while he was undersecretary for Transportation in the Department of Commerce had recommended the organization patterns for the major branches that would comprise the Department of Transportation. Among them were the Federal Aviation Administration, the Federal Highway Administration, and the Federal Railroad Administration. The last was given a miscellany of functions, each having railroads as its common denominator. These, in addition to the administration of The Alaska Railroad, included federally financed experiments with high-speed passenger transportation, formerly in the Department of Commerce, and the administration of railroad safety legislation, formerly in the Interstate Commerce Commission. Its research activities may eventually be even more important than the responsibilities for specific railroad programs transferred from other federal agencies. (See Chart 2.)

In March, 1967, Secretary Boyd appointed as federal railroad administrator A. Scheffer Lang, one of his principal assistants in the Department of Commerce and a man with long experience as a railroad official and as a teacher of railroad engineering. It was an interesting coincidence that, many years previously, the new administrator had spent a summer as an inspector in the maintenance-of-way department of The Alaska Railroad.

After April 1, 1967, the general manager of the railroad reported to the federal railroad administrator rather than to an assistant secretary of the Department of the Interior. The immediate effects of the transfer were felt hardly at all by most Alaska Railroad employees. While they have lost accustomed loyalties, they have gained a place in the government where the language of railroad rules and practices is not a foreign tongue.

# VIII

# To Bargain or Not to Bargain

In the spring of 1927, a small but select audience in New York City listened to a debate between a distinguished professor from the Economics Department of the University of Wisconsin and the president of the American Federation of Labor. The subject for debate was unemployment insurance. Professor John R. Commons spoke in favor and President William Green spoke against. Trade unionists have probably forgotten the ideological difficulties of the 1920's with which President Green was much concerned, for they have long since made their peace with social security, minimum-wage legislation, and the Fair Labor Standards Act. In 1927, however, the American Federation of Labor was uncertain as to whether or not federal and state governments might make unions obsolete by substituting legislative debate for collective bargaining.

While William Green never won accolades for brilliance, the fears that led him to oppose unemployment compensation were not irrational. He was the product of a pre–New Deal era in which union gains depended almost solely on quasi-coercive tactics at the bargaining table backed up by the thoroughly coercive right to strike. If worker salvation on a broad front was to be secured by legislation, what function would be left to the unions? With a fine, if not prophetic, instinct for self-preservation, he opposed social security measures on the ground that economic power rather than political action provides the proper instrument for advancing the cause of union labor.

In the debate, the professor was the pragmatist and the labor leader the theoretician. Professor Commons knew from his own experience that Green was tilting at windmills, that the dilemma he posed for union labor had little basis in reality, and that social security laws and trade unionism could progress together. By mixing research with politics, the economist from Wisconsin had made his home state a pioneer in labor legislation and, at the same time, had become the country's foremost protagonist of business unionism among students of labor. New Deal reforms, which included the Wagner Act as well as the Social Security Act, reinforced the validity of his position. The American Federation of Labor provided the final demonstration by abandoning, on this issue, the ideology of its president for that of Professor Commons.

Had William Green in the 1920's attempted to unionize federal workers in the face of the open-shop attitudes of many federal officials, he would have discovered that, where government was concerned, he was on firmer ground in emphasizing the conflict between legislation and collective bargaining. An understanding of these conflicting methods of advancing the welfare of government employees is necessary to an understanding of trade unionism of The Alaska Railroad and of the weakness of labor organizations in many areas of federal activity. However, social legislation has not threatened collective bargaining in government any more than it has in private industry. It was never possible that union power could win from a reluctant management the gains in workmen's compensation, unemployment compensation, and old age security that both private and government employees now enjoy. It would hardly occur to a government labor leader that he might bargain for such benefits on an individual department or agency basis.

Those laws that circumscribe or interfere with trade unionism in the federal government go to the heart of employee goals. In both government and private enterprise, the achievement of these goals has meant progressively higher standards governing hours of work, rates of pay, work rules, and the settlement of grievances. Congress can legislate in regard to these standards without harm to federal employee unions desiring to negotiate them, so long as there is left a reasonably wide area in which collective bargaining can operate. When the area of discretion for a federal manager becomes so small that bargaining seems futile, government unions have no reason for existence unless they can concentrate on other means of attaining their objectives.

## By Law or Bargaining?

The method by which a government employee's wages are determined is directly related to his interest in collective bargaining. Where Congress determines wages and salaries, as in the case of postal workers and employees subject to the classification laws, there may be trade unions but there is very little negotiation. Here, federal wage acts decide the issue and union leaders are primarily lobbyists whose chief concern is with the tactics of pressure and propaganda. There can be no negotiation as to the amounts and conditions of wage and salary rates established by Congress. Unions may influence congressmen and they may even intimidate a few, but they do not bargain with them.

The case is different for those employees whose pay rates are determined by agency wage boards "as nearly as is consistent with the public interest in accordance with prevailing rates." For them, the amount of variation in wage rates held to be "prevailing" is great enough to allow for negotiation and compromise. It is, therefore, no accident that the closest approach to industry-type collective bargaining is found among those government agencies that employ large numbers of wage-board workers.

The Tennessee Valley Authority and The Alaska Railroad

are both excluded from the coverage of the Classification Act of 1949. All their employees are wage-board whether craftsmen, machine operators, helpers and laborers (the so-called blue-collar workers) or clerks, stenographers, supervisors, professionals, or officials (the so-called white-collar workers). Both agencies have bargained and signed agreements with union representatives of their employees to a greater extent than is found elsewhere in the federal government. Several agencies with both wage-board and classified employees deal only with the former on a collective bargaining basis.

The granting to federal administrators of authority to fix wage and salary rates is by no means a guarantee that collective-bargaining relationships will be developed. There are not a few instances in which a federal executive has regarded the fixing of wages for his wage-board employees as a part of his management prerogative. Even when union participation is permitted, the members of wage boards established by such agencies often minimize the large amount of judgment involved in making wage determinations in accordance with prevailing rates. They try to maintain the fiction that fact-finding and wage computation are parts of so objective and scientific a process that there can be little room for argument about the facts and none at all about the conclusions. Here the area of collective bargaining is restricted by custom rather than law.

## Hours and Working Rules

Federal labor laws for government employees have made little distinction between classified and wage-board employees in the matter of hours of work, working rules, and grievances. For both kinds of employees, Congress has greatly narrowed the area of management discretion relating to hours, overtime, layoff and recall, seniority, and the filling of vacancies. There are two cogent reasons for this situation. When the Civil

Service system began in 1883 and trade unionism was regarded by the courts as a conspiracy against free enterprise, it was unthinkable that a government union would try to negotiate working conditions with representatives of sovereignty. Furthermore, when a benevolent Congress first began to establish labor standards for government employees, as it did in the eight-hour law of 1890 (repealed by the Work Hours Act of 1962), there was no one so confused as to argue that this was an unwarranted infringement upon the rights of businessmen. There has thus been built up over the years a code of government-worker standards embodied in Civil Service regulations that has pre-empted a large area in which government unions might otherwise function.

One of the most interesting of these laws and one that brought misfortune to the general managers of The Alaska Railroad for more than twenty years was Section 23 of the Act of March 28, 1934. This law provided that the regular hours of federal wage-board employees should not exceed 40 per week, that hours in excess of 40 should be paid for as overtime at not less than time and a half, and that, with some qualifications, wage rates should be increased so that pay for 40 hours per week should equal the pay received for the work week in effect prior to the act. These seemingly innocuous requirements proved to be in hopeless conflict with the overtime rules of the "dual system" of wage payment as contained in the railroad's agreement with the train and engine service brotherhoods. A consideration of this conflict will serve two purposes. It will illustrate the harm brought by a well-intentioned attempt to impose an inflexible formula on a large group of government employees without varying it to fit the many different situations to which it must apply. It will also permit a brief introduction to a system of wage payment that has been somewhat of a mystery to those outside the railroad industry.

The dual system of wage payment has evolved from a long-since vanished railroad formula of paying engineers, firemen, conductors, and brakemen at a fixed amount per trip. Under this pay system, in effect on The Alaska Railroad and on most private railroads in the United States, train crews are paid in cents per mile when the run is 100 miles or more and the average speed (miles run divided by the total elapsed time) is 12.5 miles per hour or more. Overtime is paid for hours worked in excess of 8 per day if the run is 100 miles or less. On runs of more than 100 miles, overtime is paid for hours by which time on duty exceeds the length of the run divided by 12.5. Thus, a run of 150 miles is paid for at a straight-time rate per mile so long as it is completed in 12 hours or less (150 divided by 12.5 equals 12). But if the run takes more than 12 hours, miles run are paid for at a straight-time rate per mile and all time over 12 hours is paid for at time and a half in freight service and straight time in passenger service. On a 150-mile run requiring more than the 12 hours on duty, the average speed is necessarily less than 12.5 miles per hour.* Since most runs can be completed at speeds exceeding 12.5 miles per hour, even though time at intermediate stops is included, train and engine men do not receive overtime for most trips.

There is a widespread delusion that the 100-mile day and the 12.5-miles-per-hour speed basis are outmoded standards and that, if they were increased, railroad management would benefit through decreased payroll costs. The 100-mile day is not a standard of performance but is a measure of a minimum day. If it were increased, railroads would pay more for every day that the minimum was not earned. The 12.5-mile speed basis has no reference to modern performance standards but merely determines the time when overtime begins. If the miles in a standard day were increased to 150 and the speed basis to

* The speed basis is 12.5 miles per hour on The Alaska Railroad in both freight and passenger service. On private railroads, it is 12.5 miles per hour in freight service and 20 miles per hour in passenger service.

25 miles, a run of 100 miles would be paid for at the mileage rate times 150 and overtime would begin after 4 hours on duty instead of after 8. So long as mileage rates remain constant, each increase in these so-called standards enables train and engine men to earn more money, not less.

It may take time with pencil and paper before the overtime rules of the dual system are thoroughly understood. Understandable or not, it is clear that they do not provide for overtime at time and a half after 40 hours per week. For private railroads, the conflict between the dual system and the 40-hour-week overtime was recognized and railroads were excluded from the overtime provisions of the Fair Labor Standards Act. No one reminded Congress that the same problem existed for The Alaska Railroad, which, in 1934, was operated on the basis of a 6-day, 48-hour straight-time work week. Within a few weeks, the Comptroller General was requested for a ruling on Section 23 of the Act of March 28, 1934, and held that it did not apply to the railroad. There followed a labor dispute that lasted nearly 20 years and was finally settled in the U.S. Court of Claims with a decision that overruled the Comptroller General and resulted in back-pay judgments for employees totaling nearly $1.5 million.*

The train and engine service brotherhoods, who brought the original suits, were unhappy with the federal overtime law, however, because the railroad's wage costs were then less than those payable under the labor agreements. The paradox of a cash award by the U.S. Court of Claims before the law was applied and a lower payroll after was in part the complex result of the court's attempt to join together two pay systems that were essentially incompatible. Since the court decision, the

* See *David F. Samples et al* v. *United States,* decided July 12, 1956. The findings in this case contain an excellent description of the dual system of wage payment for operating employees, including constructive allowances or arbitraries and various guarantees, not described herein. There were several other Alaska Railroad overtime cases decided by the U.S. Court of Claims. The first in this series was *Poggas* v. *United States,* decided December 5, 1950.

brotherhoods have joined, in friendly cooperation with management, in an attempt to avoid or minimize the overtime rules of the 1934 act to the extent that this has been legally possible. Their joint efforts included an unsuccessful try at amending the law to remove train and engine service employees from the coverage of its overtime formula.

The 1934 overtime law for wage-board employees is an unusual example of the long-term results of careless legislation. Had it been drafted with appropriate exclusions and qualifications, it would have caused fewer collective-bargaining problems. There are other federal laws that, no matter how skillfully drafted, reduce the effectiveness of collective bargaining. The most important of these are the Veterans' Preference Act of 1944 as amended and various civil service laws authorizing the selection of employees on a merit basis. Appointment and merit rating procedures do not, of themselves, affect the work rules of any government-employee labor agreement. Appointment procedures are rarely the subject of collective bargaining except when the closed shop is legally possible. Civil service law and regulation, apart from procedures governing appointments, are in serious conflict with many of the working rules that have existed for years in Alaska Railroad labor agreements.

## Veterans' Preference

The Veterans' Preference Act authorizes procedures for reduction in force that preclude the use of traditional concepts of seniority for this purpose. Civil Service rules under veterans' preference also include complicated regulations for the protection of employees against so-called adverse actions, which include discharge, suspension, and reduction in employee rank or compensation, whether or not of disciplinary origin. But the framers of the law and the regulations forgot the countless instances in an industrial type of government activity when reduction in rank or compensation occurs without disciplinary significance. Thus, the law requires time-consuming procedures, which may be appropriate to the assessment of discipline but which serve no other purpose that the average labor agreement could not accomplish a great deal better.

On The Alaska Railroad, for example, many fill-in assignments are handled by a small pool of employees specially established for this purpose, called "extra boards" in train and engine service. These extra boards cover jobs of short duration when regular employees are sick or on vacation. Extra-board employees may run an extra troop train or man an extra trick when a pile-up of yard work requires it.

Many of these services carry different rates of pay. There are also rate variations for engineers and firemen who operate heavier or multiple-unit locomotives (some Alaska Railroad freight trains require six diesels), and there are similar variations for conductors and brakemen based on length of train. As a result of all this, an extra-board train and engine man may have his rank or compensation reduced or increased with considerable frequency, and during some weeks this might happen each day. In regular or assigned service, many changes result from adding passenger trains in the spring and taking them off in the fall, or in varying assignments to suit traffic or weather conditions, or work-train requirements.

Civil Service regulations require that, for every instance of reduction in rank or compensation, the employee must have thirty days' written notice giving reasons for the change, an opportunity to reply, and the right to appeal to the Civil Service Commission if he finds the change objectionable. To observe the rule as the lower echelons of the Civil Service literally interpreted it was literally impossible, and the railroad continued to follow the rules of the labor agreement and to ignore the Civil Service rules. For many years, there were no complaints.

Finally, in 1964, the railroad's luck ran out and a yard

engineer appealed to the commission against an assignment to a firemen's extra board (even though he made more money while working from the extra board than as a yard engineer). The Seattle office of the Civil Service Commission ruled in favor of the complainant and ordered the railroad to restore him to his job. The yard engineer's motive was obscure, but there is some evidence that he was trying to prove that a veteran could not be displaced or reassigned without his consent. The railroad appealed to the commission's Board of Appeals and Review in Washington. The board remanded the case to the Seattle office for reconsideration. The Seattle office reaffirmed its original decision but, on a second appeal to Washington, the original decision was reversed. For many months before and after the case of the yard engineer, railroad and Civil Service officials in Washington worked to resolve the conflict between veterans' preference regulations and the rules of the train and engine men's agreement. Both understood that a literal application of the regulations would be sheer nonsense.* They finally put together new regulations, derived from the labor agreements and satisfactory to the railroad as well as to the commission and to train and engine service unions, which established civil service rules covering multiple appointments for operating employees. The commission published the new rules in the *Federal Register,* thus giving formal recognition to the labor-agreement provisions describing the right and the duty of train and engine employees to work different assignments at varying rates of pay. Unfortunately, there were few job relationships among non-operating employees that gave similar protection to the seniority rules in their agreements with labor.

It is significant of the equities in the conflict between the

* Let us suppose, for example, that an engineer operating a freight train to Fairbanks with six diesels had to be given 30 days' notice in writing before he could be directed to return to Anchorage with only five diesels or that an extra-board brakeman had to be given notice of reduction in his rank or compensation twice a week.

law and the labor agreements that almost all the train and engine men in the Railbelt, veteran and nonveteran alike, applauded the decision of the Appeals Board of the commission against their fellow yard engineer. They also applauded the success of Alaska Railroad officials in securing the commission's acceptance of the principle of multiple appointments. They were motivated by the high value they placed on their railroad seniority. They knew that, if the yard engineer's case had gone against the railroad and the multiple-appointment principle had not been approved by the Civil Service Commission, many of the seniority rules contained in their work agreement would have been invalidated.

## Competitive Civil Service

The basic rules of the Civil Service merit system are those governing the competitive examining and selecting of appointees for federal jobs. The system applies to wage-board appointments as well as to applicants for work in the classified civil service. For a great many years, Alaska Railroad employees had "Schedule A" appointments, which are exempt from competitive examinations and are said to be in the "excepted civil service."

Competitive appointment procedures in themselves have only a minor influence in reducing the area of collective bargaining but they bring in their wake a host of rules that are completely unnecessary where a strong union exists and that must bear part of the responsibility for the unsatisfactory state of trade unionism among federal employees. Here again, the principal villain is the Veterans' Preference Act, although, ironically, no veterans' preference is involved. "Adverse action" procedures give preference to veterans only when they are not applied to other federal employees. The Civil Service Commission has ruled, however, that in the competitive service, these procedures must be applied to both veterans and nonveterans. Only in the case of excepted-service employees do veterans have any "preference" in this respect.

On January 1, 1967, Alaska Railroad employees were transferred from the excepted to the competitive service. The area of bargaining has thus been further reduced because the adverse-action rules are now equally applicable to veterans and nonveterans. For labor-agreement rules relating to seniority, there has been substituted a civil-service kind of seniority that is strange to Alaska Railroad employees and that most of them find inferior. Only in situations where multiple appointments can be made has it proved possible to save essential seniority features of the labor-agreement rules. It has been pointed out that nonoperating agreement rules provide little opportunity for use of the multiple-appointment principle. For layoff on account of reduction in force, a complicated method of determining employee priorities must be substituted on both operating and nonoperating agreements for the simple seniority rule that the junior men in a given occupation shall be the first laid off and the senior laid-off employee shall be the first to be returned to service.

Apart from their influence on collective bargaining, regulations applying to force reduction and adverse action, together with rules relating to the examining procedures of the competitive service, are defective because they are too complicated for the average employee to understand and because they vastly increase the amount of paper work necessary to complete a personnel change.* Compare, for example, the simplicity of the railroad seniority rule "Qualifications being sufficient, seniority shall govern" with the complex structure of a reduction-in-force retention roster. Furthermore, Civil

* The few employees on The Alaska Railroad who have complained to local Civil Service officials against being transferred from one assignment to another have been completely unable to explain whether they wished to proceed under the rules applying to reduction in force or the quite different rules applying to adverse actions. In fairness to the employees, it must be said that there are railroad officials who have equal trouble in making the distinction.

Service rules are not attuned to the relatively fast pace of an industrial enterprise and were never intended to apply to them. They are tolerable to the average government bureau, not because government bureaus are fond of paper work, but because the personnel changes to which they relate are ordinarily infrequent.

Veterans' preference and competitive-service regulations are not the only Civil Service rules that restrict the freedom of management to engage in labor negotiations, but they are the most important. When these are combined with a system of establishing federal wage and salary rates by action of Congress or of authoritarian government administrators, the leaders of some government unions react by avoiding even the pretense of maintaining the attitudes and practices of traditional collective bargaining.

There is more to the story of the conflict between the Civil Service rules and labor agreements, which will have meaning after a review of the long history of the railroad's dealings with trade unions. It is enough to say at this point that a determined attempt was made to amend provisions of the Veterans' Preference Act and provisions of other Civil Service laws that place obstacles in the way of freedom to negotiate. At congressional hearings on the "Railroad Personnel Bill," as it was called, the star witnesses who spoke in favor of its enactment were Alaska Railroad employees with veterans' preference rights and John W. Macy, Jr., chairman of the Civil Service Commission.

## The Beginnings of Alaska Railroad Trade Unionism

Labor-management relations on The Alaska Railroad developed at an early date in an atmosphere favorable to the growth of trade unionism and collective bargaining. In the 1920's, the general manager's freedom to act in personnel matters was almost as great as in private enterprise. His authority was restrained far more by the Secretary of the Interior than by any Civil Service rules. Even the authority of the secretary was weakened by 3,000 miles distance and two to three weeks in time.

Among the first general managers, Noel Smith was from the Pennsylvania Railroad and Otto Ohlson from the Northern Pacific, and almost all employees came from "outside" railroads. They brought with them their operating rules, methods of wage payments, and their trade unions. In train and engine service, employees and management began negotiating agreements even before it was possible to run trains through from Seward to Fairbanks. But suppose Alaska Railroad employees had been in the classified civil service or that their pay rates, as wage-board employees, had been imposed by a centralized federal wage board. If such had been the case, most of the railroad's collective-bargaining history would have been erased. Had the Veterans' Preference Act been in existence in the 1920's and 1930's, the seniority system that employees brought from their home railroads would have been dealt a near-mortal blow. If employees had not been excepted from the rules of the competitive civil service, Alaska Railroad labor agreements would have existed, if indeed they could have existed at all, as completely different, watered-down documents. Again this is because the competitive civil service covers a great deal more than the examining requirements of applicants.

The absence of Civil Service laws and regulations did not produce a spoils system on The Alaska Railroad. Had there been any such danger, it would have been easy to apply the Tennessee Valley Authority remedy by forbidding the use of a political test or qualification on pain of forfeiture of position by both the person making a political appointment and the person receiving one. The lack of restrictive personnel laws, however, made possible a series of labor agreements altogether unlike any other in the federal government. A few of the work rules, adopted after negotiation, were indigenous to the railroad. Many more were copied from private railroad agreements. Taken together, these Alaska Railroad negotiated rules meant that employees depended upon their union agreements for protection in their jobs and for improvement in their labor standards. In federal agencies where collective bargaining does not exist, government employees tend to look to the Civil Service system for job protection and to Congress for improvement in their hours, wages, and working conditions.

In a not too important sense, The Alaska Railroad's labor-relations history began in 1916 with a spontaneous strike against a wage rate of 37.5 cents per hour established by the Alaskan Engineering Commission. Mediators from the Department of Labor intervened, and wages were increased about 20 per cent. The first real step toward trade unions for all classes and crafts on the railroad came with the signing, on April 1, 1920, of an agreement covering rules and rates of pay for locomotive engineers, conductors, firemen, and brakemen. As operating employees were the first to introduce collective bargaining to The Alaska Railroad, so they would be the last to abandon it if bargaining in government should ever lose its meaning and effectiveness.

Train and engine men are among the highest paid of all railroad workers, but they are paid for the responsibilities they assume as well as the skill they exercise. Between terminals, they are "on their own" and free from supervision more than any other railroad employee of equivalent training and experience. A four- or five-man freight crew, with a conductor as "captain" (and with an engineer sometimes a little annoyed at this fact) can be operating a train worth well over $1 million carrying a cargo worth more than $2 million. It has often been said that inexperienced brakemen and firemen arrive at high pay too quickly. There may be some truth in this conclusion. But it must be remembered that the new brakeman always begins work in yard service and that there have been a good many years in which the accidental death rates of yard firemen and brakemen have exceeded those for airplane pilots.

January 16, 1925, was a red-letter day for trade unionism on The Alaska Railroad. On that day the Brotherhood of Railroad Trainmen took over the representation of conductors and brakemen, the Brotherhood of Locomotive Firemen and Enginemen became the bargaining representatives of engineers, firemen, and hostlers, and the Order of Railroad Telegraphers were recognized as representing agent telegraphers, telegraphers, and telegrapher clerks. Today, five other unions represent the rest of the nonoperating employees (excluding foremen and other supervisors, professionals, and officials), but none was able to get a permanent foothold on the railroad for more than ten years after 1925. The attempts to organize during this period failed partly because many of the less-skilled nonoperating employees did not have a railroad background. Moreover, a division along craft lines, which has been characteristic of railroad trade unionism, meant smaller numbers for organization purposes. Often the cost of maintaining an Alaska Railroad local by a national labor organization was greatly in excess of the amount of dues collected. If organizing and maintaining the local meant trips to the Territory, the expense of such trips was, for some unions, almost prohibitive. Finally, the years between 1925 and 1937 were years of rather extraordinary wage stability. By the spring of 1937, section laborers on the railroad were still earning only 56.25 cents to 58.2 cents per hour. (The comparable section-labor rate on the Northern Pacific Railway was 41 cents per hour.)

During the early days of Alaska's economic development, all wage rates were imported, most of them from the Pacific Northwest. Prices were higher and work hardships greater in the Territory than "outside," and various devices were used to make up for these differences. Employers who hired in Seattle for work in Alaska paid transportation both ways, often provided subsistence in the Territory, and paid Seattle wage rates. As an Alaskan labor market slowly developed, the custom of paying a differential over the wage rate transplanted from the "south" became general. Current authority for giving government employees in Alaska a 25 per cent cost-of-living differential dates from 1949. General Manager Ohlson followed no consistent wage pattern, except that he tried, without being very precise about it, to give his employees the pay increases negotiated on private railroads in the Pacific Northwest plus 25 per cent.

Until 1937, no permanent union gains had been made among the nonoperating employees except for the recognition of the Order of Railroad Telegraphers in 1925. In 1937, a new dimension was added with the recognition of the American Federation of Government Employees as the bargaining agent for most of the rest of the nonoperating groups. In that year, the long period of wage stability was brought to an end. In the following ten years, four Alaska Railroad wage increases were negotiated—in 1937, 1941, 1943, and 1946. The first two increases were based generally on the accustomed pattern of 25 per cent over "stateside" railroad increases. The others were based on federal pay increases that resulted in the largest additions ever made to Alaska Railroad wages and salaries and led directly to the most bitter labor dispute in the railroad's history.

## Wage Settlement by Secretarial Order, 1948

On April 30, 1948, Oscar Chapman, as Acting Secretary of the Interior, signed Order No. 2424, which increased the rates of pay of Alaska Railroad employees in varying amounts and added nearly $1 million to the railroad's annual payroll. The increases were based on an addition to the wage rates paid by the Northern Pacific Railway for comparable occupations of an amount that, as a differential for higher living costs in

Alaska, would enable employees to earn $1,482.80 a year more than their Northern Pacific counterparts. This annual differential was included in basic pay rates and thus was included in calculations of overtime, accident compensation, sick and annual leave, and retirement. The odd amount of the differential resulted from the addition of 5 cents per hour on an annual basis to the flat cost-of-living differential of $1,350 recommended by the railroad.

Order 2424 was issued unilaterally by the secretary and was both preceded and followed by a union-management dispute so intense that, had the railroad been privately owned, its employees would have gone on strike. The convictions of management, on the other hand, were so strong that they would have shut down the railroad rather than surrender. Nevertheless, Order 2424 established an over-all wage policy that was followed for a great many years, with eventual near-to-unanimous union acquiescence and with active and vigorous support from the two operating brotherhoods.

The dispute that led to Order 2424 was inadvertently set in motion by a decision of General Manager Otto Ohlson in 1943 to abandon temporarily the railroad's practice of negotiating wage increases to correspond with increases agreed to on private railroads plus 25 per cent. He considered higher wages imperative because of critical manpower shortages, so acute that they had required the loan to the railroad of the 714th Railway Operating Battalion. Recruiting problems were frustrating in the extreme. In addition to difficulties caused by inflated wartime prices and competitive wage rates, housing shortages in both Anchorage and Fairbanks were almost absolute. A 1941 decision to allow Anchorage employees to buy at the railroad commissary had helped some, but not much.

Unfortunately, wage negotiations in the railroad industry in 1943 were unusually drawn out. Colonel Ohlson could not afford to wait and therefore requested the Secretary of the Interior for authority to offer employees a 15 per cent increase. His request denied, he turned, in some desperation, to the Comptroller General for a ruling as to whether the War Overtime Pay Act of 1943 was applicable. In a decision of August 21, 1943, the Comptroller General held that the wage-board provisions of the act applied to Alaska Railroad monthly and annually rated employees, but not to those rated hourly or daily or to pieceworkers. Under the government accounting and payroll practices in vogue at the time, all employees were regarded as monthly or annual, except laborers and train and engine men. Under the 1943 wage settlement, and in accordance with the Comptroller General's opinion, monthly and annual employees received percentage increases amounting to a maximum of $52.36 per month. By agreement, hourly workers received 15 cents an hour increase and train and engine men $1.20 per 100 miles or per 8-hour day. For nonoperating employees, the increases were greatly in excess of corresponding increases on private railroads.

The next step in the sad experiment of substituting law for negotiation came with the Federal Pay Act of 1945. While the bill was being considered by Congress, representatives of the American Federation of Government Employees asked Delegate Bartlett to include Alaska Railroad employees under its terms. Colonel Ohlson, apprehensive that such inclusion might also mean competitive service rules for Alaska Railroad employees, told union representatives that if they would withdraw their request, he would pay wage increases equivalent to those that the new pay law would guarantee. The unions complied. No consideration was given to the possibility of a 40-hour week on the railroad. The Alaska Railroad had long followed (with some clerical variations) the 48-hour week of "outside" railroads, and the general manager tried to avoid radical departures from these practices so that railroad unions would have no basis for using Alaska Railroad precedents as arguments for changes in private-railroad work rules.

On June 30, 1945, the Federal Pay Act of 1945 became

law. It placed classified employees in the federal service on a 40-hour week and substituted for the "in lieu of overtime" increases of the 1943 pay law new wage increases that would make 40-hour week earnings slightly larger than 1943 earnings for a 48-hour week. Penalty payments for overtime after 40 hours would be equal to time and a half in the lower pay brackets and were graduated downward for employees in higher grades. Basically classified employees (and others having statutory wage rates) would benefit through an additional day of free time rather than in increased earnings.

Nonoperating employees on The Alaska Railroad had been receiving time and a half for overtime after 48 hours per week since 1943. In 1945, no employer in Alaska, including the general manager, thought that the work week could be successfully reduced to 40 hours in the face of the extreme manpower shortages in the Territory. After the Federal Pay Act of 1945 became law, Colonel Ohlson found that he had promised to pay, not only the pay rates legally required, but 30 per cent more on a weekly basis because of the time-and-a-half requirement for the sixth day. Ohlson then asked his chief clerk, A. R. Sessions (whose duties often included the functions of the personnel director that the railroad did not employ) to calculate the overtime rates on the basis of the 1945 act. Ohlson was astonished at the result. After further pondering of the mathematics of overtime, he decided that the railroad could not afford such increases. He withdrew his offer to the unions and proposed a 20 per cent wage increase instead.

Union representatives now had more than a wage issue—they also had the issue of a broken promise and they proceeded to make the most of it. However sound Ohlson's logic may have been, he had made an agreed-to settlement almost impossible. Inevitably, the dispute found its way to Washington. This time the Interior Department, rather than the general manager, requested a ruling from the Comptroller General and ordered the 1943 increase continued in the interim. On November 20, 1945, after a summer and fall of heated wrangling in Alaska, the Comptroller General used the legal logic of 1943 and ruled that the Federal Pay Act of 1945 applied to the railroad's monthly and annual employees but not to the others. The employees and their union representatives thus added the Comptroller General's opinion to their arsenal of moral indignation and were more adamant than ever. The general manager, now nearly seventy years old, retired but, to the very last, refused to surrender.

When the new general manager, Colonel J. P. Johnson, took over on January 1, 1946, he had no choice but to apply the Comptroller General's decision to monthly and annual employees and to agree to equivalent increases for hourly employees and train and engine men. The new wage rates were made retroactive to July 1, 1945, the effective date of the 1945 act. In another decision, the Comptroller General agreed that the "equivalent increases" had been promised as of July 1, 1945, and were therefore "prospectively" valid as of that date.*

Even after the private railroad settlement of 1946, the 1945 increases meant that Alaska Railroad employees were receiving, not 25 per cent more, but 40 to 75 per cent more than employees in the same occupations on the Northern Pacific. For a few occupations, differentials approached 100 per cent.

* Comptroller General decisions on prospective pay established a method by which government agencies can make administrative decisions or union agreements that wage increases of unknown amounts can be paid as of the date of the decision or agreement or later date and that legal "retroactive" payments can be made to such date even though it may take months to arrive at the amount of the increase. Some of the earliest decisions establishing this principle were applied to The Alaska Railroad by the Comptroller General in 1946. Most government unions, except on The Alaska Railroad, made no attempt to utilize these decisions but lobbied for legislation legalizing retroactive wage increases. An explanation of "prospective pay" and citations to several decisions regarding it may be found in a letter of April 8, 1963, from the Comptroller General to the Secretary of the Interior.

Years later, Alaska Railroad employees refused to bargain on the basis of Alaska Railroad and Northern Pacific rates but insisted on bargaining on the basis of a comparison of wage increases only. Using this union theory in 1945, Alaska Railroad machinists received a 31 cents per hour increase, or 70 per cent more than the corresponding 18.5 cents per hour increase on the Northern Pacific. On a weekly basis, Alaska Railroad machinists received an increase of $21.55, or 143 per cent more than the $8.88 increase received by the machinists on the Northern Pacific.

After the 1943 and 1945 wage settlements, Alaska Railroad wages followed no recognizable pattern. There were neither government rates nor railroad rates. There was not even a pretense that they followed prevailing wages in Alaska or anywhere else. They were the wartime results of extreme manpower shortages, stubborn unions, a general manager's broken promise, and federal pay legislation. Less-skilled workers were dissatisfied because their pay rates were still too low. Skilled workers, realizing that they might have won too great a victory, were fearful that management might plot to deprive them of its fruits.

The new general manager had no plot against the unions. He was determined, however, not to be caught again without a plan. The railroad appointed its first personnel director, who was happily unaware that before many months the railroad would again be involved in a bitter labor struggle. Interior officials had said correctly that the railroad had no labor policy; the general manager set about to obtain one. Interior officials had said the railroad had no wage policy; the general manager was determined to remedy this lack.

On behalf of General Manager Johnson, the Department of the Interior hired Otto S. Beyer, a labor consultant with a distinguished reputation, to assist in these personnel enterprises. Beyer had been an adviser to the railroad employees department of the American Federation of Labor, to the president of the Canadian National Railways, the Tennessee Valley Authority, the federal coordinator of transportation, the Office of Defense Transportation, and had been chairman of the National Mediation Board. He devised a labor-relations program in 1947 that was issued as the "Labor Policy Statement of The Alaska Railroad" and approved on June 3, 1947. The program was based on recognition of employees' rights to join unions and to select a single union as their exclusive bargaining agent and placed on management the duty to bargain with representatives of their employees on hours, wages, and working conditions. It called for written agreements, the establishment of grievance procedures, mediation and voluntary arbitration, and committees for labor-management cooperation. It was indicative of the corrosive character of the 1945 wage dispute that union representatives refused to join with management in issuing the railroad's labor charter, even though it was the most forward-looking and progressive pro-trade-union statement that had been prepared by any government agency up to that time.

Since it was awkward for an agency of the Department of the Interior to release a statement on labor policy before the department itself had taken a position, Otto Beyer drew up the "General Labor Relations Policy for Ungraded Employees of the Department of the Interior," which was approved by the secretary on January 16, 1948. By these policy pronouncements, both the railroad and Interior assumed a pro-trade-union stance rarely found in a government agency. Armed with the directives of a liberal labor creed, Alaska Railroad officials set out to put its principles into practice and redeem labor-management relations from the low estate to which they had fallen.

Labor relations on private railroads during this period were setting no one a good example. The "outside" wage settlement of May, 1946, which gave $1.48 per basic day (100 miles) to train and engine men and 18.5 cents per hour to nonoperating employees, came at the end of a long and angry dispute. It was preceded by an arbitration award to which engineers and trainmen were not a party, by a threatened strike and a two-day walkout by these same train and engine men, by President Truman's seizure of the railroads, and by a final agreed-to conclusion minutes before the President delivered a speech to a joint session of Congress in favor of strong antistrike legislation.

This private railroad settlement corresponded to the 1945–46 Alaska Railroad settlement. Nevertheless, representatives of the American Federation of Government Employees in Anchorage asked that its increases be added to those of the 1945 pay act. The general manager indignantly refused, and the request was quickly dropped. Early in 1947, however, union representatives began to press for additions to their wages even though the 1947 wage movement on "outside" railroads was several months from settlement. The only suggestion as to how large the increase should be came from the operating brotherhoods, which asked for 30 per cent, plus 25 per cent of 30 per cent as a cost-of-living differential. The 25 per cent differential request was interesting in view of cost-of-living differentials already in Alaska Railroad wage rates that were two or three times as large.

At this point, Colonel Johnson appointed a wage board of three officials—Paul Shelmerdine, personnel director and chairman of the wage board, D. H. Nucker, budget officer, and R. A. Sharood, chief engineer. The wage board did its fact-finding with the help of Otto Beyer and the author of this book, who prepared "A Survey of the Wage and Salary Situation on The Alaska Railroad, 1937–1947." The unions that had not participated in preparing the report denounced it vigorously and suggested that no amount of "distorted" statistics could overcome the fact that turnover among railroad employees approached 100 per cent (which was true) and that the cost of living had increased (which was also true).

Wage-board members stressed the discriminatory effects of the 1945 wage increases toward low-wage employees, among whom turnover was greatest (which was true as well). The employees' case was presented by a conductor, Del Van Curler, probably the ablest and most dedicated labor leader that Alaska Railroad unions have produced.

The details of these negotiations would require a volume in themselves. Temperatures grew warmer as the dispute progressed. Demands by nonoperating employees increased with each offer and counteroffer, to the dismay of the members of the wage board and the annoyance of the operating brotherhoods that followed the union tradition of compromising downward if they intended to compromise at all. Whether the customs of bargaining were or were not followed made little difference. The dispute was more concerned with wage philosophies than with wage amounts. The unions wanted a cost-of-living allowance measured by the difference between straight-time pay on The Alaska Railroad for 40 hours and that on the Northern Pacific for 48. Management wanted a cost-of-living allowance measured by the difference between pay for 48 hours on The Alaska Railroad, including 8 hours of penalty overtime, and 48 hours straight-time pay on the Northern Pacific. In addition, the unions wanted to preserve the high gains of the 1943 and 1945 settlements for skilled employees by insisting that any addition to wages must be "across the board."

The foregoing observations apply generally to nonoperating employees rather than to train and engine men. The latter had no complaint about hours of work and overtime because they were working under the dual system of wage payment and wished to continue under its terms. While many operating employees had brought suits under the wage-board overtime law of 1934, at no time after the Comptroller General declared the law inapplicable to the railroad did they propose the inclusion of the overtime rules of the 1934 law in their collective-bargaining agreements. The operating brotherhoods joined in the 1947 dispute, not only because of an interest in presenting a united front, but because they objected to management's desire to substitute an increase in rates for a "free" 100 miles' pay on the seventh day—the layover day provided for in the then current agreement. They also opposed a wage calculation offered by management adjusting basic rates so that it required the running of 3,000 miles per month before the cost-of-living differential could be earned. Operating employees wanted higher basic rates that would permit the differential to be earned for 2,600 miles.

The dispute dragged on to an impasse in Anchorage and submission at last to Washington for a decision by the Secretary of the Interior. A hearing was held under the chairmanship of Director James Davis of the Division of Territories and Island Possessions. Union representatives from Alaska presented the employee side of the dispute. When all the speechmaking was over, Chairman Davis found in favor, with some revisions, of the final proposal of the general manager. Secretary Chapman did not act hastily but spent many hours in studying a wage problem of more than ordinary complexity. On April 30, 1948, he gave his approval to the revised recommendations and issued them as Order No. 2424, a summary of which was presented earlier in this chapter. In the "Statement and Findings" that accompanied the order, Secretary Chapman wrote:

> One of the principle values of the General Manager's wage and salary proposal is its effect in eliminating most of the inequitable pay differentials between occupations which now exist on The Alaska Railroad. Many of these occupational differentials are not the result of the deliberate adaptation of a sound and tested wage structure to Alaskan conditions. Rather, they have been the result of two factors: (1) General percentage increases which favored high wage over low wage occupations and (2) a series of individual increases which sometimes produced widely varying rates for essentially the same level of jobs.

These inequitable wage differentials have been particularly unjust to the employees in the low-wage brackets. It is thus not an accident that it is among these employees that The Alaska Railroad has encountered its greatest recruiting difficulties and its major turnover problems.

I find that in general the General Manager's proposed plan and recommendations are fair and equitable, that they conform to the prevailing wage principle, will remove presently existing inequities, and will provide a stable wage structure for the Railroad.

## Wage History Since Order 2424

In spite of union fulminations, Wage Order 2424 survived. Management attempts prior to November, 1949, to persuade union representatives to join in conciliatory conferences were unsuccessful. So drastic a revision of wage rates could hardly be made without some mistakes, and Order 2424 provided for joint union-management recommendations on changes. Union representatives refused to review the hated order, and management was forced to make the required reconsideration without assistance. Some individual changes and an across-the-board increase of 6 cents per hour were recommended to the Interior Department and approved.

In November, 1949, the curse was removed from Order 2424 when, after negotiation, the railroad agreed to a 40-hour work week for nonoperating employees. Private rail carriers had made the same change in negotiated settlements, and The Alaska Railroad followed their formula for conversion. Pay rates for nonoperating employees were increased so that those on 40-hour week schedules received the same pay, less 80 cents per week, for the 40 hours that they had previously received for 48 hours. The increases in hourly rates were greater on The Alaska Railroad than on "outside" railroads because employees had to be made whole (given 48 hours' pay, at the previous rate, for 40 hours' work) for a sixth day of work for which 8 hours at time and a half had been paid. The Northern

Pacific, which has been the railroad's measure of wage changes on private railroads, needed to include pay for 8 hours of straight time only in the rates applicable to the 40-hour week.

Wage negotiations with the operating brotherhoods took a much stormier course precisely because the 40-hour week was not involved. Order 2424's pay rates for train and engine men were expressed in terms of the dual system of wage payment and were not sharply challenged. Nevertheless, train and engine men shared with nonoperating employees their bitter hostility toward a unilateral wage order. They also had an additional grievance. In 1947, a new operating agreement had been negotiated with the railroad's personnel director. The agreement had been submitted to the Interior Department for approval, and, two years later, the Department was still unable to decide whether legal objections to some of its most important provisions were valid or invalid.

What had been a wage-rate negotiation for the nonoperating employees turned into a rules negotiation for train and engine men. The intensity of feeling generated by the Order 2424 controversy made bargaining extremely difficult. The dispute was transferred to Washington in the summer of 1950 and was continued there for several weeks. It was finally settled as a result of the kind of unpredictable accident, the possibility of which keeps men striving for lost causes when all hope seems gone. A vice-president of the Brotherhood of Railroad Trainmen, assisted by the union's general chairman in Anchorage, Van Curler, was in charge of the negotiations for the two operating unions. The item under discussion was the "layover day," previously described as a "free" 100 miles' pay for the seventh day of an employee's work week when no service was performed. The value of the layover day had been incorporated in the basic rates, and there was suspicion that employees had somehow lost out in the process.

In analyzing the layover day, the union vice-president became confused by the dual-system mathematics and made an ambiguous counter offer to a management offer that had just been indignantly refused. As the dials of a management calculating machine started to spin, Van Curler slowly turned purple as he did the arithmetic in his head and, simultaneously with the calculator, realized that the union counteroffer would result in a lower wage level than the vice-president of the trainmen's union had just rejected. The railroad's negotiator, Personnel Director Paul Shelmerdine, paused long enough to check the arithmetic and then explained the mathematics of the union's mistake and allowed the trainmen's vice-president to withdraw his offer. The meeting adjourned with confusion confined to the union side only. That night, Van Curler telephoned Shelmerdine to express his appreciation of Shelmerdine's consideration. The next day there were no more negotiating problems, and an agreement was signed.

Order 2424 was vindicated in the 1949 40-hour week negotiations, for, if Alaska Railroad management had not held to the wage formulas of the order, nonoperating employees could not have been "made whole" for the loss of 8 hours at premium pay when the 40-hour week was finally adopted. Instead, their weekly earnings would have been reduced by the equivalent of 12 hours of straight-time pay. The adoption of a 40-hour week would have cost most of the journeymen in the shops an average of $22 per week, or over $1,100 per year. In the negotiations leading up to Order 2424, in May, 1948, union representatives had insisted that they would accept such decreases as the price of receiving 40-hour week pay rates. There can be no doubt that the transition to the 40-hour week was made a great deal easier because it did not have to be done at so great a decline in income and living standards.

While the adoption of the 40-hour week in 1949 eliminated the most important employee objection to Order 2424, more than this was required to smooth feelings that had been almost continuously ruffled since 1945. Quite unexpectedly, a misunderstanding of the order by the railroad's management gave the unions an opportunity to save face and paved the way for successful negotiations in 1951. Officials of the railroad, still smarting from the barrage of name-calling that had been their long-time portion, began the 1951 wage negotiations by insisting that Order 2424 established the rules for wage-fixing not only for 1948 but for subsequent years. When the 1951 wage negotiations began, management brushed aside any suggestions that did not fit an inflexible formula version of the order. This was as unnecessary as it was unwise. Order 2424 settled but a single wage dispute. There was not a line in it to suggest that it represented a secretarial directive on the disposition of future disputes. The department no doubt hoped that the Order 2424 pattern would be followed in the future, but did not require it. Furthermore, the general manager had forgotten that he had received a letter on April 12, 1949, from Secretary of the Interior J. A. Krug that stated that negotiations could take place without regard to the provisions of Order 2424. Local officials of the nonoperating unions appealed to their national officers in Washington to intervene with Interior and secure a clarification of the negotiation procedures to be followed. At a conference of their national union representatives and Office of Territories officials, it was agreed that Order 2424 did not bind future negotiations. This was, in its way, a defeat for the general manager, but of a kind that he might well hope to see repeated. For, in return, union officials at the conference signed the following statement of principles to guide the 1951 wage negotiations:

> That the wage rates payable to the employees of the Northern Pacific Railway constitute a fair and equitable pattern to be used as the basis for determining wage rates of employees on The Alaska Railroad.
>
> That Alaska Railroad employees should receive, over and above the basic rates for comparable occupations on the North-

ern Pacific Railway, a differential which should (a) fairly reflect the difference in living cost between the Pacific Northwest areas of the United States and Alaska, and (b) give due regard for any conditions peculiar to Alaska.

The above paragraphs were included in a letter of April 3, 1951, signed by Dan Wheeler, acting director of Territories, and dispatched to the unions concerned and to the general manager of the railroad. No agreement could have been more eloquent of the effectiveness of the 40-hour-week agreement of November, 1949, in removing most of the opposition to the reviled Order 2424.

With this letter, negotiations in Anchorage resulted in a nonoperating wage agreement signed May 23, 1951, and an operating agreement signed June 9, 1951. Both agreements were based on a Department of Labor finding that in 1951 the prices of consumer goods in Anchorage and Fairbanks were, on the average, 44 per cent higher than in Seattle. This 44 per cent was applied to a "stateside" increase for nonoperating employees of 18.5 cents per hour to become in the Railbelt 26.6 cents per hour. Instead of an across-the-board increase, amounts varied from 25 cents to 35 cents per hour, with higher-wage employees receiving the larger increases. The agreement also contained an escalator clause based on changes in Department of Labor consumer price indexes. With this kind of flexibility, agreement on the principles of Order 2424 became easier for both employees and management. The operating wage agreement contained corresponding wage increases, except that yard service rates were increased 50 cents per hour based on similar special treatment in the "outside" railroad wage settlement.

The principles of Order 2424 as summarized in the Wheeler letter were applied in succeeding wage negotiations, the details of which need not concern us here. This was true of wage increases made in 1953, 1954, and 1956, as well as in 1951.

## Wages and the Cost of Living

While Alaska remained a Territory, the Bureau of Labor Statistics of the Department of Labor was only sporadically concerned with its cost of living. Limited budgets made it impossible for the bureau to satisfy all the demands made upon it for consumer price statistics. The Territory of Alaska, with a nonvoting delegate and no senators or representatives, possessed low priorities, even with strong support from the Department of the Interior.

Although statistics were inadequate, it was evident that Alaska was changing in the 1950's from its helter-skelter combination of frontier and wartime economics. The signs were unmistakable, at least to railroad officials, that the extremely high consumer prices in Alaska could not continue to rise at the same pace as prices in the Pacific Northwest. If prices in Alaska did not rise as fast as those in Seattle, the percentage differential in consumer prices between the two cities had no place to go but down. And evidence was accumulating everywhere that this was exactly what was happening. Fairbanks and Anchorage grew from towns into cities. Chain stores took over from the prosperous, small-scale merchants who had long fostered the notion that it was bad form to hold a sale or inquire about a price. The power of small monopolies to keep out cheechako competitors was breaking down. The railroad itself contributed to these transformations, for its tariff rates had changed little from 1937 and its freight charges became an increasingly smaller percentage of shelf prices in the towns and cities of the Railbelt.

In the light of these trends, management negotiators looked forward to the time when the differential between Northern Pacific and Alaska Railroad wage rates would be reduced to fit the declining differences in living costs. The 1955 wage agreement, for example, was based on adding a 25 per cent cost-of-living differential to a 14.5 cents per hour stateside increase. This was not an indication that the differential had dropped from 44 per cent to 25 per cent, but that it had dropped enough to warrant a response to the decline in the revision of wage rates.

No union likes to lose any part of what it has gained. Alaska Railroad unions, therefore, began to look for a reason other than cost of living to support wage rates, most of which were already 40 to 45 per cent higher than those on private railroads. They first turned to "conditions peculiar to Alaska" as a justification for high wage differentials. The argument was abandoned when it became obvious that, with the rehabilitation of the railroad in the 1940's and 1950's and with the rapid increase in the amenities of living that accompanied the growth of Anchorage and Fairbanks, its premises became increasingly untenable.

After Alaska Railroad nonoperating unions failed to convince even themselves that "conditions peculiar to Alaska" justified high differentials over the wages paid by outside railroads, they turned for an answer to the wage-board concept of prevailing wages. Alaska Railroad officials agreed on the concept but had long argued that they had met its requirements by translating private-railroad wage rates into the higher consumer price level of the Alaskan frontier. Aside from the White Pass and Yukon Route, with only twenty miles of railroad in Alaska and with lower wages than Railbelt unionists would have been willing to accept, The Alaska Railroad had a 100 per cent monopoly of rail transportation in the Territory.

In 1955, the nonoperating unions, led by District 44 of the International Association of Machinists (now the Federal Employees Department, International Association of Machinists and Aerospace Workers) persuaded railroad officials to join in a fact-finding hunt for prevailing wages in Alaska. Under joint union-management sponsorship, a wage survey was made that included 63 of the largest firms in Anchorage and Fairbanks, 15 local and federal government agencies in the Railbelt, and 18 contractors and job shops. Results of the survey were issued by the Department of the Interior in February, 1956, as "Wage Rates in Alaska, October, 1955." Railroad officials concluded from the survey that, with one or two exceptions, the number of employees in occupations comparable to railroad occupations was too small to permit valid comparisons. At all events, nonoperating unions made no wage proposals to the railroad based on the "prevailing wage" data collected.

In 1958 and again in 1960, the argument as to the wage rates of nonoperating employees moved back to the question of how to apply the cost-of-living differential to Northern Pacific wage rates and wage increases. In both years, the disputes were painfully prolonged, and the negotiations were shuttled back and forth between Anchorage and Washington. To the general manager, Interior Department officials seemed to go to great lengths to avoid making a final decision. To Department officials, negotiators for the railroad seemed hopelessly oblivious to the political consequences of a unilateral decision against trade unions, some with tens of thousands of members in government agencies outside the Department of the Interior and others with a like number outside the government.

Finally, both disputes successively went to arbitration in Washington—a procedure abhorrent to most government officials, even those who have made their peace with the recognition of trade unions. In both arbitrations, railroad witnesses presented evidence and argument to demonstrate that the percentage difference in cost of living between the Pacific Northwest and the Railbelt had declined and that a cost-of-living differential in Alaska Railroad wages should decline with it. In the 1958 arbitration, union representatives argued that the differential had increased rather than declined but hedged against the possibility that the neutral arbitrator would reach a contrary conclusion. They urged at one time that the cost-of-living differential should be applied against the total wage (if the differential were found to have increased) and against wage increases only (if the differential had declined). In the 1960 arbitration, both sides agreed that the differential had declined and, in the absence of convincing statistics, settled on 37 per cent as a reasonable figure. To the pleasure of the unions and the discomfiture of the railroad, the two neutral arbitrators, both with distinguished records as mediators in labor disputes, found that the wages of nonoperating employees should be increased by the amount of the corresponding increases on private railroads, plus the 37 per cent differential. Both ignored the fact that the existing cost-of-living differentials in Alaska Railroad wage rates were already substantially in excess of 37 per cent.

In the 1958 wage disputes, train and engine employees formed a united front with the nonoperating groups and resisted with equal vehemence management's evidence that the cost-of-living differential between Seattle and the Railbelt had declined. The train and engine brotherhoods submitted the dispute to Washington for a decision by the Secretary of the Interior. To the astonishment of railroad officials on the one hand and the Brotherhood of Railroad Trainmen and the Brotherhood of Locomotive Firemen and Enginemen on the other, the Department of the Interior decided in 1959 in favor of the management position and decreed that Alaska Railroad wage rates should exceed the wage rates on the Northern Pacific by only 37 per cent. Loud indignation was succeeded by lesser grumblings which then changed to acceptance as the Department of Labor began to pay the kind of statistical attention to the state that it had not afforded the Territory. Consumer price indexes as well as Alaska-Seattle consumer price differentials were inaugurated in 1960. Management's economics and economic forecasting were completely vindicated when the first survey showed that the Anchorage-Seattle consumer price differential had fallen from 37 per cent in 1951 to 27 per cent in 1960, and the Fairbanks-Seattle differential from 47 per cent in 1951 to 36 per cent in 1960. Subsequent surveys showed still further declines.

## Prevailing Wages in Alaska

The nonoperating agreement that followed the 1960 arbitration contained clauses calling for another union-management attempt to determine the prevailing wage level in Alaska. By the time the survey was undertaken, only District 44 of the International Association of Machinists favored joint collection of the data. Other nonoperating unions, less sanguine perhaps than the machinists as to the usefulness of more statistics, elected to abstain. At the same time, they went on record that if the machinists were successful in obtaining a wage increase through a wage survey in Alaska, they would insist on equal increases for the employees they represented. Among these were two shop-craft unions that had won representation disputes with the American Federation of Government Employees—the International Brotherhood of Boilermakers, Iron Shipbuilders, Blacksmiths, Forgers and Helpers in 1951, and the Brotherhood Railway Carmen in 1953. The "of," by the way, is deliberately left out of the carmen's title and its members appreciate the compliment of a correct rendition.

The survey in September, 1961, of prevailing wages in the Railbelt was hardly more convincing than the 1955 survey. The number of industrial-type employees had increased, but, except for airplane mechanics and laborers, the sampling was too small and the rates too various to permit firm conclusions on what constituted prevailing wages in Alaska. Again the machinists made no wage proposal based on the results of the

Alaska survey. The remaining nonoperating unions signed agreements based on Northern Pacific wage rates plus a differential to compensate for the higher living costs in Alaska. The machinists would not sign such an agreement and referred the dispute to the Department of the Interior in the spring of 1962. Management's position was upheld, and the machinists reluctantly accepted an agreement containing the wage increases they had previously refused. Thereafter, wage increases for employees represented by the Brotherhood of Railroad Trainmen, the Brotherhood of Locomotive Firemen and Enginemen, the Train Dispatchers Association, and the Order of Railroad Telegraphers were made equal to the Northern Pacific plus cost-of-living differential. The machinists, joined by the carmen and the boilermakers and blacksmiths, refused to negotiate on this basis and were given increases based on Order 2424 principles after receiving notice to this effect (to which they did not respond). They were joined in this "passive resistance" by the American Federation of Government Employees, who were fearful of "white collar" prevailing-wage comparisons in Alaska but hoped that any increases obtained by the shop-craft unions would somehow trickle down to them.

Disillusioned with the 1955 and 1961 wage surveys as well as with the Seattle-Alaska cost-of-living differentials, the machinists turned for comfort to the Army–Air Force wage rates paid to civilian employees at Fort Richardson and at Elmendorf. Using data collected in Alaska, the Army–Air Force wage board in Washington applied the mathematics of Cartesian coordinates and the method of least squares to determine "prevailing wages" in Alaska. Forbidden to use the wage rates paid by Alaskan contractors, they used identical rates paid in job shops. There was irony in the fact that the military machinists' rate, used most often by spokesmen for the machinists to illustrate the inadequacy of Alaska Railroad wages, was not based on a survey of machinists' wages. The

Army–Air Force wage board, finding no more than half a dozen operating and maintenance machinists employed in the Railbelt other than by The Alaska Railroad, excluded the machinists' "prevailing wage" in Alaska from their calculations.

The mathematics of the Army–Air Force wage determinations had little meaning for Alaska Railroad union officials. Their interest related mainly to comparisons with wages paid by the railroad to workers in shop-craft occupations. They were also interested in the three-step military wage-board rates, the second step being equal to the "prevailing wage." Here was a built-in device to insure that, in a period of normal turnover, the average wage would exceed that said to be "prevailing."

In proposing Army–Air Force wage-board rates for such comparable occupations as could be found on The Alaska Railroad, the machinists, the carmen, the boilermakers and blacksmiths, and a not-altogether-happy American Federation of Government Employees were consistent in their attitude toward further wage bargaining. They seemed willing to allow a military wage board, which did not permit union negotiators to participate in its deliberations, to determine Alaska Railroad pay rates. This would not be the first time that government workers offered to trade their freedom to bargain for what they hoped would be higher wages.

As far as wage negotiations were concerned, 1961 and 1962 saw a final parting of the ways between the operating unions and the telegraphers and dispatchers on the one hand,* and the remaining nonoperating employee unions on the other. The former could see no sense in comparisons with wages paid at military posts where no engineers, firemen, conductors,

* The American Train Dispatchers Association obtained representation rights on the railroad in 1949. The dispatchers are a small but select group whose heavy responsibilities give them some of the glamour of train and engine men. The use of the word "Association" in the name of any trade union indicates a certain aloofness from the rank and file.

brakemen, dispatchers, or telegraphers were employed. They decided to adhere to the traditional formulas and keep a wary eye out for any preference that nonoperating unions might obtain by avoiding wage comparisons with employees of a railroad. They were also more alert than the machinists, carmen, boilermakers, blacksmiths, and the employees represented by the American Federation of Government Employees to the relationships between labor-agreement rules and wage rates. They saw traditional railroad advantages in these rules. They pondered the fact that there was neither negotiation nor written agreement on wage rates at the military posts in Alaska, nor were there labor agreements covering the kind of work rules that form so large a part of the agreements in effect on The Alaska Railroad. The operating brotherhoods particularly valued their work rules and were about to begin a fight to save them from the increasing threat of encroaching law and regulation. In this enterprise, they would be joined by three of the four unions that no longer seemed interested in the negotiation of wage rates. Of the eight unions with labor agreements on The Alaska Railroad, only District 44 of the International Association of Machinists would be unwilling to fight for its freedom to bargain.

## Executive Order 10988

On January 17, 1962, President Kennedy issued the nation's first government-wide labor policy based on the recognition of union representation of federal employees. The policy established by Executive Order 10988 was, not unexpectedly, expressed in extremely cautious terms. Nevertheless, it marked a considerable step forward for many federal agencies, only two of which, the Department of the Interior and the Tennessee Valley Authority, had previously issued a comprehensive statement on union-management relations. It was perhaps inevitable that the report of the President's Task Force that preceded the executive order should look back as well as forward and should bear the lingering marks of a federal officialdom fearful of the consequences of allowing employee unions the right to bargain with sovereignty.* However important to the rest of the federal government, the philosophy of Order 10988 had small significance for the employees and officials of The Alaska Railroad. Both had gone far beyond the confines of the new policy a quarter of a century before.

The Department of the Interior had anticipated the union policies of the executive order by fourteen years in its 1948 policy statement for ungraded employees and by three years with its "Labor Relations Policies," issued in January, 1959, applicable in part to classified employees as well as to ungraded or wage-board employees. The reissued labor policy required that the more fundamental aspects of union-management relations be contained in a document called a "basic labor agreement," including the determination of bargaining rights, the duty to confer, written agreements, wage policy, the handling of disputes, and the creation of committees for labor-management cooperation. Policies contained in basic agreements required departmental approval before they could be made effective or before their provisions could be changed. "Supplementary agreements" contained most of the work

* The facts and judgments expressed in this chapter are at sharp variance with the judgments contained in "A Policy of Employee-Management Cooperation in the Federal Service, a Report of the President's Task Force on Employee-Management Relations in the Federal Service," November 30, 1961. Note, for example: "The Task Force wishes, finally, to note its conviction that there need be no conflict between the system of employee-management relations proposed in this report and the Civil Service merit system, which is and should remain the essential basis of the personnel policy of the Federal Government." The Task Force is not here emphasizing the Civil Service system of examining and appointment, but rather "the full range of principles and practices that make up the Civil Service System," and is at once indirectly supporting the retention of the Civil Service rules stemming from the Veterans' Preference Act and condemning that part of Alaska Railroad labor policy which has been based upon an attempt to change them.

rules of the kind that, for many years, have been included in Alaska Railroad labor agreements. These could be made effective by a bureau or agency head without reference to the Department of the Interior.

On November 10, 1960, officials of the railroad and of the two operating brotherhoods signed a "Basic Labor Agreement" under the department's new policy. It was approved by the Secretary of the Interior on February 20, 1961, and marked the end of a long period of strained relations and the beginning of an era of cooperation that has continued ever since. This turn of events had three major causes: Train and engine men, more than any other craft except dispatchers, telegraphers, and carmen, identified themselves with railroading and were not interested in abandoning railroad customs and practices; the 1960 agreement came at a time when there were no serious conflicts of interest between railroad officials and the operating brotherhoods other than a few lingering memories of past disagreements; and the men who negotiated the agreement had unusual forcefulness and ability to compromise. They were Dennis O'Neil, general chairman, Brotherhood of Locomotive Firemen and Enginemen; R. L. Shake, general chairman, Brotherhood of Railroad Trainmen, Anchorage; William Fravel, assistant to the national legislative representative, Brotherhood of Railroad Trainmen, Washington, D.C.; and D. J. Smith, general manager, and Paul Shelmerdine, personnel officer, of the railroad. In immediate charge of the negotiations were Shelmerdine for the railroad and Fravel for the brotherhoods. Both men possessed intuitive abilities to get to the essence of a labor problem and a genuine desire to understand the other side's point of view.

Basic labor agreements similar to extent and substance to the agreement signed by the train and engine crafts were negotiated in March, 1964, by the telegraphers and in May, 1964, by the train dispatchers. All three agreements contained wage provisions that followed the policies of Order 2424 and the Wheeler letter and were almost automatic in applying Alaska-Seattle cost-of-living differentials to rates based on those of the Northern Pacific. They also included adjustment board procedures for settling disputes over the interpretation of agreements or the application of the railroad's operating rules and arbitration procedures applicable to unresolved disputes over wage rates or rules.

## Defeat of a Personnel Bill

Most of the major confrontations between Alaska Railroad agreements and opposing law and regulation have been outlined. One more deserves brief reference. In 1946, when the railroad's first personnel office was established, the initial task assigned its director was the renegotiation of existing agreements to bring them up to date. Another reason for the assignment was Interior's desire that the agreements be submitted for approval and that the suspicion of illegality be removed from many of their provisions. The delegations of authority then in existence required that the agreements receive Interior's assent, but they had never been submitted to Washington for this purpose.

Once the agreements were in Washington, legal doubts grew as department officials gave a first reading to work rules that contained language nearly identical with agreements on private railroads. The agreements were returned to Anchorage without specific legal objection but with the advice that they be carefully examined for possible violation of law and Civil Service regulations. After a long period of further shuttling of agreements between Anchorage and Washington, the department gave them its reluctant approval. The most serious legal problem, namely the conflict between labor-agreement rules based on seniority and the requirements of the Veterans' Preference Act of 1944, seems to have been completely overlooked.

For fifteen years after the passage of the Veterans' Preference Act, only one employee, and he a subordinate official not covered by a labor agreement, claimed his rights under the act. Yet it is probable that in obeying the rules of the labor agreements, railroad officials were in violation of the Veterans' Preference Act a dozen times a week over those fifteen years. In 1954, a Civil Service official called the attention of his superiors in Washington to the puzzling fact that The Alaska Railroad did not seem aware of the act. His comment did not refer to veterans' preference in appointments to which railroad officials had no objection and which did not conflict with any agreement rules. He was referring to "reduction in force" and "adverse action" procedure to which the railroad had paid little attention.

Counsel for the Civil Service Commission issued a memorandum in 1954 which left no doubt that the railroad was covered by the Veterans' Preference Act. Civil Service officials, however, were impressed with the astonishing fact that no rank-and-file employee had ever made a complaint to the commission alleging violation of his veteran's rights. They also knew that both "reduction in force" and "adverse actions" were covered by elaborate rules in the labor agreements. Civil Service counsel therefore suggested that the law be enforced whenever a valid complaint was made but that, barring such a complaint, the commission would leave the railroad alone.

In 1959, about fifteen years after the enactment of the Veterans' Preference Act, a complainant brought a case to the Civil Service Commission and won because of a "procedural defect" in the railroad's handling of his discharge. The railroad had observed the agreement rules but not the veterans' preference regulations. Several similar cases followed in spite of vigorous attempts by railroad unions to prevent them. Since the railroad was admittedly not observing the required Civil Service procedures, it lost almost every case, some at an appreciable cost in retroactive pay. The railroad's position thus became untenable. The general manager was subject to attack from the unions if he disobeyed the agreement rules and from veterans if he observed them. There was only one solution—the railroad must either observe the veterans' preference regulations or secure a change in the law that imposed such regulations.

The first attempt to change the law was made by including remedial legislation in proposed bills for incorporating the railroad. When these bills failed of enactment, a separate bill known as the "Railroad Personnel Bill," was drafted. It was introduced in the Senate as S.2593 on September 21, 1961. Hearings were held by the Senate Committee on Post Office and Civil Service, and a favorable report was issued. But the bill died in the Second Section of the Eighty-seventh Congress.

In the First Session of the Eighty-eighth Congress, the Railroad Personnel Bill was reintroduced as S.622 (January 31, 1963) "to improve and encourage collective bargaining between the management of The Alaska Railroad and representatives of its employees, and to permit to the extent practicable the adoption by The Alaska Railroad of the personnel policies and practices of the railroad industry." S.622 was reported favorably by the Committee on Labor and Public Welfare and was passed by the Senate on June 24, 1963.

On August 8, 1963, hearings were held on the bill by the House Committee on Post Office and Civil Service. As in the Senate hearing during the previous year, the principal witnesses for the bill were war-veteran and union employees of The Alaska Railroad, officials of national unions, including the American Federation of Government Employees, John W. Macy, chairman of the Civil Service Commission, and officials of veterans' organizations (in opposition to the bill).

The provisions of the Railroad Personnel Bill were simple, both in language and objective. Each paragraph was designed to protect the labor-agreement rules and railroad customs from conflict with federal law and regulation. The bill permitted Alaska Railroad employees to remain in "Schedule A," that is, exempt from the examining and hiring requirements of the Civil Service system, except as veterans' preference was required in appointments. It permitted supervisory and professional employees to be hired and paid on the basis of an annual salary for all services rendered. It ensured that wage payments to train and engine employees would be deemed to comply with the federal overtime law of 1934. It permitted the establishment of performance-rating systems without regard to the Performance Rating Act of 1950. Finally, it gave unions the option to negotiate written agreements in opposition to the provisions of the Veterans' Preference Act. Contrary to the assertions of veterans' organizations, the bill did not repeal any section of the Veterans' Preference Act. It permitted the negotiation of labor-agreement rules in preference to Veterans' Preference Act procedures only if the majority of the employees in a class or craft preferred the agreement rules.

War-veteran witnesses from the railroad protested that they preferred the rules of the labor agreements and that their seniority rights would be destroyed if the bill did not pass. Railroad and Interior officials insisted that railroad safety and railroad collective bargaining would deteriorate unless the bill became law. A representative of the Brotherhood Railway Carmen testified that the Railway Labor Executives Association had gone on record as favoring passage of the bill. The chairman of the Civil Service Commission testified that "the Commission has no objection to the enactment of S.622 and believes that the recommendation of the Department of the Interior and The Alaska Railroad, the agencies responsible for this unique operation, should be respected and that the pattern of railroad personnel conditions should be permitted to apply in the operation of The Alaska Railroad." Not one veterans' organization took note of the fact that veterans' preference procedure applying to reduction in force and adverse action would be void only if employees, including veterans, elected rules, through their unions, that would give them better protection.

The House committee reported the bill favorably, but it died in a rules committee that would not permit it to come to a vote. Some Alaska Railroad employees, mostly young veterans who hoped to bump experienced nonveterans out of their jobs, opposed it. Their opposition was in large part mistaken, because the Veterans' Preference Act provides no preference for a veteran desiring to be promoted. Other Alaska Railroad employees opposed it because of an erroneous belief that the bill would prevent them from negotiating for a nonrailroad type of wage rate.

With the failure of the bill, the Civil Service Commission revoked its permission for Alaska Railroad employees to remain in the excepted service. Employees were transferred to the competitive service on January 1, 1967. The destruction or weakening of labor-agreement rules that Alaska Railroad management officials and union officials had predicted began to take place. Only in the train and engine service were the essential seniority practices left intact and this because of a system of multiple appointments that had long been followed but which existed to a very limited extent among nonoperating crafts. Faced with the realities of a different and less flexible system, many of the several hundred employees who had signed a petition requesting the application of competitive service rules questioned whether they had made a wise choice.

# IX
# Competitive Paths to Regulation

What is vice and what is virtue in business competition depend to a large extent upon point of view. This is especially so when the U.S. Government is one of the competitors. A motor carrier may lower a tariff rate to take business away from The Alaska Railroad, and its action is a meritorious exercise in sound business judgment. If The Alaska Railroad should lower a tariff rate to take business away from a motor carrier, the action represents a nefarious use of governmental power and calls for seven pages of indignant protest to the state's two senators and one congressman. Because of this relativity in economic judgment, the railroad does not compete against the motor-transport industry with the harshness that is the normal expectation in the world of private enterprise.

There are stories of a more lurid past that run counter to these comments. It is said that Colonel Otto Ohlson, general manager from 1928 to 1945, cut down truck competition by persuading the Department of the Interior to exact tolls at a major river crossing on the Richardson highway from Valdez to Fairbanks. Within limits, the story is true. It is said that, at Anchorage, the railroad placed freight cars across a road leading to a Cook Inlet dock to prevent a ship operator from delivering his freight by truck. This story is only half true. Court records reveal that the dock in question belonged to the railroad and that the ship operator was trying to avoid payment of terminal charges. At Seward, the railroad has been accused of discriminating against motor truckers by charging them for handling freight across the dock and letting interline tonnage go free when waybilled to rail points beyond. Actually, the railroad's share of the through rate from West Coast ports contains an increment for Seward terminal charges. A hearing on freight rates that is part of the story of regulation of The Alaska Railroad will shed more light on this accusation.

There was a time when the railroad came close to being an Alaskan transportation monopoly. The Territory covered so vast an area and its population was (and still is) so sparse that highway building seemed never to be adequate. Another Interior agency, the Alaska Road Commission, was responsible for road construction outside the national forest areas. It would take many years and many millions before traveling the Richardson highway from Valdez to Fairbanks would change from dangerous to routine and before black-topped highways would extend from the Alaska border to Fairbanks, from Anchorage to Glennallen on the Richardson and to Tok Junction on the Alaska Highway, and across the Canadian border to Dawson in Yukon Territory. Anchorage and Seward had their first road connection in 1951, and the Kenai Peninsula highway from Moose Pass to Homer was completed in 1952. In 1958, it was possible for the first time to drive from Anchorage and Fairbanks via Paxson into Mt. McKinley National Park. With the black-topping of these motor highways, truck transportation greatly increased and truckers did a reasonably efficient job of diverting business from The Alaska Railroad.

High transportation costs and high living costs have long been among Alaska's most sensitive economic problems. Without attempting to analyze the relation between them, it can be said that both derive from the inevitabilities of geography and the degree of sophistication of Alaska business organizations. Alaska is a noncontiguous part of the United States, and the cost of a barge or steamship haul from West Coast ports to

Alaska is a part of the price of all its goods and services. For most of its history, the usually lower costs of ocean transportation have been offset to a large extent by the long distance and low volume and by the high cost of cargo transfer at interchange points. The state of Alaska contains about 275,000 people. Fairfax County, Virginia, has 100,000 more. Alaska is so far removed from self-sufficiency and the interdependencies of mutual trade that most traffic is one way, and one-way traffic must bear the cost of two-way transportation.

A typical shipment to Alaska reaches Seattle from a point of origin in another state, must travel from Seattle 1,240 miles by boat or barge to Seward or 1,228 miles to Whittier, and then 114 miles by rail from Seward to Anchorage or 471 from Seward to Fairbanks. From Delta Alaska Junction near Vancouver, British Columbia, the ocean haul to Seward or Whittier is about 140 miles shorter than from Seattle. For shipments interchanged at Whittier, the rail distance to Anchorage is 64 miles and to Fairbanks 409 miles. Prince Rupert in British Columbia, an alternate port, is 600 ocean miles closer to Whittier than Seattle.

Highway distance to Fairbanks is 4,440 miles from Washington, D.C., 3,550 miles from Chicago, and 2,380 miles from Seattle. Yet with these handicaps of great distance and small volume, a 2,500-pound automobile can be shipped from Seattle to Anchorage for $199.25, an 82,000-pound carload of beer from Milwaukee to Fairbanks for $2,335.95, or 3.06 cents per can, and a carload of dressed chickens from Arkansas to Anchorage for 3.9 cents per pound, including refrigeration charges, or less than 9 cents per 2.5-pound chicken.

The desirability of regulating transportation in Alaska was hardly recognized before the mid-1950's. Many years before, the Attorney General had declared that The Alaska Railroad "was not a common carrier subject to the provisions of the Interstate Commerce Act." Alaskan truck transportation was not regulated because the Motor Carrier Act did not apply to a Territory. Water transportation to and from Alaskan ports was subject to a measure of regulation by the Federal Maritime Commission. Air carriers and private railroads were the only transportation agencies in Alaska subject to the same regulatory authority as the forty-eight states. The Territory of Alaska did not try to regulate intrastate truck transportation except in the matter of weight limitations, particularly during the spring thaw. Had The Alaska Railroad been privately owned, however, it would have been subject to Part I of the Interstate Commerce Act.

As a result of an informal agreement between the Secretary of the Interior and the Interstate Commerce Commission made during the railroad's construction period, Alaska Railroad tariffs were published for nearly forty subsequent years with ICC identifying numbers. These tariffs were filed with the commission and contained joint, single-factor rates applicable to the ocean haul from West Coast ports to Seward and to the rail haul to points beyond Seward. Motor carriers participated in some of these tariffs. The through rates were not subject to regulatory jurisdiction, although the water portion was subject to the Federal Maritime Commission.

In 1941, the Maritime Commission made an investigation of Alaskan rates, noted what appeared to be an anomalous filing of Alaska Railroad–Alaska Steamship Company tariffs with the Interstate Commerce Commission, and sought to regain its jurisdiction over the water portion of the joint rate. The Maritime Commission issued an opinion, advising the cancellation of these through rail-water tariffs and the filing by the Alaska Steamship Company, instead, of the port-to-port proportional rates with the Maritime Commission. The war intervened, and both the railroad and the steamship company ignored the pronouncement. The Maritime Commission again called attention to this tariff situation in 1948, but it was not until January 29, 1953, that the Interstate Commerce Commission instructed the railroad, by letter, to remove the ICC numbers from its tariffs. The commission's letter stated also that "No additional publications providing joint rates between The Alaska Railroad and water carriers subject to regulation by the Federal Maritime Board [now Commission] should be placed in the Commission's tariff files."* The railroad complied with the commission's instructions, and ceased filing tariffs with ICC numbers. At the same time, the water carriers filed proportional rates with the Maritime Commission applying to the ocean portion of the through all-water rates. Division sheets established the shares of the through rates allotted by agreement to each of the participating carriers.

The convenience to the railroad and the public of joint single-factor rates to Alaskan rail points was too great to permit these rates to lapse. After 1953, therefore, the railroad issued informational tariffs containing the rates in the tariff publications to which the Interstate Commerce Commission had objected. To preserve a continuous record, the railroad maintained its policy of sending its tariffs to the commission but identified them with ARR rather than with ICC numbers.

A shipper or a competitor could still protest against an Alaska Railroad tariff, but the protest would be to the Secretary of the Interior, who would thus sit in judgment of his own appointee, the general manager. A protest might also be submitted to the delegate from Alaska or to a friendly senator or representative. Protests lodged through such channels would carry more weight, but they would wind up in the hands of the Secretary of the Interior just the same.

Through, single-factor rates do not flourish under ambiguous regulation. Their advantages, previously alluded to, include facilitating paper work connected with freight handling, simplifying tariff quotations, removing some of the problems of assessing responsibility for loss and damage, sometimes

* When rates from Seward and Whittier were equalized in 1952, a shipper had protested against this change in tariff rates and had erroneously assumed that the Interstate Commerce Commission had authority to receive the protest.

reducing the cost of transportation. Through, single-factor rates are almost always less than the sum of the several local rates otherwise applying to a route. On some shipments to Alaska, it has been necessary to add three local rates—one regulated by the Interstate Commerce Commission, one regulated by the Federal Maritime Commission, and one subject to no regulation at all.

## First Steps Toward Regulation

In October, 1955, Senate hearings were held in Anchorage and in Juneau on problems of Alaskan transportation, including the lack of regulation of The Alaska Railroad. Many witnesses testified that they thought The Alaska Railroad should be regulated, and the Senate Interstate and Foreign Commerce Committee recommended that the Interstate Commerce Commission prepare a plan directed toward the economic and safety regulation of transportation to and from points in Alaska. The Senate committee stated that the situation was "particularly unhealthy, as between motor carriers on the one hand and The Alaska Railroad on the other."

The Interstate Commerce Commission responded to this congressional request with a regulatory proposal in February, 1957, recommending a series of amendments to the Interstate Commerce Act and related laws to cover the railroad, motor carriers, water carriers, and intrastate transport activities. One feature of the proposal that startled officials of Interior and the railroad was the establishment of a "nonpartisan Alaskan Board of three members, appointed by the Governor of Alaska" which would have "initial jurisdiction under the Interstate Commerce Act equivalent to that of a division of the Commission, in matters pertaining to transportation within Alaska." This Alaska Board would thus have had jurisdiction over The Alaska Railroad, subject to an appeal to the full commission.

The ICC recommendations, which contained indications of inadequate fact-finding in Alaska, became Senate bill S.1448. Hearings were held on the bill in Anchorage and Fairbanks in September and October, 1957, by the Surface Transportation Subcommittee of the Senate Committee on Interstate and Foreign Commerce. If The Alaska Railroad was the villain in an unregulated struggle among transportation competitors, the hearings failed to demonstrate this fact. Witnesses for Weaver Brothers, for example, a more than moderately successful Alaskan motor carrier, were frank in indicting "gypo" truckers for financial irregularities, for keeping tariffs on their cuffs, and for making it difficult, because of irresponsible rate-cutting, for a legitimate motor carrier to reveal his rates by issuing them as published tariffs. The railroad was mentioned as a competitor, but there was hardly a protest about its competitive activities. The major troubles of the motor carriers were much closer at hand. Truckers in Alaska (as in the forty-eight states before the Motor Carrier Act was passed) wanted federal regulation to eliminate a kind of business anarchy within their own ranks, to which, in the absence of regulation, they seemed to be particularly vulnerable.

At the Anchorage hearing on S.1448, General Manager John Lloyd testified against the bill but stated that he was not opposed to regulation. He noted that "The Interstate Commerce Commission prepared the proposed bill after a study which did not include visits by staff members of the Commission to Alaska" and suggested that "Some of the major difficulties of this bill seem related to the fact that no such investigaton was made."* The testimony of Howard Weaver of Weaver Brothers sheds some light on motor-carriers'

* There is little doubt that slips were showing in the ICC staff work on the regulatory plan submitted to the Senate committee. For example, in the commission's letter of February 11, 1957, to Senator Magnuson, previously cited, a misunderstanding of corporate names created two railroads out of the White Pass and Yukon Route, each alleged to have twenty miles of railroad in the Territory.

opinion, which, to the surprise of Alaska Railroad officials, contained almost no criticism of unfair governmental competition. After Weaver explained that his company had been active in Alaska since 1949, Senator Andrew F. Schoeppel of Kansas asked him, "Have you found that your business as a common carrier and the demands for your business have systematically or progressively increased each year?" The reply was "Yes, sir." This, however, was 1957. In 1959, testimony by motor carriers on the competitive practices of the railroad would make an about-face, but the attack would be led by truckers who had been somewhat less successful than Weaver Brothers in diverting tonnage to the trucks —tonnage of which the railroad once had a near monopoly.

In spite of the motor carriers' enthusiasm for regulation, S.1448 received only lukewarm support, partly because its concepts were buried in language that some witnesses frankly confessed they did not understand, but mainly because of the imminence of statehood. S.1488 had not been framed in the light of this possibility, and, with statehood, its provisions became irrelevant to the political and economic facts of a politically revitalized Alaska.

Alaska became a state in 1959 and Interstate Commerce Commission regulation thus came automatically to the state's motor carriers. By special provision of the Alaska Statehood Act, the Federal Maritime Commission kept its jurisdiction over water transportation between Alaskan deepwater ports and ports in the other states, territories, and possessions. The Statehood Act also amended Section 27 of the Merchant Marine Act of 1920 (known as the Jones Act), by removing the exclusion of Alaska from the third proviso. Thereafter, foreign vessels could operate between Canadian and Alaskan ports as they had previously been able to operate from Canadian ports to ports in all states but not to the Territory of Alaska.

## Regulation Meets a Presidential Veto

After 1958, motor truckers, airlines, ocean carriers to Alaskan ports, and private railroads in Alaska were covered by three types of federal regulation. The Alaska Railroad continued on its unfettered way, subject only to the control of the Secretary of the Interior. The surface-transportation situation in Alaska was inherently unstable, and agitation for more orderly regulations began anew. The possibility of regulating The Alaska Railroad was not the only item to demand attention. There was the question of the possible substitution of the Interstate Commerce Commission for the Federal Maritime Commission in the regulation of ocean transport to Alaska. There was the alternative question of securing through rates and the regulation thereof on either a mandatory or permissive basis by joint boards representing the Federal Maritime Commission, the Civil Aeronautics Board, and the Interstate Commerce Commission. There was also the difficult problem of "grandfather rights" (automatic certification for existing carriers) for "certain motor carriers, water carriers and freight forwarders."

The problem of the difference between regulatory standards for shipping to Alaskan ports and those for shipping between ports in other states has never received adequate attention. The major difference lies in the requirement for a certificate of convenience and necessity under Interstate Commerce Commission rules and the lack of such requirement in the rules of the Maritime Commission. Whatever the merits and demerits of these contrasting policies, it is difficult to understand why the same standards are not applied to ocean traffic between the ports of San Francisco and Seattle that are applied to traffic between San Francisco and Seattle and any port in Alaska. If competition is free in the one case, why should it not be free in the other?

The facts of life in regard to ocean transportation to Alaska suggest that the philosophy of fair but limited competition is more concordant with the public interest than unlimited competition. The latter makes price and profit the primary standards of entrepreneurial decision—if an Alaskan port cannot handle tonnage in sufficient quantity to make profitable operations possible, the port need not be served. The convenience-and-necessity doctrine of the Interstate Commerce Commission protects the ocean carrier from the effects of unlimited competition but may exact in return an obligation to serve points that may be unprofitable considered by themselves, but, nevertheless, need water transportation service.

The highly seasonal character of Alaskan transportation makes limited competition the more reasonable doctrine. Otherwise, the itinerant carrier could skim the cream of the profitable traffic and could disregard the shipping interests of the smaller ports where traffic is, for the most part, too small to be attractive. A water carrier need only take the precaution to hire U.S. registered ships, barges, and tugs and, under the unlimited-competition principle, need serve only those ports where tonnage is available in volume. In other words, a shipper with little more capital than is needed to buy a notebook can solicit traffic until a reasonable load is assured, can then lease the floating equipment necessary to complete the movement, and can (and will) abandon the trade during the lean months of winter. Alaska Railroad officials, committed to a policy of providing service to all points on its line, even where operations are unprofitable, are compelled by the logic of position and of economic event to support, in this instance, the regulatory philosophies of the Interstate Commerce Commission rather than those of the Maritime Commission.

The Senate and House committees on interstate and foreign commerce arranged for joint hearings in Alaska in the fall of 1959 to consider legislative proposals to resolve Alaska's problems of transportation regulation. The most important of these was bill S.1508, "to provide for economic regulation of The Alaska Raiload under the Interstate Commerce Act."

S.1508 was a marvel of simplicity in comparison to the language and the concepts of S.1448 (which had been made obsolete by statehood). The railroad's founding act of March 12, 1914, was used as a point of departure, and amendments were recommended that would bring the railroad under most of the provisions of Part I of the Interstate Commerce Act within 180 days of their enactment. Certain railroad safety legislation was included, as well as the Employers' Liability Act of 1908 and Title I of the Railway Labor Act—indigestible provisions in S.1508 that contributed to its failure to become law.

Hearings were held on the Alaska transportation proposals in Ketchikan, Juneau, Anchorage, Seward, Cordova, Valdez, and Fairbanks. In earlier hearings, in 1957, The Alaska Railroad had not been a prime target of the motor carriers. During the 1959 hearings, however, at Anchorage, Fairbanks, and Valdez, the railroad was subject to a barrage of accusations, the like of which it had never before experienced. Alaskan motor carriers, under the banner of the Alaska Carriers Association, were alarmed by the progress of containerization and piggyback, and charged the railroad with using federal power to destroy them. One motor carrier, for example, a survivor among several trucking companies that had attempted to compete for freight between Seward and Anchorage, called the roll of the departed and suggested that if it were not for the unfair tactics of The Alaska Railroad, these trucking firms would not have disappeared. The railroad was attacked as a competitive Machiavelli, engaged in a conspiracy to strangle motor trucking in Alaska, from Seward to Anchorage and from Valdez to Fairbanks—all in the hope of fattening itself on the fruits of monopoly.

Railroad witnesses were less emotional and were able to demonstrate the many instances in which the motor carriers' testimony was based on rumors or misinterpretation that could easily be countered by facts. In part, the difference in attitude reflected the railroad's growing confidence in the future and the rather desperate insecurity of those Alaska truckers whose operations had been on a comparatively small scale. At Valdez, for example, truckers had watched their business dwindle and their town grow smaller and genuinely believed that rate-juggling on the part of The Alaska Railroad was the prime cause of their decline. They were right in concluding that it was unfair that they should be regulated while the railroad was not. They were wrong, however, in thinking that regulation of the railroad, no matter how rigorous, would have resolved their difficulties. Even the Interstate Commerce Commission cannot make a truck operator with a few rigs and a few employees competitively equal to a large corporate motor carrier or a railroad worth $125 million, particularly when the motor carrier and the railroad have container and piggyback technology and economics working for them.

Unfortunately for the Alaskan truckers who lashed out at the railroad during the 1959 hearings, there was a great deal more to the competitive story than the question of whether the railroad was playing the game according to its own rules and changing the rules to suit the occasion. For several years, a revolution in transportation techniques had been profoundly altering the relation between the railroad and the motor carriers in Alaska. Containerization and piggyback had so changed cost-benefit ratios that the freight business that trucks had taken away from the railroad was coming back. The larger trucking companies were discovering that they could make more money by cooperating in integrated transport movements with the railroad than by trying to go it alone. This explains why the motor carriers at the Anchorage and Fairbanks hearings maintained a united front in asking for tariff regulation for the railroad but did not maintain a united front in denouncing the railroad for monopolistic conspiracy.

The same technological changes had been taking place in the forty-eight states to the south, but there neither the truck operators nor the Teamsters' Union had a government railroad as a target for their resentments. These changes would have consequences more far-reaching than a mere shift in freight between transportation modes. They would produce doubts in the Interstate Commerce Commission about ancient shibboleths of freight classification. They would make railroad presidents not so sure of their long-time opposition to through-rate agreements with motor-truck operators. They would give the notion of integrated transportation between rail, motor, ocean, and air carriers a new respectability.

Weaver Brothers has been selected as a representative motor carrier because the company is medium in size and because its officials have regarded themselves as among the railroad's principal competitors. During the 1959 Alaska hearings, witnesses for this company were as lightly critical of the railroad as they had been in 1957. It remained, however, for a witness for one of the largest motor carriers in the United States to describe part of the wave of the future for Alaskan land and water transportation. John M. Kinnaird, vice-president of Consolidated Freightways, Menlo Park, California, told the joint committee:

> The facilities of our motor carrier operation in Seattle have been melded with those of Alaska Steamship Co., The Alaska Railroad, and our own motor carrier operation in Alaska and between the continental United States and Alaska to perform, under a single-factor through-rate and under a single bill of lading, a coordinated transportation service which has contributed in a significant way to the fulfillment of our military needs, to the economic development of Alaska and the rest of the United States, and to the enhancement of the Alaskan standard of living.

Piggyback and containerization not only diverted tonnage from the small Alaskan truck operator back to the railroad; they also made the dominant Alaskan motor carriers more dominant and contributed to a concentration of trucking operations at Seward and, to an extent, at Anchorage. Other Alaskan ports, Valdez for example, where accusations against the railroad were more strident than in any other part of the Railbelt, were hurt far more by the concentration of motor carriers in Seward than by loss of business directly to the railroad. Even Alaska Freight Lines, the railroad's most bitter motor-truck competitor, moved from Valdez to Seward in 1959. The dominant motor carriers, ocean carriers, and The Alaska Railroad were showing the rest of the United States a dramatic example of what integrated transportation could accomplish. But what was meat for them was poison for the small Alaska trucker.

Before completing the story of S.1508, it should be noted that despite the repeated and probing questioning of members of the joint Senate and House committee, witnesses for the railroad and the motor carriers went to considerable lengths to avoid discussing the major issue between them—the level of freight rates. Many witnesses who were hopeful that regulation of the railroad would benefit the trucking industry denied that regulation would result in freight-rate increases. In most cases, the denial was not volunteered but was elicited in questioning by the committee. One witness even predicted that regulation would result in decreased tariff rates. Some stated that regulation would not "necessarily" increase rates, meaning, no doubt, that increases would not automatically result.

In the face of these denials, many witnesses for the motor carriers testified that they were being driven out of business by the low rates charged by the railroad. Some stated that this was due to terminal charges at Seward that were lower for shippers via the railroad than for motor carriers trucking Seward local freight or freight destined beyond Seward. Some witnesses stated that low rates on carload shipments constituted the major problem. Others insisted that the railroad's container rates were too low. Several stated that it was unfair not to require the railroad to make a reasonable return on investment. A few argued that, now that the development era for Railbelt transportation was over, the railroad should carry no commodities except those which a motor carrier was unable to haul.

Railroad witnesses also had some trouble with consistency on the subject of freight rates. Pressed as to whether they engaged in competitive rate-making, they were inclined to assume a position of lofty objectivity. An interesting cat was let out of the bag, however, when the committee counsel asked, "Do you take competition into account in establishing your rates?" The railroad witness answered, "Well, I think that is a minor part of our consideration of rates. Frankly, it's been difficult to know what the competitive rates were." The inference was fairly broad, and truthfully so, that if the railroad could find out what the motor truckers were charging, they would be able to set competitive rates on a more informed basis. Of course the railroad set rates competitively and, after some sparring, witnesses admitted that this was so.

The railroad's final stand on S.1508 was to oppose the bill on the grounds that it would subject the railroad to the same ICC regulations as had been applied to private railroads and that these regulations were not appropriate to The Alaska Railroad. However, railroad witnesses admitted the unfairness of economic regulation that restricted motor carriers but left the railroad free, and they suggested that objectors to Alaska Railroad freight rates should be given the legal right to protest such rates to the Interstate Commerce Commission. They further recommended that the ICC follow its regular adjudication procedures and then submit an advisory decision to the Secretary of the Interior. The secretary would be free to modify the recommendations in the light of the public purposes for which the railroad had been created.

Back in Washington, S.1508 was favorably reported by

both the House and Senate committees on Interstate and Foreign Commerce. Enactment of the bill was opposed by the Department of the Interior on the ground that history had demonstrated that regulation was unnecessary to protect consumers from Alaska Railroad rates alleged to be too high, and that, if the purpose of the legislation was to force an increase in railroad tariffs, success would be harmful to the development of Alaska's resources. The Comptroller General disapproved of the bill because it would create problems of conflicting standards in accounting and statistical reports between the Comptroller General's office and the Interstate Commerce Commission. The Bureau of the Budget opposed the bill on the grounds that it was improper and even unconstitutional to make the President, to whom the Congress had given the power to operate The Alaska Railroad, subservient to the regulatory authority of the ICC.

Nevertheless, S.1508 passed both houses of Congress and would have become law had it not been vetoed on July 6, 1960, by President Eisenhower. In his veto message, the President followed the reasoning of the Bureau of the Budget and the Department of the Interior and noted the anomaly of including in the bill language which made the railroad subject to the Employer's Liability Act of 1908 and the Railway Labor Act. The former established the right of railroad employees in interstate commerce to sue for damages in the case of employee accidents, and the latter would have given the employees of the railroad the right to strike. Since contradictory federal employee legislation had not been repealed, there would have been strange conflicts of federal employee labor law if S.1508 had been approved.

## Interior Turns to ICC Regulation

While the veto of S.1508 may have prevented new problems for The Alaska Railroad, it accomplished nothing toward resolving those already in existence. The smaller Alaskan trucking companies continued to maintain that railroad competition was at the bottom of most of their difficulties. They rarely brought their protests to the Secretary of the Interior, insisting that such protests were futile and that the Secretary, with line responsibility for the financial success of The Alaska Railroad, could not be expected to show impartial judgment.

Weary of criticism from motor carriers, and with no adequate forum from which to reply, Alaska Railroad officials decided to try to blunt the edge of accusation by supporting a plan for economic regulation. In the winter of 1959–60, the Department of the Interior was given an opportunity to test Interstate Commerce Commission standards and procedures in an Alaska Railroad rate case. On December 24, 1959, the railroad had announced an increase in the terminal-charge increment of its through tariffs from West Coast ports to inland Alaska destinations. The proposed increases amounted to 5 cents per 100 pounds ($1 per ton) for carload freight and 10 cents per 100 pounds ($2 per ton) on less-than-carload. When protests against the new tariff rates were received, the Secretary of the Interior suspended them and announced that a hearing, patterned on Interstate Commerce Commission lines, would be held in Anchorage to hear the protests. A retired ICC examiner was employed by Interior to conduct the hearing and was instructed by the secretary to proceed "as nearly as may be" in accordance with the principles and procedures that would have been applicable had Part I of the Interstate Commerce Act been in force on the railroad.

The rate hearings that followed in Anchorage and Fairbanks took place in an atmosphere of amiability. Motor carriers who hauled freight consigned for Seward or beyond had an interest in the case because they would be charged with similarly increased terminal charges. At congressional hearings, described previously, some truckers had alleged that the railroad provided free movement over the Seward dock for the very freight on which it was now requesting additional terminal charges. The only objection to the increase was offered by lumber dealers who maintained that the railroad was required by law to aid in the development of Alaska and that this aid would be more effective if the railroad assumed the burden of the higher terminal charges instead of Alaska's retail lumber dealers. Neither the Alaska Carriers Association nor other interested parties presented arguments against the rate increases. Somewhat surprised at the lack of public participation, the examiner mistook a new arrival at the Fairbanks hearing for a potential witness. The visitor responded that he was not concerned with the hearing and that he had come inside only to get out of the cold. In view of winter temperatures in Fairbanks, this was not at all unreasonable.

The railroad's request for the increases named in its tariff supplement was upheld by the examiner, who stated:

> The Examiner recognizes that the economy of Alaska is vitally affected by the actions of the United States Government. However, it appears that the attitude of both the executive and legislative branches of the government is that The Alaska Railroad should be operated on a strict business-like basis, according consideration to its purpose as set out in the Enabling Act, but without operation on a deficit basis.
>
> After careful study of the record made at the public hearings, the Examiner is of the opinion that the proposed increases are justified and are necessary to meet additional costs of handling the traffic on which they would apply.

Both Interior Department and railroad officials were impressed with the ease with which the tariff increases were placed in effect. They were also impressed by the tendency of vague charges to disappear when witnesses found that they were required to testify under oath. The uproar that had forced a cancellation of a 10 per cent increase in 1950 did not recur. Alaskan citizens had had their day in court, and the railroad had had an opportunity to argue for a decision based on the kind of facts and conclusions that were customarily presented at Interstate Commerce Commission tariff hearings. Regulation in this guise has its positive values for the carrier regulated. It was thus easy to decide that the railroad ought to have an affirmative policy in support of a limited judicial review of its tariffs by the Interstate Commerce Commission.

In February, 1961, Senator Warren G. Magnuson, chairman of the Senate Committee on Interstate and Foreign Commerce, met with Interior officials to discuss the problem of Alaska Railroad regulation. The senator pointed out that Alaska truckers felt as strongly as ever that it was unfair to regulate the motor carriers and not the railroad. He was informed that the general manager would be in Washington shortly with the draft of a bill to place the railroad under ICC regulation.

The general manager did bring such a proposal to Washington, but disagreement with the Interstate Commerce Commission developed as to the legislative drafting method to be followed. The commission wanted the railroad brought under Part I of the Interstate Commerce Act, except for enumerated sections from which it would be excluded. The general manager wanted the railroad brought under certain sections of Part I so that none would apply unless specifically mentioned. The commission won out, and Senator Bartlett, on August 14, 1961, introduced S.2413, drafted in accordance with the commission's plan. The bill's language was of unusual significance, in view of Alaska motor carriers' objections to Alaska Railroad tariffs deemed to be noncompensatory:

> The Interstate Commerce Commission, in determining the lawfulness of rates or charges maintained, by such railroad or railroads, shall give due consideration, among other things, to the

national public purposes which to a substantial extent prompted the construction, expansion, maintenance and improvement thereof, with particular reference to the requirements of the national defense, as well as promotion and development of natural resources, and shall, to the extent warranted by the facts, recognize for valuation and cost-finding purposes a segregation of both capital investment and operating expenses which are found to be solely attributable to such national public purposes, distinguishing them from normal railroad common carrier investment and operational expenses; nor shall such rates and charges be deemed to be unlawful solely because they fail to yield sufficient revenues to cover any amounts for taxes not actually required by law to be paid or provide a return on capital investment.

Senator Bartlett's bill was the subject of hearings before the Senate Committee on Interstate and Foreign Commerce and, with other bills, was the subject of hearings in Anchorage and Fairbanks in October, 1961. At the Anchorage hearing, General Manager Smith affirmed his belief in the principle of regulation but again objected to the means chosen by the Interstate Commerce Commission. As an alternative, he offered the bill, which he had previously proposed, that would bring the railroad under named sections of the Interstate Commerce Act. He argued that his version of a regulatory bill would avoid many problems that S.2413 introduced and would accomplish all that needed to be accomplished. The general manager averred that his bill "would permit any shipper, person, common carriers, etc., to complain to the Interstate Commerce Commission of any violation of law by The Alaska Railroad, and permit investigation and reparation of the same; permit the ICC to determine and prescribe rates and classifications based upon hearings; permit the Commission to establish through routes, joint classifications, joint rates, fares, or charges and the division thereof and determine the lawfulness of new rates, suspensions thereof, and require refunds."

## Regulation by Executive Order

At a hearing before a subcommittee of the Senate Committee on Interstate and Foreign Commerce on June 25, 1962, Assistant Secretary Carver of Interior suggested an alternative to S.2413 that would change the course of The Alaska Railroad's regulations history. Senator Bartlett presided at the hearing, and Harold Seidman of the Bureau of the Budget led off against the bill on the ground that it represented an unconstitutional limitation on the power of the President. Carver supported the principle of regulation and then suggested that the problem be resolved, not by law, but by a new delegation of authority. The President's authority and duty to operate the railroad had been delegated to the Secretary of the Interior by President Harding in 1923. Carver proposed that the old delegation order be canceled and that a new order be issued by the President giving the Secretary of the Interior the authority to operate the railroad and the Interstate Commerce Commission the authority to regulate its tariffs.*

Senator Bartlett, with the finesse in treatment of witnesses that has characterized his chairmanship of many Senate hearings, recalled the Bureau of the Budget representative for an opinion on Assistant Secretary Carver's proposal. Witness Seidman responded immediately that the suggestion of a new delegation of authority might very well resolve the problem of unconstitutional limitation upon Presidential power. Yet the practical results in terms of economic regulation could be identical under the proposed law and under the proposed executive order.

During the next few months, the Department of the Interior, the Bureau of the Budget, and the Interstate Commerce

* There is no doubt that this suggestion resolved an impasse over ICC regulation of The Alaska Railroad that had been building up for more than five years. Credit for the suggestion goes to Lewis A. Sigler, legislative counsel, Interior's Office of the Solicitor.

Commission considered the matter of appropriate language for a new delegation of authority. Differences were never wholly resolved because the ICC retained its preference for the application of Part I as a whole (with certain exceptions) as in the draft legislation. Interior and the Bureau of the Budget finally agreed on the desired language, and Executive Order 11107 was signed by President Kennedy on April 25, 1963. President Harding's executive order of 1923 was canceled, and the new order gave the Secretary of the Interior the responsibility for operating the railroad and for making a valuation of its capital to ascertain what portion of capital assets was used for public purposes. The Interstate Commerce Commission was given limited economic authority over the railroad's tariffs but was admonished to declare no tariff rate unlawful by reason of the railroad's failure to earn a return on investment.

The director of the Alaska Carriers Association, who, in peremptory language, had been demanding an explanation as to why the executive order took so long to come into existence, would shortly use similar language to denounce it. In retrospect it is clear that if Senator Bartlett's bill S.2413 had been enacted, it probably would have met the same reception. During the 1959 Alaska hearings, the Alaska Carriers Association maintained that placing Alaska Railroad tariffs under the regulating authority of the Interstate Commerce Commission would not result in an increase in railroad rates. For the 1961 hearings, the association's director abandoned this position and suggested that regulation might result in a 15 per cent increase.

In a letter of June 29, 1962, to the President, the director of the association stated:

> We further submit to you our definite request that the entire rate structure of The Alaska Railroad should be expertly examined and revised so as to place each individual rate on a proper

> earning base which will include full amortization of investment, operating and maintenance costs, taxes (or amounts in lieu thereof) to the State of Alaska and the cities and boroughs through which it runs and a token profit to be yielded to the U.S. Treasury or used for capital improvements.

The position of the Alaska Carriers Association, assuming that the quoted paragraph properly describes it, seems to boil down to the assertion that fairness to the motor truckers requires that Alaska Railroad rates be increased to yield interest on investment, amortization of investment, payments in lieu of taxes, and a token profit. If the railroad could have attracted sufficient tonnage at freight rates calculated on these standards, it would long since have been sold to private interests. The inference seemed to be that, now that trucking companies had established themselves as going concerns in Alaska, the railroad should "phase out" of the transportation business unless it could advance its rates to meet these standards. (In judging such tariff standards, it should be borne in mind that many trucking companies would be unable to meet them and that they are not the standards required of private railroads by the Interstate Commerce Commission. Further, in fairness to the railroad, it should be pointed out that an audit of user charges and public investment in highways in Alaska, in comparison with similar charges and investment amounts in other states, might well suggest that Alaskan motor carriers are not, any more than The Alaska Railroad, earning full interest on capital investment.)

It seems reasonably clear that the interest of Alaskan truck operators in S.1508, S.2413, and Executive Order 11107 represented a temporary tactic, which the logic of their indignation against government competition forced them to repudiate. The executive order was in terms of the ancient and honorable objectives of the earliest railroad tariff regulation—the protection of consumers. In this objective, the truckers were supremely disinterested. The objectives of regulation that induced them to welcome the automatic application to Alaska of the Motor Carrier Act represented a producer interest solely. Grandfather clauses, combined with certificates of convenience and necessity and with requirements for tariff issuances and financial reporting, gave them the freedom from anarchy that they genuinely needed. Their argument, that it was unfair that motor carriers should be regulated while the railroad was free, was tactical rather than real insofar as it implied that truck operators would be satisfied with eliminating the alleged unfairness by becoming deregulated themselves. Some motor carriers seemed to fear that, in the absence of a statutory requirement, the railroad might disregard its published tariffs in an effort to take business from them. Actually, the railroad has a good record of adhering to ICC rules in regard to the issuance of tariffs even when not required to do so.

It was probably inevitable that the Alaska Carriers Association would regard their "victory" in helping to bring the railroad's tariffs under ICC regulation as a hollow one. Many members of the association wanted regulation in Alaska to enable motor carriers to protect themselves from the cut-throat competition of other motor carriers and from what they expected would be cut-throat competition from the railroad. They found Executive Order 11107 weak and ineffective because they wanted the opportunity to protest against rail freight rates that they regarded as noncompensatory and because they wanted the canons of what constitutes compensatory rates so established by law that the ICC would be compelled to force Alaska Railroad freight rates upward. In instances where motor carriers maintained rates lower than rail rates (and this has occurred several times), higher railroad tariffs would make little competitive difference.

It should be noted that some sympathy with this point of view may have developed within the Interstate Commerce

Commission. In a 1966 case before the commission involving the application of Sea-Land Freight Service for authority to purchase the operating rights of the financially embarrassed Alaska Freight Lines, denunciation of The Alaska Railroad by the applicant went to astonishing extremes. The railroad was charged with "destructive competitive practices . . . aimed at securing a monopoly of transportaton in Alaska." According to the ICC examiner in the case:

> Applicants claim that the Sea-Land Companies operations has [*sic*] broken the monopolistic power of control, however exercised, of The Alaska Railroad over the cost to the public of the transportation of freight to Alaska. They state that it is a matter of public knowledge that The Alaska Railroad, a government agency, always deficit-ridden, sustained major damage in the 1964 earthquake, is the recipient of major present Congressional appropriations exceeding $5 million for 1965–66, has a history of discouraging competitors, has no published cost data, is practically exempt from ICC regulation, and is more likely to establish and maintain low-cost service under the competitive influence of the Sea-Land Service than without it.

The above statement contains an abundance of the kind of nonsense that often appears in adversary argument. Considering the history of Alaska Railroad tariffs and the complaints of Alaska motor carriers as to their alleged noncompensatory character, the last assertion in the paragraph must have seemed the unkindest cut of all to Alaska Railroad officials.

The assertions of Sea-Land Service, of no great importance in themselves, become important when they so influence the thinking of an ICC examiner that he concludes:

> Sea-Land Services makes The Alaska Railroad the "whipping boy" for all of the transportation problems in Alaska, including those of the motor carriers. The fact of the matter is that *the motor carriers are caught in an inextricable vise of competitive forces; with one jaw being the water carrier operators and the other The Alaska Railroad* [italics added].

> The Alaska Railroad is not a party to the instant proceeding and little is known of its motor carrier operations. It is closely associated with several Alaska river water carriers. . . . In any event, on the record here made, the government-owned railroad has been an unrelenting competitor to the motor carrier industry, including at the government-owned Seward port facility. However, the Commission under the existing law is powerless to grant any relief in the public interest, including the interest of the motor carrier industry. The matter rests in the hands of Congress.
>
> . . . The comparative freedom and ease with which the water carriers are able to shift their calling from one Alaska port to another has seriously affected the motor carrier industry and deprived interior Alaska points of the most expeditious transportation service. The foregoing is clearly demonstrated by the evidence of Ness which shows how motor carrier services out of Valdez suffered a severe decline when Alaska Freight shifted its port of call to Anchorage. The same change in port of call also adversely affected receivers in the Fairbanks area.
>
> Among the land carriers, The Alaska Railroad in serving the most populated segment of the State compels the service of water carriers. Under existing circumstances the prejudicial competitive position of the independent Alaska motor carriers could only be worsened by either The Alaska Railroad or the Sea-Land Companies, or both, extending their services to the port of Valdez, a situation which this Commission is powerless to prevent.

The last paragraph quoted is particularly mystifying because a year earlier, in 1965, The Alaska Railroad had extended its services to Valdez through the cooperative efforts of Puget Sound–Alaska Van Lines. Valdez is now served by a car slip, which enables loaded freight cars to be landed at the port. No railroad extends from Valdez, and The Alaska Railroad uses its trucks only in local deliveries and has no intention of establishing trucking service out of Valdez. (Valdez was completely wiped out by the earthquake, and a new town was built in a different location. The Puget Sound–Alaska Van Lines and Alaska Railroad joint facility was particularly designed to get construction materials quickly and cheaply into the new town. The freight rate on concrete blocks from Anchorage to Valdez was thus reduced from $1.19 to 47 cents per 100 pounds, a saving of $14.40 per ton.)

Debate on the rest of the examiner's conclusions would serve no useful purpose. The conclusions should be challenged, if at all, in an ICC proceeding at which witnesses can be sworn and cross-examined, for no transportation company, including a government agency, should be the subject of attack when it is not a party to the proceedings and cannot defend itself even when the attacks border on libel. The conclusions of the examiner in the Sea-Land case have been considered here because they could be meaningful to the future development of transportation regulation in Alaska.

In May, 1966, three years after The Alaska Railroad was made subject to ICC authority, the Alaska Carriers Association dispatched a long letter of protest to the Secretary of the Interior alleging unfair competition by the railroad—its tariff rates were too low and it received large revenues from illegitimate sources. The Department of the Interior replied in detail to all the charges, admitting some, refuting others. The final paragraphs of the department's reply to Alaskan truck operators constitute an appropriate conclusion to this story of competition and regulation among the several modes of transportation in Alaska:

> The Alaska Railroad situation is, in many respects, unique. The Railroad was not built as an exercise in social theory, nor has it been continued in an attempt to illustrate the advantages of government enterprise. Instead, The Alaska Railroad was the pragmatic result of a general belief that rail transportation was needed for the development of Alaska's resources in what is now called the "Railbelt area" and general recognition that private enterprise had not provided it.

> The operation of the Railroad is continued today on the same pragmatic grounds. It provides basic transportation (60 to 75 per cent of its traffic is coal, petroleum, lumber and cement) to more than half the population of Alaska. I feel quite sure that the government would be willing to sell the Railroad at a fair price to a responsible operator. None has yet come forward who was willing to assume the financial risks.

The letter from the department closed with an expression of hope that motor carriers and The Alaska Railroad would establish a coordinated system of land transportation in which each would supplement the other and each be responsible for an appropriate share of the total transportation task.

Just as The Alaska Railroad is, in many ways, unique, so is the problem of its regulation. The comparison with private railroads, made so often in these pages, can be carried just so far. Although it makes a profit, The Alaska Railroad is not meant to be a profit-making enterprise. It is competitively alert but an ICC examiner to the contrary notwithstanding, it is not competitively unrelenting. The paths of transportation regulation are just beginning to be marked out in the tremendous state of Alaska. They will be marked out wrongly if it is assumed that the final goal is primarily competitive equality, that is, the establishment and enforcement of rules under which competition with other producers may be considered fair and reasonable. For a government railroad, and someday for a private railroad, the appropriate direction will be toward the encouragement of cooperative endeavor with other modes of transportation for a common good that gives the users of transportation and the workers who produce it a slight priority over those who supply its capital funds and its managerial talent.

# X

# Earthquake

An earthquake of the magnitude that struck Alaska at 5:26 P.M. on Friday, March 27, 1964, is not easily contained within the bounds of language, whether of science, of journalism, or of literature. Those who tried to so contain it began with the common reality of earth shocks greater in intensity than had ever before been recorded in North America. But, in describing this reality, the geologist wrote of Richter scales, of epicenters, of tsunami waves, of tectonic uplift and subsidence. The journalist, with the exaggeration that often accompanies the scarcity of accurate news in times of catastrophe, wrote, in the *Evening Star* of Washington, D.C., on March 28, 1964:

> The heart of this metropolitan city [Anchorage] was virtually destroyed by an earthquake that roared through Alaska last night, leaving a death toll that may reach several hundred.

And, after a day of less uncertain news, on Sunday, March 29, in the Anchorage *Daily Times*:

> In the incredible aftermath of one of the world's mightiest earthquakes the people of Anchorage began to rebuild today on a hazy, quiet Easter Sunday.

It remained for a geologist from the Department of the Interior to combine both science and literature in the Geological Survey's first detailed report on the effects of rocks slipping deep into the earth along a major fault line. In *Geological*

*Survey Circular 491,* he began his description, which later bristled with the technical terminology of the professional, in this fashion:

> At 5:36 P.M. on Good Friday, March 27, 1964, a great earthquake with a Richter magnitude of 8.4 to 8.6 crippled south-central Alaska. It released at least twice as much energy as the 1906 earthquake which wrecked San Francisco, and was felt on land over an area of almost half a million square miles.*

The area of significant land damage extended in a great arc around the shores of the Gulf of Alaska. The southwestern end of this arc touched Kodiak Island. It reached north by east to The Alaska Railroad port cities of Seward and Whittier and to its headquarters city of Anchorage. With lessening violence, it turned toward the Matanuska Valley, where the railroad's spur to Palmer and the Matanuska coal fields begins. Along the downward curve of the area of greatest damage, there was tragic loss of life on the docks at Valdez and the town and harbor were so destroyed that the old site has been abandoned and a new Valdez built some distance away. The arc of the earthquake ended in Prince William Sound between Cordova and Yakutat. But its influence, through tsunamis, reached far beyond. One such wave raced at jet-plane speed 2,000 miles to the south and brought death and destruction to Crescent City, California.

The reactions of no two individuals among the more than 100,000 people in the disaster area were exactly the same. Each saw and felt the quake from his own small vantage point on the earth's thin and restless crust. For some, caught in slide areas of crumbling cliffs, of gaping cracks in moving earth, of crashing walls and disappearing houses, the quake was the sheer horror that *Life* magazine described as "an eternity that

* It has been pointed out earlier that the New Madrid, Missouri, earthquake of 1811–12 was of greater intensity. But this was determined by geological investigation years afterward and not by measurements at the time.

was all over in just five minutes." For some, the disaster came from the sea—a series of monstrous waves that, at port cities and Indian coastal towns, wrought more death and devastation than the earth shocks themselves. For others, it was burning oil from ruptured tanks whose volcano-like rolling swirl of smoke and flame seemed like a preview of hell itself.

Yet to many Alaskans the earthquake was not a thing of horror. In Anchorage, for example, the slide areas meant catastrophic destruction, but there were few such areas. Shocks of low intensity in southwestern Alaska had been commonplace for many years. Every long-time resident of Anchorage had felt them many times. To some, the earth tremors of Good Friday seemed merely unusually severe. They lasted longer and broke more dishes but only vaguely suggested the extent of the disaster that had befallen the area.

The great majority of the thousands of homes in Anchorage received minor damage or escaped altogether. Despite crashed buildings, broken schools, and sunken streets, despite the awful destruction caused by endlessly repeating landslides among the expensive homes of Turn-Again-by-the-Sea, the earthquake caused only nine deaths in the Anchorage area. Among the close to 1,000 employees of The Alaska Railroad, only one died, and he not from the quake but from a weakened heart that could not take the strain of the event.

Among the calmer of the citizens of Anchorage both during and after the earthquake was the chief train dispatcher of The Alaska Railroad. The keeping of a log is a part of his essential duties. Here is the earthquake entry in his log book for March 27.

> Unusual—March 27, 1964 . . . 5:36 P.M. earthquake hits Alaska. Major damage to Alaska Railroad docks, and trackage destroyed at Seward. Whittier docks damaged, track out of service Seward to Sunshine. No. 24 not heard from since last contact at Portage 4:50 P.M. account no communications. Rail cars turned over in Anchorage yard and yard tracks out of service.

Earthquake felt as far as Fairbanks. Later reports indicate track OK for service from Sunshine to Fairbanks and no apparent damage between these points. Sutton Sub Div track badly damaged. Extra 1504 South at Curry and tied up account blockade of track. No. 21 stopped at Palmer and tied up at Palmer account blockade of track.

## A $27 Million Loss

Although the chief train dispatcher's account was accurate as far as it went, it was not possible to know on the evening of March 27 that the railroad had suffered damage to track, roadway, bridges, buildings, rolling stock, motive power, docks, and equipment that would require more than $27 million for repairs and replacements. During the three to four minutes of the earthquake, the damage increased geometrically with time and The Alaska Railroad lost about one-fifth of the book value of its plant and equipment.

An accurate appraisal of the railroad's losses was slow in reaching the Department of the Interior. Communications between Anchorage and Washington, D.C., were either unreliable or nonexistent on the two days following March 27. Military communications were quickly restored, but it was rarely possible, once a telephone call was placed to Elmendorf Air Base, to get beyond to downtown Anchorage.

The first message that reached Interior with news of the extent of damage to The Alaska Railroad did not come through official channels at all. At about 4:00 A.M. on Sunday morning, March 29, a White House aide called the assistant to the general manager at his home in McLean, Virginia, and asked him to stand by for an important message from Reno, Nevada. The connection with Reno was made, and a ham-radio operator in Reno relayed word from the head of the Bureau of Land Management in Anchorage that The Alaska Railroad had suffered losses in excess of $17 million. On the afternoon of the same day, a telephone call came through from the general manager in Anchorage in which he estimated railroad damage at around $20 million. Reports a few days later increased these estimates to $27 million—an amount that proved astonishingly accurate. The subtotals changed, but the grand total remained about the same.

The story of Seward, while it included few casualties, was particularly tragic. The earthquake generated underwater landslides that not only destroyed railroad shore-side terminal facilities, but increased the depth of water in front of the little that was left of the dock and warehouses from 35 feet to more than 125 feet. Two of the three giant cranes on the apron of the dock, each nearly five stories high, crashed into the churning waters of Resurrection Bay. One of them disappeared so completely that divers were unable to find even a trace of it.

The seismic waves that followed the quake took a further terrible toll of railroad plant and equipment. One completely loaded freight train was destroyed that would have been on its way to Anchorage, had the earth stood still for another few minutes. Earthquake-generated waves crashed against boxcars in the Seward yard with such force that their wheel flanges tore out rails and popped spikes from the ties. Toward the head of the bay, the waves ruptured the big tanks of two large petroleum tank farms. Fire followed, and waves, capped with burning oil, completed the shore-side destruction. Fortunately, much of the rest of Seward was on higher ground that the flame-blanketed waters could not reach.

There were some lighter aspects to the Seward tragedy. A railroad flatcar loaded with strapped lumber landed wrong side up in front of a shop building over which a giant wave must have hurled it. When the car was finally righted, its load of lumber was delivered to the consignee in such good condition that no claim for damages was presented. A military bus was found in the debris of the railyard, apparently upright and apparently not much damaged. Inspection of the rear side, however, revealed that the big bus had been sheared almost completely in half. For reasons still unknown to Alaska Railroad traffic men, military authorities requested the railroad to deliver the bus irrespective of its condition. In due time, one half of one bus was carried on a flatcar to Anchorage and was turned over to the Army at Fort Richardson. Whether the freight charges were halved to correspond with the bus is not a matter of easily accessible record.

The visual impact of the disaster the earthquake brought to the railroad was greater at Seward than at any other point along the line. Even after six months of cleanup, there was left a shoreline scalloped by marine landslides, with twisted rail dangling crazily over the water, with burned and blackened oil tanks partially collapsed, and a mountain of destroyed railroad equipment piled high to await sorting for scrap. There was also an unnatural quiet hanging over a town that had formerly bustled with longshoremen and sling cargo and had echoed the noise of clanking cranes, of yard diesels spotting cars and assembling freight trains bound for Portage and Anchorage, and of the engine hum and grinding gears of trucks aggressively asserting their alleged superiority over locomotives.

At Whittier, the railroad's port on the south coast of the Kenai Peninsula, the story of Seward was repeated, except that there was less railroad property destroyed. This is not because the force of the earthquake was less, but because the railroad's investment in Whittier was much smaller. It will be remembered that an Alaskan transportation revolution had changed Whittier from a traditional port depending mainly on longshore gangs to a car-ferry and sea-train port joining The Alaska Railroad to every other railroad in the United States and Canada. When the Army had occupied Whittier, gangs of soldier longshoremen manipulated slings and winches and fork-lift trucks, and freight was warehoused pending rail shipment. When the military moved out and the railroad reached agreement with Canadian and U.S. railroads that loaded freight cars would be interchanged at Whittier, car-slip operators and switch crews replaced longshoremen. Freight cars from many different railroads then, for the first time in history, became common sights in Whittier and Anchorage and Fairbanks.

As a result of the earthquake, the car slip that the railroad had built to accommodate the new kind of car-load traffic was a total loss. The rebuilt Army dock that the railroad still used occasionally was badly damaged. So were the Whittier yard tracks, the warehouse, and the railroad station. One wing of the station was completely torn away from the rest of the building, yet hardly a window was broken in that part of the structure that remained. A military petroleum tank farm, more or less retired from active operation, was only touched by the earthquake. But a private tank farm that was an essential link in the shipment of gasoline and fuel oil to Anchorage and Fairbanks was the victim of the kind of rupture and fire that destroyed similar facilities in Seward. Less railroad equipment was lost than in Seward, not only because there were fewer items of such equipment in Whittier, but because the waves born of submarine landslides forced freight cars landward rather than into the bay.

Interestingly enough, the two long unlined tunnels that are part of the twelve-mile connection between Whittier and the main line at Portage were hardly damaged. This fact, plus the necessity of finding a substitute for the destroyed Whittier car slip, was to prove of dramatic importance to The Alaska Railroad and to civilian and military communities in the Railbelt during the first few weeks that followed March 27.

A strip map of The Alaska Railroad shows a good many dots that, to the outsider, would represent towns. Many are picturesquely named—Grandview, Moose Pass, Rainbow,

Gold Creek, Hurricane, and Honolulu. Most of them are not towns, however, but section points lived in by a few maintenance employees. Some have been abandoned even for this purpose. A few, like Portage, at the head of Turnagain Arm and at the junction of the twelve-mile line to Whittier with the main line from Seward, were large enough before the earthquake that "town" was not a misnomer. Portage was, in fact, sufficiently important to the railroad to warrant the building of a new railroad station at a cost of about $200,000. In retrospect, and in view of what the earthquake did to Portage, this was a somewhat excessive investment.

The junction town of Portage occupied flat land only a few feet above the level of the arm of the sea in front of it. The earthquake not only damaged or destroyed buildings in Portage, including the new railroad station, but it also lowered the land level so that most of the town was under water at high tide. The Alaska Railroad did not rebuild at Portage. Tracks were raised above flood levels, but it was not practical to attempt to raise the entire townsite. The attractive blonde who ran a restaurant and saloon across the road from the railroad station hitched a tractor to her building and hauled it up the highway to a better site in the direction of Anchorage. She and her friends ceased writing letters of protest to the Secretary of the Interior about the unfair competition of the railroad in allowing a concessionaire to sell alcoholic drinks at the railroad station. Her competition disappeared when the railroad station was sold for a junk price of $7,000.

In Anchorage, as in Seward and Whittier, The Alaska Railroad experienced multimillion-dollar earthquake damage. Buildings and yard facilities were particularly vulnerable because they were located in the narrow valley of Ship Creek between Government Hill to the north and the high land to the south that supports the main Anchorage business district. The Government Hill slide, which cut in two a new elementary school building, also engulfed an equipment-storage building in the railroad yards below the hill. Most of the machinery in the building was ruined beyond repair. The nearby wheel shop was so badly damaged that it had to be torn down and replaced. One two-track bay of the freight-car shop had to be completely rebuilt.

Across the yard tracks, and toward the place where an even larger slide destroyed three blocks of Fourth Avenue business buildings, was the big concrete and steel station and headquarters office building. Across the street from the station and down one block was a cinder-block accounting building. It was so shattered that it had to be leveled with bulldozers and the rubble trucked away. The station and office building showed only plaster cracks and a fractional-inch subsidence at one end. The type of construction made the difference. Generally, the more recently constructed buildings suffered the greatest damage.

Apart from physical damage, one of the most frustrating aspects of the quake was the scrambling of paper records and supply inventories that occurred. Almost worse than the loss of the railroad's accounting building was the mess of papers that required reassembling. In railroad warehouses, otherwise relatively unmarred, repair parts that had cascaded from supply bins created a confusion that seemed at first to defy restoration.

Buildings, however important, cannot possibly contain the essence of a railroad. It was damage to track and roadway, not to buildings or even rolling stock, that stopped the operation of The Alaska Railroad on Good Friday in 1964. This damage extended, with greater or less severity, from Seward to Matanuska Junction, at milepost 150, and from Matanuska Junction to Palmer and along the coal branch to Jonesville, a distance from the junction of 37 miles. It included twisted rail, humpbacked bridges, spectacular slides that destroyed whole sections of track, and about 35 miles of roadway subsidence. Damage along the main line north of Matanuska Junction, largely confined to bridges, became progressively less and finally disappeared above Hurricane, about 175 miles north of Anchorage.

The kind of damage that many Alaska Railroad bridges suffered resulted from the combined effect of earthquake and winter. On March 27, the ground around the bridges was still frozen. But flowing water kept the stream beds thawed. The frozen ground resisted stress, forcing the full shock of the earthquake to the thawed ground between bridge abutments. As a result, bridge after bridge buckled, or there was horizontal displacement. In the language of the geologist, most of the bridges in the 185-mile stretch of railroad from Seward to the Matanuska Valley were "cambered from compression."

With bridges, track, and roadway, as with buildings and equipment, the area of most severe destruction extended from Anchorage south. For the 50 miles to Portage, the railroad alternates with the highway in occupying tidal flats or rock ledges blasted from the Chugach Mountain shoreline of Turnagain Arm. The railroad was totally destroyed along part of this stretch, as at Potter Hill, a few miles south of Anchorage, and the rest was damaged by slides, subsidence, and flood. For about 35 miles the railroad grade sank between 5 and 6 feet and, where tracks crossed a tidal inlet, they and their supporting grade were pushed down into the muck another 5 feet or more. Before the earthquake, there had been only a few feet of freeboard for the right of way from Potter south to Portage. Therefore, after the earthquake, flood waters from abnormally high tides greatly increased the amount of damage and added correspondingly to the work of reconstruction.

Subsidence, tidal floods, and winter combined to provide a dramatic bridge story at the Twenty-Mile River near the head of Turnagain Arm. Here a multiple-span steel railroad bridge, badly shaken but not demolished, was threatened after the quake by a tidal flood that, as it receded, brought floes of river ice crashing against bridge piers and abutments. If the railroad bridge at Twenty-Mile, like the highway bridge beside it, had gone out, there would have been about ten days' delay before a temporary crossing could be built to permit train movements from Whittier through Portage to Anchorage. In the emergency, it was decided to weight down the bridge with gravel-loaded hopper cars, which, in the absence of a locomotive, had to be pushed onto the bridge track with a bulldozer. There was the obvious risk of losing both cars and bridge. But the scheme worked, the bridge held, and an invaluable ten days was saved.

For much of the 114 miles between Anchorage and Seward, highway and railroad run side by side. Thus, both were in the area of the most intense earthquake damage. Both crossed streams on many bridges. The railroad bridges were built to carry the weight of diesel locomotives of more than 2,000 horsepower, while the highway bridges were built to carry only vehicular traffic. Comparative destruction reflected these differences. In spite of damage, The Alaska Railroad did not lose a single major bridge. On the other hand, most of the major highway bridges, as at Twenty-Mile River, were either totally destroyed or destruction was close to total. It may be of some transportation significance that the railroad was back in service following temporary repairs long before the highway. It is also to be noted that, for many months after the railroad had completed permanent repairs, highway traffic was still crossing rivers on the Seward Highway on the emergency bridges that were to have been only temporary replacements.

Two more incidents of devastation wind up the history of what the great earthquake of March 27, 1964, did to The Alaska Railroad. These were large landslides, one depositing a section of the railroad into Kenai Lake, the other hurling a much larger section into the waters of Turnagain Arm. The Kenai Lake landslide was spectacular but relatively small. It left a large scar in the mountain shoreline of the lake, destroyed a thousand feet of roadway and track, and required a rerouting of the railroad above the slide area.

At Potter Hill, a few miles south of Anchorage, the land

bordering Turnagain Arm, even before the earthquake, was known to be unstable. During the quake, great sections of the hill collapsed along a mile and a half of the railroad right of way. Thousands of tons of earth slid into the ocean carrying a good deal of railroad along with it. Spikes held for part of the distance while roadway sank, and rails and ties dangled grotesquely in the air. Here the earthquake did one of its mightiest jobs of moving enormous yardage of soil and rocks. Here also the railroad accomplished a correspondingly gargantuan task of earth-moving to get track and roadway back in place.

### Comeback from Disaster

An article entitled "Comeback from Disaster" in the January, 1965, issue of *Railway Age,* paid high tribute to the accomplishment of The Alaska Railroad in solving the problems of earthquake rehabilitation. There is no question that a great disaster inspires men to forget their differences and unite in a common cause. A generous sharing of talent and possessions becomes the norm. Calculation of cost and price gives way to a more fundamental consideration of more fundamental values. And so it was in the towns and cities of the Alaska Railbelt in the months that followed Good Friday, March 27, 1964.

By Sunday, March 29, only two days after the earthquake, the general manager and his engineering staff had already made their plans for temporary and emergency repairs that would permit the resumption of rail service in the shortest possible time. For quick restoration, the port of Whittier, not Seward, turned out to be the answer. Whittier meant 62.5 miles of track and roadway to be repaired instead of 114 miles. Whittier was a sea-train and car-ferry port, whereas Seward was equipped to handle loose stow and container cargo. Although the car slip at Whittier and the docks at Seward were totally destroyed, it was much easier to improvise an alternative to the Whittier car slip than to find an emergency substitute for the Seward docks.

Yet, in those first few hectic days, some way had to be found to transfer loaded freight cars from barges and ships to tracks at Whittier without waiting for the rebuilding of a car slip. There was no time for rebuilding and Alaska Railroad officials were so doubtful of finding an acceptable substitute that their initial estimates of the time needed to get freight trains moving depended on Seward. The first telephoned report from the general manager on the seriousness of the damage reached Washington, D.C., on March 29. Except for the mention of the total destruction of the car slip, Whittier was almost ignored. The general manager summarized the loss figures and said that, because there was no damage north of the Alaska Range, coal trains were continuing to roll into Fairbanks from the Healy field. He said that it would be two weeks before coal from the Matanuska Valley mines could be brought into Anchorage and estimated that it would take three weeks before trains could move from Anchorage to Fairbanks and six weeks before tracks could be cleared to Seward.

Almost immediately, however, and as extra gangs, track machines, and work trains were beginning the job of rebuilding track between Anchorage and Portage, another solution presented itself that would cut in half the estimated six weeks for restoring freight service from the south. The general manager learned that the Army had a $1 million floating crane at Beaver, Oregon, with a lift capability of 200,000 pounds. If it could be brought to Whittier, freight cars could be lifted from ship or barge, placed on the shoreside tracks, and made up into trains for Anchorage and Fairbanks. By fortunate coincidence, the Navy tug *Sioux,* rated at 3,000 horsepower, was in Seattle. A triangle of long-distance calls among Anchorage, Seattle, and Washington, D.C., brought assurance of cooperation from both the Army and the Navy in making the big crane available and towing it to Whittier. Thus, plans to reopen Seward's rail line first were abandoned in favor of Whittier almost as soon as they were born.

With a reasonable assurance that the problem of interchanging freight cars at Whittier was about to be resolved, railroad employees turned to the enormous task of repairing the fifty miles of track between Anchorage and Portage and the twelve miles between Portage and Whittier. This meant concentration on the three principal jobs of earth moving, track relaying, and bridge repair. Communications also had to be restored, but this task was reduced because a few years previously the railroad had replaced the pole line between Anchorage and Portage with a microwave system.

Track, roadway, and bridge repair meant that the heaviest burden of reconstruction would fall on the railroad's engineering staff and upon its maintenance-of-way and bridge-and-building employees. It meant hiring several hundred additional track and roadway laborers. It meant the greatest concentration of heavy earth-moving equipment and the most extensive and intensive use of sophisticated track and roadway machines ever seen on The Alaska Railroad. The total job of completing repairs took more than two years from March, 1964. Yet management was proposing emergency repairs that, it was predicted, would permit freight to be shipped from Seattle to Anchorage and Fairbanks at the end of two weeks!

Few people outside the railroad industry realize the nature of the technological revolution that has been taking place in methods of rebuilding track and roadway. Such rebuilding once depended upon the physical labor of section men, gandy dancers as they were called, who pulled out ties, replaced them, and laid rails with principal reliance upon hand tools. The spike, maul, and shovel were symbols of the trade. Although it is true that railroad rights of way have not been built with hand shovels for many years, construction and maintenance of railroad track a quarter-century ago depended even more on muscle than on machines.

A revolution in maintaining right of way has been created by earth-moving equipment of greatly increased size and power and, more importantly, by the invention of automatic and semi-automatic machinery for spreading ballast, inserting ties, and laying rail. Power shovels, caterpillar tractors, and tie tampers were among the first of the labor-saving devices purchased for The Alaska Railroad maintenance-of-way department. Now the list includes power jacks for lifting rails and ties so that additional ballast can be spread under them, ballast-laying and spreading machines, and electronic tie tampers that automatically align track during the rail-relaying and tie-tamping process. As a result of technological innovations, eight section men working with machines can now accomplish the same amount of track work that required eighty men not more than fifteen years ago. The implications of these changes were tremendous for the earthquake repair program. Machinery made possible predictions of short-time completion of emergency track rebuilding that would have been regarded as nonsense fifteen to twenty years earlier.

On the Saturday and Sunday after March 27, officials of The Alaska Railroad sent out radio appeals to all employees to report for work on Monday, March 30. Many, of course, could not be put to their normal tasks, which would mean some work time wasted. But management's decision to ask all employees to return to duty paid off in the employee loyalty that it called forth. The fact that almost all of the railroad's rank-and-file employees are represented by trade unions did not prevent them from forgetting craft lines in the interest of the job to be done. Union officials cooperated to the fullest extent. Train-and-engine service employees, for example, told management, "Use us in any way you want. If labor-agreement penalty rules interfere with necessary work assignments, we will forget about the rules." A similar pride in getting the job done quickly was reflected in the work (and overtime) of all Alaska Railroad employees, with some special emphasis on maintenance-of-way employees, who carried the heaviest burden of reconstruction and who could see during every hour of the working day the tangible results of their labor.

The same kind of cooperation was given the railroad by other government agencies, particularly by the Army, Navy, Air Force, and the General Services Administration, and by private contractors and suppliers. Power shovels, power jacks, bulldozers, air-dump cars, cranes, dump trucks, and giant earth movers were marshaled from every available source. Such machinery was the key to speedy rehabilitation because of the hundreds of thousands of cubic yards of earth and rock that had to be moved before rail could be relaid across the Potter Hill slide area and before the sunken track over the thirty-five-mile stretch to Portage could be brought up to grade. GSA provided a tremendous assist by cutting red tape to make possible the emergency purchase of equipment and supplies.

Behind all these agencies was the effective coordinating effort of the Office of Emergency Planning in the Executive Office of the President. This agency worked closely with the Federal Reconstruction and Development Planning Commission, an organization specially created by the President to deal with the task of rebuilding.

Private railroads and railroad-equipment companies were called upon for extra and unusual assistance and were quick to respond. A bridge foreman, a bridge gang, and a fleet of flatcars were sent to the railroad by the Great Northern Railway. Pacific Fruit Express repaired forty-nine air-dump cars that had been obtained second-hand. A fleet of fifty open-top hoppers was purchased on an emergency basis from one of the larger rail equipment companies. A supplier diverted power shovels to the railroad from other purchasers. Private contractors did some of the big fill jobs. In spite of the loss of many boxcars, no real car shortage developed, and, with only one small locomotive lost, the diesel fleet was adequate.

Alaska Railroad officials had hoped to reach Whittier with a passable track and roadway by April 14. This would have been possible had not the tides at Portage risen in mid-April faster than railroad work gangs could build up the track. Track and roadway machines enabled raises of up to 12 inches at a single pass. But there were 4 or 5 feet of raise to be accomplished and twice that amount across some tidal flats. Some rebuilt track was washed out and had to be replaced. Result—another week added to the original estimate as to when the first freight train could reach Whittier from Anchorage.

While bridges were being repaired and track raised, the Navy tug *Sioux* left Seattle on April 3 for Beaver, Oregon, to pick up the Army's million-dollar floating crane. On April 5, the *Sioux* took the big crane in tow and started for the Gulf of Alaska. The skipper of the tug gambled on the weather and followed the outside passage over the open Pacific rather than the safer inside route. The gamble paid off, and the tug and floating crane arrived in Whittier on April 13. Because of the additional damage from record mid-April tides in Cook Inlet and Turnagain Arm, the crane was in Whittier a full week ahead of the railroad.

On April 20, however, a little more than three weeks after the earthquake, a train moved into Whittier from Anchorage on slow orders over temporary track, and against the threat of possible derailment. But track and roadway stood up, and, on the same day, loaded freight cars behind diesels in tandem brought the first outside freight into Anchorage since March 27. A one-freight-train-a-day policy was adopted to enable track gangs to keep on with their work with the least interference. Sometimes this meant 125 loaded cars in a single train. In the first three or four days, the congestion at Whittier was cleaned up and barge and train-ship arrivals were serviced in a more normal fashion thereafter.

The reopening of Alaska's warm-water port of Whittier was of course the climax of the first hectic days of emergency rehabilitation. Other sections of the railroad, however, had been reopened even earlier. It will be remembered that freight service north of McKinley Park was never interrupted by the earthquake. On April 6, ten days after the earthquake, freight service was restored between Anchorage and Fairbanks. On April 7, coal trains started moving toward Palmer and Anchorage from the coal branch at Jonesville. On April 11, passenger service between Anchorage and Fairbanks was resumed.

In June, 1966, when the final job of reconstruction had been accomplished, an assistant secretary of the Interior presented an Award for Meritorious Service to the officials and employees of The Alaska Railroad for their work in creating a new railroad from the chaos caused by Alaska's great earthquake. A measure of how well the award was earned during those weeks is contained in a single statistic: In May, 1964, The Alaska Railroad hauled more freight than in May of the year before.

With freight trains once more rolling northward from Whittier, there was no pressure to reopen the railroad from Portage to Seward. For a while, as will be seen later in this chapter, the specter of possible abandonment of the Seward line walked again. By fall of 1964, however, temporary track and bridge repair was far enough along to permit the first post-earthquake freight train to reach Seward from Anchorage on September 13. It would be nearly two years before new dock, warehouse, and yard facilities would be completed in Seward under the supervision of the U.S. Corps of Engineers. During this period, the citizens of Seward were both helped and, to a degree, humiliated by the fact that locally consigned rail freight could reach them only via the port of Whittier.

## The Two-year Job of Reconstruction

In contrast to emergency repairs that started freight trains moving northward from Whittier in about three weeks, the total job of rehabilitation was not completed until June, 1966, more than two years later. The crash part of the program was fast, imaginative, and extremely expensive. The hard, slogging job of permanent rebuilding was slow, less dramatic, more efficient, and much more economical. With pressure off and funds limited, it again became important to make a dollar go as far as possible. There was a three-way division of labor. Railroad forces did most of the track and bridge work, private contractors built or rebuilt large buildings, including dock and warehouse facilities, and the U.S. Corps of Engineers, relying on private contractors, was responsible for supervising the building of an entirely new port at Seward.

If Alaska had to have an earthquake, it was much better that it happened in March than in August. In March there are five, perhaps six good construction months ahead before frost and snow interfere in October. By August, two-thirds of the work season is over. Thus in April and May, 1964, engineering plans and the recruitment of additional employees could be speeded up so that both blueprints and manpower would be ready for maximum use during the warm-weather months. By the middle of June, when the work season was well underway, The Alaska Railroad had increased its forces from about 1,000 to over 1,450.

Planning also included the highly essential question as to where the money would come from. Retained earnings had made the railroad independent of appropriated funds, so the first look was toward cash on hand in the U.S. Treasury. At the end of February, 1964, this amounted to nearly $10 million. Of this sum $1.25 million was obligated for current liabilities, $2 to $3 million was needed to finance current operations, another $2 million was required to pay for the completion of items in prior capital programs, and about $2.25 million was intended for a capital improvement program in fiscal year 1965. This left from $1.5 to $2.5 million immediately available to meet initial reconstruction expenditures. The Secretary of the Interior had made plans to advance emergency Interior funds, but the railroad's "cash in the bank" made emergency advances unnecessary.

By the end of April, the over-all bill for earthquake repairs was estimated by railroad officials at $26,995,000. This total was distributed as follows:

| | |
|---|---|
| Repair line from Healy to Matanuska | $ 500,000 |
| Repair line from Matanuska to Jonesville | 125,000 |
| Repair line from Anchorage to Matanuska | 1,760,000 |
| Anchorage buildings and yard | 2,050,000 |
| Repair line from Anchorage to Portage | 5,265,000 |
| Repair Whittier yard and marine facilities and line from Portage to Whittier | 3,140,000 |
| Repair line from Portage to Seward | 3,855,000 |
| Replace motive power and equipment | 2,500,000 |
| Replace dock and yard facilities at Seward | 7,800,000 |
| | $26,995,000 |

A more graphic picture of the financing required to solve the problems of an earthquake appears from the detail for one segment of the total program—repairs to track and roadway for the fifty miles along Cook Inlet and Turnagain Arm from Anchorage to Portage.

| | |
|---|---|
| Raise 35 miles of grade to provide higher tide levels, 1,300,000 cubic yards fill, load, haul, and dump (includes equipment purchase) @ $2.00 per cubic yd. | $2,625,000 |
| Blast, load, and haul armor rock for 30 miles of line, 375,000 cubic yds. @ $3.20 per cubic yd. (includes equipment purchase) | 1,200,000 |
| Raise, line, and reballast 35 miles of track @ $17,000 per mile | 595,000 |
| Repairs to 8 steel bridges | 46,600 |
| Major repairs to 10 trestles | 116,200 |
| Minor repairs to 3 trestles | 7,200 |
| Seven new tidal relief bridges | 210,000 |
| Restore grade at Potter Hill and other locations, 232,500 cubic yds. @ $2.00 per cubic yd. | 465,000 |
| | $5,265,000 |

It has been noted that the subtotals of The Alaska Railroad repair bill changed but that the grand total remained at about $27 million. These first detailed estimates took into account the possibility of alternatives. Thus, the Seward to Portage cost included $1 million for a line change where the railroad skirts the head of Turnagain Arm. The line change proved unnecessary. The Anchorage to Portage cost did not contemplate a line change at Potter Hill, where the track and roadway were destroyed by earthslides for nearly a mile and a half. Such a line change, had it been needed, would have been priced at $1 million more.

The weakest link in the chain of estimates involved the dock, warehouse, and yard facilities at Seward, where the U.S. Corps of Engineers was in charge. The final cost at Seward was about $3 million above the estimates. Savings and overestimates for other parts of the program, however, plus a special congressional appropriation, made up these extra costs.

The inclusion of the Seward line and Seward terminal facilities in the reconstruction program was accomplished only after a struggle that shook the citizens of Seward almost as much as the earthquake itself. Ever since the completion of the Whittier tunnels, in 1943, the possibility of the abandonment of the Seward line had been discussed. The planning and building of the Anchorage-Seward highway had, in fact, been predicated on the assumption that rail service to Seward was no longer necessary. The southern end of the railroad was saved by a military decision that the defense of Alaska required that both Whittier and Portage be maintained as ports. It is somewhat ironic that this decision was made just a few years before the Department of Defense reversed itself on the military necessity of two rail-water ports and abandoned Whittier in the interests of economy.

It will be remembered that Seward was born as a railroad town when private interests started the construction of the Alaska Central in 1903. Longshore operations and rail freight have been the principal components of the town's economic activity. Without this source of jobs and payroll, despite the oil strike on the Kenai Peninsula, Seward would probably sink into a long and discouraging decline. It was inevitable, however, that the cost of rehabilitating the Seward line and the port of Seward would spotlight once more comparisons between the twelve-mile water-level haul from Whittier to Portage and the sixty-four-mile haul from Seward to Portage, which included a climb over the Kenai Mountains and at least one 3 per cent grade against southbound traffic.

The problem of Seward's post-earthquake future was one of the first to be considered by the Federal Reconstruction and Development Planning Commission for Alaska. This agency was created by President Johnson on April 2, 1964, for the purpose of coordinating the federal contribution toward Alaska's reconstruction. On April 17, the undersecretary of the Department of the Interior wrote to the chairman of the commission to urge the case for Seward. He argued that no net savings would accrue as a result of the abandonment of Seward because of the high cost of providing alternative terminal facilities at either Whittier or Anchorage. The undersecretary did not limit himself to a comparison of net advantages. His letter stated:

> The decision on reconstruction is not restricted to economic considerations alone; in many respects humane and equitable factors assume even greater significance. *The essential fact is that failure to restore rail service means that Seward will disappear as an important factor in Alaskan life.* Absent rail facilities, employment opportunity for a major segment of wage earners, those engaged in longshore operations, will no longer exist. Seward also served as a major port of entry for Alaska's petroleum supply; without the Railroad, the major oil companies must relocate.

One wonders how the Alaska Reconstruction and Development Planning Commission would have decided hat it known that the oil companies in Seward and Whittier would subsequently decide to abandon both ports, except for local sales. These companies are operating in Anchorage today from tank farms on Cook Inlet below Government Hill of a size that would be impressive, even in New Jersey.

Fortunately for Seward, perhaps, the decision was made before the oil companies moved to Anchorage. Both officials of The Alaska Railroad and members of a transportation task force appointed by the commission had recommended in its favor. Railroad officials were particularly articulate in describing the human values at stake. They wrote that:

> While costs and economics have been central to the previous discussion, there is more to the story than a matter of bookkeeping. The Federal government has the power, through a decision as to rail location, to destroy the livelihood and the property values of most of the citizens of Seward and to downgrade transport service to the entire Kenai Peninsula. If this is done, no comparable human and property values will be added to Whittier. And no Alaskan transportation costs will be reduced in sufficient amount to make the sacrifice with respect to Seward and the Kenai Peninsula worthwhile.

With the evidence in and the discussion completed, the Federal Reconstruction and Development Planning Commission for Alaska approved the rebuilding of a rail-water terminal at Seward and recommended that the U.S. Corps of Engineers be responsible for the work. It remained for The Alaska Railroad and the Department of the Interior to find the $27 million needed to finance the total railroad rehabilitation program, including costs for a new Seward.

It was obvious from the first that the railroad could not be rebuilt without heavy reliance on Congressional appropriations. This was no more true of The Alaska Railroad than of other enterprises in Alaska, both public and private, that experienced severe earthquake losses. The total federal contribution to Alaska's restoration was, in fact, in excess of $400 million. For railroad reconstruction, the Department of the Interior and the Bureau of the Budget finally decided that a 1964 deficiency appropriation request for $25.2 million should be made to Congress. This, plus the $1,795,000 that the Bureau of the Budget required the reluctant railroad to contribute from its own accumulated cash, made up the $26,995,000 needed for the total program.

Originally the Department of the Interior had hoped that the $7.8 million cost of rebuilding the port of Seward would constitute Department of Defense appropriations for expenditure by the Corps of Engineers. Had Seward's port facilities belonged to the city of Seward instead of to the federal government, the Corps of Engineers would have had an obligation to restore the port facilities damaged by flood and fire from their own appropriated funds. But a federal property does not qualify for disaster relief funds, and the $7.8 million estimated cost for Seward had to be included in a Department of the Interior appropriation bill.

Of the $25.2 million that Interior requested, Congress granted only $20 million. This was not because the Senate and House conferees on the 1964 deficiency bill thought that $25.2 was excessive. Instead, knowing that the larger sum could not all be spent or obligated in fiscal 1964, the conferees decided to project $5.2 million of the request into the next fiscal year. It was stipulated that $7.8 million of the $20 million appropriated to Interior for the railroad be transferred to the Corps of Engineers and spent under Corps supervision.

During the summer of 1964, the Corps of Engineers completed its engineering designs for a new Seward port at the head of the bay nearly two and a half miles from where the old dock and warehouses had been. Bids were requested, and the Corps hoped, with an optimism that the realities did not justify, that the project would be completed in less than a year. When bids were opened in September, the price asked by the low bidder exceeded the $7.8 million available by $1.8 million. It was not possible to present the problem to Congress and obtain additional funds within the time available to let the contract. The general manager of the railroad then agreed to underwrite the additional cost with the possibility, already partly realized, that savings in other parts of the recovery program would protect the railroad from dipping further into accumulated funds.

There was more bad news to come. In February, 1965, the Corps of Engineers informed the general manager that unforeseen increases in dredging costs would necessitate another $1.3 million. The railroad's cash on hand could not support this additional charge. A request for a supplemental appropriation in this amount was presented to the Congress, and the amount was granted.

The railroad was still short by the $5.2 million that Congress had withheld in fiscal 1964 but intended to include in Interior's appropriation bill for fiscal 1965. To the consternation of the Alaska delegation in Congress and to the distress of Alaska Railroad officials, the Bureau of the Budget would not permit Interior to request more than $3 million. The House promptly voted the $3 million, but the Senate, more mindful of the obligations of the past, voted the original amount. The conferees from the House and Senate, perhaps from force of habit, halved the difference and the railroad got $4.1 million. Total Congressional appropriations for repairing the railroad's earthquake damage thus amounted to $25.4 million.

# XI

# The Track Ahead

If an institution can be said to have had a traumatic experience, the great Alaskan earthquake of 1964 was such an experience for The Alaska Railroad. During the previous three years, operations had been relatively smooth, except for wage and labor problems. Both gross and net income had slowly increased from the low point reached after oil for the military bases began flowing through the Haines-Fairbanks pipeline. For the first time, a man who had grown up with the railroad was in charge at Anchorage. The balance sheet showed current assets, somewhat less than they had been a few years before, but still in amounts and proportions that would have been highly pleasing to any railroad. Moderate programs for capital improvements, financed from the net income and depreciation charges of the previous year, were keeping plant and equipment in good condition. If Interior officials in Washington and Alaska Railroad officials in Anchorage viewed the problems of the railroad with a certain amount of complacency, there was considerable justification for such an attitude.

Then, in about three and a half minutes on March 27, 1964, a great deal of the railroad's future was altered. It is true that freight and passenger service were both restored in remarkably short time and true also that officials and employees deserved without question the citation awarded in June, 1966, for meritorious service in meeting the earthquake's challenge. The initial traffic response actually increased gross income as reconstruction materials and supplies were rushed to devastated areas. Nevertheless, trade channels were so changed and costs so increased that moderate profits turned, in fiscal year 1965, to a loss in excess of $1 million. Official exhilaration at the tremendous restoration job that had been done became resigned discouragement in recognition of continuing financial problems that lay ahead.

The decision of three oil companies to abandon their ravaged storage facilities at Seward and Whittier and build new tank farms at Anchorage cost the railroad $1 million in annual petroleum revenues. Seward tonnage, diverted to the port of Anchorage, brightened the prospects of the municipal dock but further decreased Alaska Railroad freight revenues. Cash assets were depleted because of the extent to which the railroad used its own funds to finance earthquake repairs. As a result of revenue decline and earthquake costs, the railroad's ability to finance needed capital improvements was obviously decreased. To complete the financial gloom, the discovery of enormous reserves of natural gas incidental to Alaska's oil strikes threatened disaster to coal mining in the Matanuska Valley and even brought apprehension to coal companies in the Healy River field.

Anyone familiar with the complexities of depreciation accounting knows that an enterprise with over $135 million in assets, at cost less depreciation and with charges to depreciation of over $2.25 million, can continue to operate for a reasonably long period with annual losses of $1 million per year. With deficits of this order, The Alaska Railroad will still be able to pay its bills and will have $1.25 million per year, admittedly an inadequate sum, for capital improvements. However, unless the loss trend is reversed, deferred maintenance will eventually pile up and the quality of plant and equipment will inevitably deteriorate.

Like private railroads, The Alaska Railroad can be rescued

from financial difficulties by traffic growth, by increased efficiency and decreased costs, or by selective or across-the-board increases in its tariff rates. Unlike most private railroads (although times seem to be changing in this respect), the government railroad can be rescued from annual deficits by Congressional appropriations to meet operating expenses. As noted earlier, The Alaska Railroad has had no such appropriations since 1939. The appropriations subcommittees, which annually review the railroad's finances, have insisted that it should live within its income for capital improvements as well as for operating expenses. The General Accounting Office has gone even further, arguing that the railroad should be required to earn interest on its capital investment. On the basis of this record, it seems unlikely that the federal officials who are responsible for the railroad's operating and financial results will look upon Congressional largesse as an appropriate solution.

The Alaska Railroad is no stranger to financial difficulties. It was saved from the constant deficits of the postconstruction period by a general manager at once capable and parsimonious. It achieved incredible profits during World War II. It emerged from a postwar slump through a $100 million rehabilitation program. It survived the Haines-Fairbanks pipeline by means of containerization and the piggybacking of truck trailers. A combination of good luck, good management, technological advance, and selective increases in tariff rates may again enable the railroad to earn modest profits.

## Profit and Loss

In the foregoing rather pessimistic summary of the railroad's financial outlook, the meaning of "net income" and "profit" has been defined more by implication than by direct statement. "Does the railroad make money?" is often put to its officials. The easy response, referred to more than once in these chapters, has been an emphasis on the railroad's many years of independence from congressional appropriations. Earthquake funds were not an exception, since disasters of such magnitude always result in temporary suspension of the rules.

The reference to freedom from dependence upon appropriations satisfies most inquirers unless they happen to be Alaskan motor carriers. Truck operators are quite correct in pushing the profit question further. It is certainly an accomplishment for a short-line, single-track railroad in sparsely settled Alaska to be free from the need of subsidy. But the accomplishment, however admirable, does not provide a precise explanation of what constitutes "net income" and "profit" for The Alaska Railroad.

One way to arrive at an answer to the question of whether The Alaska Railroad makes money would be to determine the difference between income received and accrued for a given fiscal year and out-of-pocket expenses paid or accrued for the same period. On this basis, the railroad has made a profit in every year, almost without exception, since 1939. Profit in this sense has been between $2 and $3 million in most years and, in some years of World War II, more than $5 million.

Out-of-pocket costs do not, however, include depreciation. Depreciation is an accounting expense, but it is different from an expense requiring a payment in cash or its equivalent because it represents the cost of capital currently used up in the operations that produce the income. Cash expenses deplete current assets, that is, they reduce the amount of available cash. Depreciation expenses deplete fixed assets but neither add to nor subtract from currently available cash. They may be regarded as adding to a cash reserve retained for the purpose of capital replacement, but they are usually not specifically earmarked for such a purpose.

The Alaska Railroad has included charges to depreciation among its expenses since 1947. Currently, these charges amount to about $2.25 million per year and are reflected in the following record of revenue tons carried, gross revenue (including nonoperating revenue), expenditures (including nonoperating expense), and net income for fiscal years 1953 through 1966:

| *Year* | *Revenue tons* | *Revenue* | *Expenditures* | *Net income* |
|---|---|---|---|---|
| 1953 | 1,591,558 | $20,825,999 | $20,616,465 | $ 209,534 |
| 1954 | 1,596,753 | 20,313,209 | 19,593,684 | 719,525 |
| 1955 | 1,479,298 | 18,425,440 | 15,808,162 | 2,617,278 |
| 1956 | 1,473,268 | 17,905,044 | 15,827,788 | 2,077,256 |
| 1957 | 1,443,164 | 15,224,909 | 15,044,031 | 180,878 |
| 1958 | 1,447,528 | 13,350,929 | 13,241,913 | 109,016 |
| 1959 | 1,271,049 | 13,482,546 | 13,138,745 | 343,801* |
| 1960 | 1,248,542 | 14,538,646 | 14,797,101 | −258,455 |
| 1961 | 1,313,359 | 14,302,280 | 14,503,805 | −201,525 |
| 1962 | 1,447,996 | 14,455,225 | 14,202,125 | 253,100 |
| 1963 | 1,449,133 | 14,893,839 | 14,608,433 | 285,406 |
| 1964 | 1,506,882 | 15,285,311 | 14,661,625 | 623,686 |
| 1965 | 1,384,511 | 13,658,196 | 14,823,024 | −1,164,828 |
| 1966 | 1,416,359 | 13,559,506 | 14,420,978 | −861,472 |

* An extraordinary depreciation adjustment strongly recommended by the Comptroller General reduced this amount to a net loss of $150,632.

Of the fourteen fiscal years shown in the tabulation, only five were years of deficits. Of these, two were post-earthquake years and showed the largest deficits. Yet even in 1965, when the deficit was over $1 million, depreciation charges were nearly twice as large as the deficit and the railroad added more than $1 million to its revolving fund to be used, if necessary, for capital expenditures. For all fourteen years, combined gross earnings were substantially in excess of expenses, including charges to depreciation.

Some, but not all, Alaskan truck operators point out that the expenditures of The Alaska Railroad are unfairly minimized because they include neither interest on investment nor amounts in lieu of taxes. Congress has never required that the railroad's capital investment derived from appropriations be returned to the U.S. Treasury either as interest or as principal, nor has it required the Interstate Commerce Commission to consider interest on investment in determining Alaska Railroad tariff rates. Furthermore, Congress has not permitted the railroad to make payments in lieu of taxes, even when the railroad was desirous of doing so. If interest, amortization, and in-lieu-of taxes are to be treated as part of the railroad's costs, then its operations have never been profitable except in the periods of extraordinarily high earnings during World War II. The smaller truck operators in Alaska strongly insist that this is patently unfair to them and that, unless the railroad can fix its tariff rates at amounts that will permit it to earn interest on investment and in-lieu-of taxes, it should retire from the field of transportation and allow the trucking industry to take its place.

There is some logic in this argument. When a truck operator risks his capital in an Alaskan venture and goes bankrupt because he cannot meet the tariffs of a railroad that pays neither taxes nor interest on investment, he has a grievance that does not permit a quick and easy answer. It is significant, however, that few truck operators will attempt to carry this argument to its logical conclusion. In the hearings on bills to regulate The Alaska Railroad, referred to in Chapter IX, motor-carrier witnesses tried to avoid direct comment on the railroad's freight tariffs. Some insisted that regulation of The Alaska Railroad would not result in increased rail and truck tariffs in Alaska, while a member of the Teamsters Union testified that he thought the result would be a decrease in freight rates. At later hearings, motor-carrier witnesses were more frank on this point and affirmed that tariff rates would be increased if the railroad were regulated on the same basis as motor carriers, and stated that it was necessary and desirable that this should happen. No motor carrier argued that the railroad should be shut down because a privately operated motor-truck industry was capable of replacing it. Yet the fact remains that the population along the Railbelt is too small to provide the volume of traffic necessary for the railroad to earn interest on investment and an amount in lieu of taxes. If Congress should make such a requirement (and Congress, having created the railroad, should determine its policies in this respect), this would be equivalent to telling the railroad to cease operations. There are undoubtedly motor carriers who wish that this would happen, just as there are residents of Seward who wish that the Whittier cutoff had never been built. Nevertheless, shutting down The Alaska Railroad to establish an appearance of fair competition with private motor carriers is simply not practical politics. Rebellion in the Alaska Railbelt against such a policy would make current complaints of Alaskan truckers low-keyed whispers in comparison.

## The Future of Alaska Railroad Bargaining

No one who believes in the benefits of collective bargaining in a government enterprise can be other than pessimistic about the future on The Alaska Railroad of negotiated labor agreements. The Alaska Railroad personnel system has been a kind of government-industry hybrid in which government represents a recessive characteristic. In the past twenty years, there has been so great an erosion of railroad rules and practices that government rules and practices have become dominant. The protections that time and geography once gave The Alaska Railroad personnel system are gone. The protection that Executive Order 10988 gave to more primitive unionism in other branches of the government can be of no help. The inflexible formulas of law and regulation have taken over and the possibilities of softening the harsher outlines of authoritarian personnel control with a government kind of industrial democracy has lessened with each passing day. If collective bargaining is to be preserved on The Alaska Railroad, the train and engine service brotherhoods, with help from the dispatchers and telegraphers unions, will be the means by which this will be accomplished.

Alaska Railroad officials would be the first to affirm that there are many areas of personnel activity in which federal standards should be dominant. Alaska Railroad employees share laws governing retirement, sick leave and annual leave, workmen's compensation, unemployment compensation, life insurance, and medical care with other federal workers. Their faith in bargaining has been shown even here by agreed-to additions, notably in medical care, to federal statutory privileges.

Alaska Railroad collective bargaining in past years has produced a personnel system that more closely mirrors the faults and virtues of personnel organization in private industry than any other government agency, not excluding the Bonneville Power Administration or the Tennessee Valley Authority. That system has been weakened for the railroad's operating employees but is still, for them at least, very much alive. For nonoperating employees, there are many signs that collective bargaining is dying. Some dues-paying union members among their number have already pronounced it dead, but it is not certain that this diagnosis will prove correct. If bargaining should die for these federal railroaders, there will be considerable doubt as to whether the immediate cause was suicide or involuntary manslaughter through a collision with veterans' preference and the regulations of the Civil Service System.

## The Railroad and the Military

The President's Executive Order 11107, of April 25, 1963, which gave partial regulatory jurisdiction over The Alaska Railroad to the Interstate Commerce Commission, authorized the Secretary of the Interior to separate from the railroad's civilian investment that part of its capital required by military rather than by civilian needs. (The authorization still holds for the Secretary of Transportation.) An obligation to aid the military is contained in the 1914 law that created the railroad. Much of the railroad's activity has had military flavor and military backing, and there have been times when over 50 per cent of its annual tonnage and revenue has been recorded in military bills of lading.

It has been assumed that a large share of the railroad's capital structure was created because of military needs and that separating this capital from the rest might provide a reasonable investment base on which to require the railroad to pay interest. The civilian economy, for example, does not need the two ports of Seward and Whittier. The capital costs of one port, therefore, could be charged to military requirements.

In spite of the authority given in the President's executive order, no attempt has been made to separate military from civilian capital in the railroad's fixed assets. It is even doubtful whether this could be done without a great many arbitrary judgments, for there is joint military-civilian use of almost all of the railroad's right of way and equipment. Except for the two ports mentioned, it is difficult to conclude that the railroad could have been built to cheaper standards if only civilian traffic needs had to be served. Even if the capital structure of the railroad were scaled down in this manner, there is little reason to believe that the railroad could earn reasonable interest on the lesser amount.

There were probably no economists who would have regarded The Alaska Railroad as a reasonable economic investment between 1915 and 1941, even had the thought occurred to them. Yet World War II would have justified the railroad's existence, even if it had shown deficits in each year before and after. It would also have been unreasonable to abandon the railroad after the war—most of its capital was not transferrable and, even on exclusively monetary grounds, it would have been better to use up the value remaining in existing capital than destroy most of it by liquidation.

It is popular in government circles to appraise potential investments in terms of various alternatives. If The Alaska

Railroad had not been built and if World War II had required the same military bases in Alaska as now exist, the bases would have been built along a highway. Consider what the costs would have been if the bases had been constructed along the Richardson highway and if all the materials and supplies had therefore to be transported within Alaska by truck, or by river routes during short Alaskan summers. A cost accounting comparison of such alternatives would now be impossible. A rough estimate might produce trucking or riverboat costs two or three times higher than the transportation costs of the same materials and supplies moved by The Alaska Railroad. It requires no close analysis to conclude that 4,000 tons of heavy supplies can be shipped within Alaska much more cheaply by four or five men and a freight train than by the drivers and equipment necessary to ship the 4,000 tons by truck. It is not impossible that, in the location of its Alaskan bases in the Railbelt, savings to the Army and Air Force were enough to amortize the entire investment in the railroad up to World War II.

## The Railroad and the Railbelt

Any successful railroad creates values that cannot be included in its balance sheet or in its profit and loss statements. The railroads that first spanned the United States could not have been justified on the basis of a "planning-programing-budgeting" analysis of alternatives. Yet by owning land along its right of way, a railroad could accrue handsome profits by holding this land for capital gains or by marketing its natural resources. Through federal land grants to the transcontinental railroads, a great deal of the value that the existence of a railroad brought to the land along its route found its way back to the railroad instead of to the pockets of pioneer settlers.

There were thoughts of this nature in the minds of some of the congressmen who authorized the building of a railroad in

Alaska in 1914. The United States owned almost every foot of the land through which the railroad would be built. Profits from the sale of lots and acreage would help make up for the money advanced from congressional appropriations. The theory was unassailable, but the timing of its implementation was poor. The Alaskan Engineering Commission did not wait for the increased value that the land would acquire after the railroad was built and in operation. Lots in Anchorage, Wasilla, Talkeetna, and Nenana were sold at the beginning of the construction period rather than after the railroad had become a going concern. Let us suppose that The Alaska Railroad had retained all the government-owned property in the city of Anchorage at the time plans for the railroad were being formulated. Its value in 1965, according to the Alaska Municipal League, was $280 million. Had the railroad been built in another part of Alaska it is inconceivable that Anchorage real estate values could have reached this total.

There is economic significance in the adoption, by that portion of the State of Alaska that stretches nearly 500 miles from Seward to Fairbanks, of The Alaska Railroad as the source of its geographical identification. Though inscribed on no map, the "Railbelt" is its name, and the "Railbelt" it is destined to be for many years to come. The city of Anchorage, with more than 100,000 people packed within the city limits or scattered over sprawling acres from Cook Inlet to the Chugach Mountains, rarely remembers its origin as a railroad construction camp. Its citizens court a more turbulent mistress, whose home is the cold and sometimes ice-flecked waters of a tide-tossed harbor. They are hopeful that the city's future lies with maritime rather than rail transportation, and they are indignant that Alaska railroaders do not relish being short-hauled by ships. The city fathers who are closely associated with the fortunes of the port of Anchorage are firmly convinced that Alaska Railroad employees feel about the winter ice of Cook Inlet as glaziers feel about hailstones—the more ice the more business.

Time and economics, with an admixture of politics, will determine the relationship between marine-minded Anchorage and the government railroad. With its demonstration that winter port operations are possible, Anchorage has already achieved some status as a harbor city. With that status will come a greater sense of security on the part of city fathers and port officials and a decline in rivalry between the two kinds of government agencies. The city may no longer fear the railroad, and railroaders may come to accept Anchorage as a year-round port.

Seward and Fairbanks, with less suspicion of the railroad, show closer allegiance to it. Although Seward has more than once been condemned as obsolete by the railroad, it has also been saved more than once by the same railroad. When its citizens finally come to believe that abandonment of Seward is no longer contained in railroad policy, the port of Whittier may seem less of a threat. Oil, tourism, and agriculture may yet give Seward a more balanced economic base and modify its heavy dependence on maritime and railroad operations.

Fairbanks, at the northern end of the Railbelt, and with interests nearly as broad as those of Anchorage, is in some ways more of a railroad town than the headquarters city. It was a thriving, lusty, gold-rush settlement when Anchorage was scarcely a dot in the wilderness. While Anchorage has outdistanced Fairbanks in wealth and population, Fairbanks has become the guardian of the last frontier in a way that Anchorage can never be again. In Fairbanks, the railroad is one of the family rather than a jealous rival for competitive position. Even so, there is occasional indignation that railroad officials do not pay the city the attention it deserves. Fairbanks' time may come when its picture-book railroad yard handles terminal operations (for which it was in part built) for an international railroad across Yukon Territory and British Columbia to a connection with railroads in the other states.

Palmer and the Matanuska Valley are not so dependent on the railroad as Seward and the Kenai Peninsula. Yet Palmer and the farmers of the valley need the railroad and the business and industrial enterprises they hope it will foster. As declining markets threaten Matanuska coal mines with what could be permanent closure, Palmer hopes that the railroad will help contrive the miracle that will produce (if the coal mines close) an acceptable industrial substitute. Whittier, on the other hand, is a place where only a handful of railroad employees work and where none would choose to live.

Of the 275,000 persons who live in Alaska today, nearly two-thirds live in the towns and cities of the Railbelt. During the railroad's construction days in the early 1920's, this was far from the case. Population grew slowly in the Railbelt until World War II, and then quickly outdistanced the population growth of the rest of Alaska. Since the end of the war, Alaska's population has more than doubled, and the number of people in the Railbelt has increased more than 600 per cent. The number of people within the city limits of Fairbanks was 4 times as large in 1960 as in 1940, while in Anchorage the number increased 10 times. In contrast, the population of southeastern Alaska (the Panhandle) was 35 per cent of Alaska's total population in 1940 but only 16 per cent in 1960.

An impressive demonstration of the importance of the railroad to population growth can be seen in a comparison of the Railbelt with the area of the Richardson highway from Valdez to Fairbanks. The highway is far older than the railroad. It began as a military trail in about 1902 and was gradually improved until black-topping and its ocean terminal at Valdez made it the most important truck route in Alaska. The highway, cutting through the Alaska Range, is not kept open in winter, but a longer route, via Tok Junction and the Alaska Highway, allowed Valdez-Fairbanks truck transportation to continue in the wintertime.

The Richardson area might have furnished a railroad right

of way from a warm-water southwestern Alaska port—either Valdez or Cordova—to Fairbanks. It would have been a shorter route than the one finally chosen and there was much to be said for its selection. Building from Cordova would have permitted the use of a large section of the Copper River and Northwestern Railroad, then in operation.

But President Wilson chose the Seward route, partly in reaction against the Guggenheims, who owned the Copper River and Northwestern and the fabulous copper mines that had brought it into being. Today the contrast in business activity and population between the route of The Alaska Railroad and that of the Richardson highway could hardly be greater. The Railbelt is a region of bustling business activity, with major population concentrations at Anchorage and Fairbanks and minor ones at Seward, Palmer, Wasilla, Talkeetna, McKinley Park, and Healy. The Richardson highway terminates in Fairbanks, but, except for Valdez, Glennallen, and Fort Greely, there has been little development along its length. With population, as sometimes with money, growth feeds on itself. As the Railbelt grew, some Richardson highway points declined. Even before the earthquake destroyed it, Valdez was a shrinking port. Trucking not only failed to develop towns along the Richardson highway, it finally failed Valdez when a good deal of its trucking activities were moved to Seward.

The only significant difference between the relatively populous Railbelt and the sparsely settled route of the Richardson highway is the existence of a railroad in the one and not in the other. There are no major contrasts in natural resources in the two areas. Except for coal, which can be reached from either area, and oil, which creates wealth rather than population, neither the Railbelt nor the Richardson is outstanding for its resources. Had military posts in addition to Fort Greely been placed along the highway instead of along the railroad, they would have brought to the highway a measure of the increased business activity that they brought to the Railbelt.

The military chose the Railbelt for five of its six largest

bases in Alaska precisely to take advantage of rail facilities. If the railroad had been built from Valdez or Cordova to Fairbanks, it follows that Valdez or Cordova might have become the largest city in Alaska. The principal military bases would still have been located along a railroad, and the area of that railroad would have grown and prospered as the Railbelt has grown and prospered. In that event, Anchorage and Seward might have been little more than villages beside small canneries. The oil strike on the Kenai Peninsula would have made Seward the larger of the two, but petroleum tends to produce wealth for its owners, often absentee owners, more than it fosters population growth where the wells are drilled. The alternate railbelt would have included two-thirds of Alaska's population, but it would have been located north from Valdez or Cordova rather than north from Seward.

The selection of the Seward-Anchorage-Fairbanks route resulted from a combination of planning and a great deal of historical accident. It was no accident, however, that has made The Alaska Railroad the most important economic factor in the development of business enterprise along its right of way.

## A Hope in Copper?

The Alaska Railroad has several times considered expansion, but without real expectation that it would take place. With the Kenai oil strike, there had been talk of a possible extension to Homer, on the southwest coast of the peninsula at Kachemak Bay. Should a dam at Rampart ever find favor with Congress, a rail link between Fairbanks and the main construction site would be necessary. Had car-ferries and train-ships been unable at reasonable cost to bring carloads of freight from the other states to Alaska, the long-time dream of a rail connection across Canada to The Alaska Railroad might have become reality. All these are "might have beens" and have not only failed to result in additional trackage in Alaska but are unlikely to do so in the future.

More recently, a copper find at Bornite, about 400 miles northwest of Fairbanks, has created greater interest in the possible expansion of the railroad than any of the previous proposals. The ore at Bornite is by no means as rich as the bonanza discovery that resulted in the building of the Copper River and Northwestern Railroad. It is rich enough, however, to justify its mining, and apparently there are enormous quantities of it. Several million dollars of private capital have already been spent in proving out the Bornite ore, and there are commitments to spend several million more. Alaska Railroad officials have examined a possible rail route and have found no unusual difficulties. The proposed railroad would not only tap the new copper find, it would also reach Yukon River points that are now dependent on riverboat transportation (and that for only four months of the year) and would open up to more intensive exploration a vast new area of subarctic Alaska.

It may be several years before the economic feasibility of the Bornite extension can be convincingly demonstrated. If both the ore and the proposed rail extension continue to show promise, The Alaska Railroad may be on the threshold of its first major expansion since the golden spike was driven in 1923.

# APPENDIX I

# Public Law No. 69—63d Congress

(S. 48)

An Act to authorize the President of the United States to locate, construct, and operate railroads in the Territory of Alaska, and for other purposes.

*Be it enacted by the Senate and House of Representatives of the United States of America in Congress assembled,* That the President of the United States is hereby empowered, authorized, and directed to adopt and use a name by which to designate the railroad or railroads and properties to be located, owned, acquired, or operated under the authority of this Act; to employ such officers, agents, or agencies, in his discretion, as may be necessary to enable him to carry out the purposes of this Act; to authorize and require such officers, agents, or agencies to perform any or all of the duties imposed upon him by the terms of this Act; to detail and require any officer or officers in the Engineer Corps in the Army or Navy to perform service under this Act; to fix the compensation of all officers, agents, or employees appointed or designated by him; to designate and cause to be located a route or routes for a line or lines of railroad in the Territory of Alaska not to exceed in the aggregate one thousand miles, to be so located as to connect one or more of the open Pacific Ocean harbors on the southern coast of Alaska with the navigable waters in the interior of Alaska, and with a coal field or fields so as best to aid in the development of the agricultural and mineral or other resources of Alaska, and the settlement of the public lands therein, and so as to provide transportation of coal for the Army and Navy, transportation of troops, arms, munitions of war, the mails, and for other governmental and public uses, and for the transportation of passengers and property; to construct and build a railroad or railroads along such route or routes as he may so designate and locate, with the necessary branch lines, feeders, sidings, switches, and spurs; to purchase or otherwise acquire all real and personal property necessary to carry out the purposes of this Act; to exercise the power of eminent domain in acquiring property for such use, which use is hereby declared to be a public use, by condemnation in the courts of Alaska in accordance with the laws now or hereafter in force there; to acquire rights of way, terminal grounds, and all other rights; to purchase or otherwise acquire all necessary equipment for the construction and operation of such railroad or railroads; to build or otherwise acquire docks, wharves, terminal facilities, and all structures needed for the equipment and operation of such railroad or railroads; to fix, change, or modify rates for the transportation of passengers and property, which rates shall be equal and uniform, but no free transportation or passes shall be permitted except that the provisions of the interstate commerce laws relating to the transportation of employees and their families shall be in force as to the lines constructed under this Act; to receive compensation for the transportation of passengers and property, and to perform generally all the usual duties of a common carrier by railroad; to make and establish rules and regulations for the control and operation of said railroad or railroads, or any portion thereof, including telegraph and telephone lines, after completion under such terms as he may deem proper, but no lease shall be for a longer period than twenty years, or in the event of failure to lease, to operate the same until the further action of Congress: *Provided,* That if said railroad or railroads, including telegraph and telephone lines, are leased under the authority herein given, then and in that event they shall be operated under the jurisdiction and control of the provisions of the interstate commerce laws; to purchase, condemn, or otherwise acquire upon such terms as he may deem proper any other line or lines of railroad in Alaska which may be necessary to complete the construction of the line or lines of railroad designated or located by him: *Provided,* That the price to be paid in case of purchase shall in no case exceed the actual physical value of the railroad; to make contracts or agreements with any railroad or steamship company or vessel owner for joint transportation of passengers or property over the road or roads herein provided for, and such railroad or steamship line or by such vessel, and to make such other contracts as may be necessary to carry out any of the purposes of this Act; to utilize in carrying on the work herein provided for any and all machinery, equipment, instruments, material, and other property of any sort whatsoever used or acquired in connection with the construction of the Panama Canal, so far and as rapidly as the same is no longer needed at Panama, and the Isthmian Canal Commission is hereby authorized to deliver said property to such officers or persons as the President may designate, and to take credit therefor at such percentage of its original cost as the President may approve, but this amount shall not be charged against the fund provided for in this Act.

The authority herein granted shall include the power to construct, maintain, and operate telegraph and telephone lines so far as they may be necessary or convenient in the construction and operation of the railroad or railroads as herein authorized and they shall perform generally all the usual duties of telegraph and telephone lines for hire.

That it is the intent and purpose of Congress through this Act to authorize and empower the President of the United States, and he is hereby fully authorized and empowered, through such officers, agents, or agencies as he may appoint or employ, to do all necessary acts and things in addition to those specially authorized in this Act to enable him to accomplish the purposes and objects of this Act.

The President is hereby authorized to withdraw, locate, and

dispose of, under such rules and regulations as he may prescribe, such area or areas of the public domain along the line or lines of such proposed railroad or railroads for town-site purposes as he may from time to time designate.

Terminal and station grounds and rights of way through the lands of the United States in the Territory of Alaska are hereby granted for the construction of railroads, telegraph and telephone lines authorized by this Act, and in all patents for lands hereafter taken up, entered, or located in the Territory of Alaska there shall be expressed that there is reserved to the United States a right of way for the construction of railroads, telegraph and telephone lines to the extent of one hundred feet on either side of the center line of any such road and twenty-five feet on either side of the center line of any such telegraph or telephone lines, and the President may, in such manner as he deems advisable, make reservation of such lands as are or may be useful for furnishing materials for construction and for stations, terminals, docks, and for such other purposes in connection with the construction and operation of such railroad lines as he may deem necessary and desirable.

Section 2. That the cost of the work authorized by this Act shall not exceed $35,000,000, and in executing the authority granted by this Act the President shall not expend nor obligate the United States to expend more than the said sum; and there is hereby appropriated, out of any money in the Treasury not otherwise appropriated, the sum of $1,000,000 to be used for carrying out the provisions of this Act, to continue available until expended.

Section 3. That all moneys derived from the lease, sale, or disposal of any of the public lands, including townsites, in Alaska, or the coal or mineral therein contained, or the timber thereon, and the earnings of said railroad or railroads, together with the earning of the telegraph and telephone lines constructed under this Act, above maintenance charges and operating expenses, shall be paid into the Treasury of the United States as other miscellaneous receipts are paid, and a separate account thereof shall be kept and annually reported to Congress.

Section 4. That the officers, agents, or agencies placed in charge of the work by the President shall make to the President annually, and at such other periods as may be required by the President or by either House of Congress, full and complete reports of all their acts and doings and of all moneys received and expended in the construction of said work and in the operation of said work or works and in the performance of their duties in connection therewith. The annual reports herein provided for shall be by the President transmitted to Congress.

*Approved March 12, 1914*

# Public Law No. 232—84th Congress

(H.R. 3338)

---

An Act to amend section 1 of the Act of March 12, 1914.

*Be it enacted by the Senate and House of Representatives of the United States of America in Congress assembled,* That the first sentence of section 1 of the Act of March 12, 1914 (38 Stat. 305), as amended (48 U.S.C., sec. 301), is amended by striking out "but no lease shall be for a longer period than twenty years," and inserting in lieu thereof "but no lease of such railroad or railroads shall be for a longer period than twenty years and no other lease authorized in this Act shall be for a longer period than fifty-five years."

*Approved August 4, 1955*

# APPENDIX II

# Executive Order No. 1

# Alaska Railroad

By authority of an act entitled "An Act to authorize the President of the United States to locate, consruct, and operate railroads in the Territory of Alaska and for other purposes," I do now designate and cause to be located the following routes for lines of railroad in the Territory of Alaska:

For a main line of railroad—

Commencing at the town of Seward on the westerly shore of Resurrection Bay, Alaska: thence following along said westerly shore in a northerly direction to the head of said bay: thence following up the drainage of Salmon Creek to a summit between said drainage and the drainage of Snow River: thence following the drainage of Snow River to Kenai Lake: thence continuing northerly along the easterly shore of Kenai Lake, along Falls Creek, along the shores of Lower and Upper Trail Lake, and up Trail Creek to a summit in the Kenai Mountains near mile 45 from Seward: thence descending along the drainage of Placer River to the head of Turnagain Arm of Cook Inlet: thence following the northeasterly shore of said Turnagain Arm and crossing Portage Creek and Twenty Mile River to the mouth of Kern Creek near mile 71 from Seward: thence in a northwesterly direction along the shore of Turnagain Arm to near the mouth of Big Rabbit Creek: thence leaving Turnagain Arm and running northerly to a summit in section 26, Township 14 North, Range 3 West, Seward Meridian: thence running northeasterly to near the head of Knik Arm of Cook Inlet: thence running northerly across the flats at the head of said Arm and crossing Knik and Matanuska Rivers, to a point about two miles north of the Matanuska River: thence running in a westerly and northwesterly direction, crossing the little Susitna River and following along the south-westerly slopes of Bald Mountain to Willow Creek, a tributary of the Susitna River: thence in a northerly direction following the drainage of the Susitna and Chulitna Rivers to Broad Pass situated in the main Alaska Range of mountains: thence crossing Broad Pass and entering the drainage of the Nenana River: thence continuing northward following the drainage of the Nenana River to the Tanana River, the total distance from Seward being 416 miles, more or less.

Also starting from a point on the above described line, situated two miles more or less northerly from where said line crosses the Matanuska River, and thence running in an easterly direction following the drainage of said Matanuska River and its tributaries, a distance of thirty-eight miles more or less to the Matanuska Coal Fields.

And, in order to complete the construction of the lines so designated and located, I direct the Secretary of the Interior to purchase and acquire the line of railroad known as the Alaska Northern Railway and, for that purpose, to execute and enter into an agreement substantially in the form hereto annexed, which calls for the payment of a purchase price therefor not in excess of the physical value of said railway.

Woodrow Wilson

*The White House*
*April 10, 1915*

# Executive Order No. 3
# Alaska Railroad

TO THE SECRETARY OF THE INTERIOR:

By virtue of the authority vested in me by the Act of Congress approved March 12, 1914, entitled "An Act to authorize the President of the United States to locate, construct, and operate railroads in the Territory of Alaska, and for other purposes," I hereby direct that all work of the Alaskan Engineering Commission under all orders made by me and the carrying out of all contracts entered into by my direction under authority of said act, be performed under the supervision and control of the Department of the Interior, as directed by the head thereof, in all respects and to all intents and purposes the same as if said work had been placed by law under the jurisdiction and control of the Department of the Interior.

I also direct that contracts for the purchase of supplies by the Alaskan Engineering Commission shall be made after advertisement in such manner as shall best serve the interests of the Government, in the district of Alaska or otherwise, where such supplies may, in the judgment of the Chairman of the Commission, best be purchased and shall be awarded to the lowest responsible bidder.

Except so far as they are inconsistent with and changed by this Order, I direct that the Executive Order of April 10, 1915, continue in force.

WOODROW WILSON

*The White House*
*April 30, 1915*

# Executive Order No. 3861

# Alaska Railroad

By virtue of the authority vested in me by the Act of Congress approved March 12, 1914, entitled: "An Act to authorize the President of the United States to locate, construct, and operate railroads in the Territory of Alaska, and for other purposes,"

I hereby authorize and direct the Secretary of the Interior to operate the railroad or railroads, branch lines, feeders and telegraph and telephone lines incident thereto, constructed or acquired under the Act of March 12, 1914, or acts supplemental thereto, in all respects and to all intents and purposes, the same as if the operation thereof had been placed by law under the jurisdiction of the Secretary of the Interior.

WARREN G. HARDING

*The White House*
*June 8, 1923*

# Executive Order No. 11107
# Administration of Alaska Railroads

By virtue of the authority vested in me by the Act of March 12, 1914, entitled "An Act to authorize the President of the United States to locate, construct, and operate railroads in the Territory of Alaska, and for other purposes," 38 Stat. 305, as amended (hereinafter referred to as the Alaska Railroad Act), it is ordered as follows:

Section 1. *General responsibility for railroad.* The Secretary of the Interior is authorized to operate the railroad or railroads, branch lines, feeders and telegraph and telephone lines incident thereto, constructed or acquired under the Act of March 12, 1914, or Acts supplemental thereto, in all respects and to all intents and purposes as if the operation thereof had been placed by law under the jurisdiction of the Secretary of the Interior, except that the authority of the Secretary under this order "to fix, change, or modify rates for the transportation of passengers and property" shall be subject to the authority of the Interstate Commerce Commission under Section 3 of this order.

Section 2. *Rates; Secretary of the Interior.* In connection with carrying out the authority under the Alaska Railroad Act "to fix, change, or modify rates for the transportation of passengers and property," the Secretary of the Interior from time to time:

(a) Shall allocate to the national public purposes which to a substantial extent prompted the construction, expansion, maintenance, and improvement of the railroad, the proper portion of the capital investment of the railroad.

(b) Shall fix, change, or modify the rates with due regard for the actions of the Interstate Commerce Commission authorized under this order.

(c) Shall post the rates for public inspection and file them with the Interstate Commerce Commission.

Section 3. *Rates; Interstate Commerce Commission.* (a) In respect of rates filed with the Interstate Commerce Commission pursuant to the provisions of this order, the Commission may act, to the extent practicable, and subject to the limitations provided in subsection (b) of this section, in the same manner as though the railroad were subject to Sections 1(1)(a), 1(4), 1(5), 1(5½), 1(6), 6(3), 6(6), 6(9), 13(1), 13(2) (to the extent that it relates to action by the Interstate Commerce Commission on its own motion), 15 (except 15(12) and 15(14)), 15a, 202(c) (1), and 202(c)(2) of the Interstate Commerce Act, as amended.

(b) When determining the justness and reasonableness of rates or charges maintained, or from time to time proposed to be maintained by the railroad, the Interstate Commerce Commission shall exclude for valuation and cost finding purposes the portion of capital investment allocated to national public purposes by the Secretary of the Interior under Section 2(a) hereof, and such rates and charges shall not be deemed to be unjust or unreasonable by reason of failure to yield sufficient revenues to cover any amounts for taxes not actually required by law to be paid or provide a return on capital investment.

Section 4. *Transitional provisions.* (a) The issuance of this order shall not affect any action heretofore taken by the Secretary of the Interior or his representative until such action has been modified or revoked in accordance with the provisions of this order.

(b) As promptly after the date of this order as may be convenient, the Secretary of the Interior shall post for public inspection and file with the Interstate Commerce Commission rates as referred to in Section 2(c) of this order. The rates posted and filed under this subsection may be the rates in force on the date of this order, with or without subsequent changes or modifications, or new rates.

This order supersedes Executive Order No. 3861 of June 8, 1923, and shall be codified for inclusion in the Code of Federal Regulations.

JOHN F. KENNEDY

*The White House*
*April 25, 1963*

# APPENDIX III

## Statement of Assets and Liabilities of The Alaska Railroad

June 30, 1966

ASSETS

| | | |
|---|---|---|
| Current assets | | |
| Cash | $ 7,281,762.89 | |
| Accounts receivable | 3,033,651.75 | |
| Inventories of supplies and materials | 3,743,169.79 | $ 14,058,584.43 |
| Fixed assets | | |
| Road property | $ 98,315,998.64 | |
| Equipment | 30,269,989.55 | |
| Non operating property | 3,604,428.96 | |
| | 132,190,417.15 | |
| Less: Provision for depreciation | 27,518,911.25 | |
| | 104,671,505.90 | |
| Additions and betterments in progress | 1,016,077.80 | |
| Construction work in progress (Seward dock) | 10,129,886.47 | 115,817,470.17 |
| Other assets and undistributed charges | | 10,964,163.84 |
| Total assets | | $140,840,218.44 |

LIABILITIES

| | | |
|---|---|---|
| Current liabilities | | |
| Accounts payable | $ 2,647,246.72 | |
| Accrued payrolls payable | 351,572.76 | $ 2,998,819.48 |
| Other liabilities | | 778,110.48 |
| Total liabilities | | 3,776,929.96 |
| Proprietary interest of the U.S. Government | | |
| Net investment | | 139,220,907.11 |
| Retained earnings: | | |
| Retained earnings July 1, 1964 to June 30, 1965 | − 936,648.21 | |
| Current year operating results | −1,220,970.42 | −2,157,618.63 |
| Total proprietary interest of the U.S. Government | | 137,063,288.48 |
| Total liabilities and capital | | $140,840,218.44 |

# Bibliography

Most of the material for this book has come from (1) unpublished letters, memoranda, and reports in the files of The Alaska Railroad, the departments of the Interior and Transportation, and the National Archives, (2) recollections of Alaska Railroad officials, and (3) direct observations by the author. Information about The Alaska Railroad is available in any city where libraries contain government publications and periodical literature. Such libraries will contain Department of Interior and Department of Transportation appropriations hearings and reports, annual reports of the governors of Alaska, annual reports of the secretaries of Interior and Transportation, *Congressional Record* transcripts of debates and committee hearings on legislation relating to the railroad, and reports of the General Accounting Office and the Interstate Commerce Commission. Special mention should be made of the Association of American Railroads library in Washington, D.C., which has more printed material on The Alaska Railroad than either the Interior or Transportation Department.

## Background Books


BEACH, REX. *The Iron Trail.* New York: Harper & Bros., 1913. A romantic novel based on the building of the Copper River and Northwestern Railroad.

BERNHARDT, JOSHUA. *The Alaskan Engineering Commission.* New York: D. Appleton and Co., 1922. Contains an excellent bibliography.

ENGLE, ELOISE. *Earthquake.* New York: John Day Co., 1966. Journalistic account of the 1964 Alaska earthquake.

GRUENING, ERNEST. *The State of Alaska.* New York: Random House,

1954. The best book on government problems of Alaska prior to statehood.

*Guide to Alaska and Yukon.* New York: Rand McNally, 1922. Conveys the flavor of Alaska at the time the "government railroad" was under construction.

HANSON, WALLACE R., *et al. The Alaska Earthquake, March 27, 1964.* Geological Survey Professional Paper 541, U.S. Department of the Interior. Washington, D.C.: U.S. Government Printing Office, 1966. Best account of the earthquake and reconstruction period. Illustrated.

HART, WILSON R. *Collective Bargaining in the Federal Civil Service.* New York: Harper & Bros., 1961. A perceptive account of organized labor in federal agencies.

JOHNSON, HUGH A., and JORGENSON, HAROLD T. *The Land Resources of Alaska.* Printed for the University of Alaska by University Publishers, 1963. Particularly good for its restraint in describing the natural resources of Alaska. Contains a capsule history.

LAWING, NELLIE NEAL. *Alaska Nellie.* Seattle: Chieftan Press, 1940. A colorful autobiography by one of Alaska's most unforgettable characters.

PRINCE, BERNADINE. *The Alaska Railroad.* 2 vols. Anchorage: Ken Wray's Print Shop, 1964. Pictorial history,

## REPORTS, PAMPHLETS, AND PERIODICALS

*Admitting the Vessel "City of New Orleans" to American Registry.* Hearings before the Subcommittee on Merchant Marine and Fisheries of the Senate Committee on Commerce (88th Cong., 1st sess.; S.534). Washington, D.C.: U.S. Government Printing Office, 1963.

*Alaska and West Coast Transportation Problems.* Hearings before the Senate Committee on Interstate and Foreign Commerce (84th Cong., 2d sess., October, 1955). Washington, D.C.: U.S. Government Printing Office, 1956.

*The Alaska Earthquake.* Office of Emergency Planning. Washington, D.C.: Defense Printing Service, 1964.

*Alaskan and Hawaiian Transportation.* Joint hearings before the Senate and House committees on Interstate and Foreign Commerce (86th Cong., 1st sess., October-November, 1959). Washington, D.C.: U.S. Government Printing Office, 1961.

*The Alaskan Earthquake.* Department of Defense. Washington, D.C.: U.S. Government Printing Office, 1964.

*Alaskan Engineering Commission.* Reports of the Alaskan Engineering Commission for the period from March 12, 1914, to December 31, 1915 (64th Cong., 1st sess., H.R. Doc. 610, Part 2). U.S. Government Printing Office, 1916.

*The Alaska Railroad Railbelt Reporter,* published bimonthly by The Alaska Railroad.

*The Alaska Railroad Record,* a weekly newspaper published as the official record of the Alaskan Engineering Commission from November 14, 1916, to July 1, 1920.

*The Alaska Railway Bill.* Speech by Hon. James Wickersham of Alaska in the House of Representatives, January 14 and 28, 1914. Reprinted from the *Congressional Record.* Washington, D.C.: U.S. Government Printing Office, 1914.

*Alaska's 1957 Oil Discovery and Its Strategic Importance.* Anchorage Chamber of Commerce, 1957.

*Annual Report of the Alaskan Engineering Commission,* for the year ended December 31, 1916 (Senate Document No. 741). U.S. Government Printing Office, 1917.

*Applying the Provisions of the Interstate Commerce Act, as Amended, to The Alaska Railroad* (86th Cong., 1st sess.; Senate Report No. 435, February 25, 1959). Washington, D.C.: U.S. Government Printing Office, 1959.

*Assistance and Recovery, Alaska, 1964.* U.S. Coast and Geodetic Survey, U.S. Department of Commerce. Washington, D.C.: U.S. Government Printing Office, 1965.

BEYER, OTTO S., and FITCH, EDWIN M. *A Survey of the Wage and Salary Situation on The Alaska Railroad, 1937–1947.* Anchorage, 1947. Alaska Railroad files.

*Collective Bargaining Agreements in the Federal Service.* Bureau of Labor Statistics Bulletin No. 1451, U.S. Department of Labor. Washington, D.C.: U.S. Government Printing Office, 1965.

*Construction of Railroads in Alaska.* Hearings before the Senate Committee on Territories on S.48 and S.133. Washington, D.C.: U.S. Government Printing Office, 1913.

"Earthquake in Alaska," *Life,* April 10, 1964, pp. 26–38.

Federal Maritime Commission. *No. 571 Alaskan Rates, No. 572 Alaska Rate Investigation No. 2, and No. 611 Surcharge—Alaska Trade,* decided March 31, 1942. Washington, D.C.: U.S. Government Printing Office, 1942.

FITCH, EDWIN M. "The Government and Bargaining on The Alaska Railroad," *Monthly Labor Review.* Department of Labor, May, 1961.

———, and ANDERSON, R. H. "Containerized Freight on The Alaska Railroad," *National Defense Transportation Journal* (Washington, D.C.), September-October, 1960.

———, SHELMERDINE, PAUL, and JONES, HARRY F. *Wage Rates and Wage Policies of The Alaska Railroad, 1948–1955.* Alaska Railroad manuscript. Anchorage, 1956.

FORD, NANCY. "The Alaska Railroad," *Modern Railroads* (Chicago), XX (December, 1965), 72–86.

GRANTZ, ARTHUR, PLAFKER, GEORGE, and KACHADOORIAN, REUBEN. *Alaska's Good Friday Earthquake, March 27, 1964*. Geological Survey, U.S. Department of the Interior. Washington, D.C., 1964.

HANSEN, WALLACE R. *The Alaska Earthquake, March 27, 1964*. Effects on Communities, Anchorage. Geological Survey, U.S. Department of the Interior. Washington, D.C.: U.S. Government Printing Office, 1965.

*Impact of Earthquake of March 27, 1964*. Prepared for Federal Reconstruction and Development Planning Commission by the Office of Emergency Planning. Washington, D.C., 1964.

KACHADOORIAN, REUBEN. *The Alaska Earthquake, March 27, 1964*. Effects on Communities, Whittier. Geological Survey, U.S. Department of the Interior. Washington, D.C.: U.S. Government Printing Office, 1965.

*Mid-Century Alaska*. Office of Territories, U.S. Department of the Interior. Washington, D.C.: U.S. Government Printing Office, 1958.

MORGAN, DAVID P. "Cold War Railroading." *Trains,* May, 1963.

———. "Uncle Sam's Railroad Experiment," *Trains,* April, 1963.

*Natural Resources of Alaska*. U.S. Department of the Interior. Washington, D.C.: U.S. Government Printing Office, 1966.

*The Official Guide of the Railways and Steam Navigation Lines of the United States, Puerto Rico, Canada, Mexico and Cuba,* published monthly by National Railway Publication Co., New York.

*Personnel Policies of The Alaska Railroad*. Hearings before the House Committee on Post Office and Civil Service (88th Cong., 1st sess.; S.622, August 8, 1963). Washington, D.C.: U.S. Government Printing Office, 1963.

*Personnel Policies of The Alaska Railroad*. Hearings before the Subcommittee on Civil Service of the Senate Committee on Post Office and Civil Service (87th Cong., 2d sess.; S.2593, June 21, 1962). Washington, D.C.: U.S. Government Printing Office, 1962.

*Railroad Rates on Alaska Bound Freight*. Hearings before the Surface Transportation Subcommittee of the Senate Committee on Commerce (87th Cong., 2d sess.; S.1723). Washington, D.C.: U.S. Government Printing Office, 1962.

*Railroads in Alaska*. Hearings before the House Committee on the Territories. Washington, D.C.: U.S. Government Printing Office, 1906.

*Railway Routes in Alaska*. Message from the President transmitting report of The Alaska Railroad Commission (62d Cong., 3d sess.; H.R. Doc. 1346). Washington, D.C.: U.S. Government Printing Office, 1913. The most important document of the preconstruction days of the railroad.

*Regulation of Alaska Railroad* (86th Cong., 2d sess.; H.R. Report No.

1913, June 17, 1960). Washington, D.C.: U.S. Government Printing Office, 1960.

*Report of the Committee Appointed by the Secretary of the Interior to Review the Rates and Policies of The Alaska Railroad.* U.S. Department of the Interior, 1947. This is the most important and far-reaching investigation of The Alaska Railroad ever made. Committee members were Benjamin W. Thoron, chairman, George Sundborg, and Edward Margolin.

*Response to Disaster.* Federal Reconstruction and Development Planning Commission for Alaska. Washington, D.C.: U.S. Government Printing Office, 1964.

*Retirement of Employees of The Alaska Railroad.* Hearings before the Senate Committee on Civil Service on S.2293. Washington, D.C.: U.S. Government Printing Office, 1938.

SHELDON, JEROME. "The Railroad That Had It Too Good," *Trains* (Milwaukee, Wis.), XV (September, 1955), 23–30.

STONE, KIRK H. "The Matanuska Colony." Bureau of Land Management, U.S. Department of the Interior. Washington, D.C., 1950.

*Study of Alaska Transportation.* Hearings before the Senate Committee on Commerce (87th Cong., 1st sess.; S.1725, S.1839, S.1978, S.2413, and S.2484, October, 1961). Washington, D.C.: U.S. Government Printing Office, 1962.

"Toughest Railroad You Taxpayers Own," *Popular Mechanics* (Chicago), CXII (November, 1959), 117 ff.

*Transportation in Alaska.* Report of House Committee on Interstate and Foreign Commerce, Report No. 1272, January 26, 1948. Washington, D.C.: U.S. Government Printing Office, 1948.

*Transport Requirements for the Growth of Northwest North America.* Alaska International Rail and Highway Commission. Vol. 1, *Commission Report to the Congress;* Vol. 2, *Research Report by Battelle Memorial Institute;* Vol. 3, *Supplement 1 to Battelle Memorial Institute's Report* (87th Cong., 1st sess.; H.R. Doc. 176). Washington, D.C.: U.S. Government Printing Office, 1961.

"A Wage Award on The Alaska Railroad," *Monthly Labor Review.* U.S. Department of Labor, September, 1958.

# Index

| | DATE DUE | | |
|---|---|---|---|
| OCT 2 2 1985 | | | |
| JAN 5 '87 | | | |
| FEB 3 '87 | | | |
| FEB 2 3 1987 | | | |
| OCT 9 '87 | | | |
| | | | |
| NOV 1 6 '87 | | | |
| FEB 0 6 '90 | | | |
| | | | |
| | | | |
| | | | |

# GREAT ILLUSTRATED CLASSICS

# *GREAT ILLUSTRATED CLASSICS*

Adam Bede—*Eliot*
Afloat and Ashore—*Cooper*
The Arabian Nights
Around the World in Eighty Days—*Verne*
Ben-Hur—*Wallace*
The Black Arrow—*Stevenson*
Black Beauty—*Sewell*
The Call of the Wild and Other Stories—*London*
Captains Courageous and Other Stories—*Kipling*
Christmas Tales—*Dickens*
The Cloister and the Hearth—*Reade*
A Connecticut Yankee in King Arthur's Court—*Clemens*
The Cruise of the Cachalot—*Bullen*
David Copperfield—*Dickens*
The Deerslayer—*Cooper*
Emma—*Austen*
Famous Tales of Sherlock Holmes—*Doyle*
From the Earth to the Moon—*Verne*
Great Expectations—*Dickens*
Green Mansions—*Hudson*
Gulliver's Travels—*Swift*
Hawthorne's Short Stories—*Hawthorne*
Henry Esmond—*Thackeray*
The House of the Seven Gables—*Hawthorne*
Huckleberry Finn—*Clemens*
The Hunchback of Notre-Dame—*Hugo*
Ivanhoe—*Scott*
Jane Eyre—*Brontë*
A Journey to the Centre of the Earth—*Verne*
Kenilworth—*Scott*
Kidnapped—*Stevenson*
Kim—*Kipling*
King Arthur—*Malory*
The Last Days of Pompeii—*Bulwer-Lytton*
The Last of the Mohicans—*Cooper*
Little Dorrit—*Dickens*
Lord Jim—*Conrad*
Lorna Doone—*Blackmore*
The Luck of Roaring Camp and Other Stories—*Harte*
The Man in the Iron Mask—*Dumas*
Martin Chuzzlewit—*Dickens*
The Mill on the Floss—*Eliot*
The Moonstone—*Collins*
The Mysterious Island—*Verne*
Nicholas Nickleby—*Dickens*
The Odyssey—*Homer*
The Old Curiosity Shop—*Dickens*
Oliver Twist—*Dickens*
Our Mutual Friend—*Dickens*
The Pathfinder—*Cooper*
Père Goriot—*Balzac*
Pickwick Papers—*Dickens*
The Pilot—*Cooper*
The Pioneers—*Cooper*
The Prairie—*Cooper*
Pride and Prejudice—*Austen*
Quentin Durward—*Scott*
Quo Vadis—*Sienkiewicz*
The Red Badge of Courage and Other Stories—*Crane*
The Return of the Native—*Hardy*
Robinson Crusoe—*Defoe*
The Scarlet Letter—*Hawthorne*
Sense and Sensibility—*Austen*
Silas Marner—*Eliot*
The Sketch Book—*Irving*
The Spy—*Cooper*
The Strange Case of Dr. Jekyll and Mr. Hyde and Other Famous Tales—*Stevenson*
A Tale of Two Cities—*Dickens*
Tales—*Poe*
The Talisman—*Scott*
Tess of the D'Urbervilles—*Hardy*
The Three Musketeers—*Dumas*
Tom Sawyer—*Clemens*
Treasure Island—*Stevenson*
Twenty Thousand Leagues Under the Sea—*Verne*
Twenty Years After—*Dumas*
Two Years Before the Mast—*Dana*
Uncle Tom's Cabin—*Stowe*
Vanity Fair—*Thackeray*
Walden—*Thoreau*
The Way of All Flesh—*Butler*
Westward Ho!—*Kingsley*
The White Company—*Doyle*
The Wreck of the Grosvenor—*Russell*
Wuthering Heights—*Brontë*

# *GREAT ILLUSTRATED CLASSICS—TITANS*

Autobiography of Benvenuto Cellini
Barnaby Rudge—*Dickens*
Bleak House—*Dickens*
Dombey & Son—*Dickens*
Don Quixote—*Cervantes*
Everybody's Plutarch
Short Novels of Henry James—*James*

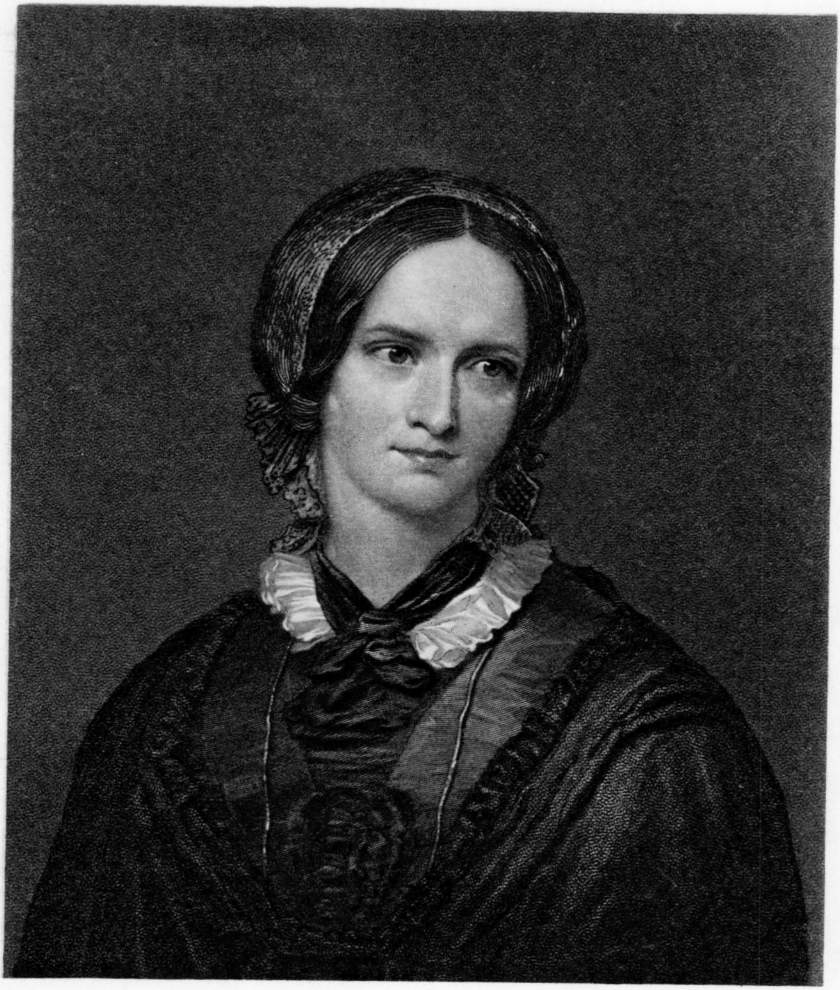

CHARLOTTE BRONTË

# JANE EYRE

*BY CHARLOTTE BRONTË*

*With illustrations made up of drawings by contemporary artists and photographs from the Jane Eyre country together with an introductory biographical sketch of the author and anecdotal captions by Basil Davenport*

NEW YORK · DODD, MEAD & COMPANY

*JANE EYRE*

PUBLISHED IN THE UNITED
STATES OF AMERICA, 1941
BY DODD, MEAD & COMPANY, INC.



PRINTED IN THE UNITED STATES OF AMERICA
BY THE CORNWALL PRESS, INC.

# CHARLOTTE BRONTË

Charlotte Brontë was born in 1816, her sister Emily in 1818, and Anne in 1820. They were the daughters of an Irish clergyman, the Reverend Patrick Brontë (his name was originally Brunty or Prunty), whose church was at Haworth, in the bleak moorland country of Yorkshire. The girls' mother died when Charlotte was five, and three years later she and Emily, with their older sisters Maria and Elizabeth, were sent to a semi-charitable school for the daughters of clergymen. From this school Maria and Elizabeth went home to die, Charlotte believed as a result of its hardships, and Charlotte and Emily were taken away. Charlotte was sent to another school which she left at nineteen; after a few years spent as teacher and governess she and Emily thought of starting a school of their own, and in preparation Charlotte spent several years studying and teaching in Brussels, at the Pensionnat Héger. In 1844 Charlotte returned home, because, it is believed, Madame Héger was jealous of her. For some years now her life was very unhappy; her father's eyesight was failing, she herself feared that she might go blind, and her brother Branwell became a confirmed drunkard and opium addict. The three sisters had always written tales and woven fancies; when they were still children they had invented a mythical kingdom for themselves; and at this time Charlotte resolved to send a volume of their poems to a publisher. Since there was at that time a prejudice against women authors, the three sisters chose pen names which might be masculine, and which preserved their initials; Charlotte called herself Currer Bell, Emily was Ellis Bell, and Anne, Acton Bell. The poems were accepted, and the sisters were encouraged to try novels. In 1847 there appeared *Wuthering Heights* by Ellis Bell, and *Agnes Grey* by Acton Bell; the following year *Jane Eyre* (pronounced "Air") was published and achieved enormous popularity. So far, the authors' identities had been kept a secret even from the publishers, but after this success the sisters came out of their retirement into a fame which two of them did not live long to enjoy; Branwell and Emily died in 1848, and Anne in 1849. Charlotte continued to write, and in 1854 married her father's curate, Arthur Bell Nicholls, but died after a year of married life.

Basil Davenport

THE PRINCIPAL WORKS OF CHARLOTTE BRONTË WITH THEIR DATES OF PUBLICATION

*NOVELS*

Jane Eyre—1847

Shirley—1849

Villette—1852

The Professor—1857

The Twelve Adventures and Other Stories—1925

The Spell—1931

Legends of Angria—1933

*VERSE*

Poems by Currer, Ellis and Acton Bell—1846

Complete Poems—1924

## PREFACE

A PREFACE to the first edition of "Jane Eyre" being unnecessary, I gave none: this second edition demands a few words both of acknowledgement and miscellaneous remark.

My thanks are due in three quarters.

To the Public, for the indulgent ear it has inclined to a plain tale with few pretensions.

To the Press, for the fair field its honest suffrage has opened to an obscure aspirant.

To my Publishers, for the aid their tact, their energy, their practical sense, and frank liberality have afforded an unknown and unrecommended Author.

The Press and the Public are but vague personifications for me, and I must thank them in vague terms; but my Publishers are definite: so are certain generous critics who have encouraged me as only large-hearted and high-minded men know how to encourage a struggling stranger; to them, *i.e.* to my Publishers and the select Reviewers, I say cordially, Gentlemen, I thank you from my heart.

Having thus acknowledged what I owe those who have aided and approved me, I turn to another class; a small one, so far as I know, but not, therefore, to be overlooked. I mean the timorous or carping few who doubt the tendency of such books as "Jane Eyre:" in whose eyes whatever is unusual is wrong; whose ears detect in each protest against bigotry — that parent of crime — an insult to piety, that regent of God on earth. I would suggest to such doubters certain obvious distinctions; I would remind them of certain simple truths.

Conventionality is not morality. Self-righteousness is not religion. To attack the first is not to assail the last. To pluck the mask from the face of the Pharisee, is not to lift an impious hand to the Crown of Thorns.

These things and deeds are diametrically opposed: they are as distinct as is vice from virtue. Men too often confound them; they should not be confounded: appearance should not be mistaken for truth; narrow human doctrines, that only tend to elate and magnify a few, should not be substituted for the world-redeeming creed of Christ There is — I repeat it — a difference; and it is a good, and not a bad action to mark broadly and clearly the line of separation between them.

The world may not like to see these ideas dissevered, for it has been accustomed to blend them; finding it convenient to make external show pass for sterling worth — to let white-washed walls vouch for clean shrines. It may hate him who dares to scrutinise and expose — to rase the gilding, and show base metal under it — to penetrate the sepulchre, and reveal charnel relics: but, hate as it will, it is indebted to him.

Ahab did not like Micaiah, because he never prophesied good concerning him, but evil: probably he liked the sycophant son of Chenaanah better; yet might Ahab have escaped a bloody death, had he but stopped his ears to flattery, and opened them to faithful counsel.

There is a man in our own days whose words are not framed to tickle delicate ears: who, to my thinking, comes before the great ones of society, much as the son of Imlah came before the throned Kings of Judah and Israel; and who speaks truth as deep, with a power as prophet-like and as vital — a mien as dauntless and as daring. Is the satirist of "Vanity Fair" admired in high places? I cannot tell; but I think if some of those amongst whom he hurls the Greek fire of his scarcasm, and over whom he flashes the levin-brand of his denunciation, were to take his warnings in time — they or their seed might yet escape a fatal Ramoth-Gilead.

Why have I alluded to this man? I have alluded to him, Reader, because I think I see in him an intellect profounder and more unique than his contemporaries have yet recognized; because I regard him as the first social regenerator of the day — as the very master of that working corps who would restore to rectitude the warped system of things; because I think no commentator on his writings has yet found the comparison that suits him, the terms which rightly characterise his talent. They say he is like Fielding: they talk of his wit, humour, comic powers. He resembles Fielding as an eagle does a vulture: Fielding could stoop on carrion, but Thackeray never does. His wit is bright, his humour attractive, but both bear the same relation to his serious genius, that the mere lambent sheet-lightning playing under the edge of the summer-cloud, does to the electric death-spark hid in its womb. Finally; I have alluded to Mr. Thackeray, because to him — if he will accept the tribute of a total stranger — I have dedicated this second edition of "JANE EYRE."

CURRER BELL.

## NOTE TO THE THIRD EDITION

I AVAIL myself of the opportunity which a third edition of "Jane Eyre" affords me, of again addressing a word to the Public, to explain that my claim to the title of novelist rests on this one work alone. If, therefore, the authorship of other works of fiction has been attributed to me, an honour is awarded where it is not merited; and consequently, denied where it is justly due.

This explanation will serve to rectify mistakes which may already have been made, and to prevent future errors.

CURRER BELL

# ILLUSTRATIONS

# JANE EYRE

## CHAPTER I

THERE was no possibility of taking a walk that day. We had been wandering, indeed, in the leafless shrubbery an hour in the morning; but since dinner (Mrs. Reed, when there was no company, dined early) the cold winter wind had brought with it clouds so sombre, and a rain so penetrating, that further out-door exercise was now out of the question.

I was glad of it: I never liked long walks, especially on chilly afternoons: dreadful to me was the coming home in the raw twilight, with nipped fingers and toes, and a heart saddened by the chidings of Bessie, the nurse, and humbled by the consciousness of my physical inferiority to Eliza, John, and Georgiana Reed.

The said Eliza, John, and Georgiana were now clustered round their mama in the drawing-room: she lay reclined on a sofa by the fireside, and with her darlings about her (for the time neither quarrelling nor crying) looked perfectly happy. Me, she had dispensed from joining the group; saying, "She regretted to be under the necessity of keeping me at a distance; but that until she heard from Bessie, and could discover by her own observation that I was endeavouring in good earnest to acquire a more sociable and childlike disposition, a more attractive and sprightly manner,— something lighter, franker, more natural as it were — she really must exclude me from privileges intended only for contented, happy little children."

"What does Bessie say I have done?" I asked.

"Jane, I don't like cavillers or questioners: besides, there is something truly forbidding in a child taking up her elders in that manner. Be seated somewhere; and until you can speak pleasantly, remain silent."

A small breakfast-room adjoined the drawing-room. I slipped in there. It contained a book-case: I soon possessed myself of a volume, taking care that it should be one stored with pictures. I mounted into the window-seat: gathering up my feet, I sat cross-legged, like a

Turk; and, having drawn the red moreen curtain nearly close, I was shrined in double retirement.

Folds of scarlet drapery shut in my view to the right hand; to the left were the clear panes of glass, protecting, but not separating me from the drear November day. At intervals, while turning over the leaves of my book, I studied the aspect of that winter afternoon. Afar, it offered a pale blank of mist and cloud; near, a scene of wet lawn and storm-beat shrub, with ceaseless rain sweeping away wildly before a long and lamentable blast.

I returned to my book — Bewick's History of British Birds: the letter-press thereof I cared little for, generally speaking; and yet there were certain introductory pages that, child as I was, I could not pass quite as a blank. They were those which treat of the haunts of sea-fowl; of "the solitary rocks and promontories" by them only inhabited; of the coast of Norway, studded with isles from its southern extremity, the Lindeness, or Naze, to the North Cape —

"Where the Northern Ocean, in vast whirls,
Boils round the naked, melancholy isles
Of farthest Thule; and the Atlantic surge
Pours in among the stormy Hebrides."

Nor could I pass unnoticed the suggestion of the bleak shores of Lapland, Siberia, Spitzbergen, Nova Zembla, Iceland, Greenland, with "the vast sweep of the Arctic Zone, and those forlorn regions of dreary space,— that reservoir of frost and snow, where firm fields of ice, the accumulation of centuries of winters, glazed in Alpine heights above heights, surround the pole, and concentre the multiplied rigours of extreme cold." Of these death-white realms I formed an idea of my own: shadowy, like all the half-comprehended notions that float dim through children's brains, but strangely impressive. The words in these introductory pages connected themselves with the succeeding vignettes, and gave significance to the rock standing up alone in a sea of billow and spray; to the broken boat stranded on a desolate coast; to the cold and ghastly moon glancing through bars of cloud at a wreck just sinking.

I cannot tell what sentiment haunted the quiet solitary churchyard, with its inscribed headstone; its gate, its two trees, its low horizon, girdled by a broken wall, and its newly-risen crescent, attesting the hour of eventide.

The two ships becalmed on a torpid sea, I believed to be marine phantoms.

The fiend pinning down the thief's pack behind him, I passed over quickly: it was an object of terror.

So was the black, horned thing seated aloof on a rock, surveying a distant crowd surrounding a gallows.

Each picture told a story; mysterious often to my undeveloped understanding and imperfect feelings, yet ever profoundly interesting: as interesting as the tales Bessie sometimes narrated on winter evenings, when she chanced to be in good humour; and when, having brought her ironing-table to the nursery-hearth, she allowed us to sit about it, and while she got up Mrs. Reed's lace frills, and crimped her night-cap borders, fed our eager attention with passages of love and adventure taken from old fairy tales and older ballads; or (as at a later period I discovered) from the pages of Pamela, and Henry, Earl of Moreland.

With Bewick on my knee, I was then happy: happy at least in my way. I feared nothing but interruption, and that came too soon. The breakfast-room door opened.

"Boh! Madame Mope!" cried the voice of John Reed; then he paused: he found the room apparently empty.

"Where the dickens is she?" he continued. "Lizzy! Georgy! (calling to his sisters) Joan is not here: tell mama she is run out into the rain — bad animal!"

"It is well I drew the curtain," thought I; and I wished fervently he might not discover my hiding-place: nor would John Reed have found it out himself; he was not quick either of vision or conception; but Eliza just put her head in at the door, and said at once: —

"She is in the window-seat, to be sure, Jack."

And I came out immediately, for I trembled at the idea of being dragged forth by the said Jack.

"What do you want?" I asked, with awkward diffidence.

"Say, 'what do you want, Master Reed,'" was the answer. "I want you to come here;" and seating himself in an armchair, he intimated by a gesture that I was to approach and stand before him.

John Reed was a schoolboy of fourteen years old; four years older than I, for I was but ten; large and stout for his age, with a dingy and unwholesome skin; thick lineaments in a spacious visage, heavy limbs and large extremities. He gorged himself habitually at table, which made him bilious, and gave him a dim and bleared eye and flabby cheeks. He ought now to have been at school; but his mama had taken him home for a month or two, "on account of his delicate health." Mr. Miles, the master, affirmed that he would do very well if he had fewer cakes and sweetmeats sent him from home; but the mother's heart turned from an opinion so harsh, and inclined rather to the more refined idea that John's sallowness was owing to over-application and, perhaps, to pining after home.

John had not much affection for his mother and sisters, and an antipathy to me. He bullied and punished me; not two or three times in the week, nor once or twice in the day, but continually: every nerve I had feared him, and every morsel of flesh on my bones shrank when he came near. There were moments when I was bewildered by the terror he inspired, because I had no appeal whatever against either his menaces or his inflictions; the servants did not like to offend their young master by taking my part against him, and Mrs. Reed was blind and deaf on the subject: she never saw him strike or heard him abuse me, though he did both now and then in her very presence; more frequently, however, behind her back.

Habitually obedient to John, I came up to his chair: he spent some three minutes in thrusting out his tongue at me as far as he could without damaging the roots: I knew he would soon strike, and while dreading the blow, I mused on the disgusting and ugly appearance of him who would presently deal it. I wonder if he read that notion in my face; for, all at once, without speaking, he struck suddenly and strongly. I tottered, and on regaining my equilibrium retired back a step or two from his chair.

"That is for your impudence in answering mama awhile since," said he, "and for your sneaking way of getting behind curtains, and for the look you had in your eyes two minutes since, you rat!"

Accustomed to John Reed's abuse, I never had an idea of replying to it; my care was how to endure the blow which would certainly follow the insult.

"What were you doing behind the curtain?" he asked.

"I was reading."

"Shew the book."

I returned to the window and fetched it thence.

"You have no business to take our books; you are a dependant, mama says; you have no money; your father left you none; you ought to beg, and not to live here with gentlemen's children like us, and eat the same meals we do, and wear clothes at our mama's expense. Now, I'll teach you to rummage my book-shelves: for they *are* mine; all the house belongs to me, or will do in a few years. Go and stand by the door, out of the way of the mirror and the windows."

I did so, not at first aware what was his intention; but when I saw him lift and poise the book and stand in act to hurl it, I instinctively started aside with a cry of alarm: not soon enough, however; the volume was flung, it hit me, and I fell, striking my head against the door and cutting it. The cut bled, the pain was sharp; my terror had passed its climax; other feelings succeeded.

"Wicked and cruel boy!" I said. "You are like a murderer — you are like a slave-driver — you are like the Roman emperors!"

I had read Goldsmith's History of Rome, and had formed my opinion of Nero, Caligula, etc. Also I had drawn parallels in silence, which I never thought thus to have declared aloud.

"What! what!" he cried. "Did you say that to me? Did you hear her, Eliza and Georgiana? Won't I tell mama? but first"—

He ran headlong at me: I felt him grasp my hair and my shoulder: he had closed with a desperate thing. I really saw in him a tyrant: a murderer. I felt a drop or two of blood from my head trickle down my neck, and was sensible of somewhat pungent sufferings: these sensations for the time predominated over fear, and I received him in frantic sort. I don't very well know what I did with my hands, but he called me "Rat! rat!" and bellowed out aloud. Aid was near him: Eliza and Georgiana had run for Mrs. Reed, who was gone upstairs; she now came upon the scene, followed by Bessie and her maid Abbot. We were parted: I heard the words: —

"Dear! dear! What a fury to fly at Master John!"

"Did ever anybody see such a picture of passion!"

Then Mrs. Reed subjoined: —

"Take her away to the red-room, and lock her in there." Four hands were immediately laid upon me, and I was borne upstairs.

## CHAPTER II

I RESISTED all the way: a new thing for me, and a circumstance which greatly strengthened the bad opinion Bessie and Miss Abbot were disposed to entertain of me. The fact is, I was a trifle beside myself; or rather *out* of myself, as the French would say: I was conscious that a moment's mutiny had already rendered me liable to strange penalties, and, like any other rebel slave, I felt resolved, in my desperation, to go all lengths.

"Hold her arms, Miss Abbot: she's like a mad cat."

"For shame! for shame!" cried the lady's-maid. "What shocking conduct, Miss Eyre, to strike a young gentleman, your benefactress's son! Your young master."

"Master! How is he my master? Am I a servant?"

"No; you are less than a servant, for you do nothing for your keep. There, sit down, and think over your wickedness."

They had got me by this time into the apartment indicated by Mrs. Reed, and had thrust me upon a stool: my impulse was to rise from it like a spring; their two pair of hands arrested me instantly.

"If you don't sit still, you must be tied down," said Bessie. "Miss Abbot, lend me your garters; she would break mine directly."

Miss Abbot turned to divest a stout leg of the necessary ligature. This preparation for bonds, and the additional ignominy it inferred, took a little of the excitement out of me.

"Don't take them off," I cried; "I will not stir."

In guarantee whereof, I attached myself to my seat by my hands.

"Mind you don't," said Bessie; and when she had ascertained that I was really subsiding, she loosened her hold of me; then she and Miss Abbot stood with folded arms, looking darkly and doubtfully on my face, as incredulous of my sanity.

"She never did so before," at last said Bessie, turning to the Abigail.

"But it was always in her," was the reply. "I've told Missis often my opinion about the child, and Missis agreed with me. She's an underhand little thing: I never saw a girl of her age with so much cover."

Bessie answered not; but ere long, addressing me, she said,—

"You ought to be aware, Miss, that you are under obligations to Mrs. Reed: she keeps you: if she were to turn you off, you would have to go to the poor-house."

I had nothing to say to these words: they were not new to me: my very first recollections of existence included hints of the same kind. This reproach of my dependence had become a vague sing-song in my ear; very painful and crushing, but only half intelligible. Miss Abbot joined in:—

"And you ought not to think yourself on an equality with the Misses Reed and Master Reed, because Missis kindly allows you to be brought up with them. They will have a great deal of money, and you will have none: it is your place to be humble, and to try to make yourself agreeable to them."

"What we tell you, is for your good," added Bessie, in no harsh voice: "you should try to be useful and pleasant, then, perhaps, you would have a home here; but if you become passionate and rude, Missis will send you away, I am sure."

"Besides," said Miss Abbot, "God will punish her: he might strike her dead in the midst of her tantrums, and then where would she go? Come, Bessie, we will leave her: I wouldn't have her heart for anything. Say your prayers, Miss Eyre, when you are by yourself; for if you don't repent, something bad might be permitted to come down the chimney and fetch you away."

They went, shutting the door, and locking it behind them.

The red-room was a spare chamber, very seldom slept in; I might say never, indeed, unless when a chance influx of visitors at Gateshead Hall rendered it necessary to turn to account all the accommodation it contained: yet it was one of the largest and stateliest chambers in the mansion. A bed supported on massive pillars of mahogany, hung with curtains of deep red damask, stood out like a tabernacle in the centre; the two large windows, with their blinds always drawn down, were half shrouded in festoons and falls of similar drapery; the carpet was red; the table at the foot of the bed was covered with a crimson cloth; the walls were a soft fawn colour, with a blush of pink in it; the wardrobe, the toilet-table, the chairs were of darkly polished old mahogany. Out of these deep surrounding shades rose high, and glared white, the piled-up mattresses and pillows of the bed, spread with a snowy Marseilles counterpane.

Scarcely less prominent was an ample, cushioned easy-chair near the head of the bed, also white, with a footstool before it; and looking, as I thought, like a pale throne.

This room was chill, because it seldom had a fire; it was silent, because remote from the nursery and kitchens; solemn, because it was known to be so seldom entered. The house-maid alone came here on Saturdays, to wipe from the mirrors and the furniture a week's quiet dust: and Mrs. Reed herself, at far intervals, visited it to review the contents of a certain secret drawer in the wardrobe, where were stored divers parchments, her jewel-casket, and a miniature of her deceased husband; and in those last words lies the secret of the red-room — the spell which kept it so lonely in spite of its grandeur.

Mr. Reed had been dead nine years: it was in this chamber he breathed his last; here he lay in state; hence his coffin was borne by the undertaker's men; and, since that day, a sense of dreary consecration had guarded it from frequent intrusion.

My seat, to which Bessie and the bitter Miss Abbot had left me riveted, was a low ottoman near the marble chimney-piece; the bed rose before me; to my right hand there was the high, dark wardrobe, with subdued, broken reflections varying the gloss of its panels; to my left were the muffled windows; a great looking-glass between them repeated the vacant majesty of the bed and room. I was not quite sure whether they had locked the door; and, when I dared move, I got up, and went to see. Alas! yes, no jail was ever more secure. Returning, I had to cross before the looking-glass; my fascinated glance involuntarily explored the depth it revealed. All looked colder and darker in that visionary hollow than in reality: and the strange little figure there gazing at me, with a white face and arms specking the gloom, and glittering eyes of fear moving where all else was still, had the effect of a real spirit: I thought it like one of the tiny phantoms, half fairy, half imp, Bessie's evening stories represented as coming out of lone, ferny dells in moors, and appearing before the eyes of belated travellers. I returned to my stool.

Superstition was with me at that moment; but it was not yet her hour for complete victory: my blood was still warm; the mood of the revolted slave was still bracing me with its bitter vigour; I had to stem a rapid rush of retrospective thought before I quailed to the dismal present.

All John Reed's violent tyrannies, all his sisters' proud indifference, all his mother's aversion, all the servants' partiality, turned up in my disturbed mind like a dark deposit in a turbid well. Why was I always suffering, always brow-beaten, always accused, for ever condemned? Why could I never please? Why was it useless to try to win any one's favour? Eliza, who was headstrong and selfish, was respected. Georgiana, who had a spoiled temper, a very acrid spite, a captious and insolent carriage, was universally indulged. Her beauty, her pink cheeks and golden curls, seemed to give delight to all who looked at her, and to purchase indemnity for every fault. John, no one thwarted, much less punished; though he twisted the necks of the pigeons, killed the little pea-chicks, set the dogs at the sheep, stripped the hothouse vines of their fruit, and broke the buds off the choicest plants in the conservatory: he called his mother "old girl," too; sometimes reviled her for her dark skin, similar to his own; bluntly disregarded her wishes; not unfrequently tore and spoiled her silk attire; and he was still "her own darling." I dared commit no fault: I strove to fulfil every duty; and I was termed naughty and tiresome, sullen and sneaking, from morning to noon, and from noon to night.

My head still ached and bled with the blow and fall I had received: no one had reproved John for wantonly striking me; and because I had turned against him to avert farther irrational violence, I was loaded with general opprobrium.

"Unjust! — unjust!" said my reason, forced by the agonising stimulus into precocious though transitory power; and Resolve, equally wrought up, instigated some strange expedient to achieve escape from insupportable oppression — as running away, or, if that could not be effected, never eating or drinking more, and letting myself die.

What a consternation of soul was mine that dreary afternoon! How all my brain was in tumult, and all my heart in insurrection! Yet in what darkness, what dense ignorance, was the mental battle fought! I could not answer the ceaseless inward question — *why* I thus suffered; now, at the distance of — I will not say how many years, I see it clearly.

I was a discord in Gateshead Hall; I was like nobody there; I had nothing in harmony with Mrs. Reed or her children, or her chosen vassalage. If they did not love me, in fact, as little did I love them.

They were not bound to regard with affection a thing that could not sympathise with one amongst them; a heterogeneous thing, opposed to them in temperament, in capacity, in propensities; a useless thing, incapable of serving their interest, or adding to their pleasure; a noxious thing, cherishing the germs of indignation at their treatment, of contempt of their judgment. I know that had I been a sanguine, brilliant, careless, exacting, handsome, romping child — though equally dependent and friendless — Mrs. Reed would have endured my presence more complacently; her children would have entertained for me more of the cordiality of fellow-feeling; the servants would have been less prone to make me the scapegoat of the nursery.

Daylight began to forsake the red-room; it was past four o'clock, and the beclouded afternoon was tending to drear twilight. I heard the rain still beating continuously on the staircase window, and the wind howling in the grove behind the hall; I grew by degrees cold as a stone, and then my courage sank. My habitual mood of humiliation, self-doubt, forlorn depression, fell damp on the embers of my decaying ire. All said I was wicked, and perhaps I might be so; what thought had I been but just conceiving of starving myself to death? That certainly was a crime: and was I fit to die? Or was the vault under the chancel of Gateshead Church an inviting bourne? In such vault I had been told did Mr. Reed lie buried; and led by this thought to recall his idea, I dwelt on it with gathering dread. I could not remember him; but I knew that he was my own uncle — my mother's brother — that he had taken me when a parentless infant to his house; and that in his last moments he had required a promise of Mrs. Reed that she would rear and maintain me as one of her own children. Mrs. Reed probably considered she had kept this promise; and so she had, I dare say, as well as her nature would permit her; but how could she really like an interloper not of her race, and unconnected with her, after her husband's death, by any tie? It must have been most irksome to find herself bound by a hard-wrung pledge to stand in the stead of a parent to a strange child she could not love, and to see an uncongenial alien permanently intruded on her own family group.

A singular notion dawned upon me. I doubted not — never doubted — that if Mr. Reed had been alive he would have treated me kindly; and now, as I sat looking at the white bed and overshadowed walls — occasionally also turning a fascinated eye towards the dimly gleaming mirror — I began to recall what I had heard of dead men, troubled in their graves by the violation of their last wishes, revisiting the earth to punish the perjured and avenge the oppressed; and I thought Mr. Reed's spirit, harassed by the wrongs of his sister's child, might quit its abode — whether in the church vault or in the unknown world of the departed — and rise before me in this chamber. I wiped my tears and hushed my sobs, fearful lest any sign of violent grief might waken a preternatural voice to comfort me, or elicit from the gloom some haloed face, bending over me with strange pity. This idea, consolatory in theory, I felt would be terrible if realised: with all my might I endeavoured to stifle it — I endeavoured to be firm. Shaking my hair from my eyes, I lifted my head and tried to look boldly round the dark room: at this moment a light gleamed on the wall. Was it, I asked myself, a ray from the moon penetrating some aperture in the blind? No; moonlight was still, and this stirred; while I gazed, it glided up to the ceiling and quivered over my head. I can now conjecture readily that this streak of light was, in all likelihood, a gleam from a lantern, carried by some one across the lawn: but then, prepared as my mind was for horror, shaken as my nerves were by agitation, I thought the swift-darting beam was a herald of some coming vision from another world. My heart beat thick, my head grew hot; a sound filled my ears, which I deemed the rushing of wings: something seemed near me; I was oppressed, suffocated: endurance broke down; I rushed to the door and shook the lock in desperate effort. Steps came running along the outer passage; the key turned, Bessie and Abbot entered.

"Miss Eyre, are you ill?" said Bessie.

"What a dreadful noise! it went quite through me!" exclaimed Abbot.

"Take me out! Let me go into the nursery!" was my cry.

"What for! Are you hurt! Have you seen something?" again demanded Bessie.

"Oh! I saw a light, and I thought a ghost would come." I had now got hold of Bessie's hand, and she did not snatch it from me.

"She has screamed out on purpose," declared Abbot, in some disgust. "And what a scream! If she had been in great pain one would have excused it, but she only wanted to bring us all here. I know her naughty tricks."

"What is all this?" demanded another voice peremptorily; and Mrs. Reed came along the corridor, her cap flying wide, her gown rustling stormily. "Abbot and Bessie, I believe I gave orders that Jane Eyre should be left in the red-room till I came to her myself."

"Miss Jane screamed so loud, ma'am," pleaded Bessie.

"Let her go," was the only answer. "Loose Bessie's hand, child: you cannot succeed in getting out by these means, be assured. I abhor artifice, particularly in children; it is my duty to show you that tricks will not answer: you will now stay here an hour longer, and it is only on condition of perfect submission and stillness that I shall liberate you then."

"Oh aunt, have pity! Forgive me! I cannot endure it—let me be punished some other way! I shall be killed if"—

"Silence! This violence is all most repulsive:" and so, no doubt, she felt it. I was a precocious actress in her eyes: she sincerely looked on me as a compound of virulent passions, mean spirit, and dangerous duplicity.

Bessie and Abbot having retreated, Mrs. Reed, impatient of my now frantic anguish and wild sobs, abruptly thrust me back and locked me in, without farther parley. I heard her sweeping away; and soon after she was gone, I suppose I had a species of fit: unconsciousness closed the scene.

## CHAPTER III

THE next thing I remember is, waking up with a feeling as if I had had a frightful night-mare, and seeing before me a terrible red glare, crossed with thick black bars. I heard voices, too, speaking with a hollow sound, and as if muffled by a rush of wind or water: agitation, uncertainty, and an all-predominating sense of terror confused my faculties. Ere long, I became aware that some one was handling me; lifting me up and supporting me in a sitting posture, and that more tenderly than I had ever been raised or upheld before. I rested my head against a pillow or an arm, and felt easy.

In five minutes more, the cloud of bewilderment dissolved: I knew quite well that I was in my own bed, and that the red glare was the nursery fire. It was night: a candle burnt on the table; Bessie stood at the bed-foot with a basin in her hand, and a gentleman sat in a chair near my pillow, leaning over me.

I felt an inexpressible relief, a soothing conviction of protection and security, when I knew that there was a stranger in the room, an individual not belonging to Gateshead, and not related to Mrs. Reed. Turning from Bessie (though her presence was far less obnoxious to me than that of Abbot, for instance, would have been), I scrutinised the face of the gentleman: I knew him; it was Mr. Lloyd, an apothecary, sometimes called in by Mrs. Reed when the servants were ailing: for herself and the children she employed a physician.

"Well, who am I?" he asked.

I pronounced his name, offering him at the same time my hand: he took it, smiling and saying, "We shall do very well by-and-by." Then he laid me down, and addressing Bessie, charged her to be very careful that I was not disturbed during the night. Having given some further directions, and intimated that he should call again the next day, he departed; to my grief: I felt so sheltered and befriended while he sat in the chair near my pillow; and as he closed the door after him, all the room darkened and my heart again sank: inexpressible sadness weighed it down.

"Do you feel as if you should sleep, Miss?" asked Bessie, rather softly.

Scarcely dared I answer her; for I feared the next sentence might be rough. "I will try."

"Would you like to drink, or could you eat anything?"

"No, thank you, Bessie."

"Then I think I shall go to bed, for it is past twelve o'clock; but you may call me if you want anything in the night."

Wonderful civility this! It emboldened me to ask a question.

"Bessie, what is the matter with me? Am I ill?"

"You fell sick, I suppose, in the red-room with crying; you'll be better soon, no doubt."

Bessie went into the housemaid's apartment which was near. I heard her say —

"Sarah, come and sleep with me in the nursery; I daren't for my life be alone with that poor child to-night; she might die; it's such a strange thing she should have that fit: I wonder if she saw anything. Missis was rather too hard."

Sarah came back with her; they both went to bed; they were whispering together for half an hour before they fell asleep. I caught scraps of their conversation, from which I was able only too distinctly to infer the main subject discussed.

"Something passed her, all dressed in white, and vanished"—"A great black dog behind him"—"Three loud raps on the chamber door"—"A light in the church-yard just over his grave"— etc., etc.

At last both slept: the fire and the candle went out. For me, the watches of that long night passed in ghastly wakefulness; ear, eye, and mind were alike strained by dread: such dread as children only can feel.

No severe or prolonged bodily illness followed this incident of the red-room: it only gave my nerves a shock, of which I feel the reverberation to this day. Yes, Mrs. Reed, to you I owe some fearful pangs of mental suffering. But I ought to forgive you, for you knew not what you did: while rending my heartstrings, you thought you were only up-rooting my bad propensities.

Next day, by noon, I was up and dressed, and sat wrapped in a shawl by the nursery hearth. I felt physically weak and broken down: but my worse ailment was an unutterable wretchedness of mind: a wretchedness which kept drawing from me silent tears; no sooner had I wiped one salt drop from my cheek than another followed. Yet I thought, I ought to have been happy, for none of the Reeds were there; they were all gone out in the carriage with their mama: Abbot, too, was sewing in another room, and Bessie, as she moved hither and thither, putting away toys and arranging drawers, addressed to me every now and then a word of unwonted kindness. This state of things should have been to me a paradise of peace, accustomed as I was to a life of ceaseless reprimand and thankless fagging; but, in fact, my racked nerves were now in such a state that no calm could soothe, and no pleasure excite them agreeably.

Bessie had been down into the kitchen, and she brought up with her a tart on a certain brightly painted china plate, whose bird of paradise, nestling in a wreath of convolvuli and rosebuds, had been wont to stir in me a most enthusiastic sense of admiration; and which plate I had petitioned to be allowed to take in my hand in order to examine it more closely, but had always hitherto been deemed unworthy of such a privilege. This precious vessel was now placed on my knee, and I was cordially invited to eat the circlet of delicate pastry upon it. Vain favour! coming, like most other favours long deferred and often wished for, too late! I could not eat the tart: and the plumage of the bird, the tints of the flowers, seemed strangely faded: I put both plate and tart away. Bessie asked if I would have a book: the word *book* acted as a transient stimulus, and I begged her to fetch Gulliver's Travels from the library. This book I had again and again perused with delight. I considered it a narrative of facts, and discovered in it a vein of interest deeper than what I found in fairy tales: for as to the elves, having sought them in vain among foxglove leaves and bells, under mushrooms and beneath the ground-ivy mantling old wall-nooks, I had at length made up my mind to the sad truth, that they were all gone out of England to some savage country where the woods were wilder and thicker, and the population more scant; whereas, Lilliput and Brobdignag being, in my creed, solid parts of the earth's surface, I doubted not that I might one day, by taking a long voyage, see with my own eyes the little fields, houses, and trees, the diminutive people, the tiny cows, sheep, and birds of the one realm; and the corn-fields forest-high, the mighty mastiffs, the monster cats, the tower-like men and women, of the other. Yet, when this cherished volume was now placed in my hand — when I turned over its leaves, and sought in its marvellous pictures the charm I had, till now, never failed to find — all was eerie and dreary; the giants were gaunt goblins, the pigmies malevolent and fearful imps, Gulliver a most desolate wanderer in most dread and dangerous regions. I closed the book, which I dared no longer peruse, and put it on the table, beside the untasted tart.

Bessie had now finished dusting and tidying the room, and having washed her hands, she opened a certain little drawer, full of splendid shreds of silk and satin, and began making a new bonnet for Georgiana's doll. Meantime she sang: her song was —

"In the days when we went gipsying,
A long time ago."

I had often heard the song before, and always with lively delight; for Bessie had a sweet voice,— at least, I thought so. But now, though her voice was still sweet, I found in its melody an indescribable sadness. Sometimes, pre-occupied with her work, she sang the refrain very low, very lingeringly: "A long time ago" came out like the saddest cadence of a funeral hymn. She passed into another ballad, this time a really doleful one.

"My feet they are sore, and my limbs they are weary;
Long is the way, and the mountains are wild;
Soon will the twilight close moonless and dreary
Over the path of the poor orphan child.

"Why did they send me so far and so lonely,
Up where the moors spread and grey rocks are piled?
Men are hard-hearted, and kind angels only
Watch'd o'er the steps of a poor orphan child.

"Yet distant and soft the night-breeze is blowing,
Clouds there are none, and clear stars beam mild.
God, in His mercy, protection is showing,
Comfort and hope to the poor orphan child.

"Ev'n should I fall o'er the broken bridge passing,
Or stray in the marshes, by false lights beguiled,
Still will my Father, with promise and blessing,
Take to His bosom the poor orphan child.

"There is a thought that for strength should avail me,
Though both of shelter and kindred despoiled;
Heaven is a home, and a rest will not fail me;
God is a friend to the poor orphan child."

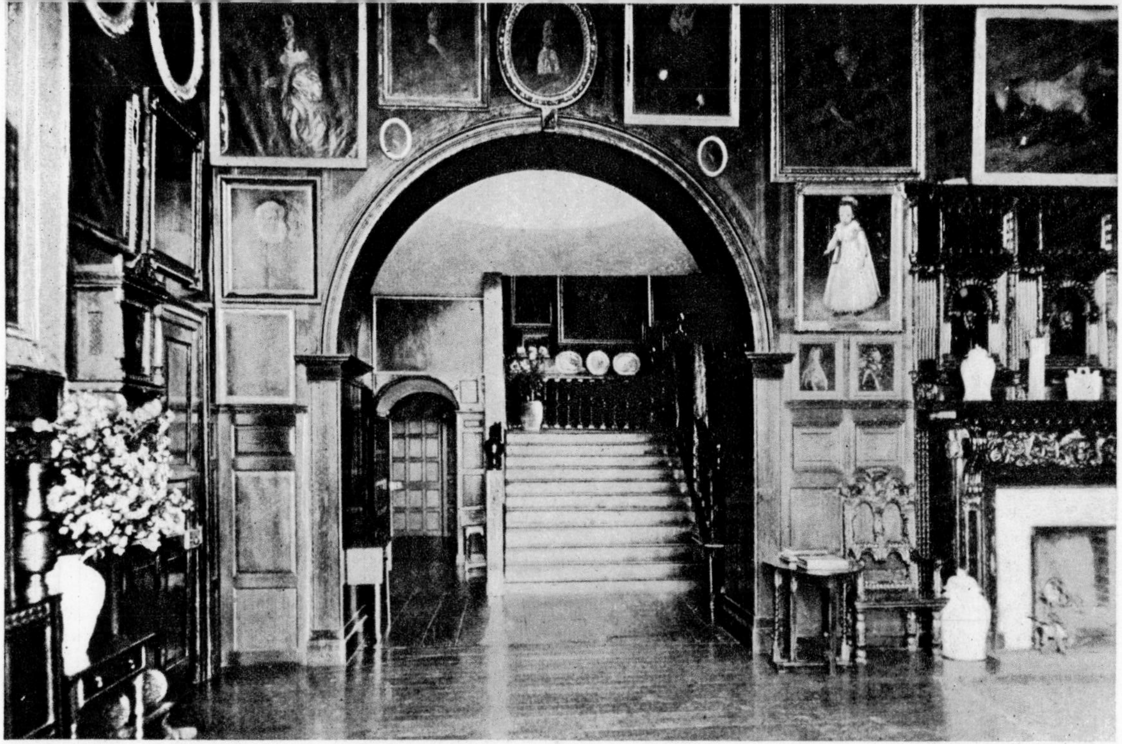

NORTON CONYERS, INTERIOR

Charlotte Brontë was much impressed by Norton Conyers, especially the staircase with its oak steps and bannisters and lofty latticed window, and the long gallery upon which the bedrooms opened. She drew on her recollections of it for the interior of "Thornfield," Mr. Rochester's magnificent and gloomy mansion. At the real Norton Conyers there is a small room in the attic called "the madwoman's room" in which a lunatic was once confined, just as at Thornfield.

"Come, Miss Jane, don't cry," said Bessie, as she finished. She might as well have said to the fire, "don't burn!" but how could she divine the morbid suffering to which I was a prey? In the course of the morning, Mr. Lloyd came again.

"What, already up!" said he, as he entered the nursery. "Well, nurse, how is she?"

Bessie answered that I was doing very well.

"Then she ought to look more cheerful. Come here, Miss Jane: your name is Jane, is it not?"

"Yes, sir, Jane Eyre."

"Well, you have been crying, Miss Jane Eyre, can you tell me what about? Have you any pain?"

"No, sir."

"Oh! I daresay she is crying because she could not go out with Missis in the carriage," interposed Bessie.

"Surely not! why, she is too old for such pettishness."

I thought so too; and my self-esteem being wounded by the false charge, I answered promptly, "I never cried for such a thing in my life: I hate going out in the carriage. I cry because I am miserable."

"Oh fie, Miss!" said Bessie.

The good apothecary appeared a little puzzled. I was standing before him; he fixed his eyes on me very steadily: his eyes were small and grey; not very bright, but I daresay I should think them shrewd now: he had a hard-featured yet good-natured looking face. Having considered me at leisure, he said —

"What made you ill yesterday?"

"She had a fall," said Bessie, again putting in her word.

"Fall! why that is like a baby again! Can't she manage to walk at her age? She must be eight or nine years old."

"I was knocked down," was the blunt explanation jerked out of me by another pang of mortified pride: "but that did not make me ill," I added; while Mr. Lloyd helped himself to a pinch of snuff.

As he was returning the box to his waistcoat pocket, a loud bell rang for the servants' dinner; he knew what it was. "That's for you, nurse," said he; "you can go down; I'll give Miss Jane a lecture till you come back."

Bessie would rather have stayed, but she was obliged to go, because punctuality at meals was rigidly enforced at Gateshead Hall.

“The fall did not make you ill; what did, then?” pursued Mr. Lloyd, when Bessie was gone.

“I was shut up in a room where there is a ghost, till after dark.”

I saw Mr. Lloyd smile and frown at the same time: “Ghost! What, you are a baby after all! You are afraid of ghosts?”

“Of Mr. Reed's ghost I am: he died in that room, and was laid out there. Neither Bessie nor any one else will go into it at night, if they can help it; and it was cruel to shut me up alone without a candle,— so cruel that I think I shall never forget it.”

“Nonsense! And is it that makes you so miserable? Are you afraid now in daylight?”

“No: but night will come again before long: and besides,— I am unhappy,— very unhappy, for other things.”

“What other things? Can you tell me some of them?”

How much I wished to reply fully to this question! How difficult it was to frame any answer! Children can feel, but they cannot analyse their feelings; and if the analysis is partially effected in thought, they know not how to express the result of the process in words. Fearful, however, of losing this first and only opportunity of relieving my grief by imparting it, I, after a disturbed pause, contrived to frame a meagre, though, as far as it went, true response.

“For one thing, I have no father or mother, brothers or sisters.”

“You have a kind aunt and cousins.”

Again I paused; then bunglingly announced:

“But John Reed knocked me down, and my aunt shut me up in the red-room.”

Mr. Lloyd a second time produced his snuff-box.

“Don't you think Gateshead Hall a very beautiful house?” asked he. “Are you not very thankful to have such a fine place to live at?”

“It is not my house, sir; and Abbot says I have less right to be here than a servant.”

“Pooh! you can't be silly enough to wish to leave such a splendid place?”

“If I had anywhere else to go, I should be glad to leave it; but I can never get away from Gateshead till I am a woman.”

“Perhaps you may — who knows? Have you any relations besides Mrs. Reed?”

“I think not, sir.”

“None belonging to your father?”

"I don't know: I asked aunt Reed once, and she said possibly I night have some poor, low relations called Eyre, but she knew nothng about them."

"If you had such, would you like to go to them?"

I reflected. Poverty looks grim to grown people; still more so to hildren: they have not much idea of industrious, working, respectble poverty; they think of the word only as connected with ragged lothes, scanty food, fireless grates, rude manners, and debasing vices: overty for me was synonymous with the degradation.

"No; I should not like to belong to poor people," was my reply.

"Not even if they were kind to you?"

I shook my head: I could not see how poor people had the means of eing kind; and then to learn to speak like them, to adopt their maners, to be uneducated, to grow up like one of the poor women I saw ometimes nursing their children or washing their clothes at the cotage doors of the village of Gateshead: no, I was not heroic enough o purchase liberty at the price of caste.

"But are your relatives so very poor? Are they working people?"

"I cannot tell; aunt Reed says if I have any, they must be a beggarly set: I should not like to go a begging."

"Would you like to go to school?"

Again I reflected: I scarcely knew what school was; Bessie someimes spoke of it as a place where young ladies sat in the stocks, wore ackboards, and were expected to be exceedingly genteel and preise: John Reed hated his school, and abused his master; but John Reed's tastes were no rule for mine, and if Bessie's accounts of schoolliscipline (gathered from the young ladies of a family where she ad lived before coming to Gateshead) were somewhat appalling, her letails of certain accomplishments attained by these same young adies were, I thought, equally attractive. She boasted of beautiful paintings of landscapes and flowers by them executed; of songs they could sing and pieces they could play, of purses they could net, of French books they could translate; till my spirit was moved to emulation as I listened. Besides, school would be a complete change: it implied a long journey, an entire separation from Gateshead, an entrance into a new life.

"I should indeed like to go to school," was the audible conclusion of my musings.

"Well, well; who knows what may happen?" said Mr. Lloyd as he got up: "The child ought to have change of air and scene," he added, speaking to himself; "nerves not in a good state."

Bessie now returned; at the same moment the carriage was heard rolling up the gravel-walk.

"Is that your mistress, nurse?" asked Mr. Lloyd. "I should like to speak to her before I go."

Bessie invited him to walk into the breakfast-room, and led the way out. In the interview which followed between him and Mrs. Reed, I presume, from after-occurrences, that the apothecary ventured to recommend my being sent to school; and the recommendation was no doubt readily enough adopted; for as Abbot said, in discussing the subject with Bessie when both sat sewing in the nursery one night, after I was in bed, and, as they thought, asleep, "Missis was, she dared say, glad enough to get rid of such a tiresome, ill-conditioned child, who always looked as if she were watching everybody, and scheming plots underhand." Abbot, I think, gave me credit for being a sort of infantine Guy Fawkes.

On that same occasion I learned, for the first time, from Miss Abbot's communications to Bessie, that my father had been a poor clergyman; that my mother had married him against the wishes of her friends, who considered the match beneath her; that my grandfather Reed was so irritated at her disobedience, he cut her off without a shilling; that after my mother and father had been married a year, the latter caught the typhus fever while visiting among the poor of a large manufacturing town where his curacy was situated, and where that disease was then prevalent; that my mother took the infection from him, and both died within a month of each other.

Bessie, when she heard this narrative, sighed and said, "Poor Miss Jane is to be pitied, too, Abbot."

"Yes," responded Abbot; "if she were a nice, pretty child, one might compassionate her forlornness; but one really cannot care for such a little toad as that."

"Not a great deal to be sure," agreed Bessie: "at any rate, a beauty like Miss Georgiana would be more moving in the same condition."

"Yes, I doat on Miss Georgiana!" cried the fervent Abbot. "Little darling! — with her long curls and her blue eyes, and such a sweet colour as she has; just as if she were painted! — Bessie, I could fancy a Welsh rabbit for supper."

"So could I — with a roast onion. Come, we'll go down." They went.

## CHAPTER IV

FROM my discourse with Mr. Lloyd, and from the above reported conference between Bessie and Abbot, I gathered enough of hope to suffice as a motive for wishing to get well: a change seemed near,— I desired and waited it in silence. It tarried, however: days and weeks passed: I had regained my normal state of health, but no new allusion was made to the subject over which I brooded. Mrs. Reed surveyed me at times with a severe eye, but seldom addressed me: since my illness, she had drawn a more marked line of separation than ever between me and her own children; appointing me a small closet to sleep in by myself, condemning me to take my meals alone, and pass all my time in the nursery, while my cousins were constantly in the drawing-room. Not a hint, however, did she drop about sending me to school: still I felt an instinctive certainty that she would not long endure me under the same roof with her; for her glance, now more than ever, when turned on me, expressed an insuperable and rooted aversion.

Eliza and Georgiana, evidently acting according to orders, spoke to me as little as possible: John thrust his tongue in his cheek whenever he saw me, and once attempted chastisement; but as I instantly turned against him, roused by the same sentiment of deep ire and desperate revolt which had stirred my corruption before, he thought it better to desist, and ran from me uttering execrations, and vowing I had burst his nose. I had indeed levelled at that prominent feature as hard a blow as my knuckles could inflict; and when I saw that either that or my look daunted him, I had the greatest inclination to follow up my advantage to purpose; but he was already with his mama. I heard him in a blubbering tone commence the tale of how "that nasty Jane Eyre" had flown at him like a mad cat: he was stopped rather harshly—

"Don't talk to me about her, John: I told you not to go near her; she is not worthy of notice; I do not choose that either you or your sisters should associate with her."

Here, leaning over the banister, I cried out suddenly, and without at all deliberating on my words,—

"They are not fit to associate with me."

Mrs. Reed was rather a stout woman; but, on hearing this strange and audacious declaration, she ran nimbly up the stair, swept me like a whirlwind into the nursery, and crushing me down on the edge of my crib, dared me in an emphatic voice to rise from that place, or utter one syllable during the remainder of the day.

"What would uncle Reed say to you, if he were alive?" was my scarcely voluntary demand. I say scarcely voluntary, for it seemed as if my tongue pronounced words without my will consenting to their utterance: something spoke out of me over which I had no control.

"What?" said Mrs. Reed under her breath: her usually cold composed grey eye became troubled with a look like fear; she took her hand from my arm, and gazed at me as if she really did not know whether I were child or fiend. I was now in for it.

"My uncle Reed is in heaven, and can see all you do and think; and so can papa and mama: they know how you shut me up all day long, and how you wish me dead."

Mrs. Reed soon rallied her spirits: she shook me most soundly, she boxed both my ears, and then left me without a word. Bessie supplied the hiatus by a homily of an hour's length, in which she proved beyond a doubt that I was the most wicked and abandoned child ever reared under a roof. I half believed her; for I felt indeed only bad feelings surging in my breast.

November, December, and half of January passed away. Christmas and the New Year had been celebrated at Gateshead with the usual festive cheer; presents had been interchanged, dinners and evening parties given. From every enjoyment I was, of course, excluded: my share of the gaiety consisted in witnessing the daily apparelling of Eliza and Georgiana, and seeing them descend to the drawing-room, dressed out in thin muslin frocks and scarlet sashes, with hair elaborately ringletted; and afterwards, in listening to the sound of the piano or the harp played below, to the passing to and fro of the butler and footman, to the jingling of glass and china as refreshments were handed, to the broken hum of conversation as the drawing-room doors opened and closed. When tired of this occupation, I would retire from the stair-head to the solitary and silent nursery: there, though somewhat sad, I was not miserable. To speak the truth, I had not the least wish to go into company, for in company I was very rarely noticed; and if Bessie had been kind and companionable, I should have deemed it a treat to spend the evenings quietly with her, instead of passing them under the formidable eye of Mrs. Reed, in a room full of ladies and gentlemen. But Bessie, as soon as she had dressed her young ladies, used to take herself off to the lively regions of the kitchen and housekeeper's room, generally bearing the candle along with her. I then sat with my doll on my knee, till the fire got low, glancing round occasionally to make sure that nothing worse than myself haunted the shadowy room; and when the embers sank to a dull red, I undressed hastily, tugging at knots and strings as I best might, and sought shelter from cold and darkness in my crib. To this crib I always took my doll; human beings must love something, and in the dearth of worthier objects of affection, I contrived to find a pleasure in loving and cherishing a faded graven image, shabby as a miniature scarecrow. It puzzles me now to remember with what absurd sincerity I doated on this little toy, half fancying it alive and capable of sensation. I could not sleep unless it was folded in my night-gown; and when it lay there safe and warm, I was comparatively happy, believing it to be happy likewise.

Long did the hours seem while I waited the departure of the company, and listened for the sound of Bessie's step on the stairs: sometimes she would come up in the interval to seek her thimble or her scissors, or perhaps to bring me something by way of supper — a bun or a cheese-cake — then she would sit on the bed while I ate it, and when I had finished, she would tuck the clothes round me, and twice she kissed me, and said, "Good-night, Miss Jane." When thus gentle, Bessie seemed to me the best, prettiest, kindest being in the world; and I wished most intensely that she would always be so pleasant and amiable, and never push me about, or scold, or task me unreasonably, as she was too often wont to do. Bessie Lee must, I think, have been a girl of good natural capacity, for she was smart in all she did, and had a remarkable knack of narrative; so, at least, I judge from the impression made on me by her nursery tales. She was pretty, too, if my recollections of her face and person are correct. I remember her as a slim young woman, with black hair, dark eyes, very nice features, and good, clear complexion; but she had a capricious and hasty temper, and indifferent ideas of principle or justice: still, such as she was, I preferred her to any one else at Gateshead Hall.

It was the fifteenth of January, about nine o'clock in the morning: Bessie was gone down to breakfast; my cousins had not yet been summoned to their mama; Eliza was putting on her bonnet and warm garden-coat to go and feed her poultry, an occupation of which she was fond: and not less so of selling the eggs to the housekeeper and hoarding up the money she thus obtained. She had a turn of traffic, and a marked propensity for saving; shown not only in the vending of eggs and chickens, but also in driving hard bargains with the gardener about flower-roots, seeds, and slips of plants, that functionary having orders from Mrs. Reed to buy of his young lady all the products of her parterre she wished to sell: and Eliza would have sold the hair off her head if she could have made a handsome profit thereby. As to her money, she first secreted it in odd corners, wrapped in a rag or an old curl-paper; but some of these hoards having been discovered by the housemaid, Eliza, fearful of one day losing her valued treasure, consented to intrust it to her mother, at a usurious rate of interest — fifty or sixty per cent.; which interest she exacted every quarter, keeping her accounts in a little book with anxious accuracy.

Georgiana sat on a high stool, dressing her hair at the glass, and interweaving her curls with artificial flowers and faded feathers, of which she had found a store in a drawer in the attic. I was making my bed, having received strict orders from Bessie to get it arranged before she returned (for Bessie now frequently employed me as a sort of under-nurserymaid, to tidy the room, dust the chairs, etc.). Having spread the quilt and folded my night-dress, I went to the window-seat to put in order some picture-books and doll's house furniture scattered there; an abrupt command from Georgiana to let her playthings alone (for the tiny chairs and mirrors, the fairy plates and cups were her property) stopped my proceedings; and then, for lack of other occupation, I fell to breathing on the frost-flowers with which the window was fretted, and thus clearing a space in the glass through which I might look out on the grounds, where all was still and petrified under the influence of a hard frost.

From this window were visible the porter's lodge and the carriage-road, and just as I had dissolved so much of the silver-white foliage veiling the panes, as left room to look out, I saw the gates thrown open and a carriage roll through. I watched it ascending the drive with indifference: carriages often came to Gateshead, but none ever brought visitors in whom I was interested; it stopped in front of the house, the door-bell rang loudly, the new comer was admitted. All this being nothing to me, my vacant attention soon found livelier attraction in the spectacle of a little hungry robin, which came and chirruped on the twigs of the leafless cherry-tree nailed against the wall near the casement. The remains of my breakfast of bread and milk stood on the table, and having crumbled a morsel of roll, I was tugging at the sash to put out the crumbs on the window-sill, when Bessie came running upstairs into the nursery.

"Miss Jane, take off your pinafore: what are you doing there? Have you washed your hands and face this morning?" I gave another tug before I answered, for I wanted the bird to be secure of its bread: the sash yielded; I scattered the crumbs, some on the stone sill, some on the cherry-tree bough, then, closing the window, I replied:—

"No, Bessie; I have only just finished dusting."

"Troublesome, careless child! and what are you doing now? You look quite red, as if you had been about some mischief: what were you opening the window for?"

I was spared the trouble of answering, for Bessie seemed in too great a hurry to listen to explanations; she hauled me to the wash-stand, inflicted a merciless, but happily brief scrub on my face and hands with soap, water, and a coarse towel; disciplined my head with a bristly brush, denuded me of my pinafore, and then hurrying me to the top of the stairs, bid me go down directly, as I was wanted in the breakfast room.

I would have asked who wanted me: I would have demanded if Mrs. Reed was there; but Bessie was already gone, and had closed the nursery-door upon me: I slowly descended. For nearly three months, I had never been called to Mrs. Reed's presence: restricted so long to the nursery, the breakfast, dining, and drawing-rooms were become for me awful regions, on which it dismayed me to intrude.

I now stood in the empty hall; before me was the breakfast-room door, and I stopped, intimidated and trembling. What a miserable little poltroon had fear, engendered of unjust punishment, made of me in those days! I feared to return to the nursery, and feared to go forward to the parlor; ten minutes I stood in agitated hesitation: the vehement ringing of the breakfast-room bell decided me; I *must* enter.

"Who could want me?" I asked inwardly, as with both hands I

turned the stiff door-handle which, for a second or two, resisted my efforts. "What should I see besides aunt Reed in the apartment?—a man or a woman?" The handle turned, the door unclosed, and passing through and curtseying low, I looked up at — a black pillar! — such, at least, appeared to me, at first sight, the straight, narrow sable-clad shape standing erect on the rug: the grim face at the top was like a carved mask, placed above the shaft by way of capital.

Mrs. Reed occupied her usual seat by the fireside: she made a signal to me to approach: I did so, and she introduced me to the stranger with the words: "This is the little girl respecting whom I applied to you."

*He,* for it was a man, turned his head slowly towards where I stood, and having examined me with the two inquisitive-looking grey eyes which twinkled under a pair of bushy brows, said solemnly, and in a bass voice: "Her size is small: what is her age?"

"Ten years."

"So much?" was the doubtful answer; and he prolonged his scrutiny for some minutes. Presently he addressed me:—

"Your name, little girl?"

"Jane Eyre, sir."

In uttering these words, I looked up: he seemed to me a tall gentleman; but then I was very little: his features were large, and they and all the lines of his frame were equally harsh and prim.

"Well, Jane Eyre, and are you a good child?"

Impossible to reply to this in the affirmative: my little world held a contrary opinion: I was silent. Mrs. Reed answered for me by an expressive shake of the head, adding soon, "Perhaps the less said on that subject the better, Mr. Brocklehurst."

"Sorry indeed to hear it! she and I must have some talk;" and bending from the perpendicular, he installed his person in the arm-chair, opposite Mrs. Reed's. "Come here," he said.

I stepped across the rug; he placed me square and straight before him. What a face he had, now that it was almost on a level with mine! what a great nose! and what a mouth! and what large prominent teeth!

"No sight so sad as that of a naughty child," he began, "especially a naughty little girl. Do you know where the wicked go after death?"

"They go to hell," was my ready and orthodox answer.

"And what is hell? Can you tell me that?"

"A pit full of fire."

"And should you like to fall into that pit, and to be burning there forever?"

"No, sir."

"What must you do to avoid it?"

I deliberated a moment; my answer, when it did come, was objectionable: "I must keep in good health, and not die."

"How can you keep in good health? Children younger than you die daily. I buried a little child of five years old only a day or two since,— a good little child, whose soul is now in heaven. It is to be feared the same could not be said of you, were you to be called hence."

Not being in a condition to remove his doubts I only cast my eyes down on the two large feet planted on the rug, and sighed, wishing myself far enough away.

"I hope that sigh is from the heart, and that you repent of ever having been the occasion of discomfort to your excellent benefactress."

"Benefactress! benefactress!" said I, inwardly: "they all call Mrs. Reed my benefactress; if so, a benefactress is a disagreeable thing."

"Do you say your prayers night and morning?" continued my interrogator.

"Yes, sir."

"Do you read your Bible?"

"Sometimes."

"With pleasure? Are you fond of it?"

"I like Revelation, and the book of Daniel, and Genesis and Samuel, and a little bit of Exodus, and some parts of Kings and Chronicles, and Job and Jonah."

"And the Psalms? I hope you like them?"

"No, sir."

"No? oh, shocking! I have a little boy, younger than you, who knows six Psalms by heart: and when you ask him which he would rather have, a ginger-bread nut to eat, or a verse of a Psalm to learn, he says: 'Oh! the verse of a Psalm! angels sing Psalms;' says he, 'I wish to be a little angel here below;' he then gets two nuts in recompense for his infant piety."

"Psalms are not interesting," I remarked.

"That proves you have a wicked heart; and you must pray to God to change it: to give you a new and clean one: to take away your heart of stone and give you a heart of flesh."

I was about to propound a question, touching the manner in which that operation of changing my heart was to be performed, when Mrs. Reed interposed, telling me to sit down; she then proceeded to carry on the conversation herself.

"Mr. Brocklehurst, I believe I intimated in the letter which I wrote to you three weeks ago, that this little girl has not quite the character and disposition I could wish: should you admit her into Lowood school, I should be glad if the superintendent and teachers were requested to keep a strict eye on her, and above all, to guard against her worst fault, a tendency to deceit. I mention this in your hearing, Jane, that you may not attempt to impose on Mr. Brocklehurst."

Well might I dread, well might I dislike Mrs. Reed; for it was her nature to wound me cruelly; never was I happy in her presence: however carefully I obeyed, however strenuously I strove to please her, my efforts were still repulsed and repaid by such sentences as the above. Now, uttered before a stranger, the accusation cut me to the heart: I dimly perceived that she was already obliterating hope from the new phase of existence which she destined me to enter; I felt, though I could not have expressed the feeling, that she was sowing aversion and unkindness along my future path; I saw myself transformed under Mr. Brocklehurst's eye into an artful, noxious child, and what could I do to remedy the injury?

"Nothing, indeed!" thought I, as I struggled to repress a sob, and hastily wiped away some tears, the impotent evidences of my anguish.

"Deceit is, indeed, a sad fault in a child," said Mr. Brocklehurst; "it is akin to falsehood, and all liars will have their portion in the lake burning with fire and brimstone: she shall, however, be watched, Mrs. Reed; I will speak to Miss Temple and the teachers."

"I should wish her to be brought up in a manner suiting her prospects," continued my benefactress; "to be made useful, to be kept humble: as for the vacations, she will, with your permission, spend them always at Lowood."

"Your decisions are perfectly judicious, madam," returned Mr. Brocklehurst. "Humility is a Christian grace, and one peculiarly appropriate to the pupils of Lowood; I, therefore, direct that especial care shall be bestowed on its cultivation amongst them. I have studied how best to mortify in them the worldly sentiment of pride; and, only the other day, I had a pleasing proof of my success. My second daughter, Augusta, went with her mama to visit the school, and on her return she exclaimed: 'Oh, dear papa, how quiet and plain all the girls at Lowood look; with their hair combed behind their ears, and their long pinafores, and those little holland pockets outside their frocks — they are almost like poor people's children! and,' said she, 'they looked at my dress and mama's, as if they had never seen a silk gown before.'"

"This is the state of things I quite approve," returned Mrs. Reed; "had I sought all England over, I could scarcely have found a system more exactly fitting a child like Jane Eyre. Consistency, my dear Mr. Brocklehurst; I advocate consistency in all things."

"Consistency, madam, is the first of Christian duties; and it has been observed in every arrangement connected with the establishment of Lowood: plain fare, simple attire, unsophisticated accommodations, hardy and active habits; such is the order of the day in the house and its inhabitants."

"Quite right, sir. I may then depend upon this child being received as a pupil at Lowood, and there being trained in conformity to her position and prospects?"

"Madam, you may: she shall be placed in that nursery of chosen plants — and I trust she will show herself grateful for the inestimable privilege of her election."

"I will send her, then, as soon as possible, Mr. Brocklehurst; for, I assure you, I feel anxious to be relieved of a responsibility that was becoming too irksome."

"No doubt, no doubt, madam, and now I wish you good morning. I shall return to Brocklehurst Hall in the course of a week or two: my good friend, the Archdeacon, will not permit me to leave him sooner. I shall send Miss Temple notice that she is to expect a new girl, so that there will be no difficulty about receiving her. Good-by."

"Good-by, Mr. Brocklehurst; remember me to Mrs. and Miss Brocklehurst, and to Augusta and Theodore, and Master Broughton Brocklehurst."

"I will, madam. Little girl, here is a book entitled the 'Child's Guide'; read it with prayer, especially that part containing 'an account of the awfully sudden death of Martha G——, a naughty child addicted to falsehood and deceit.'"

With these words Mr. Brocklehurst put into my hand a thin pamphlet sewn in a cover, and having rung for his carriage, he departed.

Mrs. Reed and I were left alone: some minutes passed in silence; she was sewing, I was watching her. Mrs. Reed might be at that time some six or seven and thirty; she was a woman of robust frame, square-shouldered and strong-limbed, not tall, and, though stout, not obese: she had a somewhat large face, the under-jaw being much developed and very solid; her brow was low, her chin large and prominent, mouth and nose sufficiently regular; under her light eyebrows glimmered an eye devoid of ruth; her skin was dark and opaque, her hair nearly flaxen; her constitution was sound as a bell — illness never came near her; she was an exact, clever manager, her household and tenantry were thoroughly under her control; her children, only, at times defied her authority, and laughed it to scorn; she dressed well, and had a presence and port calculated to set off handsome attire.

Sitting on a low stool, a few yards from her arm-chair, I examined her figure; I perused her features. In my hand I held the tract, containing the sudden death of the Liar: to which narrative my attention had been pointed as to an appropriate warning. What had just passed; what Mrs. Reed had said concerning me to Mr. Brocklehurst; the whole tenor of their conversation, was recent, raw, and stinging in my mind; I had felt every word as acutely as I had heard it plainly, and a passion of resentment fomented now within me.

Mrs. Reed looked up from her work; her eye settled on mine, her fingers at the same time suspended their nimble movements.

"Go out of the room; return to the nursery," was her mandate. My look or something else must have struck her as offensive, for she spoke with extreme, though suppressed irritation. I got up, I went to the door; I came back again; I walked to the window, across the room, then close up to her.

*Speak* I must: I had been trodden on severely, and *must* turn: but how? What strength had I to dart retaliation at my antagonist? I gathered my energies and launched them in this blunt sentence:—

"I am not deceitful: if I were, I should say I loved *you;* but I declare I do not love you: I dislike you the worst of anybody in the world except John Reed; and this book about the liar, you may give to your girl, Georgiana, for it is she who tells lies, and not I."

Mrs. Reed's hands still lay on her work inactive: her eye of ice continued to dwell freezingly on mine.

"What more have you to say?" she asked, rather in the tone in which a person might address an opponent of adult age than such as is ordinarily used to a child.

That eye of hers, that voice stirred every antipathy I had. Shaking from head to foot, thrilled with ungovernable excitement, I continued:—

"I am glad you are no relation of mine: I will never call you aunt again as long as I live. I will never come to see you when I am grown up; and if any one asks me how I liked you, and how you treated me, I will say the very thought of you makes me sick, and that you treated me with miserable cruelty."

"How dare you affirm that, Jane Eyre?"

"How dare I, Mrs. Reed? How dare I? Because it is the *truth*. You think I have no feelings, and that I can do without one bit of love or kindness; but I cannot live so: and you have no pity. I shall remember how you thrust me back — roughly and violently thrust me back — into the red-room, and locked me up there, to my dying day; though I was in agony; though I cried out, while suffocating with distress, 'Have mercy! Have mercy, aunt Reed!' And that punishment you made me suffer because your wicked boy struck me — knocked me down for nothing. I will tell anybody who asks me questions, this exact tale. People think you a good woman, but you are bad; hard-hearted. *You* are deceitful!"

Ere I had finished this reply, my soul began to expand, to exult, with the strangest sense of freedom, of triumph, I ever felt. It seemed as if an invisible bond had burst, and that I had struggled out into unhoped-for liberty. Not without cause was this sentiment: Mrs. Reed looked frightened; her work had slipped from her knee; she was lifting up her hands, rocking herself to and fro, and even twisting her face as if she would cry.

"Jane, you are under a mistake: what is the matter with you? Why do you tremble so violently? Would you like to drink some water?"

"No, Mrs. Reed."

"Is there anything else you wish for, Jane? I assure you, I desire to be your friend."

"Not you. You told Mr. Brocklehurst I had a bad character, a deceitful disposition; and I'll let everybody at Lowood know what you are, and what you have done."

"Jane, you don't understand these things: children must be corrected for their faults."

"Deceit is not my fault!" I cried out in a savage, high voice.

"But you are passionate, Jane, that you must allow; and now return to the nursery — there's a dear — and lie down a little."

"I am not your dear; I cannot lie down: send me to school soon, Mrs. Reed, for I hate to live here."

"I will indeed send her to school soon," murmured Mrs. Reed, *sotto voce;* and gathering up her work, she abruptly quitted the apartment.

I was left there alone — winner of the field. It was the hardest battle I had fought, and the first victory I had gained: I stood awhile on the rug, where Mr. Brocklehurst had stood, and I enjoyed my conqueror's solitude. First, I smiled to myself and felt elate; but this fierce pleasure subsided in me as fast as did the accelerated throb of my pulses. A child cannot quarrel with its elders, as I had done, cannot give its furious feelings uncontrolled play, as I had given mine, without experiencing afterwards the pang of remorse and the chill of reaction. A ridge of lighted heath, alive, glancing, devouring, would have been a meet emblem of my mind when I accused and menaced Mrs. Reed: the same ridge, black and blasted after the flames are dead, would have represented as meetly my subsequent condition, when half an hour's silence and reflection had shown me the madness of my conduct, and the dreariness of my hated and hating position.

Something of vengeance I had tasted for the first time; as aromatic wine it seemed, on swallowing, warm and racy: its after-flavour, metallic and corroding, gave me a sensation as if I had been poisoned. Willingly would I now have gone and asked Mrs. Reed's pardon; but I knew, partly from experience and partly from instinct, that was the way to make her repulse me with double scorn, thereby re-exciting every turbulent impulse of my nature.

I would fain exercise some better faculty than that of fierce speaking; fain find nourishment for some less fiendish feeling than that of sombre indignation. I took a book — some Arabian tales; I sat down and endeavoured to read. I could make no sense of the subject; my own thoughts swam always between me and the page I had usually found fascinating. I opened the glass-door in the breakfast-room: the shrubbery was quite still: the black frost reigned, unbroken by sun or breeze, through the grounds. I covered my head and arms with the skirt of my frock, and went out to walk in a part of the plantation which was quite sequestered: but I found no pleasure in the silent trees, the falling fir-cones, the congealed relics of autumn, russet leaves, swept by past winds in heaps, and now stiffened together. I leaned against a gate, and looked into an empty field where no sheep were feeding, where the short grass was nipped and blanched. It was a very grey day; a most opaque sky, "onding on snaw," canopied all; thence flakes fell at intervals, which settled on the hard path and on the hoary lea without melting. I stood, a wretched child enough, whispering to myself over and over again, "What shall I do? — what shall I do?"

All at once I heard a clear voice call, "Miss Jane! where are you? Come to lunch!"

It was Bessie, I knew well enough; but I did not stir; her light step came tripping down the path.

"You naughty little thing!" she said. "Why don't you come when you are called?"

Bessie's presence, compared with the thoughts over which I had been brooding, seemed cheerful; even though, as usual, she was somewhat cross. The fact is, after my conflict with and victory over Mrs. Reed, I was not disposed to care much for the nursemaid's transitory anger; and I *was* disposed to bask in her youthful lightness of heart. I just put my two arms round her, and said, "Come, Bessie! don't scold."

The action was more frank and fearless than any I was habituated to indulge in: somehow it pleased her.

"You are a strange child, Miss Jane," she said, as she looked down at me: "a little roving, solitary thing: and you are going to school, I suppose?"

I nodded.

"And won't you be sorry to leave poor Bessie?"

"What does Bessie care for me? She is always scolding me."

"Because you're such a queer, frightened, shy little thing. You should be bolder."

"What! to get more knocks?"

"Nonsense! But you are rather put upon, that's certain. My mother said, when she came to see me last week, that she would not like a little one of her own to be in your place.— Now, come in, and I've some good news for you."

"I don't think you have, Bessie."

"Child! what do you mean? What sorrowful eyes you fix on me! Well! but Missis and the young ladies and Master John are going out to tea this afternoon, and you shall have tea with me. I'll ask cook to bake you a little cake, and then you shall help me to look over your drawers; for I am soon to pack your trunk. Missis intends you to leave Gateshead in a day or two, and you shall choose what toys you like to take with you."

"Bessie, you must promise not to scold me any more till I go."

"Well, I will: but mind you are a very good girl, and don't be afraid of me. Don't start when I chance to speak rather sharply: it's so provoking."

"I don't think I shall ever be afraid of you again, Bessie, because I have got used to you; and I shall soon have another set of people to dread."

"If you dread them, they'll dislike you."

"As you do, Bessie?"

"I don't dislike you, Miss; I believe I am fonder of you than of all the others."

"You don't show it."

"You little sharp thing! you've got quite a new way of talking. What makes you so venturesome and hardy?"

"Why, I shall soon be away from you, and besides—" I was going to say something about what had passed between me and Mrs. Reed; but on second thoughts I considered it better to remain silent on that head.

"And so you're glad to leave me?"

"Not at all, Bessie; indeed, just now I am rather sorry."

"Just now! and rather! How coolly my little lady says it! I daresay now if I were to ask you for a kiss you wouldn't give it to me: you'd say you'd *rather* not."

"I'll kiss you and welcome: bend your head down." Bessie

stooped; we mutually embraced, and I followed her into the house quite comforted. That afternoon lapsed in peace and harmony; and in the evening Bessie told me some of her most enchanting stories, and sang me some of her sweetest songs. Even for me life had its gleams of sunshine.

## CHAPTER V

FIVE o'clock had hardly struck on the morning of the 19th of January, when Bessie brought a candle into my closet and found me already up and nearly dressed. I had risen half an hour before her entrance, and had washed my face, and put on my clothes by the light of a half-moon just setting, whose rays streamed through the narrow window near my crib. I was to leave Gateshead that day by a coach which passed the lodge gates at 6 A. M. Bessie was the only person yet risen; she had lit a fire in the nursery, where she now proceeded to make my breakfast. Few children can eat when excited with the thoughts of a journey; nor could I. Bessie, having pressed me in vain to take a few spoonfuls of the boiled milk and bread she had prepared for me, wrapped up some biscuits in a paper and put them into my bag; then she helped me on with my pelisse and bonnet, and wrapping herself in a shawl, she and I left the nursery. As we passed Mrs. Reed's bed-room, she said, "Will you go in and bid Missis good-by?"

"No, Bessie: she came to my crib last night when you were gone down to supper, and said I need not disturb her in the morning, or my cousins either; and she told me to remember that she had always been my best friend, and to speak of her and be grateful to her accordingly."

"What did you say, Miss?"

"Nothing: I covered my face with the bed-clothes, and turned from her to the wall."

"That was wrong, Miss Jane."

"That was quite right, Bessie: your Missis has not been my friend: she has been my foe."

"Oh, Miss Jane! don't say so!"

"Good-by to Gateshead!" cried I, as we passed through the hall and went out at the front door.

The moon was set, and it was very dark; Bessie carried a lantern, whose light glanced on wet steps and gravel road soddened by a recent thaw. Raw and chill was the winter morning: my teeth chattered as I hastened down the drive. There was a light in the porter's lodge: when we reached it, we found the porter's wife just kindling her fire: my trunk, which had been carried down the evening before, stood corded at the door. It wanted but a few minutes of six, and shortly after that hour had struck, the distant roll of wheels announced the coming coach; I went to the door and watched its lamps approach rapidly through the gloom.

"Is she going by herself?" asked the porter's wife.

"Yes."

"And how far is it?"

"Fifty miles."

"What a long way! I wonder Mrs. Reed is not afraid to trust her so far alone."

The coach drew up; there it was at the gates with its four horses and its top laden with passengers: the guard and coachman loudly urged haste; my trunk was hoisted up; I was taken from Bessie's neck, to which I clung with kisses.

"Be sure and take good care of her," cried she to the guard, as he lifted me into the inside.

"Ay, ay!" was the answer: the door was slapped to, a voice exclaimed, "All right," and on we drove. Thus was I severed from Bessie and Gateshead: thus whirled away to unknown, and, as I then deemed, remote and mysterious regions.

I remember but little of the journey: I only know that the day seemed to me of a preternatural length, and that we appeared to travel over hundreds of miles of road. We passed through several towns, and in one, a very large one, the coach stopped; the horses were taken out, and the passengers alighted to dine. I was carried into an inn, where the guard wanted me to have some dinner; but, as I had no appetite, he left me in an immense room with a fireplace at each end, a chandelier pendent from the ceiling, and a little red gallery high up against the wall filled with musical instruments. Here I walked about for a long time, feeling very strange, and mortally apprehensive of some one coming in and kidnapping me; for I believed in kidnappers, their exploits having frequently figured in Bessie's fireside chronicles. At last the guard returned: once more I was stowed away in the coach, my protector mounted his own seat, sounded his hollow horn, and away we rattled over the "stony street" of L——.

The afternoon came on wet and somewhat misty: as it waned into dusk, I began to feel that we were getting very far indeed from Gateshead: we ceased to pass through towns; the country changed; great grey hills heaved up round the horizon: as twilight deepened, we descended a valley, dark with wood, and long after night had overclouded the prospect, I heard a wild wind rushing amongst trees.

Lulled by the sound, I at last dropped asleep: I had not long slumbered when the sudden cessation of motion awoke me; the coach-door was open, and a person like a servant was standing at it: I saw her face and dress by the light of the lamps.

"Is there a little girl called Jane Eyre here?" she asked. I answered "Yes," and was then lifted out; my trunk was handed down, and the coach instantly drove away.

I was stiff with long sitting, and bewildered with the noise and motion of the coach: gathering my faculties, I looked about me. Rain, wind, and darkness filled the air; nevertheless, I dimly discerned a wall before me and a door open in it. Through this door I passed with my new guide: she shut and locked it behind her. There was now visible a house or houses — for the building spread far — with many windows and lights burning in some; we went up a broad pebbly path, splashing wet, and were admitted at a door; then the servant led me through a passage into a room with a fire, where she left me alone.

I stood and warmed my numbed fingers over the blaze, then I looked round; there was no candle, but the uncertain light from the hearth showed, by intervals, papered walls, carpet, curtains, shining mahogany furniture: it was a parlour, not so spacious or splendid as the drawing-room at Gateshead, but comfortable enough. I was puzzling to make out the subject of a picture on the wall, when the door opened, and an individual carrying a light entered; another followed close behind.

The first was a tall lady with dark hair, dark eyes, and a pale and large forehead; her figure was partly enveloped in a shawl, her countenance was grave, her bearing erect.

"The child is very young to be sent alone," said she, putting her candle down on the table. She considered me attentively for a minute or two, then further added,—

"She had better be put to bed soon; she looks tired: are you tired?" she asked, placing her hand on my shoulder.

"A little, ma'am."

"And hungry too, no doubt: let her have some supper before she goes to bed, Miss Miller. Is this the first time you have left your parents to come to school, my little girl?"

I explained to her that I had no parents. She inquired how long they had been dead; then how old I was, what was my name, whether I could read, write, and sew a little: then she touched my cheek gently with her forefinger, and saying, "She hoped I should be a good child," dismissed me along with Miss Miller.

The lady I had left might be about twenty-nine; the one who went with me appeared to be some years younger: the first impressed me by her voice and air. Miss Miller was more ordinary; ruddy in complexion, though of a careworn countenance; hurried in gait and action, like one who had always a multiplicity of tasks on hand: she looked, indeed, what I afterwards found she really was, an under-teacher. Led by her, I passed from compartment to compartment, from passage to passage, of a large and irregular building; till, emerging from the total and somewhat dreary silence pervading that portion of the house we had traversed, we came upon the hum of many voices, and presently entered a wide, long room, with great deal tables, two at each end, on each of which burnt a pair of candles, and seated all round on benches, a congregation of girls of every age, from nine or ten to twenty. Seen by the dim light of the dips, their number to me appeared countless, though not in reality exceeding eighty; they were uniformly dressed in brown stuff frocks of quaint fashion, and long holland pinafores. It was the hour of study; they were engaged in conning over their to-morrow's task, and the hum I had heard was the combined result of their whispered repetitions.

Miss Miller signed to me to sit on a bench near the door, then walking up to the top of the long room, she cried out,—

"Monitors, collect the lesson-books and put them away!"

Four tall girls arose from the different tables, and going around, gathered the books and removed them. Miss Miller again gave the word of command,—

"Monitors, fetch the supper-trays!"

The tall girls went out and returned presently, each bearing a tray, with portions of something, I knew not what, arranged thereon, and a pitcher of water and mug in the middle of each tray. The portions were handed round; those who liked took a draught of the water, the mug being common to all. When it came to my turn, I drank, for I was thirsty, but did not touch the food, excitement and fatigue rendering me incapable of eating: I now saw, however, that it was a thin oaten cake, shared into fragments.

The meal over, prayers were read by Miss Miller, and the classes filed off, two and two, upstairs. Overpowered by this time with weariness, I scarcely noticed what sort of a place the bed-room was; except that, like the school-room, I saw it was very long. To-night I was to be Miss Miller's bed-fellow; she helped me to undress: when laid down I glanced at the long rows of beds, each of which was quickly filled with two occupants; in ten minutes the single light was extinguished; amid silence and complete darkness, I fell asleep.

The night passed rapidly: I was too tired even to dream; I only once awoke to hear the wind rave in furious gusts, and the rain fall in torrents, and to be sensible that Miss Miller had taken her place by my side. When I again unclosed my eyes, a loud bell was ringing: the girls were up and dressing; day had not yet begun to dawn, and a rushlight or two burnt in the room. I too rose reluctantly; it was bitter cold, and I dressed as well as I could for shivering, and washed when there was a basin at liberty, which did not occur soon, as there was but one basin to six girls, on the stands down the middle of the room. Again the bell rang: all formed in file, two and two, and in that order descended the stairs and entered the cold and dimly-lit school-room: here prayers were read by Miss Miller; afterwards she called out:—

"Form classes!"

A great tumult succeeded for some minutes, during which Miss Miller repeatedly exclaimed, "Silence!" and "Order!" When it subsided, I saw them all drawn up in four semi-circles, before four chairs, placed at the four tables; all held books in their hands, and a great book, like a Bible, lay on each table, before the vacant seat. A pause of some seconds succeeded, filled up by the low, vague hum of numbers; Miss Miller walked from class to class, hushing this indefinite sound.

A distant bell tinkled: immediately three ladies entered the room, each walked to a table and took her seat; Miss Miller assumed the fourth vacant chair, which was that nearest the door, and around which the smallest of the children were assembled: to this inferior class I was called, and placed at the bottom of it.

Business now began: the day's Collect was repeated, then certain texts of Scripture were said, and to these succeeded a protracted reading of chapters in the Bible, which lasted an hour. By the time that exercise was terminated, day had fully dawned. The indefatigable bell now sounded for the fourth time: the classes were marshalled and marched into another room to breakfast: how glad I was to behold a prospect of getting something to eat! I was now nearly sick from inanition, having taken so little the day before.

The refectory was a great, low-ceiled, gloomy room; on two long tables smoked basins of something hot, which, however, to my dismay, sent forth an odour far from inviting. I saw a universal manifestation of discontent when the fumes of the repast met the nostrils of those destined to swallow it; from the van of the procession, the tall girls of the first class, rose the whispered words:—

"Disgusting! The porridge is burnt again!"

"Silence!" ejaculated a voice; not that of Miss Miller, but one of the upper teachers, a little and dark personage, smartly dressed, but of somewhat morose aspect, who installed herself at the top of one table, while a more buxom lady presided at the other. I looked in vain for her I had first seen the night before; she was not visible: Miss Miller occupied the foot of the table where I sat, and a strange, foreign looking, elderly lady, the French teacher, as I afterwards found, took the corresponding seat at the other board. A long grace was said and a hymn sung; then a servant brought in some tea for the teachers, and the meal began.

Ravenous, and now very faint, I devoured a spoonful or two of my portion without thinking of its taste; but the first edge of hunger blunted, I perceived I had got in hand a nauseous mess: burnt porridge is almost as bad as rotten potatoes; famine itself soon sickens over it. The spoons were moved slowly: I saw each girl taste her food and try to swallow it; but in most cases the effort was soon relinquished. Breakfast was over, and none had breakfasted. Thanks being returned for what we had not got, and a second hymn chanted, the refectory was evacuated for the school-room. I was one of the last to go out, and in passing the tables, I saw one teacher take a basin of the porridge and taste it; she looked at the others; all their countenances expressed displeasure, and one of them, the stout one, whispered:—

"Abominable stuff! How shameful!"

A quarter of an hour passed before lessons again began, during which the school-room was in a glorious tumult; for that space of time, it seemed to be permitted to talk loud and more freely, and they used their privilege. The whole conversation ran on the breakfast, which one and all abused roundly. Poor things! it was the sole consolation they had. Miss Miller was now the only teacher in the room: a group of great girls standing about her, spoke with serious and sullen gestures. I heard the name of Mr. Brocklehurst pronounced by some lips; at which Miss Miller shook her head disapprovingly; but she made no great effort to check the general wrath: doubtless she shared in it.

A clock in the school-room struck nine; Miss Miller left her circle, and standing in the middle of the room, cried:—

"Silence! To your seats!"

Discipline prevailed: in five minutes the confused throng was resolved into order, and comparative silence quelled the Babel clamour of tongues. The upper teachers now punctually resumed their posts: but still, all seemed to wait. Ranged on benches down the sides of the room, the eighty girls sat motionless and erect: a quaint assemblage they appeared, all with plain locks combed from their faces, not a curl visible; in brown dresses, made high and surrounded by a narrower tucker about the throat, with little pockets of holland (shaped something like a Highlander's purse) tied in front of their frocks, and designed to serve the purpose of a work-bag: all too wearing woollen stockings and country-made shoes, fastened with brass buckles. About twenty of these clad in this costume were full-grown girls, or rather young women; it suited them ill, and gave an air of oddity even to the prettiest.

I was still looking at them, and also at intervals examining the teachers — none of whom precisely pleased me; for the stout one was a little coarse, the dark one not a little fierce, the foreigner harsh and grotesque, and Miss Miller, poor thing! looked purple, weather-beaten, and over-worked — when, as my eye wandered from face to face, the whole school rose simultaneously, as if moved by a common spring.

What was the matter? I had heard no order given: I was puzzled. Ere I had gathered my wits, the classes were again seated: but as all eyes were now turned to one point, mine followed the general direction, and encountered the personage who had received me last night. She stood at the bottom of the long room, on the hearth; for there was a fire at each end: she surveyed the two rows of girls silently and gravely. Miss Miller approaching, seemed to ask her a question, and having received her answer, went back to her place, and said aloud,—

"Monitor of the first class, fetch the globes!"

While the direction was being executed, the lady consulted moved slowly up the room. I suppose I have a considerable organ of Veneration, for I retain yet the sense of admiring awe with which my eyes traced her steps. Seen now, in broad daylight, she looked tall, fair, and shapely; brown eyes, with a benignant light in their irids, and a fine pencilling of long lashes round, relieved the whiteness of her large front; on each of her temples her hair, of a very dark brown, was clustered in round curls, according to the fashion of those times, when neither smooth bands nor long ringlets were in vogue; her dress, also in the mode of the day, was of purple cloth, relieved by a sort of Spanish trimming of black velvet; a gold watch (watches were not so common then as now) shone at her girdle. Let the reader add, to complete the picture, refined features; a complexion, if pale, clear; and a stately air and carriage, and he will have, at least, as clearly as words can give it, a correct idea of the exterior of Miss Temple — Maria Temple, as I afterwards saw the name written in a prayer-book entrusted to me to carry to church.

The superintendent of Lowood (for such was this lady) having taken her seat before a pair of globes placed on one of the tables, summoned the first class round her, and commenced giving a lesson in geography; the lower classes were called by the teachers: repetitions in history, grammar, etc., went on for an hour; writing and arithmetic succeeded, and music lessons were given by Miss Temple to some of the elder girls. The duration of each lesson was measured by the clock, which at last struck twelve. The superintendent rose: —

"I have a word to address to the pupils," said she.

The tumult of cessation from lessons was already breaking forth, but it sank at her voice. She went on: —

"You had this morning a breakfast which you could not eat; you must be hungry: — I have ordered that a lunch of bread and cheese shall be served to all."

The teachers looked at her with a sort of surprise.

"It is to be done on my responsibility," she added, in an explanatory tone to them, and immediately afterwards left the room.

The bread and cheese was presently brought in and distributed, to the high delight and refreshment of the whole school. The order was now given "To the garden!" Each put on a coarse straw bonnet, with strings of coloured calico, and a cloak of grey frieze. I was similarly equipped, and, following the stream, I made my way into the open air.

The garden was a wide enclosure, surrounded with walls so high as to exclude every glimpse of prospect; a covered verandah ran down one side, and broad walks bordered a middle space divided into scores of little beds: these beds were assigned as gardens for the pupils to cultivate, and each bed had an owner. When full of flowers they would doubtless look pretty; but now, at the latter end of January, all was wintry blight and brown decay. I shuddered as I stood and looked around me: it was an inclement day for outdoor exercise; not positively rainy, but darkened by a drizzling yellow fog; all underfoot was still soaking wet with the floods of yesterday. The stronger among the girls ran about and engaged in active games, but sundry pale and thin ones herded together for shelter and warmth in the verandah; and amongst these, as the dense mist penetrated to their shivering frames, I heard frequently the sound of a hollow cough.

As yet I had spoken to no one, nor did anybody seem to take notice of me; I stood lonely enough: but to that feeling of isolation I was accustomed; it did not oppress me much. I leant against a pillar of the verandah, drew my grey mantle close about me, and, trying to forget the cold which nipped me without, and the unsatisfied hunger which gnawed me within, delivered myself up to the employment of watching and thinking. My reflections were too undefined and fragmentary to merit record: I hardly yet knew where I was; Gateshead and my past life seemed floated away to an immeasurable distance; the present was vague and strange, and of the future I could form no conjecture. I looked round the convent-like garden, and then up at the house; a large building, half of which seemed grey and old, the other half quite new. The new part, containing the school-room and dormitory, was lit by mullioned and latticed windows, which gave it a church-like aspect; a stone tablet over the door, bore this inscription:—

"Lowood Institution.— This portion was rebuilt A. D.—, by Naomi Brocklehurst, of Brocklehurst Hall, in this county." "Let your light so shine before men that they may see your good works, and glorify your Father which is in Heaven."— St. Matt. v. 16.

I read these words over and over again: I felt that an explanation belonged to them, and was unable fully to penetrate their import. I was still pondering the signification of "Institution," and endeavouring to make out a connection between the first words and the verse of Scripture, when the sound of a cough close behind me, made me turn my head. I saw a girl sitting on a stone bench near; she had bent over a book, on the perusal of which she seemed intent: from where I stood I could see the title — it was "Rasselas;" a name that struck me as strange, and consequently attractive. In turning a leaf she happened to look up, and I said to her directly: —

"Is your book interesting?" I had already formed the intention of asking her to lend it to me some day.

"I like it," she answered, after a pause of a second or two, during which she examined me.

"What is it about?" I continued. I hardly know where I found the hardihood thus to open a conversation with a stranger; the step was contrary to my nature and habits: but I think her occupation touched a chord of sympathy somewhere; for I too liked reading, though of a frivolous and childish kind; I could not digest or comprehend the serious or substantial.

"You may look at it," replied the girl, offering me the book.

I did so; a brief examination convinced me that the contents were less taking than the title: "Rasselas" looked dull to my trifling taste; I saw nothing about fairies, nothing about genii; no bright variety seemed spread over the closely-printed pages. I returned it to her; she received it quietly, and without saying anything she was about to relapse into her former studious mood: again I ventured to disturb her: —

"Can you tell me what the writing on that stone over the door means? What is Lowood Institution?"

"This house where you are come to live."

"And why do they call it Institution? Is it in any way different from other schools?"

"It is partly a charity-school: you and I, and all the rest of us, are charity-children. I suppose you are an orphan: are not either your father or your mother dead?"

"Both died before I can remember."

"Well, all the girls here have lost either one or both parents, and this is called an institution for educating orphans."

"Do we pay no money? Do they keep us for nothing?"

"We pay, or our friends pay, fifteen pounds a year for each."

"Then why do they call us charity-children?"

"Because fifteen pounds is not enough for board and teaching, and the deficiency is supplied by subscription."

"Who subscribes?"

"Different benevolent-minded ladies and gentlemen in this neighbourhood and in London."

"Who was Naomi Brocklehurst?"

"The lady who built the new part of this house as that tablet records, and whose son overlooks and directs everything here."

"Why?"

"Because he is treasurer and manager of the establishment."

"Then this house does not belong to that tall lady who wears a watch, and who said we were to have some bread and cheese."

"To Miss Temple? Oh, no! I wish it did: she has to answer to Mr. Brocklehurst for all she does. Mr. Brocklehurst buys all our food and all our clothes."

"Does he live here?"

"No — two miles off, at a large hall."

"Is he a good man?"

"He is a clergyman, and is said to do a great deal of good."

"Did you say that tall lady was called Miss Temple?"

"Yes."

"And what are the other teachers called?"

"The one with red cheeks is called Miss Smith; she attends to the work, and cuts out — for we make our own clothes, our frocks, and pelisses, and everything; the little one with black hair is Miss Scatcherd; she teaches history and grammar, and hears the second class repetitions; and the one who wears a shawl, and has a pocket-handkerchief tied to her side with a yellow riband, is Madame Pierrot: she comes from Lisle, in France, and teaches French."

"Do you like the teachers?"

"Well enough."

"Do you like the little black one, and the Madame—?—I cannot pronounce her name as you do."

"Miss Scatcherd is hasty — you must take care not to offend her; Madame Pierrot is not a bad sort of person."

"But Miss Temple is the best — isn't she?"

"Miss Temple is very good, and very clever; she is above the rest, because she knows far more than they do."

"Have you been long here?"

"Two years."

"Are you an orphan?"

"My mother is dead."

"Are you happy here?"

"You ask rather too many questions. I have given you answers enough for the present: now I want to read."

But at that moment the summons sounded for dinner: all re-entered the house. The odour which now filled the refectory was scarcely more appetising than that which had regaled our nostrils at breakfast: the dinner was served in two huge tin-plated vessels, whence rose a strong steam redolent of rancid fat. I found the mess to consist of indifferent potatoes and strange shreds of rusty meat, mixed and cooked together. Of this preparation a tolerably abundant plateful was apportioned to each pupil. I ate what I could, and wondered within myself whether every day's fare would be like this.

After dinner, we immediately adjourned to the school-room: lessons recommended, and were continued till five o'clock.

The only marked event of the afternoon was, that I saw the girl with whom I had conversed in the verandah, dismissed in disgrace, by Miss Scatcherd, from a history class, and sent to stand in the middle of the large school-room. The punishment seemed to me in a high degree ignominious, especially for so great a girl — she looked thirteen or upwards. I expected she would show signs of great distress and shame; but to my surprise she neither wept nor blushed: composed, though grave, she stood, the central mark of all eyes. "How can she bear it so quietly — so firmly?" I asked of myself. "Were I in her place, it seems to me I should wish the earth to open and swallow me up. She looks as if she were thinking of something beyond her punishment — beyond her situation: of something not round nor before her. I have heard of day-dreams — is she in a day-dream now? Her eyes are fixed on the floor, but I am sure they do not see it — her sight seems turned in, gone down into her heart: she is looking at what she can remember, I believe; not at what is really present. I wonder what sort of a girl she is — whether good or naughty."

Soon after five P. M. we had another meal, consisting of a small mug of coffee, and half a slice of brown bread. I devoured my bread and drank my coffee with relish; but I should have been glad of as much more — I was still hungry. Half an hour's recreation succeeded, then study; then the glass of water and the piece of oat-cake, prayers, and bed. Such was my first day at Lowood.

## CHAPTER VI

THE next day commenced as before, getting up and dressing by rushlight: but this morning we were obliged to dispense with the ceremony of washing: the water in the pitchers was frozen. A change had taken place in the weather the preceding evening, and a keen north-east wind, whistling through the crevices of our bed-room windows all night long, had made us shiver in our beds, and turned the contents of the ewers to ice.

Before the long hour and a half of prayers and Bible reading was over, I felt ready to perish with cold. Breakfast-time came at last, and this morning the porridge was not burnt; the quality was eatable, the quantity small; how small my portion seemed! I wished it had been doubled.

In the course of the day I was enrolled a member of the fourth class, and regular tasks and occupations were assigned me: hitherto, I had only been a spectator of the proceedings at Lowood, I was now to become an actor therein. At first, being little accustomed to learn by heart, the lessons appeared to me both long and difficult: the frequent change from task to task, too, bewildered me; and I was glad, when, about three o'clock in the afternoon, Miss Smith put into my hands a border of muslin two yards long, together with needle, thimble, etc., and sent me to sit in a quiet corner of the school-room, with direction to hem the same. At that hour most of the others were sewing likewise; but one class still stood round Miss Scatcherd's chair reading, and as all was quiet, the subject of their lessons could be heard, together with the manner in which each girl acquitted herself, and the animadversions or commendations of Miss Scatcherd on the performance. It was English history: among the readers, I observed my acquaintance of the verandah: at the commencement of the lesson, her place had been at the top of the class, but for some error of pronunciation or some inattention to stops, she was suddenly sent to the very bottom. Even in that obscure position, Miss Scatcherd continued to make her an object of constant notice: she was continually addressing to her such phrases as the folowing:—

"Burns" (such it seems was her name: the girls here were all called by their surnames, as boys are elsewhere), "Burns, you are standing on the side of your shoe, turn your toes out immediately." "Burns, you poke your chin most unpleasantly, draw it in." "Burns, I insist on your holding your head up; I will not have you before me in that attitude," etc., etc.

A chapter having been read through twice, the books were closed and the girls examined. The lesson had comprised part of the reign of Charles I., and there were sundry questions about tonnage and poundage, and ship-money, which most of them appeared unable to answer; still, every little difficulty was solved instantly when it reached Burns: her memory seemed to have retained the substance of the whole lesson, and she was ready with answers on every point. I kept expecting that Miss Scatcherd would praise her attention; but, instead of that, she suddenly cried out: —

"You dirty, disagreeable girl! you have never cleaned your nails this morning!"

Burns made no answer: I wondered at her silence.

"Why," thought I, "does she not explain that she could neither clean her nails nor wash her face, as the water was frozen?"

My attention was now called off by Miss Smith desiring me to hold a skein of thread: while she was winding it, she talked to me from time to time, asking whether I had ever been at school before, whether I could mark, stitch, knit, etc.; till she dismissed me, I could not pursue my observations on Miss Scatcherd's movements. When I returned to my seat, that lady was just delivering an order, of which I did not catch the import; but Burns immediately left the class, and, going into the small inner room where the books were kept, returned in half a minute, carrying in her hand a bundle of twigs tied together at one end. This ominous tool she presented to Miss Scatcherd with a respectful courtesy; then she quietly, and without being told, unloosed her pinafore, and the teacher instantly and sharply inflicted on her neck a dozen strokes with the bunch of twigs. Not a tear rose to Burns' eye; and, while I paused from my sewing, because my fingers quivered at this spectacle with a sentiment of unavailing and impotent anger, not a feature of her pensive face altered its ordinary expression.

"Hardened girl!" exclaimed Miss Scatcherd; "nothing can correct you of your slatternly habits: carry the rod away."

Burns obeyed; I looked at her narrowly as she emerged from the

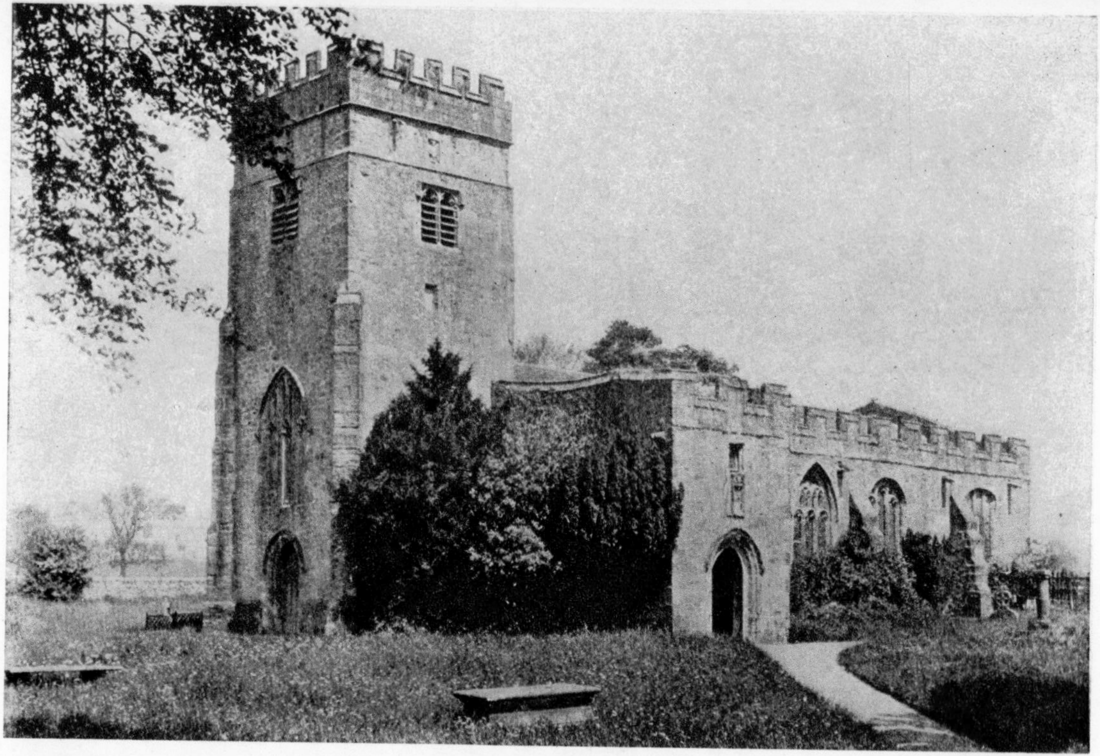

TUNSTALL CHURCH

The Reverend W. Carus-Wilson, the founder and headmaster of the Clergy Daughters' School, was rector of Tunstall, and the girls of the school attended two services every Sunday in Tunstall Church. Charlotte Brontë has drawn Mr. Carus-Wilson as "Mr. Brocklehurst," and Tunstall Church as "Brocklebury." Over the door of the transept can be seen the window of the little chamber where the pupils ate their cold lunch between the morning and book-closet; she was just putting back her handkerchief into her pocket, and the trace of a tear glistened on her thin cheek.

The play-hour in the evening I thought the pleasantest fraction of the day at Lowood: the bit of bread, the draught of coffee swallowed at five o'clock had revived vitality, if it had not satisfied hunger; the long restraint of the day was slackened; the school-room felt warmer than in the morning — its fires being allowed to burn a little more brightly to supply, in some measure, the place of candles, not yet introduced: the ruddy gloaming, the licensed uproar, the confusion of many voices gave one a welcome sense of liberty.

On the evening of the day on which I had seen Miss Scatcherd flog her pupil, Burns, I wandered as usual among the forms and tables and laughing groups without a companion, yet not feeling lonely: when I passed the windows, I now and then lifted a blind and looked out; it snowed fast, a drift was already forming against the lower panes; putting my ear close to the window, I could distinguish from the gleeful tumult within, the disconsolate moan of the wind outside.

Probably, if I had lately left a good home and kind parents, this would have been the hour when I should most keenly have regretted the separation: that wind would then have saddened my heart: this obscure chaos would have disturbed my peace: as it was, I derived from both a strange excitement, and, reckless and feverish, I wished the wind to howl more wildly, the gloom to deepen to darkness, and the confusion to rise to clamour.

Jumping over forms, and creeping under tables, I made my way to one of the fire-places; there, kneeling by the high wire fender, I found Burns, absorbed, silent, abstracted from all round her by the companionship of a book, which she read by the dim glare of the embers.

"It is still Rasselas?" I asked, coming up behind her.

"Yes," she said, "and I have just finished it."

And in five minutes more she shut it up. I was glad of this.

"Now," thought I, "I can perhaps get her to talk."

I sat down by her on the floor.

"What is your name besides Burns?"

"Helen."

"Do you come a long way from here?"

"I come from a place further north; quite on the borders of Scotland."

"Will you ever go back?"

"I hope so; but nobody can be sure of the future."

"You must wish to leave Lowood?"

"No: why should I? I was sent to Lowood to get an education; and it would be of no use going away until I have attained that object."

"But that teacher, Miss Scatcherd, is so cruel to you?"

"Cruel? Not at all! She is severe: she dislikes my faults."

"And if I were in your place I should dislike her; I should resist her; if she struck me with that rod, I should get it from her hand; I should break it under her nose."

"Probably you would do nothing of the sort: but if you did, Mr. Brocklehurst would expel you from the school; that would be a great grief to your relations. It is far better to endure patiently a smart which nobody feels but yourself than to commit a hasty action whose evil consequences will extend to all connected with you; and, besides, the Bible bids us return good for evil."

"But then it seems disgraceful to be flogged, and to be sent to stand in the middle of a room full of people; and you are such a great girl: I am far younger than you, and I could not bear it."

"Yet it would be your duty to bear it, if you could not avoid it: it is weak and silly to say you *cannot bear* what it is your fate to be required to bear."

I heard her with wonder: I could not comprehend this doctrine of endurance; and still less could I understand or sympathise with the forbearance she expressed for her chastiser. Still I felt that Helen Burns considered things by a light invisible to my eyes. I suspected she might be right and I wrong; but I would not ponder the matter deeply: like Felix, I put it off to a more convenient season.

"You say you have faults, Helen: what are they: To me you seem very good."

"Then learn from me, not to judge by appearances: I am, as Miss Scatcherd said, slatternly; I seldom put, and never keep, things in order; I am careless; I forget rules; I read when I should learn my lessons; I have no method; and sometimes I say, like you, I cannot *bear* to be subjected to systematic arrangements. This is all very provoking to Miss Scatcherd, who is naturally neat, punctual, and particular."

"And cross and cruel," I added; but Helen Burns would not admit my addition; she kept silence.

"Is Miss Temple as severe to you as Miss Scatcherd?"

At the utterance of Miss Temple's name, a soft smile flitted over her grave face.

"Miss Temple is full of goodness: it pains her to be severe to any one, even the worst in the school: she sees my errors, and tells me of them gently; and, if I do anything worthy of praise, she gives me my meed liberally. One strong proof of my wretchedly defective nature is, that even her expostulations, so mild, so rational, have no influence to cure me of my faults; and even her praise, though I value it most highly, cannot stimulate me to continued care and foresight."

"That is curious," said I: "it is so easy to be careful."

"For *you* I have no doubt it is. I observed you in your class this morning, and saw you were closely attentive: your thoughts never seemed to wander while Miss Miller explained the lesson and questioned you. Now, mine continually rove away: when I should be listening to Miss Scatcherd, and collecting all she says with assiduity, often I lose the very sound of her voice; I fall into a sort of dream. Sometimes I think I am in Northumberland, and that the noises I hear round me are the bubbling of a little brook which runs through Deepden, near our house; — then, when it comes to my turn to reply, I have to be wakened; and, having heard nothing of what was read for listening to the visionary brook, I have no answer ready."

"Yet how well you replied this afternoon."

"It was mere chance: the subject on which we had been reading had interested me. This afternoon, instead of dreaming of Deepden, I was wondering how a man who wished to do right could act so unjustly and unwisely as Charles the First sometimes did; and I thought what a pity it was that, with his integrity and conscientiousness, he could see no farther than the prerogatives of the crown. If he had but been able to look to a distance, and see how what they call the spirit of the age was tending! Still, I like Charles — I respect him — I pity him, poor murdered king! Yes, his enemies were the worst: they shed blood they had no right to shed. How dared they kill him!"

Helen was talking to herself now: she had forgotten I could not very well understand her — that I was ignorant, or nearly so, of the subject she discussed. I recalled her to my level.

"And when Miss Temple teaches you, do your thoughts wander then?"

"No, certainly, not often; because Miss Temple has generally something to say which is newer than my own reflections: her language is singularly agreeable to me, and the information she communicates is often just what I wished to gain."

"Well, then, with Miss Temple you are good?"

"Yes, in a passive way: I make no effort; I follow as inclination guides me. There is no merit in such goodness."

"A great deal: you are good to those who are good to you. It is all I ever desire to be. If people were always kind and obedient to those who are cruel and unjust, the wicked people would have it all their own way: they would never feel afraid, and so they would never alter, but would grow worse and worse. When we are struck at without a reason, we should strike back again very hard; I am sure we should — so hard as to teach the person who struck us never to do it again."

"You will change your mind, I hope, when you grow older: as yet you are but a little untaught girl."

"But I feel this, Helen: I must dislike those who, whatever I do to please them, persist in disliking me; I must resist those who punish me unjustly. It is as natural as that I should love those who show me affection, or submit to punishment when I feel it is deserved."

"Heathens and savage tribes hold that doctrine; but Christians and civilised nations disown it."

"How? I don't understand."

"It is not violence that best overcomes hate — nor vengeance that most certainly heals injury."

"What then?"

"Read the New Testament, and observe what Christ says, and how he acts; make his word your rule, and his conduct your example."

"What does he say?"

"Love your enemies; bless them that curse you; do good to them that hate you and despitefully use you."

"Then I should love Mrs. Reed, which I cannot do; I should bless her son John, which is impossible."

In her turn, Helen Burns asked me to explain; and I proceeded forthwith to pour out, in my own way, the tale of my sufferings and resentments. Bitter and truculent when excited, I spoke as I felt, without reserve or softening.

Helen heard me patiently to the end: I expected she would then make a remark, but she said nothing.

"Well," I asked impatiently, "is not Mrs. Reed a hard-hearted, bad woman?"

"She has been unkind to you, no doubt; because, you see, she dislikes your cast of character, as Miss Scatcherd does mine: but how minutely you remember all she has done and said to you! What a singularly deep impression her injustice seems to have made on your heart! No ill-usage so brands its record on my feelings. Would you not be happier if you tried to forget her severity, together with the passionate emotions it excited? Life appears to me too short to be spent in nursing animosity, or registering wrongs. We are, and must be, one and all, burdened with faults in this world: but the time will soon come when, I trust, we shall put them off in putting off our corruptible bodies; when debasement and sin will fall from us with this cumbrous frame of flesh, and only the spark of the spirit will remain,— the impalpable principle of life and thought, pure as when it left the Creator to inspire the creature: whence it came it will return; perhaps again to be communicated to some being higher than man — perhaps to pass through gradations of glory, from the pale human soul to brighten to the seraph! Surely it will never, on the contrary, be suffered to degenerate from man to fiend? No; I cannot believe that: I hold another creed; which no one ever taught me, and which I seldom mention; but in which I delight, and to which I cling: for it extends hope to all: it makes Eternity a rest — a mighty home, not a terror and an abyss. Besides, with this creed, I can so clearly distinguish between the criminal and his crime; I can so sincerely forgive the first while I abhor the last: with this creed revenge never worries my heart, degradation never too deeply disgusts me, injustice never crushes me too low: I live in calm, looking to the end."

Helen's head, always drooping, sank a little lower as she finished this sentence. I saw by her look she wished no longer to talk to me, but rather to converse with her own thoughts. She was not allowed much time for meditation: a monitor, a great rough girl, presently came up, exclaiming in a strong Cumberland accent,—

"Helen Burns, if you don't go and put your drawer in order, and fold up your work this minute, I'll tell Miss Scatcherd to come and look at it!"

Helen sighed as her reverie fled, and getting up, obeyed the monitor without reply as without delay.

# CHAPTER VII

MY first quarter at Lowood seemed an age; and not the golden age either: it comprised an irksome struggle with difficulties in habituating myself to new rules and unwonted tasks. The fear of failure in these points harassed me worse than the physical hardships of my lot; though these were no trifles.

During January, February, and part of March, the deep snows, and, after their melting, the almost impassable roads, prevented our stirring beyond the garden walls, except to go to church; but within these limits we had to pass an hour every day in the open air. Our clothing was insufficient to protect us from the severe cold: we had no boots, the snow got into our shoes and melted there; our ungloved hands became numbed and covered with chilblains, as were our feet: I remember well the distracting irritation I endured from this cause every evening, when my feet inflamed; and the torture of thrusting the swelled, raw, and stiff toes into my shoes in the morning. Then the scanty supply of food was distressing: with the keen appetites of growing children, we had scarcely sufficient to keep alive a delicate invalid. From this deficiency of nourishment resulted an abuse, which pressed hardly on the younger pupils: whenever the famished great girls had an opportunity, they would coax or menace the little ones out of their portion. Many a time I have shared between two claimants the precious morsel of brown bread distributed at tea-time; and after relinquishing to a third, half the contents of my mug of coffee, I have swallowed the remainder with an accompaniment of secret tears, forced from me by the exigency of hunger.

Sundays were dreary days in that wintry season. We had to walk two miles to Brocklebridge Church, where our patron officiated. We set out cold, we arrived at church colder: during the morning service we became almost paralysed. It was too far to return to dinner, and an allowance of cold meat and bread, in the same penurious proportion observed in our ordinary meals, was served round between the services.

At the close of the afternoon service we returned by an exposed and hilly road, where the bitter winter wind, blowing over a range of snowy summits to the north, almost flayed the skin from our faces.

I can remember Miss Temple walking lightly and rapidly along our drooping line, her plaid cloak, which the frosty wind fluttered, gathered close about her, and encouraging us, by precept and example, to keep up our spirits, and march forward, as she said, "like stalwart soldiers." The other teachers, poor things, were generally themselves too much dejected to attempt the task of cheering others.

How we longed for the light and heat of a blazing fire when we got back! But, to the little ones at least, this was denied: each hearth in the school-room was immediately surrounded by a double row of great girls, and behind them the younger children crouched in groups, wrapping their starved arms in their pinafores.

A little solace came at tea-time, in the shape of a double ration of bread — a whole, instead of a half, slice — with the delicious addition of a thin scrape of butter: it was the hebdomadal treat to which we all looked forward from Sabbath to Sabbath. I generally contrived to reserve a moiety of this bounteous repast for myself; but the remainder I was invariably obliged to part with.

The Sunday evening was spent in repeating, by heart, the Church Catechism, and the fifth, sixth, and seventh chapters of St. Matthew; and in listening to a long sermon, read by Miss Miller, whose irrepressible yawns attested her weariness. A frequent interlude of these performances was the enactment of the part of Eutychus by some half dozen of little girls; who, overpowered with sleep, would fall down, if not out of the third loft, yet off the fourth form, and be taken up half dead. The remedy was, to thrust them forward into the centre of the school-room, and oblige them to stand there till the sermon was finished. Sometimes, their feet failed them, and they sank together in a heap; they were then propped up with the monitors' high stools.

I have not yet alluded to the visits of Mr. Brocklehurst; and indeed that gentleman was from home during the greater part of the first month after my arrival; perhaps prolonging his stay with his friend the archdeacon: his absence was a relief to me. I need not say that I had my own reasons for dreading his coming: but come he did at last.

One afternoon (I had then been three weeks at Lowood), as I

was sitting with a slate in my hand, puzzling over a sum in long division, my eyes, raised in abstraction to the window, caught sight of a figure just passing: I recognised almost instinctively that gaunt outline; and when, two minutes after, all the school, teachers included, rose *en masse*, it was not necessary for me to look up in order to ascertain whose entrance they thus greeted. A long stride measured the school-room, and presently beside Miss Temple, who herself had risen, stood the same back column which had frowned on me so ominously from the hearth-rug of Gateshead. I now glanced sideways at this piece of architecture. Yes, I was right: it was Mr. Brocklehurst, buttoned up in a surtout, and looking longer, narrower, and more rigid than ever.

I had my own reasons for being dismayed at this apparition: too well I remembered the perfidious hints given by Mrs. Reed about my disposition, etc.; the promise pledged by Mr. Brocklehurst to apprise Miss Temple and the teachers of my vicious nature. All along I had been dreading the fulfilment of this promise,— I had been looking out daily for the "Coming Man," whose information respecting my past life and conversation was to brand me as a bad child for ever: now there he was. He stood at Miss Temple's side; he was speaking low in her ear: I did not doubt he was making disclosures of my villainy; and I watched her eye with painful anxiety, expecting every moment to see its dark orb turn on me a glance of repugnance and contempt. I listened too; and as I happened to be seated quite at the top of the room, I caught most of what he said: its import relieved me from immediate apprehension.

"I suppose, Miss Temple, the thread I bought at Lowton will do; it struck me that it would be just of the quality for the calico chemises, and I sorted the needles to match. You may tell Miss Smith that I forgot to make a memorandum of the darning needles, but she shall have some papers sent in next week; and she is not, on any account, to give out more than one at a time to each pupil: if they have more, they are apt to be careless and lose them. And, oh ma'am! I wish the woollen stockings were better looked to!— when I was here last, I went into the kitchen-garden and examined the clothes drying on the line; there was a quantity of black hose in a very bad state of repair: from the size of the holes in them I was sure they had not been well-mended from time to time."

He paused.

"Your directions shall be attended to, sir," said Miss Temple.

"And, ma'am," he continued, "the laundress tells me some of the girls have two clean tuckers in the week: it is too much; the rules limit them to one."

"I think I can explain that circumstance, sir. Agnes and Catherine Johnstone were invited to take tea with some friends at Lowton last Thursday, and I gave them leave to put on clean tuckers for the occasion."

Mr. Brocklehurst nodded.

"Well, for once it may pass; but please not to let the circumstance occur too often. And there is another thing which surprised me: I find, in settling accounts with the house-keeper, that a lunch, consisting of bread and cheese, has twice been served out to the girls during the past fortnight. How is this? I look over the regulations, and I find no such meal as lunch mentioned. Who introduced this innovation? and by what authority?"

"I must be responsible for the circumstance, sir," replied Miss Temple: "the breakfast was so ill-prepared that the pupils could not possibly eat it; and I dared not allow them to remain fasting till dinner time."

"Madam, allow me an instant.—You are aware that my plan in bringing up these girls is, not to accustom them to habits of luxury and indulgence, but to render them hardy, patient, self-denying. Should any little accidental disappointment of the appetite occur, such as the spoiling of a meal, the under or the over dressing of a dish, the incident ought not to be neutralised by replacing with something more delicate the comfort lost, thus pampering the body and obviating the aim of this institution; it ought to be improved to the spiritual edification of the pupils, by encouraging them to evince fortitude under the temporary privation. A brief address on those occasions would not be mistimed, wherein a judicious instructor would take the opportunity of referring to the sufferings of the primitive Christians; to the torments of martyrs; to the exhortations of our blessed Lord himself, calling upon his disciples to take up their cross and follow him; to his warnings that man shall not live by bread alone, but by every word that proceedeth out of the mouth of God; to his divine consolations, 'if ye suffer hunger or thirst for my sake, happy are ye.' Oh, madam, when you put bread and cheese, instead of burnt porridge, into these children's mouths, you may indeed feed their vile bodies, but you little think how you starve their immortal souls!"

Mr. Brocklehurst again paused — perhaps overcome by his feelings. Miss Temple had looked down when he first began to speak to her; but she now gazed straight before her, and her face, naturally pale as marble, appeared to be assuming also the coldness and fixity of that material; especially her mouth closed as if it would have required a sculptor's chisel to open it, and her brow settled gradually into petrified severity.

Meantime, Mr. Brocklehurst, standing on the hearth with his hands behind his back, majestically surveyed the whole school. Suddenly his eye gave a blink, as if it had met something that either dazzled or shocked its pupil; turning, he said in more rapid accents than he had hitherto used:—

"Miss Temple, Miss Temple, what — *what* is that girl with curled hair? Red hair, ma'am, curled — curled all over?" And extending his cane he pointed to the awful object, his hand shaking as he did so.

"It is Julia Severn," replied Miss Temple, very quietly.

"Julia Severn, ma'am! And why has she, or any other, curled hair? Why, in defiance of every precept and principle of this house, does she conform to the world so openly — here in an evangelical, charitable establishment — as to wear her hair one mass of curls?"

"Julia's hair curls naturally," returned Miss Temple, still more quietly.

"Naturally! Yes, but we are not to conform to nature: I wish these girls to be the children of Grace: and why that abundance? I have again and again intimated that I desire the hair to be arranged closely, modestly, plainly. Miss Temple, that girl's hair must be cut off entirely; I will send a barber to-morrow: and I see others who have far too much of the excrescence — that tall girl, tell her to turn round. Tell all the first form to rise up and direct their faces to the wall."

Miss Temple passed her handkerchief over her lips, as if to smooth away the involuntary smile that curled them; she gave the order, however, and when the first class could take in what was required of them, they obeyed. Leaning a little back on my bench, I could see the looks and grimaces with which they commented on this manœuvre: it was a pity Mr. Brocklehurst could not see them too;

he would perhaps have felt that, whatever he might do with the outside of the cup and platter, the inside was further beyond his interference than he imagined.

He scrutinised the reverse of these living medals some five minutes, then pronounced sentence. These words fell like the knell of doom:—

"All those top-knots must be cut off."

Miss Temple seemed to remonstrate.

"Madam," he pursued, "I have a Master to serve whose kingdom is not of this world: my mission is to mortify in these girls the lusts of the flesh; to teach them to clothe themselves with shame-facedness and sobriety, not with braided hair and costly apparel; and each of the young persons before us has a string of hair twisted in plaits which vanity itself might have woven: these, I repeat, must be cut off; think of the time wasted, of——"

Mr. Brocklehurst was here interrupted: three other visitors, ladies, now entered the room. They ought to have come a little sooner to have heard his lecture on dress, for they were splendidly attired in velvet, silk, and furs. The two younger of the trio (fine girls of sixteen and seventeen) had grey beaver hats, then in fashion, shaded with ostrich plumes, and from under the brim of this graceful head-dress fell a profusion of light tresses, elaborately curled; the elderly lady was enveloped in a costly velvet shawl, trimmed with ermine, and she wore a false front of French curls.

These ladies were deferentially received by Miss Temple, as Mrs. and Misses Brocklehurst, and conducted to seats of honour at the top of the room. It seems they had come in the carriage with their reverend relative, and had been conducting a rummaging scrutiny of the rooms upstairs, while he transacted business with the housekeeper, questioned the laundress, and lectured the superintendent. They now proceeded to address divers remarks and reproofs to Miss Smith, who was charged with the care of the linen and the inspection of the dormitories: but I had no time to listen to what they said; other matters called off and enchained my attention.

Hitherto, while gathering up the discourse of Mr. Brocklehurst and Miss Temple, I had not, at the same time, neglected precautions to secure my personal safety; which I thought would be effected, if I could only elude observation. To this end, I had sat well back on the form, and while seeming to be busy with my sum, had held my slate in such a manner as to conceal my face: I might have escaped notice, had not my treacherous slate somehow happened to slip from my hand, and falling with an obtrusive crash, directly drawn every eye upon me; I knew it was all over now, and, as I stooped to pick up the two fragments of slate, I rallied my forces for the worst. It came.

"A careless girl!" said Mr. Brocklehurst, and immediately after —"It is the new pupil, I perceive." And before I could draw breath, "I must not forget I have a word to say respecting her." Then aloud: how loud it seemed to me! "Let the child who broke her slate, come forward!"

Of my own accord, I could not have stirred; I was paralysed: but the two great girls who sat on each side of me, set me on my legs and pushed me towards the dread judge, and then Miss Temple gently assisted me to his very feet, and I caught her whispered counsel,—

"Don't be afraid, Jane, I saw it was an accident; you shall not be punished."

The kind whisper went to my heart like a dagger.

"Another minute, and she will despise me for a hypocrite," thought I; and an impulse of fury against Reed, Brocklehurst, and Co. bounded in my pulses at the conviction. I was no Helen Burns.

"Fetch that stool," said Mr. Brocklehurst, pointing to a very high one from which a monitor had just risen: it was brought.

"Place the child upon it."

And I was placed there, by whom I don't know: I was in no condition to note particulars; I was only aware that they had hoisted me up to the height of Mr. Brocklehurst's nose, that he was within a yard of me, and that a spread of shot orange and purple silk pelisses, and a cloud of silvery plumage extended and waved below me.

Mr. Brocklehurst hemmed.

"Ladies," said he, turning to his family; "Miss Temple, teachers, and children, you all see this girl?"

Of course they did; for I felt their eyes directed like burning-glass against my scorched skin.

"You see she is yet young; you observe she possesses the ordinary form of childhood; God has graciously given her the shape that He has given to all of us; no signal deformity points her out as a marked character. Who would think that the Evil One had already found a servant and agent in her? Yet such, I grieve to say, is the case."

A pause — in which I began to steady the palsy of my nerves, and to feel that the Rubicon was passed; and that the trial, no longer to be shirked, must be firmly sustained.

"My dear children," pursued the black marble clergyman, with pathos, "this is a sad, a melancholy occasion; for it becomes my duty to warn you, that this girl, who might be one of God's own lambs, is a little castaway: not a member of the true flock, but evidently an interloper and an alien. You must be on your guard against her; you must shun her example: if necessary, avoid her company, exclude her from your sports, and shut her out from your converse. Teachers, you must watch her: keep your eyes on her movements, weigh well her words, scrutinise her actions, punish her body to save her soul: if, indeed, such salvation be possible, for (my tongue falters while I tell it) this girl, this child, the native of a Christian land, worse than many a little heathen who says its prayers to Brahma and kneels before Juggernaut — this girl is — a liar!"

Now came a pause of ten minutes; during which I, by this time in perfect possession of my wits, observed all the female Brocklehursts produce their pocket-handkerchiefs and apply them to their optics, while the elderly lady swayed herself to and fro, and the two younger ones whispered, "How shocking!"

Mr. Brocklehurst resumed.

"This I learned from her benefactress; from the pious and charitable lady who adopted her in her orphan state, reared her as her own daughter, and whose kindness, whose generosity the unhappy girl repaid by an ingratitude so bad, so dreadful, that at last her excellent patroness was obliged to separate her from her own young ones, fearful lest her vicious example should contaminate their purity: she has sent her here to be healed, even as the Jews of old sent their diseased to the troubled pool of Bethesda; and, teachers, superintendent, I beg of you not to allow the waters to stagnate round her."

With this sublime conclusion, Mr. Brocklehurst adjusted the top button of his surtout, muttered something to his family, who rose, bowed to Miss Temple, and then all the great people sailed in state from the room. Turning at the door, my judge said:—

"Let her stand half an hour longer on that stool, and let no one speak to her during the remainder of the day."

There was I, then, mounted aloft: I, who had said I could not bear the shame of standing on my natural feet in the middle of the room, was now exposed to general view on a pedestal of infamy. What my sensations were, no language can describe; but just as they all rose, stifling my breath and constricting my throat, a girl came up and passed me: in passing, she lifted her eyes. What a strange light inspired them! What an extraordinary sensation that ray sent through me! How the new feeling bore me up! It was as if a martyr, a hero, had passed a slave or victim, and imparted strength in the transit. I mastered the rising hysteria, lifted up my head, and took a firm stand on the stool. Helen Burns asked some slight question about her work of Miss Smith, was chidden for the triviality of the inquiry, returned to her place, and smiled at me as she again went by. What a smile! I remember it now, and I know that it was the effluence of fine intellect, of true courage; it lit up her marked lineaments, her thin face, her sunken grey eye, like a reflection from the aspect of an angel. Yet at that moment Helen Burns wore on her arm "the untidy badge"; scarcely an hour ago I had heard her condemned by Miss Scatcherd to a dinner of bread and water on the morrow, because she had blotted an exercise in copying it out. Such is the imperfect nature of man! such spots are there on the disc of the clearest planet; and eyes like Miss Scatcherd's can only see those minute defects, and are blind to the full brightness of the orb.

## CHAPTER VIII

ERE the half-hour ended, five o'clock struck; school was dismissed, and all were gone into the refectory to tea. I now ventured to descend: it was deep dusk; I retired into a corner and sat down on the floor. The spell by which I had been so far supported began to dissolve; reaction took place, and soon, so overwhelming was the grief that seized me, I sank prostrate with my face to the ground. Now I wept: Helen Burns was not here; nothing sustained me; left to myself I abandoned myself, and my tears watered the boards. I had meant to be so good, and to do so much at Lowood: to make so many friends, to earn respect, and win affection. Already I had made visible progress: that very morning I had reached the head of my class; Miss Miller had praised me warmly; Miss Temple had smiled approbation; she had promised to teach me drawing, and to let me learn French, if I continued to make similar improvement two months longer: and then I was well-received by my fellow-pupils; treated as an equal by those of my own age, and not molested by any; now, here I lay again crushed and trodden on; and could I ever rise more?

"Never," I thought; and ardently I wished to die. While sobbing out this wish in broken accents, some one approached: I started up — again Helen Burns was near me; the fading fires just showed her coming up the long, vacant room; she brought my coffee and bread.

"Come, eat something," she said; but I put both away from me, feeling as if a drop or a crumb would have choked me in my present condition. Helen regarded me, probably with surprise: I could not now abate my agitation, though I tried hard; I continued to weep aloud. She sat down on the ground near me, embraced her knees with her arms, and rested her head upon them; in that attitude she remained silent as an Indian. I was the first who spoke: —

"Helen, why do you stay with a girl whom everybody believes to be a liar?"

"Everybody, Jane? Why, there are only eighty people who have heard you called so, and the world contains hundreds of millions."

"But what have I to do with millions? The eighty I know despise me."

"Jane, you are mistaken: probably not one in the school either despises or dislikes you: many, I am sure, pity you much."

"How can they pity me after what Mr. Brocklehurst said?"

"Mr. Brocklehurst is not a god: nor is he even a great and admired man: he is little liked here; he never took steps to make himself liked. Had he treated you as an especial favourite, you would have found enemies declared or covert, all around you; as it is, the greater number would offer you sympathy if they dared. Teachers and pupils may look coldly on you for a day or two, but friendly feelings are concealed in their hearts; and if you persevere in doing well, these feelings will ere long appear so much the more evidently for their temporary suppression. Besides, Jane,"—— she paused.

"Well, Helen?" said I, putting my hand into hers: she chafed my fingers gently to warm them, and went on:—

"If all the world hated you, and believed you wicked, while your own conscience approved you, and absolved you from guilt, you would not be without friends."

"No; I know I should think well of myself; but that is not enough; if others don't love me, I would rather die than live — I cannot bear to be solitary and hated, Helen. Look here; to gain some real affection from you, or Miss Temple, or any other whom I truly love, I would willingly submit to have the bone of my arm broken, or let a bull toss me, or to stand behind a kicking horse, and let it dash its hoof at my chest,"—

"Hush, Jane! you think too much of the love of human beings; you are too impulsive, too vehement: the sovereign hand that created your frame, and put life into it, has provided you with other resources than your feeble self, or than creatures feeble as you. Besides this earth, and besides the race of men, there is an invisible world and a kingdom of spirits: that world is round us, for it is everywhere; and those spirits watch us, for they are commissioned to guard us; and if we were dying in pain and shame, if scorn smote us on all sides, and hatred crushed us, angels see our tortures, recognise our innocence (if innocent we be: as I know you are of this charge which Mr. Brocklehurst has weakly and pompously repeated at second-hand from Mrs. Reed; for I read a sincere nature in your ardent eyes and on your clear front), and God waits only the separation of spirit from flesh to crown us with a reward. Why, then, should we ever sink overwhelmed with distress, when life is so soon over, and death is so certain an entrance to happiness — to glory?"

I was silent: Helen had calmed me; but in the tranquillity she imparted there was an alloy of inexpressible sadness. I felt the impression of woe as she spoke, but I could not tell whence it came; and when, having done speaking, she breathed a little fast and coughed a short cough, I momentarily forgot my own sorrows to yield to a vague concern for her.

Resting my head on Helen's shoulder, I put my arms round her waist; she drew me to her, and we reposed in silence. We had not sat long thus, when another person came in. Some heavy clouds, swept from the sky by a rising wind, had left the moon bare; and her light, streaming in through a window near, shone full both on us and on the approaching figure, which we at once recognised as Miss Temple.

"I came on purpose to find you, Jane Eyre," said she; "I want you in my room; and as Helen Burns is with you, she may come too."

We went; following the superintendent's guidance, we had to thread some intricate passages, and mount a staircase before we reached her apartment; it contained a good fire, and looked cheerful. Miss Temple told Helen Burns to be seated in a low arm-chair on one side of the hearth, and herself taking another, she called me to her side.

"Is it all over?" she asked, looking down at my face. "Have you cried your grief away?"

"I'm afraid I never shall do that."

"Why?"

"Because I have been wrongly accused; and you, ma'am, and everybody else will now think me wicked."

"We shall think you what you prove yourself to be, my child. Continue to act as a good girl, and you will satisfy me."

"Shall I, Miss Temple?"

"You will," said she, passing her arm round me. "And now tell me who is the lady whom Mr. Brocklehurst called your benefactress?"

"Mrs. Reed, my uncle's wife. My uncle is dead, and he left me to her care."

"Did she not, then, adopt you of her own accord?"

"No, ma'am; she was sorry to have to do it: but my uncle, as I have often heard the servants say, got her to promise before he died, that she would always keep me."

"Well now, Jane, you know, or at least I will tell you, that when a criminal is accused, he is always allowed to speak in his own defence. You have been charged with falsehood; defend yourself to me as well as you can. Say whatever your memory suggests as true; but add nothing and exaggerate nothing."

I resolved, in the depth of my heart, that I would be most moderate — most correct; and, having reflected a few minutes in order to arrange coherently what I had to say, I told her all the story of my bad childhood. Exhausted by emotion, my language was more subdued than it generally was when it developed that sad theme; and mindful of Helen's warnings against the indulgence of resentment, I infused into the narrative far less of gall and wormwood than ordinary. Thus restrained and simplified, it sounded more credible: I felt as I went on that Miss Temple fully believed me.

In the course of the tale I had mentioned Mr. Lloyd as having come to see me after the fit: for I never forgot the, to me, frightful episode of the red-room; in detailing which, my excitement was sure, in some degree, to break bounds; for nothing could soften in my recollection the spasm of agony which clutched my heart when Mrs. Reed spurned my wild supplication for pardon, and locked me a second time in the dark and haunted chamber.

I had finished: Miss Temple regarded me a few minutes in silence; she then said —

"I know something of Mr. Lloyd; I shall write to him; if his reply agrees with your statement, you shall be publicly cleared from every imputation: to me, Jane, you are clear now."

She kissed me, and still keeping me at her side (where I was well contented to stand, for I derived a child's pleasure from the contemplation of her face, her dress, her one or two ornaments, her white forehead, her clustered and shining curls, and beaming dark eyes), she proceeded to address Helen Burns.

"How are you to-night, Helen? Have you coughed much today?"

"Not quite so much I think, ma'am."

"And the pain in your chest?"

"It is a little better."

Miss Temple got up, took her hand and examined her pulse; then she returned to her own seat: as she resumed it, I heard her sigh low. She was pensive a few minutes, then rousing herself, she said cheerfully:—

"But you two are my visitors to-night; I must treat you as such." She rang her bell.

"Barbara," she said to the servant who answered it, "I have not yet had tea; bring the tray, and place cups for these two young ladies."

And a tray was soon brought. How pretty, to my eyes, did the china and bright teapot look, placed on the little round table near the fire! How fragrant was the steam of the beverage, and the scent of the toast! of which, however, I, to my dismay (for I was beginning to be hungry), discerned only a very small portion: Miss Temple discerned it too:—

"Barbara," said she, "can you not bring a little more bread and butter? There is not enough for three."

Barbara went out: she returned soon:—

"Madam, Mrs. Harden says she has sent up the usual quantity."

Mrs. Harden, be it observed, was the housekeeper: a woman after Mr. Brocklehurst's own heart, made up of equal parts of whalebone and iron.

"Oh, very well!" returned Miss Temple; "we must make it do, Barbara, I suppose." And as the girl withdrew, she added, smiling, "Fortunately, I have it in my power to supply deficiencies for this once."

Having invited Helen and me to approach the table, and placed before each of us a cup of tea with one delicious but thin morsel of toast, she got up, unlocked a drawer, and taking from it a parcel wrapped in paper, disclosed presently to our eyes a good-sized seed-cake.

"I meant to give each of you some of this to take with you," said she; "but as there is so little toast, you must have it now," and she proceeded to cut slices with a generous hand.

We feasted that evening as on nectar and ambrosia; and not the least delight of the entertainment was the smile of gratification with which our hostess regarded us, as we satisfied our famished appetites on the delicate fare she liberally supplied. Tea over and tray removed, she again summoned us to the fire; we sat one on each side of her, and now a conversation followed between her and Helen, which it was indeed a privilege to be admitted to hear.

Miss Temple had always something of serenity in her air, of state in her mien, of refined propriety in her language, which precluded deviation into the ardent, the excited, the eager: something which chastened the pleasure of those who looked on her and listened to her, by a controlling sense of awe; and such was my feeling now: but as to Helen Burns, I was struck with wonder.

The refreshing meal, the brilliant fire, the presence and kindness of her beloved instructress, or, perhaps, more than all these, something in her own unique mind, had roused her powers within her. They woke, they kindled: first, they glowed in the bright tint of her cheek, which till this hour I had never seen but pale and bloodless; then they shone in the liquid lustre of her eyes, which had suddenly acquired a beauty more singular than that of Miss Temple's — a beauty neither of fine colour nor long eyelash, nor pencilled brow, but of meaning, of movement, of radiance. Then her soul sat on her lips, and language flowed, from what source I cannot tell: has a girl of fourteen a heart large enough, vigorous enough to hold the swelling spring of pure, full, fervid eloquence? Such was the characteristic of Helen's discourse on that, to me, memorable evening; her spirit seemed hastening to live within a very brief span as much as many live during a protracted existence.

They conversed of things I had never heard of; of nations and times past; of countries far away: of secrets of nature discovered or guessed at: they spoke of books: how many they had read! What stores of knowledge they possessed! Then they seemed so familiar with French names and French authors: but my amazement reached its climax when Miss Temple asked Helen if she sometimes snatched a moment to recall the Latin her father had taught her, and taking a book from a shelf, bade her read and construe a page of "Virgil"; and Helen obeyed, my organ of Veneration expanding at every sounding line. She had scarcely finished ere the bell announced bedtime: no delay could be admitted; Miss Temple embraced us both, saying, as she drew us to her heart:—

"God bless you, my children!"

Helen she held a little longer than me: she let her go more reluctantly; it was Helen her eye followed to the door; it was for her she a second time breathed a sad sigh; for her she wiped a tear from her cheek.

On reaching the bed-room, we heard the voice of Miss Scatcherd: she was examining drawers; she had just pulled out Helen Burns's, and when we entered Helen was greeted with a sharp reprimand, and told that to-morrow she should have half a dozen of untidily folded articles pinned to her shoulder.

"My things were indeed in shameful disorder," murmured Helen to me, in a low voice: "I intended to have arranged them, but I forgot."

Next morning, Miss Scatcherd wrote in conspicuous characters on a piece of pasteboard the word "Slattern," and bound it like a phylactery round Helen's large, mild, intelligent, and benign-looking forehead. She wore it till evening, patient, unresentful, regarding it as a deserved punishment. The moment Miss Scatcherd withdrew after afternoon-school, I ran to Helen, tore it off, and thrust it into the fire: the fury of which she was incapable had been burning in my soul all day, and tears, hot and large, had continually been scalding my cheek; for the spectacle of her sad resignation gave me an intolerable pain at the heart.

About a week subsequently to the incidents above narrated, Miss Temple, who had written to Mr. Lloyd, received his answer: it appeared that what he said went to corroborate my account. Miss Temple, having assembled the whole school, announced that inquiry had been made into the charges alleged against Jane Eyre, and that she was most happy to be able to pronounce her completely cleared from every imputation. The teachers then shook hands with me and kissed me, and a murmur of pleasure ran through the ranks of my companions.

Thus relieved of a grievous load, I from that hour set to work afresh, resolved to pioneer my way through every difficulty: I toiled hard, and my success was proportionate to my efforts; my memory, not naturally tenacious, improved with practice; exercise sharpened my wits; in a few weeks I was promoted to a higher class; in less than two months I was allowed to commence French and drawing. I learned the first two tenses of the verb *Etre,* and sketched my first cottage (whose walls, by-the-by, outrivalled in slope those of the leaning tower of Pisa), on the same day. That night, on going to bed, I forgot to prepare in imagination the Barmecide supper of hot roast potatoes, or white bread and new milk, with which I was wont to amuse my inward cravings: I feasted instead on the spectacle of ideal drawings, which I saw in the dark; all the work of my own hands: freely pencilled houses and trees, picturesque rocks and ruins, Cuyp-like groups of cattle, sweet paintings of butterflies hovering over unblown roses, of birds picking at ripe cherries, of wrens' nests enclosing pearl-like eggs, wreathed about with young ivy sprays. I examined, too, in thought, the possibility of my ever being able to translate currently a certain little French story-book which Madame Pierrot had that day shown me; nor was that problem solved to my satisfaction ere I fell sweetly asleep.

Well has Solomon said—"Better is a dinner of herbs where love is, than a stalled ox and hatred therewith."

I would not now have exchanged Lowood with all its privations, for Gateshead and its daily luxuries.

## CHAPTER IX

BUT the privations, or rather the hardships, of Lowood lessened. Spring drew on, she was indeed already come; the frosts of winter had ceased; its snows were melted, its cutting winds ameliorated. My wretched feet, flayed and swollen to lameness by the sharp air of January, began to heal and subside under the gentler breathings of April; the nights and mornings no longer by their Canadian temperature froze the very blood in our veins; we could now endure the play-hour in the garden: sometimes on a sunny day it began even to be pleasant and genial, and a greenness grew over those brown beds, which, freshening daily, suggested the thought that Hope traversed them at night, and left each morning brighter traces of her steps. Flowers peeped out amongst the leaves; snow-drops, crocuses, purple auriculas, and golden-eyed pansies. On Thursday afternoons (half-holidays) we now took walks, and found still sweeter flowers opening by the wayside, under the hedges.

I discovered, too, that a great pleasure, an enjoyment which the horizon only bounded, lay all outside the high and spike-guarded walls of our garden: this pleasure consisted in prospect of noble summits girdling a great hill-hollow, rich in verdure and shadow: in a bright beck, full of dark stones and sparkling eddies. How different had this scene looked when I viewed it laid out beneath the iron sky of winter, stiffened in frost, shrouded with snow! — when mists as chill as death wandered to the impulse of east winds along those purple peaks, and rolled down "ing" and holm till they blended with the frozen fog of the beck! That beck itself was then a torrent, turbid and curbless: it tore asunder the wood, and sent a raving sound through the air, often thickened with wild rain or whirling sleet; and for the forest on its banks, *that* showed only ranks of skeletons.

April advanced to May: a bright, serene May it was; days of blue sky, placid sunshine, and soft western or southern gales filled up its duration. And now vegetation matured with vigour; Lowood shook loose its tresses; it became all green, all flowery; its great elm, ash, and oak skeletons were restored to majestic life; woodland plants sprang up profusely in its recesses; unnumbered varieties of moss filled its hollows, and it made a strange ground-sunshine out of the wealth of its wild primrose plants: I have seen their pale gold gleam in overshadowed spots like scatterings of the sweetest lustre. All this I enjoyed often and fully, free, unwatched, and almost alone; for this unwonted liberty and pleasure there was a cause, to which it now becomes my task to advert.

Have I not described a pleasant site for a dwelling, when I speak of it as bosomed in hill and wood, and rising from the verge of a stream? Assuredly, pleasant enough: but whether healthy or not is another question.

That forest-dell, where Lowood lay, was the cradle of fog and fog-bred pestilence; which, quickening with the quickening spring, crept into the Orphan Asylum, breathed typhus through its crowded school-room and dormitory, and, ere May arrived, transformed the seminary into an hospital.

Semi-starvation and neglected colds had predisposed most of the pupils to receive infection: forty-five out of the eighty girls lay ill at one time. Classes were broken up, rules relaxed. The few who continued well were allowed almost unlimited licence; because the medical attendant insisted on the necessity of frequent exercise to keep them in health: and had it been otherwise, no one had leisure to watch or restrain them. Miss Temple's whole attention was absorbed by the patients: she lived in the sick-room, never quitting it except to snatch a few hours' rest at night. The teachers were fully occupied with packing up and making other necessary preparations for the departure of those girls who were fortunate enough to have friends and relations able and willing to remove them from the seat of contagion. Many, already smitten, went home only to die; some died at the school, and were buried quietly and quickly, the nature of the malady forbidding delay.

While disease had thus become an inhabitant of Lowood, and death its frequent visitor; while there was gloom and fear within its walls; while its rooms and passages steamed with hospital smells, the drug and the pastille striving vainly to overcome the effluvia of mortality, that bright May shone unclouded over the bold hills and beautiful woodland out of doors. Its garden, too, glowed with flowers: hollyhocks had sprung up tall as trees, lilies had opened, tulips and roses were in bloom; the borders of the little beds were gay with pink thrift and crimson double-daisies; the sweet-briars gave out, morning and evening, their scent of spice and apples; and these fragrant treasures were all useless for most of the inmates of Lowood, except to furnish now and then a handful of herbs and blossoms to put in a coffin.

But I, and the rest who continued well, enjoyed fully the beauties of the scene and season; they let us ramble in the wood, like gipsies, from morning till night; we did what we liked, went where we liked: we lived better too. Mr. Brocklehurst and his family never came near Lowood now: household matters were not scrutinised into: the cross housekeeper was gone, driven away by the fear of infection; her successor, who had been matron at the Lowton Dispensary, unused to the ways of her new abode, provided with comparative liberality. Besides, there were fewer to feed: the sick could eat little; our breakfast-basins were better filled: when there was no time to prepare a regular dinner, which often happened, she would give us a large piece of cold pie, or a thick slice of bread and cheese, and this we carried away with us to the wood, where we each chose the spot we liked best, and dined sumptuously.

My favourite seat was a smooth and broad stone, rising white and dry from the very middle of the beck, and only to be got at by wading through the water; a feat I accomplished barefoot. The stone was just broad enough to accommodate, comfortably, another girl and me, at that time my chosen comrade — one Mary Ann Wilson; a shrewd observant personage, whose society I took pleasure in, partly because she was witty and original, and partly because she had a manner which set me at my ease. Some years older than I, she knew more of the world, and could tell me many things I liked to hear: with her my curiosity found gratification: to my faults also she gave ample indulgence, never imposing curb or rein on anything I said. She had a turn for narrative, I for analysis; she liked to inform, I to question; so we got on swimmingly together, deriving much entertainment, if not much improvement, from our mutual intercourse.

And where, meantime, was Helen Burns? Why did I not spend these sweet days of liberty with her? Had I forgotten her? or was I so worthless as to have grown tired of her pure society? Surely the Mary Ann Wilson I have mentioned was inferior to my first acquaintance: she could only tell me amusing stories, and reciprocate any racy and pungent gossip I chose to indulge in; while, if I have spoken truth of Helen, she was qualified to give those who enjoyed the privilege of her converse, a taste of far higher things.

True, reader; and I knew and felt this: and though I am a defective being, with many faults and few redeeming points, yet I never tired of Helen Burns; nor ever ceased to cherish for her a sentiment of attachment, as strong, tender, and respectful as any that ever animated my heart. How could it be otherwise, when Helen, at all times and under all circumstances, evinced for me a quiet and faithful friendship, which ill-humour never soured, nor irritation ever troubled? But Helen was ill at present: for some weeks she had been removed from my sight to I knew not what room upstairs. She was not, I was told, in the hospital portion of the house with the fever patients; for her complaint was consumption, not typhus: and by consumption I, in my ignorance, understood something mild, which time and care would be sure to alleviate.

I was confirmed in this idea by the fact of her once or twice coming downstairs on very warm sunny afternoons, and being taken by Miss Temple into the garden: but, on these occasions, I was not allowed to go and speak to her; I only saw her from the schoolroom window, and then not distinctly; for she was much wrapped up, and sat at a distance under the verandah.

One evening, in the beginning of June, I had stayed out very late with Mary Ann in the wood; we had, as usual, separated ourselves from the others, and had wandered far: so far that we lost our way, and had to ask it at a lonely cottage, where a man and woman lived, who looked after a herd of half-wild swine that fed on the mast in the wood. When we got back, it was after moon-rise: a pony, which we knew to be the surgeon's, was standing at the garden door. Mary Ann remarked that she supposed some one must be very ill, as Mr. Bates had been sent for at that time of the evening. She went into the house: I stayed behind a few minutes to plant in my garden a handful of roots I had dug up in the forest, and which I feared would wither if I left them till the morning. This done, I lingered yet a little longer: the flowers smelt so sweet as the dew fell; it was such a pleasant evening, so serene, so warm; the still glowing west promised so fairly another fine day on the morrow; the moon rose with such majesty in the grave east. I was noting these things and enjoying them as a child might, when it entered my mind as it had never done before: —

"How sad to be lying now on a sick bed, and to be in danger of dying! This world is pleasant — it would be dreary to be called from it, and to have to go who knows where?"

And then my mind made its first earnest effort to comprehend what had been infused into it concerning heaven and hell: and for the first time it recoiled, baffled; and for the first time glancing behind, on each side, and before it, it saw all round an unfathomed gulf: it felt the one point where it stood — the present; all the rest was formless cloud and vacant depth: and it shuddered at the thought of tottering, and plunging amid that chaos. While pondering this new idea, I heard the front door open; Mr. Bates came out, and with him was a nurse. After she had seen him mount his horse and depart, she was about to close the door, but I ran up to her.

"How is Helen Burns?"

"Very poorly," was the answer.

"Is it her Mr. Bates has been to see?"

"Yes."

"And what does he say about her?"

"He says she'll not be here long."

This phrase, uttered in my hearing yesterday, would have only conveyed the notion that she was about to be removed to Northumberland, to her own home. I should not have suspected that it meant she was dying; but I knew instantly now; it opened clear on my comprehension that Helen Burns was numbering her last days in this world, and that she was going to be taken to the region of spirits, if such region there were. I experienced a shock of horror, then a strong thrill of grief, then a desire — a necessity to see her; and I asked in what room she lay.

"She is in Miss Temple's room," said the nurse.

"May I go up and speak to her?"

"Oh, no, child! It is not likely; and now it is time for you to come in; you'll catch the fever if you stop out when the dew is falling."

The nurse closed the front door; I went in by the side entrance which led to the school-room: I was just in time; it was nine o'clock, and Miss Miller was calling the pupils to go to bed.

It might be two hours later, probably near eleven, when I — not having been able to fall asleep, and deeming, from the perfect silence of the dormitory, that my companions were all wrapt in profound repose — rose softly, put on my frock over my night-dress, and, without shoes, crept from the apartment, and set off in quest of Miss Temple's room. It was quite at the other end of the house; but I knew my way; and the light of the unclouded summer moon, entering here and there at passage windows, enabled me to find it without difficulty. An odour of camphor and burnt vinegar warned me when I came near the fever room: and I passed its door quickly, fearful lest the nurse who sat up all night should hear me. I dreaded being discovered and sent back; for I *must* see Helen,— I must embrace her before she died,— I must give her one last kiss, exchange with her one last word.

Having descended a staircase, traversed a portion of the house below, and succeeded in opening and shutting, without noise, two doors, I reached another flight of steps; these I mounted, and then just opposite to me was Miss Temple's room. A light shone through the key-hole, and from under the door; a profound stillness pervaded the vicinity. Coming near, I found the door slightly ajar; probably to admit some fresh air into the close abode of sickness. Indisposed to hesitate, and full of impatient impulses — soul and senses quivering with keen throes — I put it back and looked in. My eye sought Helen, and feared to find death.

Close by Miss Temple's bed, and half covered with its white curtains, there stood a little crib. I saw the outline of a form under the clothes, but the face was hid by the hangings: the nurse I had spoken to in the garden sat in an easy chair, asleep; an unsnuffed candle burnt dimly on the table. Miss Temple was not to be seen: I knew afterwards that she had been called to a delirious patient in the fever room. I advanced; then paused by the crib side: my hand was on the curtain, but I preferred speaking before I withdrew it. I still recoiled at the dread of seeing a corpse.

"Helen!" I whispered softly; "are you awake?"

She stirred herself, put back the curtain, and I saw her face, pale, wasted, but quite composed: she looked so little changed that my fear was instantly dissipated.

"Can it be you, Jane?" she asked in her own gentle voice.

"Oh!" I thought, "she is not going to die; they are mistaken: she could not speak and look so calmly if she were."

I got on to her crib and kissed her; her forehead was cold and her cheek both cold and thin, and so were her hand and wrist; but she smiled as of old.

"Why are you come here, Jane? It is past eleven o'clock: I heard it strike some minutes since."

"I came to see you, Helen: I heard you were very ill, and I could not sleep till I had spoken to you."

"You came to bid me good-bye, then: you are just in time probably."

"Are you going somewhere, Helen? Are you going home?"

"Yes; to my long home — my last home."

"No, no, Helen!" I stopped, distressed. While I tried to devour my tears, a fit of coughing seized Helen; it did not, however, wake the nurse; when it was over, she lay some minutes exhausted; then she whispered: —

"Jane, your little feet are bare; lie down and cover yourself with my quilt."

I did so: she put her arm over me, and I nestled close to her. After a long silence, she resumed; still whispering, —

"I am very happy, Jane; and when you hear that I am dead, you must be sure and not grieve: there is nothing to grieve about. We all must die one day, and the illness which is removing me is not painful; it is gentle and gradual: my mind is at rest. I leave no one to regret me much: I have only a father; and he is lately married, and will not miss me. By dying young, I shall escape great sufferings. I had not qualities or talents to make my way very well in the world: I should have been continually at fault."

"But where are you going to, Helen? Can you see? Do you know?"

"I believe; I have faith: I am going to God."

"Where is God? What is God?"

"My Maker and yours, who will never destroy what he created. I rely implicitly on his power, and confide wholly in his goodness: I count the hours till that eventful one arrives which shall restore me to him, reveal him to me."

"You are sure, then, Helen, that there is such a place as heaven; and that our souls can get to it when we die?"

"I am sure there is a future state; I believe God is good; I can resign my immortal part to him without any misgiving. God is my father; God is my friend: I love him; I believe he loves me."

"And shall I see you again, Helen, when I die?"

"You will come to the same region of happiness: be received by the same mighty, universal Parent, no doubt, dear Jane."

Again I questioned; but this time only in thought. "Where is that region? Does it exist?" And I clasped my arms closer round Helen; she seemed dearer to me than ever; I felt as if I could not let her go; I lay with my face hidden on her neck. Presently she said in the sweetest tone,—

"How comfortable I am! That last fit of coughing has tired me a little; I feel as if I could sleep: but don't leave me, Jane; I like to have you near me."

"I'll stay with you, *dear* Helen: no one shall take me away."

"Are you warm, darling?"

"Yes."

"Good-night, Jane."

"Good-night, Helen."

She kissed me, and I her; and we both soon slumbered.

When I awoke it was day; an unusual movement roused me; I looked up; I was in somebody's arms; the nurse held me; she was carrying me through the passage back to the dormitory. I was not reprimanded for leaving my bed; people had something else to think about: no explanation was afforded then to my many questions; but a day or two afterwards I learned that Miss Temple, on returning to her own room at dawn, had found me laid in a little crib; my face against Helen Burns's shoulder, my arms round her neck. I was asleep, and Helen was — dead.

Her grave is in Brocklebridge churchyard: for fifteen years after her death it was only covered by a grassy mound; but now a gray marble tablet marks the spot, inscribed with her name, and the word "Resurgam."

## CHAPTER X

HITHERTO I have recorded in detail the events of my insignificant existence: to the first ten years of my life, I have given almost as many chapters. But this is not to be a regular autobiography: I am only bound to invoke memory where I know her responses will possess some degree of interest; therefore I now pass a space of eight years almost in silence: a few lines only are necessary to keep up the links of connection.

When the typhus fever had fulfilled its mission of devastation at Lowood, it gradually disappeared from thence; but not till its virulence and the number of its victims had drawn public attention on the school. Inquiry was made into the origin of the scourge, and by degrees various facts came out which excited public indignation in a high degree. The unhealthy nature of the site; the quantity and quality of the children's food; the brackish, fetid water used in its preparation; the pupils' wretched clothing and accommodations: all these things were discovered; and the discovery produced a result mortifying to Mr. Brocklehurst, but beneficial to the institution.

Several wealthy and benevolent individuals in the county subscribed largely for the erection of a more convenient building in a better situation; new regulations were made; improvements in diet and clothing introduced; the funds of the school were entrusted to the management of a committee. Mr. Brocklehurst, who, from his wealth and family connections, could not be overlooked, still retained the post of treasurer; but he was aided in the discharge of his duties by gentlemen of rather more enlarged and sympathising minds: his office of inspector, too, was shared by those who knew how to combine reason with strictness, comfort with economy, compassion with uprightness. The school, thus improved, became in time a truly useful and noble institution. I remained an inmate of its walls, after its regeneration, for eight years: six as pupil, and two as teacher; and in both capacities I bear my testimony to its value and importance.

During these eight years my life was uniform: but not unhappy, because it was not inactive. I had the means of an excellent edu-

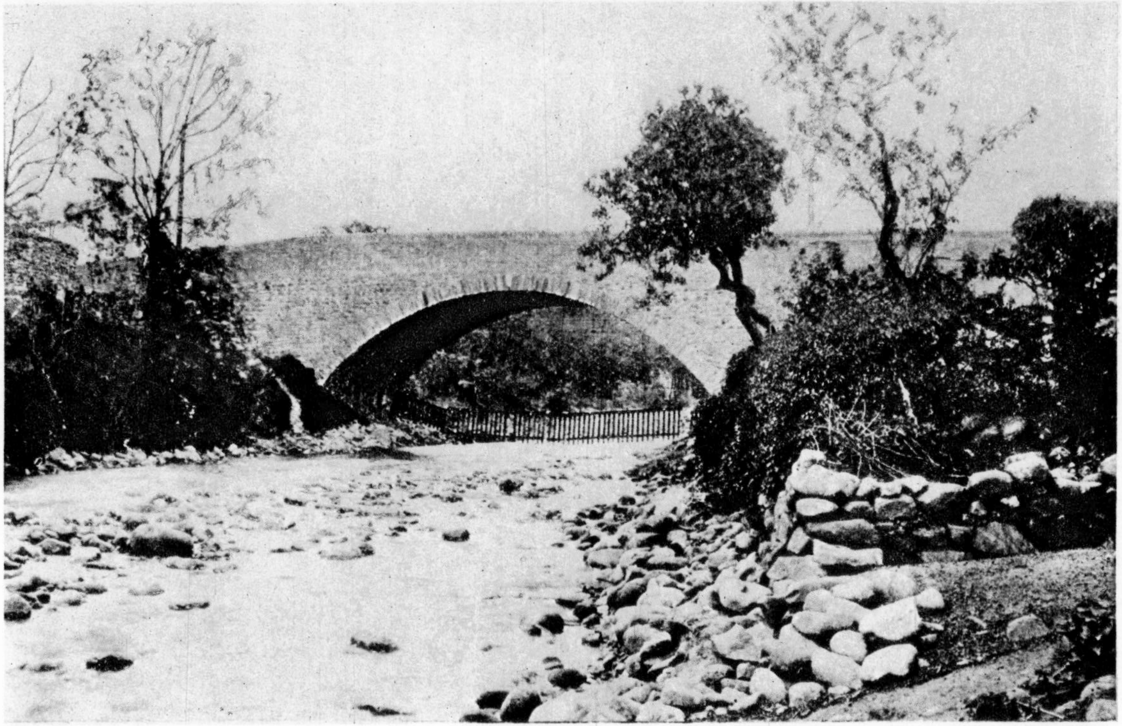

COWAN BRIDGE

"My favorite seat," says Jane Eyre, "was a smooth and broad stone, rising white and dry from the very middle of the brook, and only to be got at by wading through the waters." Charlotte Brontë was here thinking of her own lonely days at school, when for the first time she was away from home. It is interesting that her journey from her home at Haworth to Cowan Bridge took her past Eshley Hall, the residence of a Miss Currer who was famous for her collection of books. Charlotte must have envied her, for she remembered her when she came to adopt her pen name, Currer Bell.

cation placed within my reach; a fondness for some of my studies, and a desire to excel in all, together with a great delight in pleasing my teachers, especially such as I loved, urged me on: I availed myself fully of the advantages offered me. In time I rose to be the first girl of the first class; then I was invested with the office of teacher; which I discharged with zeal for two years: but at the end of that time I altered.

Miss Temple, through all changes, had thus far continued superintendent of the seminary: to her instruction I owed the best part of my acquirements; her friendship and society had been my continual solace; she had stood me in the stead of mother, governess, and, latterly, companion. At this period she married, removed with her husband (a clergyman, an excellent man, almost worthy of such a wife) to a distant county, and consequently was lost to me.

From the day she left I was no longer the same: with her was gone every settled feeling, every association that had made Lowood in some degree a home to me. I had imbibed from her something of her nature and much of her habits: more harmonious thoughts: what seemed better regulated feelings had become the inmates of my mind. I had given in allegiance to duty and order; I was quiet; I believed I was content: to the eyes of others, usually even to my own, I appeared a disciplined and subdued character.

But destiny, in the shape of the Rev. Mr. Nasmyth, came between me and Miss Temple: I saw her in her travelling dress step into a post-chaise, shortly after the marriage ceremony; I watched the chaise mount the hill and disappear beyond its brow; and then retired to my own room, and there spent in solitude the greatest part of the half-holiday granted in honour of the occasion.

I walked about the chamber most of the time. I imagined myself only to be regretting my loss, and thinking how to repair it; but when my reflections were concluded, and I looked up and found that the afternoon was gone, and evening far advanced, another discovery dawned on me, namely, that in the interval I had undergone a transforming process; that my mind had put off all it had borrowed of Miss Temple — or rather that she had taken with her the serene atmosphere I had been breathing in her vicinity — and that now I was left in my natural element, and beginning to feel the stirring of old emotions. It did not seem as if a prop were withdrawn, but rather as if a motive were gone: it was not the power to be tranquil which had failed me, but the reason for tranquillity was no more. My world had for some years been in Lowood: my experience had been of its rules and systems; now I remembered that the real world was wide, and that a varied field of hopes and fears, of sensations and excitements, awaited those who had courage to go forth into its expanse, to seek real knowledge of life amidst its perils.

I went to my window, opened it, and looked out. There were the two wings of the building; there was the garden; there were the skirts of Lowood; there was the hilly horizon. My eye passed all other objects to rest on those most remote, the blue peaks: it was those I longed to surmount; all within their boundary of rock and heath seemed prison-ground, exile limits. I traced the white road winding round the base of one mountain, and vanishing in a gorge between two: how I longed to follow it further! I recalled the time when I had travelled that very road in a coach; I remembered descending that hill at twilight: an age seemed to have elapsed since the day which brought me first to Lowood, and I had never quitted it since. My vacations had all been spent at school: Mrs. Reed had never sent for me to Gateshead; neither she nor any of her family had ever been to visit me. I had had no communication by letter or message with the outer world: school-rules, school-duties, school-habits and notions, and voices, and faces, and phrases, and costumes, and preferences, and antipathies: such was what I knew of existence. And now I felt that it was not enough: I tired of the routine of eight years in one afternoon. I desired liberty; for liberty I gasped; for liberty I uttered a prayer; it seemed scattered on the wind then faintly blowing. I abandoned it and framed a humbler supplication; for change, stimulus: that petition, too, seemed swept off into vague space: "Then," I cried, half desperate, "grant me at least a new servitude!"

Here a bell, ringing the hour of supper, called me downstairs.

I was not free to resume the interrupted chain of my reflections till bedtime: even then a teacher who occupied the same room with me kept me from the subject to which I longed to recur, by a prolonged effusion of small talk. How I wished sleep would silence her! It seemed as if, could I but go back to the idea which had last entered my mind as I stood at the window, some inventive suggestion would rise for my relief.

Miss Gryce snored at last; she was a heavy Welshwoman, and till now her habitual nasal strains had never been regarded by me in any other light than as a nuisance; to-night I hailed the first deep notes with satisfaction; I was debarrassed of interruption; my half-effaced thought instantly revived.

"A new servitude! There is something in that," I soliloquised (mentally, be it understood; I did not talk aloud). "I know there is, because it does not sound too sweet; it is not like such words as Liberty, Excitement, Enjoyment: delightful sounds truly; but no more than sounds for me; and so hollow and fleeting that it is mere waste of time to listen to them. But Servitude! That must be matter of fact. Any one may serve: I have served here eight years; now all I want is to serve elsewhere. Can I not get so much of my own will? Is not the thing feasible? Yes — yes — the end is not so difficult; if I had only a brain active enough to ferret out the means of attaining it."

I sat up in bed by way of arousing this said brain: it was a chilly night; I covered my shoulders with a shawl, and then I proceeded *to think* again with all my might.

"What do I want? A new place, in a new house, amongst new faces, under new circumstances: I want this because it is of no use wanting anything better. How do people do to get a new place? They apply to friends, I suppose: I have no friends. There are many others who have no friends, who must look about for themselves and be their own helpers; and what is their resource?"

I could not tell: nothing answered me; I then ordered my brain to find a response, and quickly. It worked and worked faster: I felt the pulses throb in my head and temples; but for nearly an hour it worked in chaos, and no result came of its efforts. Feverish with vain labour, I got up and took a turn in the room; undrew the curtain, and noted a star or two, shivered with cold, and again crept to bed.

A kind fairy, in my absence, had surely dropped the required suggestion on my pillow; for as I lay down it came quietly and naturally to my mind: — "Those who want situations advertise; you must advertise in the ——*shire Herald."*

"How? I know nothing about advertising."

Replies rose smooth and prompt now: —

"You must inclose the advertisement and the money to pay for it under a cover directed to the Editor of the *Herald;* you must put it, the first opportunity you have, into the post at Lowton; answers must be addressed to J. E. at the post-office there: you can go and inquire in about a week after you send your letter, if any are come, and act accordingly."

This scheme I went over twice, thrice; it was then digested in my mind: I had it in a clear, practical form; I felt satisfied, and fell asleep.

With earliest day, I was up: I had my advertisement written, enclosed, and directed before the bell rang to rouse the school; it ran thus:—

"A young lady accustomed to tuition" (had I not been a teacher two years?) "is desirous of meeting with a situation in a private family where the children are under fourteen (I thought that as I was barely eighteen, it would not do to undertake the guidance of pupils nearer my own age). She is qualified to teach the usual branches of a good English education, together with French, Drawing, and Music" (in those days, reader, this now narrow catalogue of accomplishments, would have been held tolerably comprehensive). "Address J. E., Post-office, Lowton, ——shire."

This document remained locked in my drawer all day: after tea, I asked leave of the new superintendent to go to Lowton, in order to perform some small commissions for myself and one or two of my fellow-teachers; permission was readily granted; I went. It was a walk of two miles, and the evening was wet, but the days were still long; I visited a shop or two, slipped the letter into the post-office, and came back through heavy rain, with streaming garments, but with a relieved heart.

The succeeding week seemed long: it came to an end at last, however, like all sublunary things, and once more, towards the close of a pleasant autumn day, I found myself afoot on the road to Lowton. A picturesque track it was, by the way; lying along the side of the beck and through the sweetest curves of the dale: but that day I thought more of the letters, that might or might not be awaiting me at the little burgh whither I was bound, than of the charms of lea and water.

My ostensible errand on this occasion was to get measured for a pair of shoes; so I discharged that business first, and when it was done, I stepped across the clean and quiet little street from the shoemaker's to the post-office: it was kept by an old dame, who wore horn spectacles on her nose, and black mittens on her hands.

"Are there any letters for J. E.?" I asked.

She peered at me over her spectacles, and then she opened a drawer and fumbled among its contents for a long time, so long that my hopes began to falter. At last, having held a document before her glasses for nearly five minutes, she presented it across the counter, accompanying the act by another inquisitive and mistrustful glance — it was for J. E.

"Is there only one?" I demanded.

"There are no more," said she; and I put it in my pocket and turned my face homeward: I could not open it then; rules obliged me to be back by eight, and it was already half-past seven.

Various duties awaited me on my arrival: I had to sit with the girls during their hour of study; then it was my turn to read prayers; to see them to bed: afterwards I supped with the other teachers. Even when we finally retired for the night, the inevitable Miss Gryce was still my companion: we had only a short end of a candle in our candlestick, and I dreaded lest she should talk till it was all burnt out; fortunately, however, the heavy supper she had eaten produced a soporific effect: she was already snoring, before I had finished undressing. There still remained an inch of candle: I now took out my letter; the seal was an initial F.; I broke it; the contents were brief.

"If J. E., who advertised in the ——*shire Herald* of last Thursday, possesses the acquirements mentioned; and if she is in a position to give satisfactory references as to character and competency; a situation can be offered her where there is but one pupil, a little girl, under ten years of age; and, where the salary is thirty pounds per annum. J. E. is requested to send references, name, address, and all particulars to the direction:—

"Mrs. Fairfax, Thornfield, near Millcote, ——shire."

I examined the document long; the writing was old-fashioned and rather uncertain, like that of an elderly lady. This circumstance was satisfactory: a private fear had haunted me, that in thus acting for myself, and by my own guidance, I ran the risk of getting into some scrape; and, above all things, I wished the result of my endeavours to be respectable, proper, *en règle*. I now felt that an elderly lady was no bad ingredient in the business I had on hand.

Mrs. Fairfax! I saw her in a black gown and widow's cap; frigid, perhaps, but not uncivil: a model of elderly English respectability. Thornfield! that, doubtless, was the name of her house: a neat, orderly spot, I was sure; though I failed in my efforts to conceive a correct plan of the premises. Millcote, ——shire; I brushed up my recollections of the map of England; yes, I saw it; both the shire and the town. ——shire was seventy miles nearer London than the remote county where I now resided: that was a recommendation to me. I longed to go where there was life and movement: Millcote was a large manufacturing town on the banks of the A——; a busy place enough, doubtless: so much the better; it would be a complete change at least. Not that my fancy was much captivated by the idea of long chimneys and clouds of smoke—"but," I argued, "Thornfield will, probably, be a good way from the town."

Here the socket of the candle dropped, and the wick went out.

Next day new steps were to be taken: my plans could no longer be confined to my own breast; I must impart them in order to achieve their success. Having sought and obtained an audience of the superintendent, during the noontide recreation, I told her I had a prospect of getting a new situation where the salary would be double what I now received (for, at Lowood, I only got £15 per annum); and requested she would break the matter for me to Mr. Brocklehurst, or some of the committee, and ascertain whether they would permit me to mention them as references. She obligingly consented to act as mediatrix in the matter. The next day she laid the affair before Mr Brocklehurst, who said that Mrs. Reed must be written to, as she was my natural guardian. A note was accordingly addressed to that lady, who returned for answer, that "I might do as I pleased: she had long relinquished all interference in my affairs." This note went the round of the committee, and at last, after what appeared to me most tedious delay, formal leave was given me to better my condition if I could; and an assurance added, that as I had always conducted myself well, both as teacher and pupil, at Lowood, a testimonial of character and capacity, signed by the inspectors of that institution, should forthwith be furnished me.

This testimonial I accordingly received in about a month, forwarded a copy of it to Mrs. Fairfax, and got the lady's reply, stating that she was satisfied, and fixing that day fortnight as the period for my assuming the post of governess in her house.

I now busied myself in preparations: the fortnight passed rapidly. I had not a very large wardrobe, though it was adequate to my wants; and the last day sufficed to pack my trunk,— the same I had brought with me eight years ago from Gateshead.

The box was corded, the card nailed on. In half an hour the carrier was to call for it to take it to Lowton, whither I myself was to repair at an early hour the next morning to meet the coach. I had brushed my black stuff travelling dress, prepared my bonnet, gloves, and muff; sought in all my drawers to see that no article was left behind; and now, having nothing more to do, I sat down and tried to rest. I could not; though I had been on foot all day, I could not now repose an instant; I was too much excited. A phase of my life was closing to-night, a new one opening to-morrow: impossible to slumber in the interval; I must watch feverishly while the change was being accomplished.

"Miss," said a servant who met me in the lobby, where I was wandering like a troubled spirit, "a person below wishes to see you."

"The carrier, no doubt," I thought, and ran downstairs without inquiry. I was passing the back parlour, or teachers' sitting-room, the door of which was half open, to go to the kitchen, when some one ran out: —

"It's her, I am sure! — I could have told her anywhere!" cried the individual who stopped my progress and took my hand.

I looked: I saw a woman attired like a well-dressed servant, matronly, yet still young; very good-looking, with black hair and eyes, and lively complexion.

"Well, who is it?" she asked in a voice and with a smile I half recognised; "you've not quite forgotten me, I think, Miss Jane?"

In another second I was embracing and kissing her rapturously: "Bessie! Bessie! Bessie!" that was all I said; whereat she half laughed, half cried, and we both went into the parlour. By the fire stood a little fellow of three years old, in plaid frock and trousers.

"That is my little boy," said Bessie, directly.

"Then you are married, Bessie?"

"Yes: nearly five years since, to Robert Leaven, the coachman; and I've a little girl besides Bobby there, that I've christened Jane."

"And you don't live at Gateshead?"

"I live at the lodge: the old porter has left."

"Well, and how do they all get on? Tell me everything about

them, Bessie: but sit down first; and, Bobby, come and sit on my knee, will you?" but Bobby preferred sidling over to his mother.

"You've not grown so very tall, Miss Jane, nor so very stout," continued Mrs. Leaven. "I dare say they've not kept you too well at school: Miss Reed is the head and shoulders taller than you are; and Miss Georgiana would make two of you in breadth."

"Georgiana is handsome, I suppose, Bessie?"

"Very. She went up to London last winter with her mama, and there everybody admired her, and a young lord fell in love with her: but his relations were against the match; and — what do you think? — he and Miss Georgiana made it up to run away: but they were found out and stopped. It was Miss Reed that found them out: I believe she was envious; and now she and her sister lead a cat and dog life together; they are always quarrelling."

"Well, and what of John Reed?"

"Oh, he is not doing so well as his mama could wish. He went to college, and he got — plucked, I think they call it: and then his uncles wanted him to be a barrister, and study the law: but he is such a dissipated young man, they will never make much of him, I think."

"What does he look like?"

"He is very tall: some people call him a fine looking young man; but he has such thick lips."

"And Mrs. Reed?"

"Missis looks stout and well enough in the face, but I think she's not quite easy in her mind: Mr. John's conduct does not please her — he spends a deal of money."

"Did she send you here, Bessie?"

"No, indeed: but I have long wanted to see you, and when I heard that there had been a letter from you, and that you were going to another part of the country, I thought I'd just set off, and get a look at you before you were quite out of my reach."

"I am afraid you are disappointed in me, Bessie." I said this laughing: I perceived that Bessie's glance, though it expressed regard, did in no shape denote admiration.

"No, Miss Jane, not exactly: you are genteel enough; you look like a lady, and it is as much as ever I expected of you: you were no beauty as a child."

I smiled at Bessie's frank answer: I felt that it was correct, but I confess I was not quite indifferent to its import: at eighteen most people wish to please, and the conviction that they have not an exterior likely to second that desire brings anything but gratification.

"I dare say you are clever, though," continued Bessie, by way of solace. "What can you do? Can you play on the piano?"

"A little."

There was one in the room; Bessie went and opened it, and then asked me to sit down and give her a tune: I played a waltz or two, and she was charmed.

"The Miss Reeds could not play as well!" said she exultingly, "I always said you would surpass them in learning: and can you draw?"

"That is one of my paintings over the chimney-piece." It was a landscape in water colours, of which I had made a present to the superintendent, in acknowledgment of her obliging mediation with the committe on my behalf, and which she had framed and glazed.

"Well, that is beautiful, Miss Jane! It is as fine a picture as any Miss Reed's drawing-master could paint, let alone the young ladies themselves, who could not come near it: and have you learnt French?"

"Yes, Bessie, I can both read it and speak it."

"And you can work on muslin and canvas?"

"I can."

"Oh, you are quite a lady, Miss Jane! I knew you would be; you will get on whether your relations notice you or not. There was something I wanted to ask you. Have you ever heard anything from your father's kinsfolk, the Eyres?"

"Never in my life."

"Well, you know Missis always said they were poor and quite despicable: and they may be poor; but I believe they are as much gentry as the Reeds are; for one day, nearly seven years ago, a Mr. Eyre came to Gateshead and wanted to see you; Missis said you were at school fifty miles off; he seemed so much disappointed, for he could not stay: he was going on a voyage to a foreign country, and the ship was to sail from London in a day or two. He looked quite a gentleman, and I believe he was your father's brother."

"What foreign country was he going to, Bessie?"

"An island thousands of miles off, where they make wine — the butler did tell me"—

"Madeira!" I suggested.

"Yes, that is it — that is the very word."

"So he went?"

"Yes; he did not stay many minutes in the house: Missis was very high with him; she called him afterwards a 'sneaking tradesman.' My Robert believes he was a wine-merchant."

"Very likely," I returned; "or perhaps clerk or agent to a wine-merchant."

Bessie and I conversed about old times an hour longer, and then she was obliged to leave me: I saw her again for a few minutes the next morning at Lowton, while I was waiting for the coach. We parted finally at the door of the Brocklehurst Arms there: each went her separate way; she set off for the brow of Lowood Fell to meet the conveyance which was to take her back to Gateshead, I mounted the vehicle which was to bear me to new duties and a new life in the unknown environs of Millcote.

# CHAPTER XI

A NEW chapter in a novel is something like a new scene in a play; and when I draw up the curtain this time, reader, you must fancy you see a room in the George Inn at Millcote, with such large figured papering on the walls as inn rooms have; such a carpet, such furniture, such ornaments on the mantel-piece, such prints; including a portrait of George the Third, and another of the Prince of Wales, and a representation of the death of Wolfe. All this is visible to you by the light of an oil lamp hanging from the ceiling, and by that of an excellent fire, near which I sit in my cloak and bonnet; my muff and umbrella lie on the table, and I am warming away the numbness and chill contracted by sixteen hours' exposure to the rawness of an October day: I left Lowton at four o'clock A. M., and the Millcote town clock is now just striking eight.

Reader, though I look comfortably accommodated, I am not very tranquil in my mind. I thought when the coach stopped here there would be some one to meet me; I looked anxiously round as I descended the wooden steps the "boots" placed for my convenience, expecting to hear my name pronounced, and to see some description of carriage waiting to convey me to Thornfield. Nothing of the sort was visible: and when I asked a waiter if any one had been to inquire after a Miss Eyre, I was answered in the negative: so I had no resource but to request to be shown into a private room: and here I am waiting, while all sorts of doubts and fears are troubling my thoughts.

It is a very strange sensation to inexperienced youth to feel itself quite alone in the world, cut adrift from every connection, uncertain whether the port to which it is bound can be reached, and prevented by many impediments from returning to that it has quitted. The charm of adventure sweetens that sensation, the glow of pride warms it; but then the throb of fear disturbs it; and fear with me became predominant, when half an hour elapsed and still I was alone. I bethought myself to ring the bell.

"Is there a place in this neighbourhood called Thornfield?" I asked of the waiter who answered the summons.

"Thornfield? I don't know, ma'am; I'll inquire at the bar." He vanished, but reappeared instantly: —

"Is your name Eyre, Miss?"

"Yes."

"Person here waiting for you."

I jumped up, took my muff and umbrella, and hastened into the inn-passage: a man was standing by the open door, and in the lamp-lit street I dimly saw a one-horse conveyance.

"This will be your luggage, I suppose?" said the man rather abruptly when he saw me, pointing to my trunk in the passage.

"Yes." He hoisted it on to the vehicle, which was a sort of car, and then I got in: before he shut me up, I asked him how far it was to Thornfield.

"A matter of six miles."

"How long shall we be before we get there?"

"Happen an hour and a half."

He fastened the car door, climbed to his own seat outside, and we set off. Our progress was leisurely, and gave me ample time to reflect: I was content to be at length so near the end of my journey; and as I leaned back in the comfortable though not elegant conveyance, I meditated much at my ease.

"I suppose," thought I, "judging from the plainness of the servant and carriage, Mrs. Fairfax is not a very dashing person: so much the better; I never lived amongst fine people but once, and I was very miserable with them. I wonder if she lives alone except for this little girl; if so, and if she is in any degree amiable, I shall surely be able to get on with her; I will do my best: it is a pity that doing one's best does not always answer. At Lowood, indeed, I took that resolution, kept it, and succeeded in pleasing; but with Mrs. Reed, I remember my best was always spurned with scorn. I pray God Mrs. Fairfax may not turn out a second Mrs. Reed; but if she does, I am not bound to stay with her: let the worst come to the worst, I can advertise again. How far are we on our road now, I wonder?"

I let down the window and looked out: Millcote was behind us; judging by the number of its lights, it seemed a place of considerable magnitude, much larger than Lowton. We were now, as far as I could see, on a sort of common; but there were houses scattered all over the district; I felt we were in a different region to Lowood, more populous, less picturesque; more stirring, less romantic.

The roads were heavy, the night misty; my conductor let his horse walk all the way, and the hour and a half extended, I verily believe, to two hours; at last he turned in his seat and said: —

"You're noan so far fro' Thornfield now."

Again I looked out: we were passing a church: I saw its low broad tower against the sky, and its bell was tolling a quarter; I saw a narrow galaxy of lights too, on a hillside, marking a village or hamlet. About ten minutes after, the driver got down and opened a pair of gates; we passed through, and they clashed to behind us. We now slowly ascended a drive, and came upon the long front of a house: candle-light gleamed from one curtained bow-window; all the rest were dark. The car stopped at the front door; it was opened by a maid-servant; I alighted and went in.

"Will you walk this way, ma'am," said the girl: and I followed her across a square hall with high doors all round; she ushered me into a room whose double illumination of fire and candle at first dazzled me, contrasting as it did with the darkness to which my eyes had been for two hours inured; when I could see, however, a cozy and agreeable picture presented itself to my view.

A snug, small room; a round table by a cheerful fire; an arm-chair high-backed and old-fashioned, wherein sat the neatest imaginable little elderly lady, in widow's cap, black silk gown and snowy muslin apron; exactly like what I had fancied Mrs. Fairfax, only less stately and milder looking. She was occupied in knitting; a large cat sat demurely at her feet; nothing in short was wanting to complete the beau-ideal of domestic comfort. A more reassuring introduction for a new governess could scarcely be conceived: there was no grandeur to overwhelm, no stateliness to embarrass; and then, as I entered, the old lady got up, and promptly and kindly came forward to meet me.

"How do you do, my dear? I am afraid you have had a tedious ride; John drives so slowly: you must be cold, come to the fire."

"Mrs. Fairfax, I suppose?" said I.

"Yes, you are right: do sit down."

She conducted me to her own chair, and then began to remove my shawl and untie my bonnet-strings: I begged she would not give herself so much trouble.

"Oh, it is no trouble; I dare say your own hands are almost

numbed with cold. Leah, make a little hot negus and cut a sandwich or two: here are the keys of the store-room."

And she produced from her pocket a most housewifely bunch of keys, and delivered them to the servant.

"Now, then, draw nearer to the fire," she continued. "You've brought your luggage with you, haven't you, my dear?"

"Yes, ma'am."

"I'll see it carried into your room," she said, and bustled out.

"She treats me like a visitor," thought I. "I little expected such a reception; I anticipated only coldness and stiffness: this is not like what I have heard of the treatment of governesses; but I must not exult too soon."

She returned; with her own hands cleared her knitting apparatus and a book or two from the table, to make room for the tray which Leah now brought, and then herself handed me the refreshments. I felt rather confused at being the object of more attention than I had ever before received, and that, too, shown by my employer and superior; but as she did not herself seem to consider she was doing anything out of her place, I thought it better to take her civilities quietly.

"Shall I have the pleasure of seeing Miss Fairfax to-night?" I asked, when I had partaken of what she offered me.

"What did you say, my dear? I am a little deaf," returned the good lady, approaching her ear to my mouth.

I repeated the question more distinctly.

"Miss Fairfax? Oh, you mean Miss Varens! Varens is the name of your future pupil."

"Indeed! Then she is not your daughter?"

"No,— I have no family."

I should have followed up my first inquiry, by asking in what way Miss Varens was connected with her; but I recollected it was not polite to ask too many questions: besides, I was sure to hear in time.

"I am so glad," she continued, as she sat down opposite to me, and took the cat on her knee; "I am so glad you are come; it will be quite pleasant living here now with a companion. To be sure it is pleasant at any time; for Thornfield is a fine old hall, rather neglected of late years perhaps, but still it is a respectable place; yet you know in winter time one feels dreary quite alone, in the best quarters. I say alone — Leah is a nice girl to be sure, and John and his wife are very decent people; but then you see they are only servants, and one can't converse with them on terms of equality: one must keep them at due distance, for fear of losing one's authority. I'm sure last winter (it was a very severe one, if you recollect, and when it did not snow, it rained and blew), not a creature but the butcher and the postman came to the house, from November till February; and I really got quite melancholy with sitting night after night alone; I had Leah in to read to me sometimes; but I don't think the poor girl liked the task much: she felt it confining. In spring and summer one got on better: sunshine and long days make such a difference; and then, just at the commencement of this autumn, little Adela Varens came and her nurse: a child makes a house alive all at once; and now you are here I shall be quite gay."

My heart really warmed to the worthy lady as I heard her talk; and I drew my chair a little nearer to her, and expressed my sincere wish that she might find my company as agreeable as she anticipated.

"But I'll not keep you sitting up late to-night," she said; "it is on the stroke of twelve now, and you have been travelling all day: you must feel tired. If you have got your feet well warmed, I'll show you your bed-room. I've had the room next to mine prepared for you; it is only a small apartment, but I thought you would like it better than one of the large front chambers: to be sure they have finer furniture, but they are so dreary and solitary, I never sleep in them myself."

I thanked her for her considerate choice, and as I really felt fatigued with my long journey, expressed my readiness to retire. She took her candle, and I followed her from the room. First she went to see if the hall-door was fastened; having taken the key from the lock, she led the way upstairs. The steps and banisters were of oak; the staircase window was high and latticed; both it and the long gallery into which the bed-room doors opened, looked as if they belonged to a church rather than a house. A very chill and vault-like air pervaded the stairs and gallery, suggesting cheerless ideas of space and solitude; and I was glad, when finally ushered into my chamber, to find it of small dimensions, and furnished in ordinary modern style.

When Mrs. Fairfax had bidden me a kind good-night, and I had fastened my door, gazed leisurely round, and in some measure effaced the eerie impression made by that wide hall, that dark and spacious staircase, and that long, cold gallery, by the livelier aspect of my little room, I remembered that after a day of bodily fatigue and mental anxiety, I was now at last in safe haven. The impulse of gratitude swelled my heart, and I knelt down at the bedside, and offered up thanks where thanks were due; not forgetting, ere I rose, to implore aid on my further path, and power of meriting the kindness which seemed so frankly offered me before it was earned. My couch had no thorns in it that night; my solitary room no fears. At once weary and content, I slept soon and soundly: when I awoke it was broad day.

The chamber looked such a bright little place to me as the sun shone in between the gay blue chintz window curtains, showing papered walls and a carpeted floor, so unlike the bare planks and stained plaster of Lowood, that my spirits rose at the view. Externals have a great effect on the young: I thought that a fairer era of life was beginning for me, one that was to have its flowers and pleasures, as well as its thorns and toils. My faculties, roused by the change of scene, the new field offered to hope, seemed all astir. I cannot precisely define what they expected, but it was something pleasant: not perhaps that day or that month, but at an indefinite future period.

I rose; I dressed myself with care: obliged to be plain — for I had no article of attire that was not made with extreme simplicity — I was still by nature solicitous to be neat. It was not my habit to be disregardful of appearance, or careless of the impression I made: on the contrary, I ever wished to look as well as I could, and to please as much as my want of beauty would permit. I sometimes regretted that I was not handsomer: I sometimes wished to have rosy cheeks, a straight nose, and small cherry mouth; I desired to be tall, stately, and finely developed in figure; I felt it a misfortune that I was so little, so pale, and had features so irregular and so marked. And why had I these aspirations and these regrets? It would be difficult to say: I could not then distinctly say it to myself; yet I had a reason, and a logical, natural reason too. However, when I had brushed my hair very smooth, and put on my black frock — which, Quakerlike as it was, at least had the merit of fitting to a nicety — and adjusted my clean white tucker, I thought I should do respectably enough to appear before Mrs. Fairfax; and that my new pupil would not at least recoil from me with antipathy. Having opened my chamber window, and seen that I left all things straight and neat on the toilet table, I ventured forth.

Traversing the long and matted gallery, I descended the slippery steps of oak; then I gained the hall: I halted there a minute; I looked at some pictures on the walls (one I remember represented a grim man in a cuirass, and one a lady with powdered hair and a pearl necklace), at a bronze lamp pendent from the ceiling, at a great clock whose case was of oak curiously carved, and ebon black with time and rubbing. Everything appeared very stately and imposing to me: but then I was so little accustomed to grandeur. The hall-door, which was half of glass, stood open; I stepped over the threshold. It was a fine autumn morning; the early sun shone serenely on embrowned groves and still green fields: advancing on to the lawn, I looked up and surveyed the front of the mansion. It was three stories high, of proportions not vast, though considerable: a gentleman's manorhouse, not a nobleman's seat: battlements round the top gave it a picturesque look. Its grey front stood out well from the background of a rookery, whose cawing tenants were now on the wing: they flew over the lawn and grounds to alight in a great meadow, from which these were separated by a sunk fence, and where an array of mighty old thorn trees, strong, knotty, and broad as oaks, at once explained the etymology of the mansion's designation. Farther off were hills: not so lofty as those round Lowood, nor so craggy, nor so like barriers of separation from the living world; but yet quiet and lonely hills enough, and seeming to embrace Thornfield with a seclusion I had not expected to find existent so near the stirring locality of Millcote. A little hamlet, whose roofs were blent with trees, straggled up the side of one of these hills; the church of the district stood nearer Thornfield: its old tower-top looked over a knoll between the house and gates.

I was yet enjoying the calm prospect and pleasant fresh air, yet listening with delight to the cawing of the rooks, yet surveying the wide, hoary front of the hall, and thinking what a great place it was for one lonely little dame like Mrs. Fairfax to inhabit, when that lady appeared at the door.

"What! out already?" said she. "I see you are an early riser." I went up to her, and was received with an affable kiss and shake of the hand.

"How do you like Thornfield?" she asked. I told her I liked it very much.

"Yes," she said, "it is a pretty place; but I fear it will be getting out of order, unless Mr. Rochester should take it into his head to come and reside here permanently; or, at least, visit it rather oftener: great houses and fine grounds require the presence of the proprietor."

"Mr. Rochester!" I exclaimed. "Who is he?"

"The owner of Thornfield," she responded quietly. "Did you not know he was called Rochester?"

Of course I did not — I had never heard of him before; but the old lady seemed to regard his existence as a universally understood fact, with which everybody must be acquainted by instinct.

"I thought," I continued, "Thornfield belonged to you."

"To me? Bless you, child; what an idea! To me? I am only the housekeeper — the manager. To be sure I am distantly related to the Rochesters by the mother's side; or, at least, my husband was: he was a clergyman, incumbent of Hay — that little village yonder on the hill — and that church near the gates was his. The present Mr. Rochester's mother was a Fairfax, and second cousin to my husband; but I never presume on the connection — in fact it is nothing to me; I consider myself quite in the light of an ordinary housekeeper: my employer is always civil, and I expect nothing more."

"And the little girl — my pupil?"

"She is Mr. Rochester's ward; he commissioned me to find a governess for her. He intends to have her brought up in ——shire, I believe. Here she comes, with her 'bonne,' as she calls her nurse." The enigma then was explained: this affable and kind little widow was no great dame, but a dependant like myself. I did not like her the worse for that; on the contrary, I felt better pleased than ever. The equality between her and me was real; not the mere result of condescension on her part: so much the better — my position was all the freer.

As I was meditating on this discovery, a little girl, followed by her attendant, came running up the lawn. I looked at my pupil, who did not at first appear to notice me: she was quite a child, perhaps seven or eight years old, slightly built, with a pale, small-featured face, and a redundancy of hair falling in curls to her waist.

"Good morning, Miss Adela," said Mrs. Fairfax. "Come and

speak to the lady who is to teach you, and to make you a clever woman some day." She approached.

"C'est là ma gouverante?" said she, pointing to me, and addressing her nurse; who answered:

"Mais oui, certainement."

"Are they foreigners?" I inquired, amazed at hearing the French language.

"The nurse is a foreigner, and Adela was born on the Continent; and, I believe, never left it till within six months ago. When she first came here she could speak no English; now she can make shift to talk it a little: I don't understand her, she mixes it so with French; but you will make out her meaning very well, I daresay."

Fortunately I had had the advantage of being taught French by a French lady; and as I had always made a point of conversing with Madame Pierrot, as often as I could, and had, besides, during the last seven years, learnt a portion of French by heart daily — applying myself to take pains with my accent, and imitating as closely as possible the pronunciation of my teacher — I had acquired a certain degree of readiness and correctness in the language, and was not likely to be much at a loss with Mademoiselle Adela. She came and shook hands with me when she heard that I was her governess; and as I led her in to breakfast, I addressed some phrases to her in her own tongue: she replied briefly at first, but after we were seated at the table, and she had examined me some ten minutes with her large hazel eyes, she suddenly commenced chattering fluently.

"Ah," cried she, in French, "you speak my language as well as Mr. Rochester does: I can talk to you as I can to him, and so can Sophie. She will be glad: nobody here understands her: Madame Fairfax is all English. Sophie is my nurse; she came with me over the sea in a great ship with a chimney that smoked — how it did smoke! — and I was sick, and so was Sophie, and so was Mr. Rochester. Mr. Rochester lay down on a sofa in a pretty room called the salon, and Sophie and I had little beds in another place. I nearly fell out of mine; it was like a shelf. And, Mademoiselle —— what is your name?"

"Eyre — Jane Eyre."

"Aire? Bah! I cannot say it. Well: our ship stopped in the morning, before it was quite daylight, at a great city — a huge city, with very dark houses and all smoky; not at all like the pretty clean town I came from; and Mr. Rochester carried me in his arms over a plank to the land, and Sophie came after, and we all got into a coach, which took us to a beautiful large house, larger than this and finer, called an hotel. We stayed there nearly a week: I and Sophie used to walk every day in a great green place full of trees, called the Park; and there were many children there besides me, and a pond with beautiful birds in it, that I fed with crumbs."

"Can you understand her when she runs on so fast?" asked Mrs. Fairfax.

I understood her very well, for I had been accustomed to the fluent tongue of Madame Pierrot.

"I wish," continued the good lady, "you would ask her a question or two about her parents: I wonder if she remembers them?"

"Adèle," I inquired, "with whom did you live when you were in that pretty clean town you spoke of?"

"I lived long ago with mama; but she is gone to the Holy Virgin. Mama used to teach me to dance and sing, and to say verses. A great many gentlemen and ladies came to see mama, and I used to dance before them, or to sit on their knees and sing to them: I liked it. Shall I let you hear me sing now?"

She had finished her breakfast, so I permitted her to give a specimen of her accomplishments. Descending from her chair, she came and placed herself on my knee; then, folding her little hands demurely before her, shaking back her curls and lifting her eyes to the ceiling, she commenced singing a song from some opera. It was the strain of a forsaken lady, who, after bewailing the perfidy of her lover, calls pride to her aid; desires her attendant to deck her in her brightest jewels and richest robes, and resolves to meet the false one that night at a ball, and prove to him, by the gaiety of her demeanour, how little his desertion had affected her.

The subject seemed strangely chosen for an infant singer; but I suppose the point of the exhibition lay in hearing the notes of love and jealousy warbled with the lisp of childhood; and in very bad taste that point was: at least I thought so.

Adèle sang the canzonette tunefully enough, and with the naïveté of her age. This achieved, she jumped from my knee and said, "Now, Mademoiselle, I will repeat you some poetry."

Assuming an attitude, she began "La Ligue des Rats, fable de La Fontaine." She then declaimed the little piece with an attention to punctuation and emphasis, a flexibility of voice and an appropriateness of gesture, very unusual indeed at her age, and which proved she had been carefully trained.

"Was it your mama who taught you that piece?" I asked.

"Yes, and she just used to say it in this way: 'Qu'avez vous donc? lui dit un de ces rats; parlez!' She made me lift my hand — so — to remind me to raise my voice at the question. Now shall I dance for you?"

"No, that will do: but after your mama went to the Holy Virgin, as you say, with whom did you live then?"

"With Madame Frédéric and her husband: she took care of me, but she is nothing related to me. I think she is poor, for she had not so fine a house as mama. I was not long there. Mr Rochester asked me if I would like to go and live with him in England, and I said yes; for I knew Mr. Rochester before I knew Madame Frédéric, and he was always kind to me and gave me pretty dresses and toys: but you see he has not kept his word, for he has brought me to England, and now he has gone back again himself, and I never see him."

After breakfast, Adèle and I withdrew to the library; which room, it appears, Mr. Rochester had directed should be used as the school-room. Most of the books were locked up behind glass doors; but there was one bookcase left open containing everything that could be needed in the way of elementary works, and several volumes of light literature, poetry, biography, travels, a few romances, etc. I suppose he had considered that these were all the governess would require for her private perusal; and, indeed, they contented me amply for the present; compared with the scanty pickings I had now and then been able to glean at Lowood, they seemed to offer an abundant harvest of entertainment and information. In this room, too, there was a cabinet piano, quite new and of superior tone; also an easel for painting, and a pair of globes.

I found my pupil sufficiently docile, though disinclined to apply: she had not been used to regular occupation of any kind. I felt it would be injudicious to confine her too much at first; so, when I had talked to her a great deal, and got her to learn a little, and when the morning had advanced to noon, I allowed her to return to her nurse. I then proposed to occupy myself till dinner-time in drawing some little sketches for her use.

As I was going upstairs to fetch my portfolio and pencils, Mrs. Fairfax called to me: "Your morning school-hours are over now, I suppose," said she. She was in a room the folding-doors of which stood open: I went in when she addressed me. It was a large, stately apartment, with purple chairs and curtains, a Turkey carpet, walnut-panelled walls, one vast window rich in stained glass, and a lofty ceiling, nobly moulded. Mrs. Fairfax was dusting some vases of fine purple spar, which stood on a sideboard.

"What a beautiful room!" I exclaimed, as I looked round; for I had never before seen any half so imposing.

"Yes; this is the dining-room. I have just opened the window, to let in a little air and sunshine; for everything gets so damp in apartments that are seldom inhabited: the drawing-room yonder feels like a vault."

She pointed to a wide arch corresponding to the window, and hung like it with a Tyrian-dyed curtain, now looped up. Mounting to it by two broad steps and looking through, I thought I caught a glimpse of a fairy place, so bright to my novice-eyes appeared the view beyond. Yet it was merely a very pretty drawing-room, and within it a boudoir, both spread with white carpets, on which seemed laid brilliant garlands of flowers; both ceiled with snowy mouldings of white grapes and vine-leaves, beneath which glowed in rich contrast crimson couches and ottomans; while the ornaments on the pale Parian mantel-piece were of sparkling Bohemian glass, ruby red; and between the windows large mirrors repeated the general blending of snow and fire.

"In what order you keep these rooms, Mrs. Fairfax!" said I. "No dust, no canvass coverings: except that the air feels chilly, one would think they were inhabited daily."

"Why, Miss Eyre, though Mr. Rochester's visits here are rare, they are always sudden and unexpected; and as I observed that it put him out to find everything swathed up, and to have a bustle of arrangement on his arrival, I thought it best to keep the rooms in readiness."

"Is Mr. Rochester an exacting, fastidious sort of man?"

"Not particularly so; but he has a gentleman's tastes and habits, and he expects to have things managed in conformity to them."

"Do you like him? Is he generally liked?"

"Oh, yes; the family have always been respected here. Almost all the land in this neighbourhood, as far as you can see, has belonged to the Rochesters time out of mind."

"Well, but, leaving his land out of the question, do you like him? Is he liked for himself?"

"*I* have no cause to do otherwise than like him; and I believe he is considered a just and liberal landlord by his tenants: but he has never lived much amongst them."

"But has he no peculiarities? What, in short, is his character?"

"Oh! his character is unimpeachable, I suppose. He is rather peculiar, perhaps: he has travelled a great deal, and seen a great deal of the world, I should think. I dare say he is clever: but I never had much conversation with him."

"In what way is he peculiar?"

"I don't know — it is not easy to describe — nothing striking, but you feel it when he speaks to you: you cannot be always sure whether he is in jest or earnest, whether he is pleased or the contrary; you don't thoroughly understand him, in short — at least, I don't: but it is of no consequence, he is a very good master."

This was all the account I got from Mrs. Fairfax, of her employer and mine. There are people who seem to have no notion of sketching a character, or observing and describing salient points, either in persons or things: the good lady evidently belonged to this class; my queries puzzled, but did not draw her out. Mr. Rochester was Mr. Rochester in her eyes; a gentleman, a landed proprietor — nothing more: she inquired and searched no further, and evidently wondered at my wish to gain a more definite notion of his identity.

When we left the dining-room, she proposed to show me over the rest of the house; and I followed her upstairs and downstairs, admiring as I went; for all was well-arranged and handsome. The large front chambers I thought especially grand; and some of the third story rooms, though dark and low, were interesting from their air of antiquity. The furniture once appropriated to the lower apartments had from time to time been removed here, as fashions changed: and the imperfect light entering by their narrow casements showed bedsteads of a hundred years old; chests in oak or walnut, looking, with their strange carvings of palm branches and cherubs' heads, like types of the Hebrew ark; rows of venerable chairs, high-backed and narrow; stools still more antiquated, on whose cushioned tops were yet apparent traces of half-effaced embroideries, wrought by fingers that for two generations had been coffin-dust. All these relics gave to the third story of Thornfield Hall the aspect of a home of the past: a shrine of memory. I liked the hush, the gloom, the quaintness of these retreats in the day; but I by no means coveted a night's repose on one of those wide and heavy beds: shut in, some of them with doors of oak; shaded, others with wrought old English hangings crusted with thick work, portraying effigies of strange flowers, and stranger birds, and strangest human beings,— all which would have looked strange, indeed, by the pallid gleam of moonlight.

"Do the servants sleep in these rooms?" I asked.

"No; they occupy a range of smaller apartments to the back; no one ever sleeps here: one would almost say that, if there were a ghost at Thornfield Hall, this would be its haunt."

"So I think: you have no ghost, then?"

"None that I ever heard of," returned Mrs. Fairfax, smiling.

"Nor any traditions of one? no legends or ghost stories?"

"I believe not. And yet it is said, the Rochesters have been rather a violent than a quiet race in their time: perhaps, though, that is the reason they rest tranquilly in their graves now."

"Yes—'after life's fitful fever they sleep well,'" I muttered. "Where are you going now, Mrs. Fairfax?" for she was moving away.

"On to the leads; will you come and see the view from thence?" I followed still, up a very narrow staircase to the attics, and thence by a ladder and through a trap-door to the roof of the hall. I was now on a level with the crow colony, and could see into their nests. Leaning over the battlements and looking far down, I surveyed the grounds laid out like a map: the bright and velvet lawn closely girding the grey base of the mansion; the field, wide as a park, dotted with its ancient timber; the wood, dun and sere, divided by a path visibly overgrown, greener with moss than the trees were with foliage; the church at the gates, the road, the tranquil hills, all reposing in the autumn day's sun; the horizon bounded by a propitious sky, azure, marbled with pearly white. No feature in the scene was extraordinary, but all was pleasing. When I turned from it and repassed the trap-door, I could scarcely see my way down the ladder; the attic seemed black as a vault compared with that arch of blue air to which I had been looking up, and to that sunlit scene of grove, pasture, and green hill of which the hall was the centre, and over which I had been gazing with delight.

Mrs. Fairfax stayed behind a moment to fasten the trap-door; I, by dint of groping, found the outlet from the attic, and proceeded to descend the narrow garret staircase. I lingered in the long passage to which this led, separating the front and back rooms of the third story: narrow, low, and dim, with only one little window at the far end, and looking, with its two rows of small black doors all shut, like a corridor in some Bluebeard's castle.

While I paced softly on, the last sound I expected to hear in so still a region, a laugh, struck my ear. It was a curious laugh; distinct, formal, mirthless. I stopped: the sound ceased only for an instant; it began again, louder: for at first, though distinct, it was very low. It passed off in a clamorous peal that seemed to wake an echo in every lonely chamber; though it originated but in one, and I could have pointed out the door whence the accents issued.

"Mrs. Fairfax!" I called out: for I now heard her descending the great stairs. "Did you hear that loud laugh? Who is it?"

"Some of the servants, very likely," she answered: "perhaps Grace Poole."

"Did you hear it?" I again inquired.

"Yes, plainly: I often hear her; she sews in one of these rooms. Sometimes Leah is with her: they are frequently noisy together."

The laugh was repeated in its low, syllabic tone, and terminated in an odd murmur.

"Grace!" exclaimed Mrs. Fairfax.

I really did not expect any Grace to answer; for the laugh was as tragic, as preternatural a laugh as any I ever heard; and, but that it was high noon, and that no circumstance of ghostliness accompanied the curious cachinnation, but that neither scene nor season favoured fear, I should have been superstitiously afraid. However, the event showed me I was a fool for entertaining a sense even of surprise.

The door nearest me opened, and a servant came out,— a woman of between thirty and forty; a set, square-made figure, red-haired, and with a hard, plain face: any apparition less romantic or less ghostly could scarcely be conceived.

"Too much noise, Grace," said Mrs. Fairfax. "Remember directions!" Grace curtseyed silently and went in.

"She is a person we have to sew and assist Leah in her housemaid's work," continued the widow; "not altogether unobjectionable in some points, but she does well enough. By-the-bye, how have you got on with your new pupil this morning?"

The conversation, thus turned on Adèle, continued till we reached the light and cheerful region below. Adèle came running to meet us in the hall, exclaiming —

"Mesdames, vous êtes servies!" adding "J'ai bien faim, moi!"

We found dinner ready and waiting for us in Mrs. Fairfax's room.

# CHAPTER XII

THE promise of a smooth career, which my first calm introduction to Thornfield Hall seemed to pledge, was not belied on a longer acquaintance with the place and its inmates. Mrs. Fairfax turned out to be what she appeared, a placid-tempered, kind-natured woman, of competent education and average intelligence. My pupil was a lively child, who had been spoilt and indulged, and therefore was sometimes wayward; but as she was committed entirely to my care, and no injudicious interference from any quarter ever thwarted my plans for her improvement, she soon forgot her little freaks, and became obedient and teachable. She had no great talents, no marked traits of character, no peculiar development of feeling or taste which raised her one inch above the ordinary level of childhood; but neither had she any deficiency or vice which sunk her below it. She made reasonable progress, entertained for me a vivacious, though perhaps not very profound, affection; and by her simplicity, gay prattle, and efforts to please, inspired me, in return, with a degree of attachment sufficient to make us both content in each other's society.

This, *par parenthèse,* will be thought cool language by persons who entertain solemn doctrines about the angelic nature of children, and the duty of those charged with their education to conceive for them an idolatrous devotion: but I am not writing to flatter paternal egotism, to echo cant, or prop up humbug; I am merely telling the truth. I felt a conscientious solicitude for Adèle's welfare and progress, and a quiet liking to her little self; just as I cherished towards Mrs. Fairfax a thankfulness for her kindness, and a pleasure in her society proportionate to the tranquil regard she had for me, and the moderation of her mind and character.

Anybody may blame me who likes, when I add further, that, now and then, when I took a walk by myself in the grounds; when I went down to the gates and looked through them along the road; or when, while Adèle played with her nurse, and Mrs. Fairfax made jellies in the store-room, I climbed the three staircases, raised the trap-door of the attic, and having reached the leads, looked out afar over sequestered field and hill, and along dim sky-line — that then I longed for a power of vision which might overpass that limit; which might reach the busy world, towns, regions full of life I had heard of but never seen; that then I desired more of practical experience than I possessed; more of intercourse with my kind, of acquaintance with variety of character, than was here within my reach. I valued what was good in Mrs. Fairfax, and what was good in Adèle; but I believed in the existence of other and more vivid kinds of goodness, and what I believed in I wished to behold.

Who blames me? Many, no doubt; and I shall be called discontented. I could not help it: the restlessness was in my nature; it agitated me to pain sometimes. Then my sole relief was to walk along the corridor of the third story, backwards and forwards, safe in the silence and solitude of the spot, and allow my mind's eye to dwell on whatever bright visions rose before it — and, certainly they were many and glowing; to let my heart be heaved by the exultant movement, which, while it swelled it in trouble, expanded it with life; and, best of all, to open my inward ear to a tale that was never ended — a tale my imagination created, and narrated continuously; quickened with all of incident, life, fire, feeling, that I desired and had not in my actual existence.

It is in vain to say human beings ought to be satisfied with tranquillity: they must have action; and they will make it if they cannot find it. Millions are condemned to a stiller doom than mine, and millions are in silent revolt against their lot. Nobody knows how many rebellions besides political rebellions ferment in the masses of life which people earth. Women are supposed to be very calm generally: but women feel just as men feel; they need exercise for their faculties, and a field for their efforts as much as their brothers do; they suffer from too rigid a constraint, too absolute a stagnation, precisely as men would suffer; and it is narrow-minded in their more privileged fellow-creatures to say that they ought to confine themselves to making puddings and knitting stockings, to playing on the piano and embroidering bags. It is thoughtless to condemn them, or laugh at them, if they seek to do more or learn more than custom has pronounced necessary for their sex.

When thus alone, I not unfrequently heard Grace Poole's laugh: the same peal, the same low, slow ha! ha! which, when first heard, had thrilled me: I heard, too, her eccentric murmurs; stranger than her laugh. There were days when she was quite silent; but there were others when I could not account for the sounds she made. Sometimes I saw her: she would come out of her room with a basin, or a plate, or a tray in her hand, go down to the kitchen and shortly return, generally (oh, romantic reader, forgive me for telling the plain truth!) bearing a pot of porter. Her appearance always acted as a damper to the curiosity raised by her oral oddities: hard-featured and staid, she had no point to which interest could attach. I made some attempts to draw her into conversation, but she seemed a person of few words: a monosyllabic reply usually cut short every effort of that sort.

The other members of the household, viz., John and his wife, Leah the housemaid, and Sophie the French nurse, were decent people; but in no respect remarkable: with Sophie I used to talk French, and sometimes I asked her questions about her native country; but she was not of a descriptive or narrative turn, and generally gave such vapid and confused answers as were calculated rather to check than encourage inquiry.

October, November, December passed away. One afternoon in January, Mrs. Fairfax had begged a holiday for Adèle, because she had a cold; and, as Adèle seconded the request with an ardour that reminded me how precious occasional holidays had been to me in my own childhood, I accorded it, deeming that I did well in showing pliability on the point. It was a fine, calm day, though very cold; I was tired of sitting still in the library through a whole long morning: Mrs. Fairfax had just written a letter which was waiting to be posted, so I put on my bonnet and cloak and volunteered to carry it to Hay; the distance, two miles, would be a pleasant winter afternoon walk. Having seen Adèle comfortably seated in her little chair by Mrs. Fairfax's parlour fireside, and given her her best wax doll (which I usually kept enveloped in silver paper in a drawer) to play with, and a story-book for change of amusement; and having replied to her "Revenez bientôt, ma bonne amie, ma chère Mdlle. Jeannette," with a kiss, I set out.

The ground was hard, the air was still, my road was lonely; I walked fast till I got warm, and then I walked slowly to enjoy and analyse the species of pleasure brooding for me in the hour and situation. It was three o'clock; the church bell tolled as I passed under the belfry; the charm of the hour lay in its approaching dimness, in the low-gliding and pale-beaming sun. I was a mile from Thornfield, in a lane noted for wild roses in summer, for nuts and blackberries in autumn, and even now possessing a few coral treasures in hips and haws, but whose best winter delight lay in its utter solitude and leafless repose. If a breath of air stirred, it made no sound here; for there was not a holly, not an evergreen to rustle, and the stripped hawthorn and hazel bushes were as still as the white, worn stones which causewayed the middle of the path. Far and wide, on each side, there were only fields, where no cattle now browsed; and the little brown birds, which stirred occasionally in the hedge, looked like single russet leaves that had forgotten to drop.

This lane inclined up-hill all the way to Hay: having reached the middle, I sat down on a stile which led thence into a field. Gathering my mantle about me, and sheltering my hands in my muff, I did not feel the cold, though it froze keenly; as was attested by a sheet of ice covering the causeway, where a little brooklet, now congealed, had overflowed after a rapid thaw some days since. From my seat I could look down on Thornfield: the grey and battlemented hall was the principal object in the vale below me; its woods and dark rookery rose against the west. I lingered till the sun went down amongst the trees, and sank crimson and clear behind them. I then turned eastward.

On the hill-top above me sat the rising moon; pale yet as a cloud, but brightening momently: she looked over Hay, which, half lost in trees, sent up a blue smoke from its few chimneys; it was yet a mile distant, but in the absolute hush I could hear plainly its thin murmurs of life. My ear too felt the flow of currents; in what dales and depths I could not tell: but there were many hills beyond Hay, and doubtless many becks threading their passes. That evening calm betrayed alike the tinkle of the nearest streams, the sough of the most remote.

A rude noise broke on these fine ripplings and whisperings, at once so far away and so clear: a positive tramp, tramp; a metallic clatter, which effaced the soft wave-wanderings; as, in a picture, the solid mass of a crag, or the rough boles of a great oak, drawn in dark and strong on the foreground, efface the aërial distance of azure hill, sunny horizon, and blended clouds, where tint melts into tint.

The din was on the causeway: a horse was coming; the windings of the lane yet hid it, but it approached. I was just leaving the stile; yet, as the path was narrow, I sat still to let it go by. In those days I was young, and all sorts of fancies bright and dark tenanted my mind: the memories of nursery stories were there amongst other rubbish; and when they recurred, maturing youth added to them a vigour and vividness beyond what childhood could give. As this horse approached, and as I watched for it to appear through the dusk, I remembered certain of Bessie's tales, wherein figured a North-of-England spirit, called a "Gytrash"; which, in the form of horse, mule, or large dog, haunted solitary ways, and sometimes came upon belated travellers, as this horse was now coming upon me.

It was very near, but not yet in sight; when, in addition to the tramp, tramp, I heard a rush under the hedge, and close down by the hazel stems glided a great dog, whose black and white colour made him a distinct object against the trees. It was exactly one mask of Bessie's Gytrash,— a lion-like creature with long hair and a huge head: it passed me, however, quietly enough; not staying to look up, with strange pretercanine eyes, in my face, as I half expected it would. The horse followed,— a tall steed, and on its back a rider. The man, the human being, broke the spell at once. Nothing ever rode the Gytrash: it was always alone; and goblins, to my notions, though they might tenant the dumb carcasses of beasts, could scarce covet shelter in the commonplace human form. No Gytrash was this,— only a traveller taking the short cut to Millcote. He passed, and I went on; a few steps, and I turned: a sliding sound and an exclamation of "What the deuce is to do now?" and a clattering tumble, arrested my attention. Man and horse were down; they had slipped on the sheet of ice which glazed the causeway. The dog came bounding back, and seeing his master in a predicament, and hearing the horse groan, barked till the evening hills echoed the sound, which was deep in proportion to his magnitude. He snuffed round the prostrate group, and then he ran up to me; it was all he could do,— there was no other help at hand to summon. I obeyed him, and walked down to the traveller, by this time struggling himself free of his steed. His efforts were so vigorous, I thought he could not be much hurt; but I asked him the question: —

"Are you injured, sir?"

I think he was swearing, but am not certain; however, he was pronouncing some formula which prevented him from replying to me directly.

"Can I do anything?" I asked again.

"You must just stand on one side," he answered as he rose, first to his knees, and then to his feet. I did; whereupon began a heaving, stamping, clattering process, accompanied by a barking and baying which removed me effectually some yards distant; but I would not be driven quite away till I saw the event. This was finally fortunate; the horse was re-established, and the dog was silenced with a "Down, Pilot!" The traveller now, stooping, felt his foot and leg, as if trying whether they were sound; apparently something ailed them, for he halted to the stile whence I had just risen, and sat down.

I was in the mood for being useful, or at least officious, I think, for I now drew near him again.

"If you are hurt, and want help, sir, I can fetch some one either from Thornfield Hall or from Hay."

"Thank you; I shall do: I have no broken bones,—only a sprain;" and again he stood up and tried his foot, but the result extorted an involuntary "Ugh!"

Something of daylight still lingered, and the moon was waxing bright: I could see him plainly. His figure was enveloped in a riding cloak, fur collared, and steel clasped; its details were not apparent, but I traced the general points of middle height, and considerable breadth of chest. He had a dark face, with stern features and a heavy brow; his eyes and gathered eyebrows looked ireful and thwarted just now; he was past youth, but had not reached middle age; perhaps he might be thirty-five. I felt no fear of him, and but little shyness. Had he been a handsome, heroic-looking young gentleman, I should not have dared to stand thus questioning him against his will, and offering my services unasked. I had hardly ever seen a handsome youth; never in my life spoken to one. I had a theoretical reverence and homage for beauty, elegance, gallantry, fascination; but had I met those qualities incarnate in masculine shape, I should have known instinctively that they neither had nor could have sympathy with anything in me, and should have shunned them as one would fire, lightning, or anything else that is bright but antipathetic.

If even this stranger had smiled and been good-humoured to me

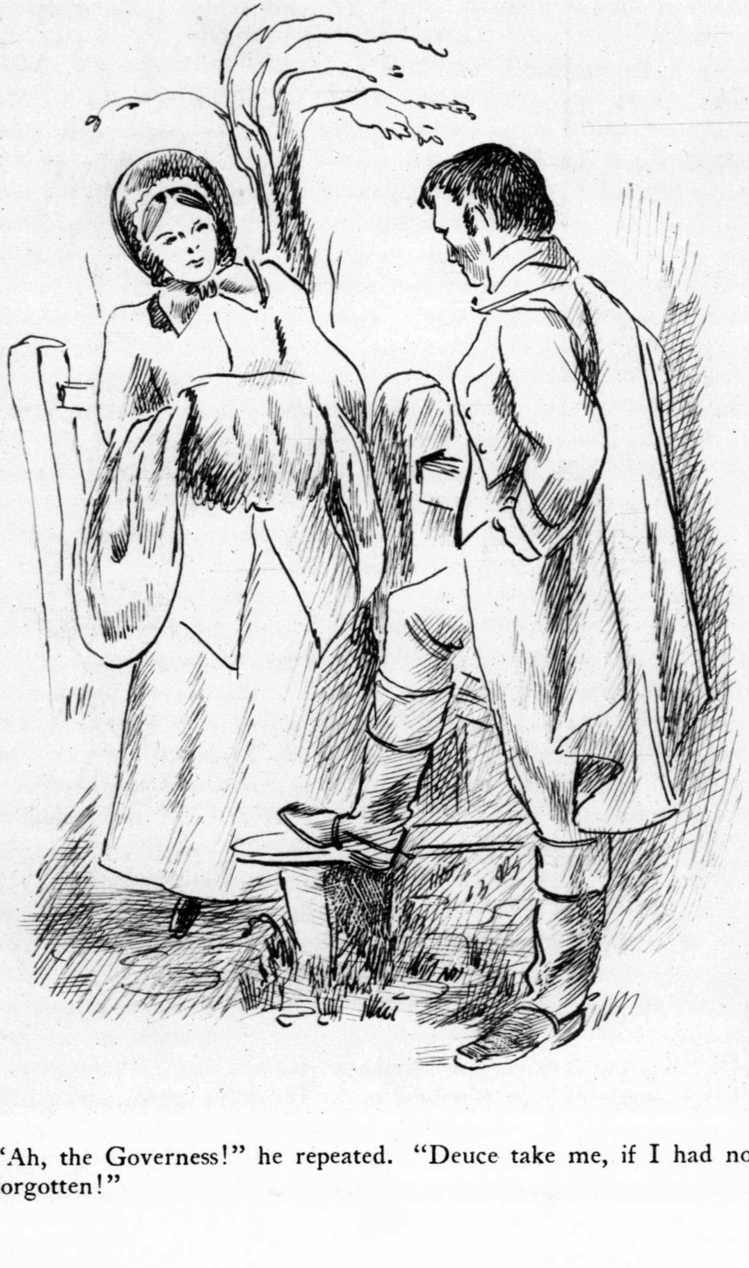

"Ah, the Governess!" he repeated. "Deuce take me, if I had not forgotten!"

when I addressed him; if he had put off my offer of assistance gaily and with thanks, I should have gone on my way and not felt any vocation to renew inquiries: but the frown, the roughness of the traveller set me at my ease: I retained my station when he waved to me to go, and announced:—

"I cannot think of leaving you, sir, at so late an hour, in this solitary lane, till I see you are fit to mount your horse."

He looked at me when I said this: he had hardly turned his eyes in my direction before.

"I should think you ought to be at home yourself," said he, "if you have a home in this neighbourhood: where do you come from?"

"From just below; and I am not at all afraid of being out late when it is moonlight: I will run over to Hay for you with pleasure, if you wish it; indeed, I am going there to post a letter."

"You live just below — do you mean at that house with the battlements?"— pointing to Thornfield Hall, on which the moon cast a hoary gleam, bringing it out distinct and pale from the woods, that, by contrast with the western sky, now seemed one mass of shadow.

"Yes, sir."

"Whose house is it?"

"Mr. Rochester's."

"Do you know Mr. Rochester?"

"No, I have never seen him."

"He is not resident, then?"

"No."

"Can you tell me where he is?"

"I cannot."

"You are not a servant at the hall, of course. You are"—— He stopped, ran his eye over my dress, which, as usual, was quite simple: a black merino cloak, a black beaver bonnet; neither of them half fine enough for a lady's maid. He seemed puzzled to decide what I was: I helped him.

"I am the governess."

"Ah, the governess!" he repeated; "deuce take me, if I had not forgotten! The governess!" and again my raiment underwent scrutiny. In two minutes he rose from the stile: his face expressed pain when he tried to move.

"I cannot commission you to fetch help," he said; "but you may help me a little yourself, if you will be so kind."

"Yes, sir."

"You have not an umbrella that I can use as a stick?"

"No."

"Try to get hold of my horse's bridle and lead him to me: you are not afraid?"

I should have been afraid to touch a horse when alone, but when told to do it, I was disposed to obey. I put down my muff on the stile, and went up to the tall steed; I endeavoured to catch the bridle, but it was a spirited thing, and would not let me come near its head; I made effort on effort, though in vain: meantime, I was mortally afraid of its trampling forefeet. The traveller waited and watched for some time, and at last he laughed.

"I see," he said, "the mountain will never be brought to Mahomet, so all you can do is to aid Mahomet to go to the mountain; I must beg you to come here."

I came. "Excuse me," he continued; "necessity compels me to make you useful." He laid a heavy hand on my shoulder, and leaning on me with some stress, limped to his horse. Having once caught the bridle, he mastered it directly, and sprang to his saddle; grimacing grimly as he made the effort, for it wrenched his sprain.

"Now," said he, releasing his under lip from a hard bite, "just hand me my whip; it lies there under the hedge."

I sought it and found it.

"Thank you; now make haste with the letter to Hay, and return as fast as you can."

A touch of a spurred heel made his horse first start and rear, and then bound away; the dog rushed in his traces: all three vanished,

"Like heath that, in the wilderness,
The wild wind whirls away."

I took up my muff and walked on. The incident had occurred and was gone for me: it *was* an incident of no moment, no romance, no interest in a sense; yet it marked with change one single hour of a monotonous life. My help had been needed and claimed; I had given it: I was pleased to have done something; trivial, transitory though the deed was, it was yet an active thing, and I was weary of an existence all passive. The new face, too, was like a new picture introduced to the gallery of memory; and it was dissimilar to all the others hanging there: firstly, because it was masculine; and, secondly, because it was dark, strong, and stern. I had it still before me when I entered Hay, and slipped the letter into the post-office; I saw it as I walked fast down hill all the way home. When I came to the stile, I stopped a minute, looked round and listened, with an idea that a horse's hoofs might ring on the causeway again, and that a rider in a cloak, and a Gytrash-like Newfoundland dog, might be again apparent: I saw only the hedge and a pollard willow before me, rising up still and straight to meet the moonbeams; I heard only the faintest waft of wind roaming fitful among the trees round Thornfield, a mile distant; and when I glanced down in the direction of the murmur, my eyes, traversing the hall-front, caught a light kindling in a window: it reminded me that I was late, and I hurried on.

I did not like re-entering Thornfield. To pass its threshold was to return to stagnation; to cross the silent hall, to ascend the darksome staircase, to seek my own lonely little room, and then to meet tranquil Mrs. Fairfax, and spend the long winter evening with her, and her only, was to quell wholly the faint excitement wakened by my walk,— to slip again over my faculties the viewless fetters of an uniform and too still existence; of an existence whose very privileges of security and ease I was becoming incapable of appreciating. What good it would have done me at that time to have been tossed in the storms of an uncertain struggling life, and to have been taught by rough and bitter experience to long for the calm amidst which I now repined! Yes, just as much good as it would do a man tired of sitting still in a "too easy chair" to take a long walk: and just as natural was the wish to stir, under my circumstances, as it would be under his.

I lingered at the gates; I lingered on the lawn; I paced backwards and forwards on the pavement: the shutters of the glass door were closed; I could not see into the interior; and both my eyes and spirit seemed drawn from the gloomy house — from the grey hollow filled with rayless cells, as it appeared to me — to that sky expanded before me — a blue sea absolved from taint of cloud; the moon ascending it in solemn march; her orb seeming to look up as she left the hill tops, from behind which she had come, far and farther below her, and aspired to the zenith, midnight-dark in its fathomless depth and measureless distance: and for those trembling stars that followed her course; they made my heart tremble, my veins glow when

I viewed them. Little things recall us to earth: the clock struck in the hall; that sufficed; I turned from moon and stars, opened a side-door, and went in.

The hall was not dark, nor yet was it lit, only by the high-hung bronze lamp: a warm glow suffused both it and the lower steps of the oak staircase. This ruddy shine issued from the great dining-room, whose two-leaved door stood open, and showed a genial fire in the grate, glancing on marble hearth and brass fire-irons, and revealing purple draperies and polished furniture, in the most pleasant radiance. It revealed, too, a group near the mantelpiece: I had scarcely caught it, and scarcely become aware of a cheerful mingling of voices, amongst which I seemed to distinguish the tones of Adèle, when the door closed.

I hastened to Mrs. Fairfax's room: there was a fire there too, but no candle, and no Mrs. Fairfax. Instead, all alone, sitting upright on the rug, and gazing with gravity at the blaze, I beheld a great black and white long-haired dog, just like the Gytrash of the lane. It was so like it that I went forward and said,—

"Pilot," and the thing got up and came to me and snuffed me. I caressed him, and he wagged his great tail: but he looked an eerie creature to be alone with, and I could not tell whence he had come. I rang the bell, for I wanted a candle; and I wanted, too, to get an account of this visitant. Leah entered.

"What dog is this?"

"He came with master."

"With whom?"

"With master — Mr. Rochester — he is just arrived."

"Indeed! and is Mrs. Fairfax with him?"

"Yes, and Miss Adèle, they are in the dining-room, and John is gone for a surgeon: for master has had an accident; his horse fell and his ankle is sprained."

"Did the horse fall in Hay Lane?"

"Yes, coming down hill; it slipped on some ice?"

"Ah! Bring me a candle, will you, Leah?"

Leah brought it; she entered, followed by Mrs. Fairfax, who repeated the news; adding that Mr. Carter the surgeon was come, and was now with Mr. Rochester: then she hurried out to give orders about tea, and I went upstairs to take off my things.

## CHAPTER XIII

MR. ROCHESTER, it seems by the surgeon's orders, went to bed early that night; nor did he rise soon next morning. When he did come down, it was to attend to business: his agent and some of his tenants were arrived, and waiting to speak with him.

Adèle and I had now to vacate the library: it would be in daily requisition as a reception-room for callers. A fire was lit in an apartment upstairs, and there I carried our books, and arranged it for the future school-room. I discerned in the course of the morning that Thornfield Hall was a changed place: no longer silent as a church, it echoed every hour or two to a knock at the door, or a clang of the bell; steps, too, often traversed the hall, and new voices spoke in different keys below; a rill from the outer world was flowing through it; it had a master: for my part, I liked it better.

Adèle was not easy to teach that day; she could not apply: she kept running to the door looking over the banisters to see if she could get a glimpse of Mr. Rochester; then she coined pretexts to go downstairs, in order, as I shrewdly suspected, to visit the library, where I knew she was not wanted; then, when I got a little angry, and made her sit still, she continued to talk incessantly of her "ami, Monsieur Edouard Fairfax *de* Rochester," as she dubbed him (I had not before heard his prenomens), and to conjecture what presents he had brought her: for it appears he had intimated the night before, that when his luggage came from Millcote, there would be found amongst it a little box in whose contents she had an interest.

"Et cela doit signifier," said she, "qu'il y aura là dedans un cadeau pour moi, et peutêtre pour vous aussi, mademoiselle. Monsieur a parlé de vous: il m'a demandé le nom de ma gouvernante, et si elle n'était pas une petite personne, assez mince et un peu pâle. J'ai dit qu'oui: car c'est vrai, n'est-ce pas, mademoiselle?"

I and my pupil dined as usual in Mrs. Fairfax's parlour; the afternoon was wild and snowy, and we passed it in the school-room. At dark I allowed Adèle to put away books and work, and to run downstairs; for, from the comparative silence below, and from the cessation of appeals to the doorbell, I conjectured that Mr. Rochester was now at liberty. Left alone, I walked to the window; but nothing was to be seen thence: twilight and snow-flakes together thickened the air, and hid the very shrubs on the lawn. I let down the curtain and went back to the fireside.

In the clear embers I was tracing a view, not unlike a picture I remembered to have seen of the castle of Heidelberg, on the Rhine, when Mrs. Fairfax came in, breaking up by her entrance the fiery mosaic I had been piecing together, and scattering too some heavy unwelcome thoughts that were beginning to throng on my solitude.

"Mr. Rochester would be glad if you and your pupil would take tea with him in the drawing-room this evening," said she: "he has been so much engaged all day that he could not ask to see you before."

"When is his tea-time?" I inquired.

"Oh, at six o'clock: he keeps early hours in the country. You had better change your frock now; I will go with you and fasten it. Here is a candle."

"Is it necessary to change my frock?"

"Yes, you had better: I always dress for the evening when Mr. Rochester is here."

This additional ceremony seemed somewhat stately: however, I repaired to my room, and, with Mrs. Fairfax's aid, replaced my black stuff dress by one of black silk; the best and the only additional one I had, except one of light grey, which, in my Lowood notions of the toilette, I thought too fine to be worn, except on first-rate occasions.

"You want a brooch," said Mrs. Fairfax. I had a single little pearl ornament which Miss Temple gave me as a parting keepsake: I put it on, and then we went downstairs. Unused as I was to strangers, it was rather a trial to appear thus formally summoned in Mr. Rochester's presence. I let Mrs. Fairfax precede me into the dining-room, and kept in her shade as we crossed that apartment; and, passing the arch, whose curtain was now dropped, entered the elegant recess beyond.

Two wax candles stood lighted on the table, and two on the mantelpiece; basking in the light and heat of a superb fire, lay Pilot — Adèle knelt near him. Half reclined on a couch appeared Mr. Rochester, his foot supported by the cushion; he was looking at

Adèle and the dog: the fire shone full on his face. I knew my traveller with his broad and jetty eyebrows; his square forehead, made squarer by the horizontal sweep of his black hair. I recognised his decisive nose, more remarkable for character than beauty; his full nostrils, denoting, I thought, choler; his grim mouth, chin, and jaw — yes, all three were very grim, and no mistake. His shape, now divested of cloak, I perceived harmonised in squareness with his physiognomy: I suppose it was a good figure in the athletic sense of the term — broad chested and thin flanked, though neither tall nor graceful.

Mr. Rochester must have been aware of the entrance of Mrs. Fairfax and myself; but it appeared he was not in the mood to notice us, for he never lifted his head as we approached.

"Here is Miss Eyre, sir," said Mrs. Fairfax, in her quiet way. He bowed, still not taking his eyes from the group of the dog and child.

"Let Miss Eyre be seated," said he: and there was something in the forced stiff bow, in the impatient yet formal tone, which seemed further to express, "What the deuce is it to me whether Miss Eyre be there or not? At this moment I am not disposed to accost her."

I sat down quite disembarrassed. A reception of finished politeness would probably have confused me: I could not have returned or repaid it by answering grace and elegance on my part; but harsh caprice laid me under no obligation; on the contrary, a decent quiescence, under the freak of manner, gave me the advantage. Besides, the eccentricity of the proceeding was piquant: I felt interested to see how he would go on.

He went on as a statue would, that is, he neither spoke nor moved. Mrs. Fairfax seemed to think it necessary that some one should be amiable, and she began to talk. Kindly, as usual — and, as usual, rather trite — she condoled with him on the pressure of business he had had all day; on the annoyance it must have been to him with that painful sprain: then she commended his patience and perseverance in going through with it.

"Madame, I should like some tea," was the sole rejoinder she got. She hastened to ring the bell; and, when the tray came, she proceeded to arrange the cups, spoons, etc., with assiduous celerity. I and Adèle went to the table; but the master did not leave his couch.

"Will you hand Mr. Rochester's cup?" said Mrs. Fairfax to me; "Adèle might perhaps spill it."

I did as requested. As he took the cup from my hand, Adèle, thinking the moment propitious for making a request in my favour, cried out:—

"N'est-ce pas, monsieur, qu'il y un cadeau pour Mademoiselle Eyre, dans votre petit coffre?"

"Who talks of cadeaux?" said he, gruffly: "did you expect a present, Miss Eyre? Are you fond of presents?" and he searched my face with eyes that I saw were dark, irate, and piercing.

"I hardly know, sir; I have little experience of them: they are generally thought pleasant things."

"Generally thought? But what do *you* think?"

"I should be obliged to take time, sir, before I could give you an answer worthy of your acceptance: a present has many faces to it, has it not? and one should consider all, before pronouncing an opinion as to its nature."

"Miss Eyre, you are not so unsophisticated as Adèle: she demands a 'cadeau,' clamorously, the moment she sees me: you beat about the bush."

"Because I have less confidence in my deserts than Adèle has: she can prefer the claim of old acquaintance, and the right too of custom; for she says you have always been in the habit of giving her playthings; but if I had to make out a case I should be puzzled, since I am a stranger, and have done nothing to entitle me to an acknowledgment."

"Oh, don't fall back on over-modesty! I have examined Adèle, and find you have taken great pains with her: she is not bright, she has no talents; yet in a short time she has made much improvement."

"Sir, you have now given me my 'cadeau'; I am obliged to you; it is the mood teachers most covet; praise of their pupils' progress."

"Humph!" said Mr. Rochester, and he took his tea in silence.

"Come to the fire," said the master, when the tray was taken away, and Mrs. Fairfax had settled into a corner with her knitting; while Adèle was leading me by the hand round the room, showing me the beautiful books and ornaments on the consoles and chiffonnières. We obeyed, as in duty bound; Adèle wanted to take a seat on my knee, but she was ordered to amuse herself with Pilot.

"You have been resident in my house three months?"

"Yes, sir."

"And you came from——?"

"From Lowood school, in ——shire."

"Ah! a charitable concern.—How long were you there?"

"Eight years."

"Eight years! you must be tenacious of life. I thought half the time in such a place would have done up any constitution! No wonder you have rather the look of another world. I marvelled where you had got that sort of a face. When you came on me in Hay Lane last night, I thought unaccountably of fairy tales, and had half a mind to demand whether you had bewitched my horse: I am not sure yet. Who are your parents?"

"I have none."

"Nor ever had, I suppose: do you remember them?"

"No."

"I thought not. And so you were waiting for your people when you sat on that stile?"

"For whom, sir?"

"For the men in green: it was a proper moonlight evening for them. Did I break through one of your rings, that you spread that damned ice on the causeway?"

I shook my head. "The men in green all forsook England a hundred years ago," said I, speaking as seriously as he had done. "And not even in Hay Lane, or the fields about it, could you find a trace of them. I don't think either summer or harvest, or winter moon, will ever shine on their revels more."

Mrs. Fairfax had dropped her knitting, and, with raised eyebrows, seemed wondering what sort of talk this was.

"Well," resumed Mr. Rochester, "if you disown parents, you must have some sort of kinsfolk: uncles and aunts?"

"No; none that I ever saw."

"And your home?"

"I have none."

"Where do your brothers and sisters live?"

"I have no brothers or sisters."

"Who recommended you to come here?"

"I advertised, and Mrs. Fairfax answered my advertisement."

"Yes," said the good lady, who now knew what ground we were upon, "and I am daily thankful for the choice Providence led me to make. Miss Eyre has been an invaluable companion to me, and a kind and careful teacher to Adèle."

"Don't trouble yourself to give her a character," returned Mr. Rochester: "eulogiums will not bias me; I shall judge for myself. She began by felling my horse."

"Sir?" said Mrs. Fairfax.

"I have to thank her for this sprain."

The widow looked bewildered.

"Miss Eyre, have you ever lived in a town?"

"No, sir."

"Have you seen much society?"

"None but the pupils and teachers of Lowood; and now the inmates of Thornfield."

"Have you read much?"

"Only such books as came in my way; and they have not been numerous, or very learned."

"You have lived the life of a nun: no doubt you are well drilled in religious forms; — Brocklehurst, who I understand directs Lowood, is a parson, is he not?"

"Yes, sir."

"And you girls probably worshipped him, as a convent full of religieuses would worship their director."

"Oh, no."

"You are very cool! No! What! a novice not worship her priest! That sounds blasphemous."

"I disliked Mr. Brocklehurst; and I was not alone in the feeling He is a harsh man; at once pompous and meddling: he cut off our hair; and for economy's sake bought us bad needles and thread, with which we could hardly sew."

"That was very false economy," remarked Mrs. Fairfax, who now again caught the drift of the dialogue.

"And was that the head and front of his offending?" demanded Mr. Rochester.

"He starved us when he had the sole superintendence of the provision department, before the committee was appointed; and he bored us with long lectures once a week, and with evening readings from books of his own inditing, about sudden deaths and judgments, which made us afraid to go to bed."

"What age were you when you went to Lowood?"

"About ten."

"And you stayed there eight years: and are now, then, eighteen?"

I assented.

"Arithmetic, you see, is useful: without its aid, I should hardly have been able to guess your age. It is a point difficult to fix where the features and countenance are so much at variance as in your case. And now what did you learn at Lowood? Can you play?"

"A little."

"Of course: that is the established answer. Go into the library — I mean, if you please.— (Excuse my tone of command; I am used to say 'Do this,' and it is done: I cannot alter my customary habits for one new inmate.) — Go, then, into the library; take a candle with you; leave the door open; sit down to the piano, and play a tune."

I departed, obeying his directions.

"Enough!" he called out in a few minutes. "You play *a little,* I see; like any other English school-girl: perhaps rather better than some, but not well."

I closed the piano, and returned. Mr. Rochester continued.

"Adèle showed me some sketches this morning, which she said were yours. I don't know whether they were entirely of your doing: probably a master aided you?"

"No, indeed!" I interjected.

"Ah! that pricks pride. Well, fetch me your portfolio, if you can vouch for its contents being original; but don't pass your word unless you are certain: I can recognise patchwork."

"Then I will say nothing, and you shall judge for yourself, sir."

I brought the portfolio from the library.

"Approach the table," said he; and I wheeled it to his couch. Adèle and Mrs. Fairfax drew near to see the pictures.

"No crowding," said Mr. Rochester: "take the drawings from my hand as I finish with them; but don't push your faces up to mine."

He deliberately scrutinised each sketch and painting. Three he laid aside; the others, when he had examined them, he swept from him.

"Take them off to the other table, Mrs. Fairfax," said he, "and look at them with Adèle; — you" (glancing at me) "resume your seat, and answer my questions. I perceived these pictures were done by one hand: was that hand yours?"

"Yes."

"And when did you find time to do them? They have taken much time, and some thought."

"I did them in the last two vacations I spent at Lowood, when I had no other occupation."

"Where did you get your copies?"

"Out of my head."

"That head I see now on your shoulders?"

"Yes, sir."

"Has it other furniture of the same kind within?"

"I should think it may have: I should hope — better."

He spread the pictures before him, and again surveyed them alternately.

While he is so occupied, I will tell you, reader, what they are: and first, I must premise that they are nothing wonderful. The subjects had, indeed, risen vividly on my mind. As I saw them with the spiritual eye, before I attempted to embody them, they were striking; but my hand would not second my fancy, and in each case it had wrought out but a pale portrait of the thing I had conceived.

These pictures were in water colours. The first represented clouds low and vivid, rolling over a swollen sea: all the distance was in eclipse; so, too, was the foreground; or, rather, the nearest billows, for there was no land. One gleam of light lifted into relief a half-submerged mast, on which sat a cormorant, dark and large, with wings flecked with foam; its beak held a gold bracelet, set with gems, that I had touched with as brilliant tints as my palette could yield, and as glittering distinctness as my pencil could impart. Sinking below the bird and mast, a drowned corpse glanced through the green water; a fair arm was the only limb clearly visible, whence the bracelet had been washed or torn.

The second picture contained for foreground only the dim peak of a hill, with grass and some leaves slanting as if by a breeze. Beyond and above spread an expanse of sky, dark blue as at twilight: rising into the sky was a woman's shape to the bust, portrayed in tints as dusk and soft as I could combine. The dim forehead was crowned with a star; the lineaments below were seen as through the suffusion of vapour; the eyes shone dark and wild; the hair streamed shadowy, like a beamless cloud torn by storm or by electric travail. On the neck lay a pale reflection like moonlight; the same faint lustre touched the train of thin clouds from which rose and bowed this vision of the Evening Star.

The third showed the pinnacle of an iceberg piercing a polar winter sky: a muster of northern lights reared their dim lances, close serried, along the horizon. Throwing these into distance, rose, in the foreground, a head,— a colossal head, inclined towards the iceberg, and resting against it. Two thin hands, joined under the forehead, and supporting it, drew up before the lower features a sable veil; a brow quite bloodless, white as bone, and an eye hollow and fixed, blank of meaning but for the glassiness of despair, alone were visible. Above the temples, amidst wreathed turban folds of black drapery, vague in its character and consistency as cloud, gleamed a ring of white flame, gemmed with sparkles of a more lurid tinge. This pale crescent was "The likeness of a Kingly Crown"; what it diademed was "the shape which shape had none."

"Were you happy when you painted these pictures?" asked Mr. Rochester, presently.

"I was absorbed, sir: yes, and I was happy. To paint them, in short, was to enjoy one of the keenest pleasures I have ever known."

"That is not saying much. Your pleasures, by your own account, have been few; but I daresay you did exist in a kind of artist's dreamland while you blent and arranged these strange tints. Did you sit at them long each day?"

"I had nothing else to do, because it was the vacation, and I sat at them from morning till noon, and from noon till night: the length of the midsummer days favoured my inclination to apply."

"And you felt self-satisfied with the result of your ardent labours?"

"Far from it. I was tormented by the contrast between my ideas and my handiwork: in each case I had imagined something which I was quite powerless to realise."

"Not quite: you have secured the shadow of your thought; but no more, probably. You had not enough of the artist's skill and science to give it full being: yet the drawings are, for a school girl, peculiar. As to the thoughts, they are elfish. These eyes in the Evening Star you must have seen in a dream. How could you make them look so clear, and yet not at all brilliant? for the planet above quells their rays. And what meaning is that in their solemn depth? And who taught you to paint wind. There is a high gale in that sky, and on this hill-top. Where did you see Latmos? For that is Latmos. There,— put the drawings away!"

I had scarce tied the strings of the portfolio, when, looking at his watch, he said abruptly —

"It is nine o'clock: what are you about, Miss Eyre, to let Adèle sit up so long? Take her to bed."

Adèle went to kiss him before quitting the room: he endured the caress, but scarcely seemed to relish it more than Pilot would have done, nor so much.

"I wish you all good-night, now," said he, making a movement of the hands towards the door, in token that he was tired of our company, and wished to dismiss us. Mrs. Fairfax folded up her knitting: I took my portfolio: we curtseyed to him, received a frigid bow in return, and so withdrew.

"You said Mr. Rochester was not strikingly peculiar, Mrs. Fairfax," I observed, when I rejoined her in her room, after putting Adèle to bed.

"Well, is he?"

"I think so: he is very changeful and abrupt."

"True: no doubt he may appear so to a stranger, but I am so accustomed to his manner, I never think of it; and then, if he has peculiarities of temper, allowance should be made."

"Why?"

"Partly because it is his nature — and we can none of us help our nature; and, partly, he has painful thoughts, no doubt, to harass him, and make his spirits unequal."

"What about?"

"Family troubles, for one thing."

"But he has no family."

"Not now, but he has had — or, at least, relatives. He lost his elder brother a few years since."

"His *elder* brother?"

"Yes. The present Mr. Rochester has not been very long in possession of the property; only about nine years."

"Nine years is a tolerable time. Was he so very fond of his brother as to be still inconsolable for his loss?"

"Why, no — perhaps not. I believe there were some misunderstandings between them. Mr. Rowland Rochester was not quite just to Mr. Edward; and, perhaps, he prejudiced his father against him. The old gentleman was fond of money, and anxious to keep the family estate together. He did not like to diminish the property by division, and yet he was anxious that Mr. Edward should have wealth, too, to keep up the consequence of the name; and, soon after he was of age, some steps were taken that were not quite fair, and made a great deal of mischief. Old Mr. Rochester and Mr. Rowland combined to bring Mr. Edward into what he considered a painful position, for the sake of making his fortune: what the precise nature of that position was I never clearly knew, but his spirit could not brook what he had to suffer in it. He is not very forgiving: he broke with his family, and now for many years he has led an unsettled kind of life. I don't think he has ever been resident at Thornfield for a fortnight together, since the death of his brother without a will left him master of the estate; and, indeed, no wonder he shuns the old place."

"Why should he shun it?"

"Perhaps he thinks it gloomy."

The answer was evasive — I should have liked something clearer; but Mrs. Fairfax either could not, or would not, give me more explicit information of the origin and nature of Mr. Rochester's trials. She averred they were a mystery to herself, and that what she knew was chiefly from conjecture. It was evident, indeed, that she wished me to drop the subject, which I did accordingly.

## CHAPTER XIV

FOR several subsequent days I saw little of Mr. Rochester. In the mornings he seemed much engaged with business, and, in the afternoon, gentlemen from Millcote or the neighbourhood called, and sometimes stayed to dine with him. When his sprain was well enough to admit of horse exercise, he rode out a good deal; probably to return these visits, as he generally did not come back till late at night.

During this interval, even Adèle was seldom sent for to his presence, and all my acquaintance with him was confined to an occasional rencontre in the hall, on the stairs, or in the gallery, when he would sometimes pass me haughtily and coldly, just acknowledging my presence by a distant nod or a cool glance, and sometimes bow and smile with gentleman-like affability. His changes of mood did not offend me, because I saw that I had nothing to do with their alternation; the ebb and flow depended on causes quite disconnected with me.

One day he had had company to dinner, and had sent for my portfolio; in order, doubtless, to exhibit its contents: the gentlemen went away early, to attend a public meeting at Millcote, as Mrs. Fairfax informed me; but the night being wet and inclement, Mr. Rochester did not accompany them. Soon after they were gone, he rang the bell: a message came that I and Adèle were to go downstairs. I brushed Adèle's hair and made her neat, and having ascertained that I was myself in my usual Quaker trim, where there was nothing to retouch — all being too close and plain, braided locks included, to admit of disarrangement — we descended, Adèle wondering whether the *petit coffre* was at length come; for, owing to some mistake, its arrival had hitherto been delayed. She was gratified: there it stood, a little carton, on the table when we entered the dining-room. She appeared to know it by instinct.

"Ma boite! ma boite!" exclaimed she, running towards it.

"Yes — there is your 'boite' at last: take it into a corner, you genuine daughter of Paris, and amuse yourself with disembowelling it," said the deep rather sarcastic voice of Mr. Rochester, proceeding from the depths of an immense easy chair at the fireside. "And mind," he continued, "don't bother me with any details of the anatomical process, or any notice of the condition of the entrails: let your operation be conducted in silence: tiens-toi tranquille, enfant; comprends tu?"

Adèle seemed scarcely to need the warning; she had already retired to a sofa with her treasure, and was busy untying the cord which secured the lid. Having removed this impediment, and lifted certain silvery envelopes of tissue paper, she merely exclaimed:—

"Oh ciel! Que c'est beau!" and then remained absorbed in ecstatic contemplation.

"Is Miss Eyre there?" now demanded the master, half rising from his seat to look round to the door, near which I still stood.

"Ah! well; come forward: be seated here." He drew a chair near his own. "I am not fond of the prattle of children," he continued; "for, old bachelor as I am, I have no pleasant associations connected with their lisp. It would be intolerable to me to pass a whole evening *tête-à-tête* with a brat. Don't draw that chair further off, Miss Eyre; sit down exactly where I placed it—if you please, that is. Confound these civilities! I continually forget them. Nor do I particularly affect simple-minded old ladies. By-the-by, I must have mine in mind; it won't do to neglect her; she is a Fairfax, or wed to one; and blood is said to be thicker than water."

He rang and despatched an invitation to Mrs. Fairfax, who soon arrived, knitting-basket in hand.

"Good-evening, madam; I sent to you for a charitable purpose: I have forbidden Adèle to talk to me about her presents, and she is bursting with repletion; have the goodness to serve her as auditress and interlocutrice: it will be one of the most benevolent acts you ever performed."

Adèle, indeed, no sooner saw Mrs. Fairfax, than she summoned her to her sofa and there quickly filled her lap with the percelain, the ivory, the waxen contents of her "boite"; pouring out, meantime, explanations and raptures in such broken English as she was mistress of.

"Now I have performed the part of a good host," pursued Mr. Rochester, "put my guests into the way of amusing each other, I ought to be at liberty to attend to my own pleasure. Miss Eyre, draw your chair still a little further forward: you are yet too far back; I cannot see you without disturbing my position in this comfortable chair, which I have no mind to do."

I did as I was bid, though I would much rather have remained somewhat in the shade: but Mr. Rochester had such a direct way of giving orders, it seemed a matter of course to obey him promptly.

We were, as I have said, in the dining-room: the lustre, which had been lit for dinner, filled the room with a festal breadth of light; the large fire was all red and clear; the purple curtains hung rich and ample before the lofty window and loftier arch; everything was still, save the subdued chat of Adèle (she dared not speak loud), and, filling up each pause, the beating of winter rain against the panes.

Mr. Rochester, as he sat in his damask-covered chair, looked different to what I had seen him look before; not quite so stern — much less gloomy. There was a smile on his lips, and his eyes sparkled, whether with wine or not, I am not sure; but I think it very probable. He was, in short, in his after-dinner mood; more expanded and genial, and also more self-indulgent than the frigid and rigid temper of the morning: still he looked preciously grim, cushioning his massive head against the swelling back of his chair, and receiving the light of the fire on his granite-hewn features, and in his great dark eyes; for he had great dark eyes, and very fine eyes, too — not without a certain change in their depths sometimes, which, if it was not softness, reminded you, at least, of that feeling.

He had been looking two minutes at the fire, and I had been looking the same length of time at him, when, turning suddenly, he caught my gaze fastened on his physiognomy.

"You examine me, Miss Eyre," said he: "do you think me handsome?"

I should, if I had deliberated, have replied to this question by something conventionally vague and polite; but the answer somehow slipped from my tongue before I was aware: —"No, sir."

"Ah! By my word! there is something singular about you," said he: "you have the air of a little nonnette; quaint, quiet, grave, and simple, as you sit with your hands before you, and your eyes generally bent on the carpet (except, by-the-by, when they are directed piercingly to my face; as just now, for instance); and when one asks you a question, or makes a remark to which you are obliged to reply, you rap out a round rejoinder, which, if not blunt, is at least brusque. What do you mean by it?"

"Sir, I was too plain: I beg your pardon. I ought to have replied that it was not easy to give an impromptu answer to a question about appearances; that tastes differ; that beauty is of little consequence, or something of that sort."

"You ought to have replied no such thing. Beauty of little consequence, indeed! And so, under pretence of softening the previous outrage, of stroking and soothing me into placidity, you stick a sly penknife under my ear! Go on: what fault do you find with me, pray? I suppose I have all my limbs and all my features like any other man?"

"Mr. Rochester, allow me to disown my first answer: I intended no pointed repartee: it was only a blunder."

"Just so: I think so: and you shall be answerable for it. Criticise me: does my forehead not please you?"

He lifted up the sable waves of hair which lay horizontally over his brow, and showed a solid enough mass of intellectual organs, but an abrupt deficiency where the suave sign of benevolence should have risen.

"Now, ma'am, am I a fool?"

"Far from it, sir. You would, perhaps, think me rude if I inquired in return whether you are a philanthropist?"

"There again! Another stick of the penknife, when she pretended to pat my head: and that is because I said I did not like the society of children and old women (low be it spoken!). No, young lady, I am not a general philanthropist; but I bear a conscience;" and he pointed to the prominences which are said to indicate that faculty, and which, fortunately for him, were sufficiently conspicuous; giving, indeed, a marked breadth to the upper part of his head: "and, besides, I once had a kind of rude tenderness of heart. When I was as old as you, I was a feeling fellow enough; partial to the unfledged, unfostered, and unlucky; but fortune has knocked me about since: she has even kneaded me with her knuckles, and now I flatter myself I am hard and tough as an India-rubber ball; pervious, though, through a chink or two still, and with one sentient point in the middle of the lump. Yes: does that leave hope for me?"

"Hope of what, sir?"

"Of my final re-transformation from India-rubber back to flesh?"

"Decidedly he has had too much wine," I thought; and I did not know what answer to make to his queer question: how could I tell whether he was capable of being re-transformed?

"You look very puzzled, Miss Eyre; and though you are not pretty any more than I am handsome, yet a puzzled air becomes you; besides, it is convenient, for it keeps those searching eyes of yours away from my physiognomy, and busies them with the worsted flowers of the rug; so puzzle on. Young lady, I am disposed to be gregarious and communicative to-night."

With this announcement he rose from his chair, and stood, leaning his arm on the marble mantelpiece; in that attitude his shape was seen plainly as well as his face; his unusual breadth of chest, disproportionate almost to his length of limb. I am sure most people would have thought him an ugly man; yet there was so much unconscious pride in his port: so much ease in his demeanour; such a look of complete indifference to his own external appearance; so haughty a reliance on the power of other qualities, intrinsic or adventitious, to atone for the lack of mere personal attractiveness, that, in looking at him, one inevitably shared the indifference, and, even in a blind, imperfect sense, put faith in the confidence.

"I am disposed to be gregarious and communicative to-night," he repeated; "and that is why I sent for you: the fire and the chandelier were not sufficient company for me; nor would Pilot have been, for none of these can talk. Adèle is a degree better, but still far below the mark; Mrs. Fairfax ditto; you, I am persuaded, can suit me if you will: you puzzled me the first evening I invited you down here. I have almost forgotten you since: other ideas have driven yours from my head; but to-night I am resolved to be at ease; to dismiss what importunes, and recall what pleases. It would please me now to draw you out — to learn more of you — therefore speak."

Instead of speaking, I smiled; and not a very complacent or submissive smile either.

"Speak," he urged.

"What about, sir?"

"Whatever you like. I leave both the choice of subject and the manner of treating it entirely to yourself."

Accordingly I sat and said nothing: "If he expects me to talk for the mere sake of talking and showing off, he will find he has addressed himself to the wrong person," I thought.

"You are dumb, Miss Eyre."

I was dumb still. He bent his head a little towards me, and with a single hasty glance seemed to dive into my eyes.

"Stubborn?" he said, "and annoyed. Ah, it is consistent. I put my request in an absurd, almost insolent form. Miss Eyre, I beg your pardon. The fact is, once for all, I don't wish to treat you like an inferior: that is (correcting himself), I claim only such superiority as must result from twenty years' difference in age and a century's advance in experience. This is legitimate, et j'y tiens, as Adèle would say; and it is by virtue of this superiority and this alone that I desire you to have the goodness to talk to me a little now, and divert my thoughts, which are galled with dwelling on one point — cankering as a rusty nail."

He had deigned an explanation; almost an apology: I did not feel insensible to his condescension, and would not seem so.

"I am willing to amuse you if I can, sir: quite willing but I cannot introduce a topic, because how do I know what will interest you? Ask me questions, and I will do my best to answer them."

"Then, in the first place, do you agree with me that I have a right to be a little masterful, abrupt; perhaps exacting, sometimes, on the grounds I stated; namely, that I am old enough to be your father, and that I have battled through a varied experience with men of many nations, and roamed over half the globe, while you have lived quietly with one set of people in one house?"

"Do as you please, sir."

"That is no answer; or rather it is a very irritating, because a very evasive one; reply clearly."

"I don't think, sir, you have a right to command me, merely because you are older than I, or because you have seen more of the world than I have; your claim to superiority depends on the use you have made of your time and experience."

"Humph! Promptly spoken. But I won't allow that, seeing that it would never suit my case; as I have made an indifferent, not to say a bad, use of both advantages. Leaving superiority out of the question then, you must still agree to receive my orders now and then, without being piqued or hurt by the tone of command — will you?"

I smiled: I thought to myself Mr. Rochester *is peculiar*—he seems to forget that he pays me £30 per annum for receiving his orders.

"The smile is very well," said he, catching instantly the passing expression; "but speak too."

"I was thinking, sir, that very few masters would trouble themselves to inquire whether or not their paid subordinates were piqued and hurt by their orders."

"Paid subordinates! What, you are my paid subordinate, are you? Oh yes, I had forgotten the salary! Well then, on that mercenary ground, will you agree to let me hector a little?"

"No, sir, not on that ground: but, on the ground that you did forget it, and that you care whether or not a dependent is comfortable in his dependency, I agree heartily."

"And will you consent to dispense with a great many conventional forms and phrases, without thinking that the omission arises from insolence?"

"I am sure, sir, I should never mistake informality for insolence: one I rather like, the other nothing free-born would submit to, even for a salary."

"Humbug! Most things free-born will submit to anything for a salary; therefore, keep to yourself, and don't venture on generalities of which you are intensely ignorant. However, I mentally shake hands with you for your answer, despite its inaccuracy; and as much for the manner in which it was said, as for the substance of the speech: the manner was frank and sincere; one does not often see such a manner: no, on the contrary, affectation, or coldness, or stupid, coarse-minded misapprehension of one's meaning are the usual rewards of candour. Not three in three thousand raw schoolgirl governesses would have answered me as you have just done. But I don't mean to flatter you: if you are cast in a different mould to the majority, it is no merit of yours: Nature did it. And then, after all, I go too fast in my conclusions: for what I yet know, you may be no better than the rest; you may have intolerable defects to counterbalance your few good points."

"And so may you," I thought. My eye met his as the idea crossed my mind: he seemed to read the glance, answering as if its import had been spoken as well as imagined:—

"Yes, yes, you are right," said he; "I have plenty of faults of my own: I know it, and I don't wish to palliate them, I assure you. God wot I need not be too severe about others; I have a past existence, a series of deeds, a colour of life to contemplate within my own breast, which might well call my sneers and censures from my neighbours to myself. I started, or rather (for, like other defaulters, I like to lay half the blame on ill fortune and adverse circumstances) was thrust on to a wrong tack at the age of one and twenty, and have never recovered the right course since: but I might have been very different; I might have been as good as you — wiser — almost as stainless. I envy you your peace of mind, your clean conscience, your unpolluted memory. Little girl, a memory without blot or contamination must be an exquisite treasure — an inexhaustible source of pure refreshment: is it not?"

"How was your memory when you were eighteen, sir?"

"All right then; limpid, salubrious: no gush of bilge water had turned it to fetid puddle. I was your equal at eighteen — quite your equal. Nature meant me to be, on the whole, a good man, Miss Eyre: one of the better end; and you see I am not so. You would say you don't see it: at least I flatter myself I read as much in your eye (beware, by-the-by, what you express with that organ, I am quick at interpreting its language). Then take my word for it,— I am not a villain: you are not to suppose that — not to attribute to me any such bad eminence; but, owing, I verily believe, rather to circumstances than to my natural bent, I am a trite, commonplace sinner, hackneyed in all the poor petty dissipations with which the rich and worthless try to put on life. Do you wonder that I avow this to you? Know, that in the course of your future life you will often find yourself elected the involuntary confidant of your acquaintances' secrets: people will instinctively find out, as I have done, that it is not your forte to tell of yourself, but to listen while others talk of themselves; they will feel, too, that you listen with no malevolent scorn of their indiscretion, but with a kind of innate sympathy; not the less comforting and encouraging because it is very unobtrusive in its manifestations."

"How do you know? — how can you guess all this, sir?"

"I know it well; therefore I proceed almost as freely as if I were writing my thoughts in a diary. You would say, I should have been superior to circumstances: so I should — so I should; but you see I was not. When fate wronged me, I had not the wisdom to remain cool: I turned desperate; then I degenerated. Now, when any vicious simpleton excites my disgust by his paltry ribaldry, I cannot flatter myself that I am better than he: I am forced to confess that he and I are on a level. I wish I had stood firm — God knows I do! Dread remorse when you are tempted to err, Miss Eyre: remorse is the poison of life."

"Repentance is said to be its cure, sir."

"It is not its cure. Reformation may be its cure; and I could reform — I have strength yet for that — if — but where is the use of thinking of it, hampered, burdened, cursed as I am? Besides, since happiness is irrevocably denied me, I have a right to get pleasure out of life: and I *will* get it, cost what it may."

"Then you will degenerate still more, sir."

"Possibly: yet why should I, if I can get sweet, fresh pleasure? And I may get it as sweet and fresh as the wild honey the bee gathers on the moor."

"It will sting — it will taste bitter, sir."

"How do you know? — you never tried it. How very serious — how very solemn you look; and you are as ignorant of the matter as this cameo head" (taking one from the mantelpiece). "You have no right to preach to me, you neophyte, that have not passed the porch of life, and are absolutely unacquainted with its mysteries."

"I only remind you of your own words, sir: you said error brought remorse, and you pronounced remorse the poison of existence."

"And who talks of error now? I scarcely think the notion that flittered across my brain was an error. I believe it was an inspiration rather than a temptation: it was very genial, very soothing,— I know that. Here it comes again! It is no devil, I assure you; or if it be, it has put on the robes of an angel of light. I think I must admit so fair a guest when it asks entrance to my heart."

"Distrust it, sir; it is not a true angel."

"Once more, how do you know? By what instinct do you pretend to distinguish between a fallen seraph of the abyss and a messenger from the eternal throne — between a guide and a seducer?"

"I judged by your countenance, sir; which was troubled: when you said the suggestion had returned upon you. I feel sure it will work you more misery if you listen to it."

"Not at all — it bears the most gracious message in the world: for the rest, you are not my conscience-keeper, so don't make yourself uneasy. Here, come in, bonny wanderer!"

He said this as if he spoke to a vision, viewless to any eye but his own; then, folding his arms, which he had half extended, on his chest, he seemed to enclose in their embrace the invisible being.

"Now," he continued, again addressing me, "I have received the pilgrim — a disguised deity, as I verily believe. Already it has done me good: my heart was a sort of charnel; it will now be a shrine."

"To speak truth, sir, I don't understand you at all: I cannot keep up the conversation, because it has got out of my depth. Only one thing I know: you said you were not as good as you should like to be, and that you regretted your own imperfection; — one thing I can comprehend: you intimated that to have a sullied memory was a perpetual bane. It seems to me, that if you tried hard, you would in time find it possible to become what you yourself would approve; and that if from this day you began with resolution to correct your thoughts and actions, you would in a few years have laid up a new and stainless store of recollections, to which you might revert with pleasure."

"Justly thought; rightly said, Miss Eyre; and, at this moment, I am paving hell with energy."

"Sir?"

"I am laying down good intentions, which I believe durable as flint. Certainly, my associates and pursuits shall be other than they have been."

"And better?"

"And better — so much better as pure ore is than foul dross. You seem to doubt me; I don't doubt myself: I know what my aim is, and what my motives are; and at this moment I pass a law, unalterable as that of the Medes and Persians, that both are right."

"They cannot be, sir, if they require a new statute to legalise them."

"They are, Miss Eyre, though they absolutely require a new statute: unheard-of combinations of circumstances demand unheard-of rules."

"That sounds a dangerous maxim, sir; because one can see at once that it is liable to abuse."

"Sententious sage! so it is: but I swear by my household gods not to abuse it."

"You are human and fallible."

"I am: so are you — what then?"

"The human and fallible should not arrogate a power with which the divine and perfect alone can be safely entrusted."

"What power?"

"That of saying of any strange, unsanctioned line of action, — 'Let it be right.'"

"'Let it be right' — the very words: you have pronounced them."

"*May* it be right, then," I said, as I rose, deeming it useless to continue a discourse which was all darkness to me; and, besides, sensible that the character of my interlocutor was beyond my penetration; at least, beyond its present reach; and feeling the uncertainty, the vague sense of insecurity, which accompanied a conviction of ignorance.

"Where are you going?"

"To put Adèle to bed: it is past her bedtime."

"You are afraid of me, because I talk like a Sphynx."

"Your language is enigmatical, sir: but though I am bewildered, I am certainly not afraid."

"You *are afraid* — your self-love dreads a blunder."

"In that sense I do not feel apprehensive — I have no wish to talk nonsense."

"If you did, it would be in such a grave, quiet manner, I should mistake it for sense. Do you never laugh, Miss Eyre? Don't trouble yourself to answer — I see, you laugh rarely; but you can laugh very merrily: believe me, you are not naturally austere, any more than I am naturally vicious. The Lowood constraint still clings to you somewhat; controlling your features, muffling your voice, and restricting your limbs; and you fear in the presence of a man and a brother — father, or master, or what you will — to smile too gaily, speak too freely, or move too quickly: but, in time, I think you will learn to be natural with me, as I find it impossible to be conventional with you; and then your looks and movements will have more vivacity and variety than they dare offer now. I see at intervals the glance of a curious sort of bird through the close-set bars of a cage: a vivid, restless, resolute captive is there; were it but free, it would soar cloud-high. You are still bent on going?"

"It has struck nine, sir."

"Never mind,— wait a minute: Adèle is not ready to go to bed yet. My position, Miss Eyre, with my back to the fire, and my face to the room, favours observation. While talking to you, I have also occasionally watched Adèle; (I have my own reasons for thinking her a curious study,— reasons that I may, nay that I shall, impart to you some day;) she pulled out of her box, about ten minutes ago, a little pink silk frock; rapture lit her face as she unfolded it; coquetry runs in her blood, blends with her brains, and seasons the marrow of her bones. 'Il faut que je l'essaie!' cried she; 'et à l'instant même!' and she rushed out of the room. She is now with Sophie, undergoing a robing process: in a few minutes she will re-enter; and I know what I shall see,— a miniature of Céline Varens, as she used to appear on the boards at the rising of —— : but never mind that. However, my tenderest feelings are about to receive a shock: such is my presentiment; stay now, to see whether it will be realised."

Ere long, Adèle's little foot was heard tripping across the hall. She entered, transformed as her guardian had predicted. A dress of rose-coloured satin, very short, and as full in the skirt as it could be gathered, replaced the brown frock she had previously worn; a wreath of rosebuds circled her forehead; her feet were dressed in silk stockings and small white satin sandals.

"Est-ce que ma robe va bien?" cried she, bounding forwards; "et mes souliers? et mes bas? Tenez, je crois que je vais danser!"

And spreading out her dress, she chasséed across the room; till, having reached Mr. Rochester, she wheeled lightly round before him on tip-toe, then dropped on one knee at his feet exclaiming: —

"Monsieur, je vous remercie mille fois de votre bonté;" then rising, she added, "C'est comme cela que maman faisait, n'est-ce pas, monsieur?"

"Pre-cise-ly!" was the answer; "and 'comme cela,' she charmed my English gold out of my British breeches' pocket. I have been green, too, Miss Eyre,— ay, grass green: not a more vernal tint freshens you now than once freshened me. My Spring is gone, however: but it has left me that French floweret on my hands; which, in some moods, I would fain be rid of. Not valuing now the root whence it sprang; having found that it was of a sort which nothing but gold dust could manure, I have but half a liking to the blossom: especially when it looks so artificial as just now. I keep it and rear it rather on the Roman Catholic principle of expiating numerous sins, great or small, by one good work. I'll explain all this some day. Good-night."

## CHAPTER XV

MR. ROCHESTER did, on a future occasion, explain it. It was one afternoon, when he chanced to meet me and Adèle in the grounds; and while she played with Pilot and her shuttlecock, he asked me to walk up and down a long beech avenue within sight of her.

He then said that she was the daughter of a French opera-dancer, Céline Varens, towards whom he had once cherished what he called a "grande passion." This passion Céline had professed to return with even superior ardour. He thought himself her idol; ugly as he was: he believed, as he said, that she preferred his "taille d'athlète" to the elegance of the Apollo Belvidere.

"And, Miss Eyre, so much was I flattered by this preference of the Gallic sylph for her British gnome, that I installed her in an hotel; gave her a complete establishment of servants, a carriage, cashmeres, diamonds, dentelles, etc. In short, I began the process of ruining myself in the received style, like any other spoony. I had not, it seems, the originality to chalk out a new road to shame and destruction, but trode the old track with stupid exactness not to deviate an inch from the beaten centre. I had — as I deserved to have — the fate of all other spoonies. Happening to call one evening, when Céline did not expect me, I found her out; but it was a warm night, and I was tired with strolling through Paris, so I sat down in her boudoir; happy to breathe the air consecrated so lately by her presence. No,— I exaggerate; I never thought there was any consecrating virtue about her: it was rather a sort of pastille perfume she had left; a scent of musk and amber, than an odour of sanctity. I was just beginning to stifle with the fumes of conservatory flowers and sprinkled essences, when I bethought myself to open the window and step out on the balcony. It was moonlight and gas-light besides, and very still and serene. The balcony was furnished with a chair or two; I sat down, took out a cigar,— I will take one now, if you will excuse me."

Here ensued a pause, filled up by the producing and lighting of a cigar; having placed it to his lips and breathed a trail of Havannah incense on the freezing and sunless air, he went on:—

"I liked bonbons too, in those days, Miss Eyre, and I was *croquant* — (overlook the barbarism) *croquant* chocolate comfits, and smoking alternately, watching meantime the equipages that rolled along the fashionable streets towards the neighbouring opera-house, when in an elegant close carriage drawn by a beautiful pair of English horses, and distinctly seen in the brilliant city-night, I recognised the 'voiture' I had given Céline. She was returning: of course my heart thumped with impatience against the iron rails I leant upon. The carriage stopped, as I had expected, at the hotel door; my flame (that is the very word for an opera inamorata) alighted: though muffled in a cloak — an unnecessary encumbrance, by-the-by, on so warm a June evening — I knew her instantly by her little foot, seen peeping from the skirt of her dress, as she skipped from the carriage-step. Bending over the balcony I was about to murmur, 'Mon ange'— in a tone, of course, which should be audible to the ear of love alone — when a figure jumped from the carriage after her; cloaked also; but that was a spurred heel which had rung on the pavement, and that was a hatted head which now passed under the arched *porte cochère* of the hotel.

"You never felt jealousy, did you, Miss Eyre? Of course not: I need not ask you; because you never felt love. You have both sentiments yet to experience; your soul sleeps; the shock is yet to be given which shall waken it. You think all existence lapses in as quiet a flow as that in which your youth has hitherto slid away. Floating on with closed eyes and muffled ears, you neither see the rocks bristling not far off in the bed of the flood, nor hear the breakers boil at their base. But I tell you — and you may mark my words — you will come some day to a craggy pass of the channel, where the whole of life's stream will be broken up into whirl and tumult, foam and noise: either you will be dashed to atoms on crag points, or lifted up and borne on by some master wave into a calmer current — as I am now.

"I like this day: I like that sky of steel; I like the sternness and stillness of the world under this frost. I like Thornfield; its grey façade, and lines of dark windows reflecting that metal welkin: and yet how long have I abhorred the very thought of it; shunned it like a great plague-house! How I do still abhor"——

He ground his teeth and was silent: he arrested his step and struck his boot against the hard ground. Some hated thought seemed to have him in its grip, and to hold him so tightly that he could not advance.

We were ascending the avenue when he thus paused; the hall was before us. Lifting his eye to its battlements, he cast over them a glare such as I never saw before or since. Pain, shame, ire — impatience, disgust, detestation — seemed momentarily to hold a quivering conflict in the large pupil dilating under his ebon eyebrow. Wild was the wrestle which should be paramount; but another feeling rose and triumphed: something hard and cynical; self-willed and resolute: it settled his passion and petrified his countenance: he went on: —

"During the moment I was silent, Miss Eyre, I was arranging a point with my destiny. She stood there, by that beech-trunk — a hag like one of those who appeared to Macbeth on the heath of Forres. 'You like Thornfield?' she said, lifting her finger; and then she wrote in the air a memento, which ran in lurid hieroglyphics all along the house-front, between the upper and lower row of windows. 'Like it if you can! Like it if you dare!'

"'I will like it,' said I. 'I dare like it;' and (he subjoined moodily) I will keep my word: I will break obstacles to happiness, to goodness — yes, goodness; I wish to be a better man than I have been; than I am — as Job's leviathan broke the spear, the dart and the habergeon, hinderances which others count as iron and brass, I will esteem but straw and rotten wood."

Adèle here ran before him with her shuttlecock. "Away!" he cried harshly; "keep at a distance, child; or go in to Sophie!" Continuing then to pursue his walk in silence, I ventured to recall him to the point whence he had abruptly diverged: —

"Did you leave the balcony, sir," I asked, "when Mdlle. Varens entered?"

I almost expected a rebuff for this hardly well-timed question: but, on the contrary, waking out of his scowling abstraction, he turned his eyes towards me, and the shade seemed to clear off his brow. "Oh, I had forgotten Céline! Well, to resume. When I saw my charmer thus come in accompanied by a cavalier, I seemed to hear a hiss, and the green snake of jealousy, rising on undulating coils from the moonlit balcony, glided within my waistcoat, and ate its way in two minutes to my heart's core. Strange!" he exclaimed, suddenly starting again from the point. "Strange that I should choose you for the confidant of all this, young lady: passing strange that you should listen to me quietly, as if it were the most usual thing in the world for a man like me to tell stories of his opera-mistresses to a quaint, inexperienced girl like you! But the last singularity explains the first, as I intimated once before: you, with your gravity, considerateness, and caution were made to be the recipient of secrets. Besides, I know what sort of a mind I have placed in communication with my own: I know it is not one liable to take infection: it is a peculiar mind; it is an unique one. Happily I do not mean to harm it: but, if I did, it would not take harm from me. The more you and I converse, the better; for while I cannot blight you, you may refresh me." After this digression he proceeded:—

"I remained in the balcony. 'They will come to her boudoir no doubt,' thought I: 'let me prepare an ambush.' So putting my hand in through the open window, I drew the curtain over it, leaving only an opening through which I could take observations; then I closed the casement, all but a chink just wide enough to furnish an outlet to lovers' whispered vows: then I stole back to my chair; and as I resumed it the pair came in. My eye was quickly at the aperture. Céline's chamber-maid entered, lit a lamp, left it on the table and withdrew. The couple were thus revealed to me clearly: both removed their cloaks, and there was 'the Varens' shining in satin and jewels,—my gifts of course,—and there was her companion in an officer's uniform; and I knew him for a young roué of a vicomte—a brainless and vicious youth whom I had sometimes met in society, and had never thought of hating because I despised him so absolutely. On recognising him, the fang of the snake, jealousy, was instantly broken; because at the same moment my love for Céline sank under an extinguisher. A woman who could betray me for such a rival was not worth contending for: she deserved only scorn; less, however, than I, who had been her dupe.

"They began to talk; their conversation eased me completely: frivolous, mercenary, heartless, and senseless, it was rather calculated to weary than enrage a listener. A card of mine lay on the table; this being perceived brought my name under discussion. Neither of them possessed energy or wit to belabour me soundly;

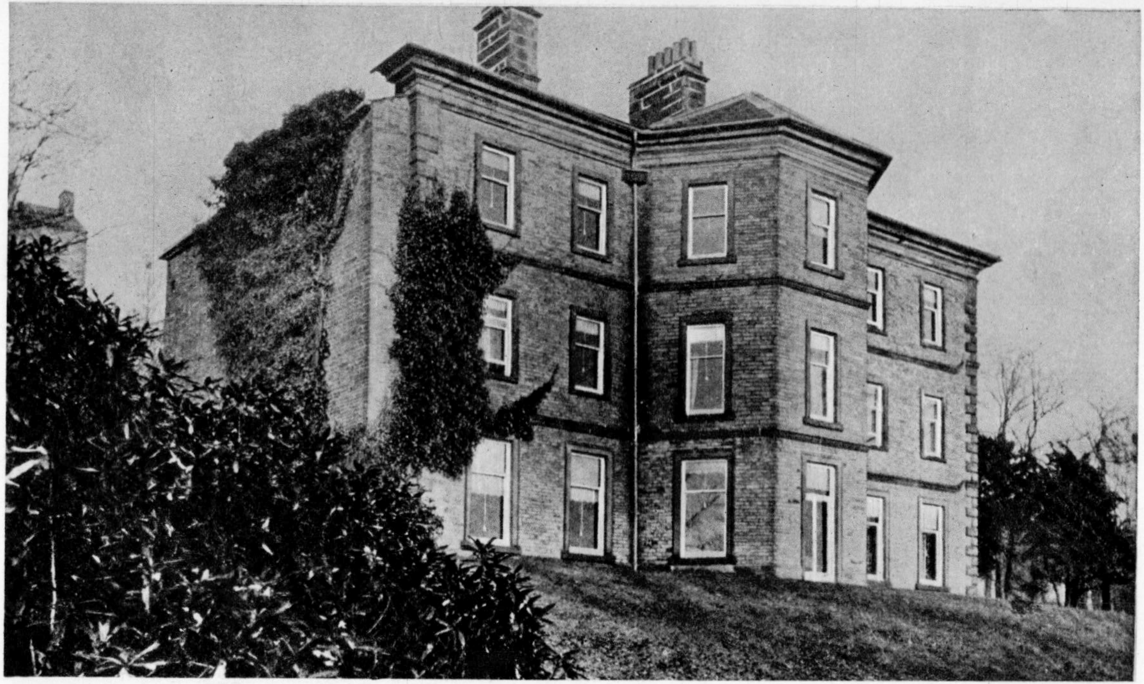

STONEGAPPE

In 1839 Charlotte became a governess in the family residing at Stonegappe, which she described as "Gateshead Hall." She was twenty-three, and had already spent three years teaching at her old school; but it is plain that she did not get on well with children, and her time at Stonegappe was an unhappy one. From here she wrote to her sister Emily: "The country, the house, the grounds are, as I have said, divine; but alack-a-day! there is such a thing as seeing all beautiful around you—pleasant woods, white paths, green lawns, and the blue sunshiny sky—and not having a free moment or a free thought to enjoy them." The family are proud of their house's connection with *Jane Eyre*, and point but they insulted me as coarsely as they could in their little way: especially Céline; who even waxed rather brilliant on my personal defects — deformities she termed them. Now it had been her custom to launch out into fervent admiration of what she called my 'beauté mâle': wherein she differed diametrically from you, who told me point blank, at the second interview, that you did not think me handsome. The contrast struck me at the time, and "——

Adèle here came running up again.

"Monsieur, John has just been to say that your agent has called and wishes to see you."

"Ah! in that case I must abridge. Opening the window, I walked in upon them; liberated Céline from my protection; gave her notice to vacate her hotel; offered her a purse for immediate exigencies; disregarded screams, hysterics, prayers, protestations, convulsions; made an appointment with the vicomte for a meeting at the Bois de Boulogne. Next morning I had the pleasure of encountering him; left a bullet in one of his poor, etiolated arms, feeble as the wing of a chicken in the pip, and then thought I had done with the whole crew. But unluckily the Varens, six months before, had given me this filette Adèle; who she affirmed was my daughter; and perhaps she may be, though I see no proofs of such grim paternity written in her countenance: Pilot is more like me than she. Some years after I had broken with the mother, she abandoned her child and ran away to Italy with a musician or singer. I acknowledge no natural claim on Adèle's part to be supported by me; nor do I now acknowledge any, for I am not her father; but hearing that she was quite destitute, I e'en took the poor thing out of the slime and mud of Paris, and transplanted it here, to grow up clean in the wholesome soil of an English country garden. Mrs. Fairfax found you to train it; but now you know that it is the illegitimate offspring of a French opera-girl, you will perhaps think differently of your post and protegée: you will be coming to me some day with notice that you have found another place — that you beg me to look out for a new governess, etc.— eh?"

"No: Adèle is not answerable for either her mother's faults or yours; I have a regard for her, and now that I know she is, in a sense, parentless — forsaken by her mother and disowned by you, sir — I shall cling closer to her than before. How could I possibly prefer the spoilt pet of a wealthy family, who would hate her governess as a nuisance, to a lonely little orphan, who leans towards her as a friend?"

"Oh, that is the light in which you view it! Well, I must go in now; and you too: it darkens."

But I stayed out a few minutes longer with Adèle and Pilot — ran a race with her, and played a game of battledore and shuttlecock. When we went in and I had removed her bonnet and coat, I took her on my knee; kept her there an hour, allowing her to prattle as she liked: not rebuking even some little freedoms and trivialities into which she was apt to stray when much noticed; and which betrayed in her a superficiality of character, inherited probably from her mother, hardly congenial to an English mind. Still she had her merits; and I was disposed to appreciate all that was good in her to the utmost. I sought in her countenance and features a likeness to Mr. Rochester, but found none: no trait, no turn of expression announced relationship. It was a pity: if she could but have been proved to resemble him, he would have thought more of her.

It was not till after I had withdrawn to my own chamber for the night, that I steadily reviewed the tale Mr. Rochester had told me. As he had said, there was probably nothing at all extraordinary in the substance of the narrative itself: a wealthy Englishman's passion for a French dancer, and her treachery to him, were everyday matters enough, no doubt, in society; but there was something decidedly strange in the paroxysm of emotion which had suddenly seized him, when he was in the act of expressing the present contentment of his mood, and his newly revived pleasure in the old hall and its environs. I meditated wonderingly on this incident: but gradually quitting it, as I found it for the present inexplicable, I turned to the consideration of my master's manner to myself. The confidence he had thought fit to repose in me seemed a tribute to my discretion: I regarded and accepted it as such. His deportment had now for some weeks been more uniform towards me than at the first. I never seemed in his way; he did not take fits of chilling hauteur: when he met me unexpectedly, the encounter seemed welcome; he had always a word and sometimes a smile for me: when summoned by formal invitation to his presence, I was honoured by a cordiality of reception that made me feel I really possessed the power to amuse him, and that these evening conferences were sought as much for his pleasure as for my benefit.

I, indeed, talked comparatively little; but I heard him talk with relish. It was his nature to be communicative; he liked to open to a mind unacquainted with the world, glimpses of its scenes and ways (I do not mean its corrupt scenes and wicked ways, but such as derived their interest from the great scale on which they were acted, the strange novelty by which they were characterised); and I had a keen delight in receiving the new ideas he offered, in imagining the new pictures he portrayed, or followed him in thought through the new regions he disclosed, never startled or troubled by one noxious allusion.

The ease of his manner freed me from painful restraint: the friendly frankness, as correct as cordial, with which he treated me, drew me to him. I felt at times as if he were my relation, rather than my master: yet he was imperious sometimes still; but I did not mind that; I saw it was his way. So happy, so gratified did I become with this new interest added to life, that I ceased to pine after kindred: my thin crescent-destiny seemed to enlarge; the blanks of existence were filled up; my bodily health improved; I gathered flesh and strength.

And was Mr. Rochester now ugly in my eyes? No, reader: gratitude, and many associations, all pleasurable and genial, made his face the object I best liked to see; his presence in a room was more cheering than the brightest fire. Yet I had not forgotten his faults: indeed, I could not, for he brought them frequently before me. He was proud, sardonic, harsh to inferiority of every description: in my secret soul I knew that his great kindness to me was balanced by unjust severity to many others. He was moody, too; unaccountably so: I more than once, when sent for to read to him, found him sitting in his library alone, with his head bent on his folded arms; and, when he looked up, a morose, almost a malignant scowl, blackened his features. But I believed that his moodiness, his harshness, and his former faults of morality (I say *former*, for now he seemed corrected of them) had their source in some cruel cross of fate. I believed he was naturally a man of better tendencies, higher principles, and purer tastes than such as circumstances had developed, education instilled, or destiny encouraged. I thought there were excellent materials in him; though for the present they hung together somewhat spoiled and tangled. I cannot deny that

I grieved for his grief, whatever that was, and would have given much to assuage it.

Though I had now extinguished my candle and was laid down in bed, I could not sleep, for thinking of his look when he paused in the avenue, and told how his destiny had risen up before him, and dared him to be happy at Thornfield.

"Why not?" I asked myself. "What alienates him from the house? Will he leave it again soon? Mrs. Fairfax said he seldom stayed here longer than a fortnight at a time; and he has now been resident eight weeks. If he does go, the change will be doleful. Suppose he should be absent, spring, summer, and autumn: how joyless sunshine and fine days will seem!"

I hardly know whether I had slept or not after this musing; at any rate, I started wide awake on hearing a vague murmur, peculiar and lugubrious, which sounded, I thought, just above me. I wished I had kept my candle burning: the night was drearily dark; my spirits were depressed. I rose and sat up in bed, listening. The sound was hushed.

I tried again to sleep; but my heart beat anxiously: my inward tranquillity was broken. The clock, far down in the hall, struck two. Just then it seemed my chamber-door was touched; as if fingers had swept the panels in groping a way along the dark gallery outside. I said, "Who is there?" Nothing answered. I was chilled with fear.

All at once I remembered that it might be Pilot: who, when the kitchen-door chanced to be left open, not unfrequently found his way up to the threshold of Mr. Rochester's chamber: I had seen him lying there myself, in the mornings. The idea calmed me somewhat: I lay down. Silence composes the nerves; and as an unbroken hush now reigned again through the whole house, I began to feel the return of slumber. But it was not fated that I should sleep that night. A dream had scarcely approached my ear, when it fled affrightened, scared by a marrow-freezing incident enough.

This was a demoniac laugh — low, suppressed, and deep — uttered, as it seemed, at the very key-hole of my chamber door. The head of my bed was near the door, and I thought at first the goblin-laughter stood at my bedside — or rather, crouched by my pillow: but I rose, looked round, and could see nothing; while, as I still gazed, the unnatural sound was reiterated: and I knew it came from behind the panels. My first impulse was to rise and fasten the bolt; my next, again to cry out, "Who is there?"

Something gurgled and moaned. Ere long, steps retreated up the gallery towards the third story staircase: a door had lately been made to shut in that staircase; I heard it open and close, and all was still.

"Was that Grace Poole? and is she possessed with a devil?" thought I. Impossible now to remain longer by myself: I must go to Mrs. Fairfax. I hurried on my frock and a shawl; I withdrew the bolt and opened the door with a trembling hand. There was a candle burning just outside, left on the matting in the gallery. I was surprised at this circumstance: but still more was I amazed to perceive the air quite dim, as if filled with smoke; and, while looking to the right hand and left, to find whence these blue wreaths issued, I became further aware of a strong smell of burning.

Something creaked: it was a door ajar, and that door was Mr. Rochester's, and the smoke rushed in a cloud from thence. I thought no more of Mrs. Fairfax; I thought no more of Grace Poole or the laugh: in an instant, I was within the chamber. Tongues of flame darted round the bed: the curtains were on fire. In the midst of blaze and vapour, Mr. Rochester lay stretched motionless, in deep sleep.

"Wake! wake!" I cried — I shook him, but he only murmured and turned: the smoke had stupefied him. Not a moment could be lost: the very sheets were kindling. I rushed to his basin and ewer; fortunately, one was wide and the other deep, and both were filled with water. I heaved them up, deluged the bed and its occupant, flew back to my own room, brought my own water-jug, baptised the couch afresh, and, by God's aid, succeeded in extinguishing the flames which were devouring it.

The hiss of the quenched element, the breakage of a pitcher which I had flung from my hand when I had emptied it, and, above all, the splash of the shower-bath I had liberally bestowed, roused Mr. Rochester at last. Though it was now dark, I knew he was awake; because I heard him fulminating strange anathemas at finding himself lying in a pool of water.

"Is there a flood?" he cried.

"No, sir," I answered; "but there has been a fire: get up, do, you are quenched now; I will fetch you a candle."

"In the name of all the elves in Christendom, is that Jane Eyre?" he demanded. "What have you done with me, witch, sorceress? Who is in the room besides you? Have you plotted to drown me?"

"I will fetch you a candle, sir; and, in Heaven's name, get up. Somebody has plotted something: you cannot too soon find out who and what it is."

"There — I am up now; but at your peril you fetch a candle yet: wait two minutes till I get into some dry garments, if any dry there be — yes, here is my dressing-gown. Now run!"

I did run; I brought the candle which still remained in the gallery. He took it from my hand, held it up, and surveyed the bed, all blackened and scorched, the sheets drenched, the carpet round swimming in water.

"What is it? and who did it?" he asked.

I briefly related to him what had transpired: the strange laugh I had hear in the gallery; the step ascending to the third story; the smoke,— the smell of fire which had conducted me to his room; in what state I had found matters there, and how I had deluged him with all the water I could lay hands on.

He listened very gravely; his face, as I went on, expressed more concern than astonishment; he did not immediately speak when I had concluded.

"Shall I call Mrs. Fairfax?" I asked.

"Mrs. Fairfax? No: what the deuce would you call her for? What can she do? Let her sleep unmolested."

"Then I will fetch Leah, and wake John and his wife."

"Not at all: just be still. You have a shawl on? if you are not warm enough, you may take my cloak yonder; wrap it about you, and sit down in the arm-chair: there,— I will put it on. Now place your feet on the stool, to keep them out of the wet. I am going to leave you a few minutes. I shall take the candle. Remain where you are till I return; be as still as a mouse. I must pay a visit to the second story. Don't move, remember, or call any one."

He went: I watched the light withdraw. He passed up the gallery very softly, unclosed the staircase door with as little noise as possible, shut it after him, and the last ray vanished. I was left in total darkness. I listened for some noise, but heard nothing. A very long time elapsed. I grew weary: it was cold, in spite of the cloak; and then I did not see the use of staying, as I was not to rouse the house. I was on the point of risking Mr. Rochester's displeasure, by disobeying his orders, when the light once more gleamed dimly on the gallery-wall, and I heard his unshod feet tread the matting. "I hope it is he," thought I, "and not something worse."

He re-entered, pale and very gloomy. "I have found it all out," said he, setting his candle down on the washstand; "it is as I thought."

"How, sir?"

He made no reply, but stood with his arms folded, looking on the ground. At the end of a few minutes, he inquired in rather a peculiar tone:—

"I forget whether you said you saw anything when you opened your chamber door."

"No, sir, only the candlestick on the ground."

"But you heard an odd laugh? You have heard that laugh before, I should think, or something like it?"

"Yes, sir: there is a woman who sews here, called Grace Poole,—she laughs in that way. She is a singular person."

"Just so. Grace Poole—you have guessed it. She is, as you say, singular,—very. Well, I shall reflect on the subject. Meantime, I am glad that you are the only person, besides myself, acquainted with the precise details of to-night's incident. You are no talking fool: say nothing about it. I will account for this state of affairs (pointing to the bed): and now return to your own room. I shall do very well on the sofa in the library for the rest of the night. It is near four:—in two hours the servants will be up."

"Good-night, then, sir," said I, departing.

He seemed surprised—very inconsistently so, as he had just told me to go.

"What!" he exclaimed, "are you quitting me already: and in that way?"

"You said I might go, sir."

"But not without taking leave; not without a word or two of acknowledgment and good will: not, in short, in that brief, dry fashion. Why, you have saved my life!—snatched me from a horrible and excruciating death! — and you walk past me as if we were mutual strangers! At least shake hands."

He held out his hand; I gave him mine: he took it first in one, then in both his own.

"You have saved my life: I have a pleasure in owing you so immense a debt. I cannot say more. Nothing else that has being would have been tolerable to me in the character of creditor for such an obligation: but you: it is different; — I feel your benefits no burden, Jane."

He paused; gazed at me; words almost visible trembled on his lips,— but his voice was checked.

"Good-night again, sir. There is no debt, benefit, burden, obligation, in the case."

"I knew," he continued, "you would do me good in some way, at some time; — I saw it in your eyes when I first beheld you: their expression and smile did not — (again he stopped) — did not (he proceeded hastily) strike delight to my very inmost heart so for nothing. People talk of natural sympathies; I have heard of good genii: — there are grains of truth in the wildest fable. My cherished preserver, good-night!"

Strange energy was in his voice; strange fire in his look.

"I am glad I happened to be awake," I said: and then I was going.

"What! you *will* go?"

"I am cold, sir."

"Cold? Yes,— and standing in a pool! Go, then, Jane; go!" But he still retained my hand, and I could not free it. I bethought myself of an expedient.

"I think I hear Mrs. Fairfax move, sir," said I.

"Well, leave me:" he relaxed his fingers, and I was gone.

I regained my couch, but never thought of sleep. Till morning dawned I was tossed on a buoyant but unquiet sea, where billows of trouble rolled under surges of joy. I thought sometimes I saw beyond its wild waters a shore, sweet as the hills of Beulah; and now and then a freshening gale, wakened by hope, bore my spirit triumphantly towards the bourne: but I could not reach it, even in fancy,— a counteracting breeze blew off land, and continually drove me back. Sense would resist delirium: judgment would warn passion. Too feverish to rest, I rose as soon as day dawned.

## CHAPTER XVI

I BOTH wished and feared to see Mr. Rochester on the day which followed this sleepless night: I wanted to hear his voice again, yet feared to meet his eye. During the early part of the morning, I momentarily expected his coming; he was not in the frequent habit of entering the school-room; but he did step in for a few minutes sometimes, and I had the impression that he was sure to visit it that day.

But the morning passed just as usual: nothing happened to interrupt the quiet course of Adèle's studies; only, soon after breakfast, I heard some bustle in the neighbourhood of Mr. Rochester's chamber, Mrs. Fairfax's voice, and Leah's and the cook's — that is, John's wife — and even John's own gruff tones. There were exclamations of "What a mercy master was not burnt in his bed!" "It is always dangerous to keep a candle lit at night." "How providential that he had presence of mind to think of the water-jug!" "I wonder he waked nobody!" "It is to be hoped he will not take cold with sleeping on the library sofa," etc.

To much confabulation succeeded a sound of scrubbing and setting to rights; and when I passed the room, in going downstairs to dinner, I saw through the open door that all was again restored to complete order; only the bed was stripped of its hangings. Leah stood up in the window seat, rubbing the panes of glass dimmed with smoke. I was about to address her, for I wished to know what account had been given of the affair: but, on advancing, I saw a second person in the chamber — a woman sitting on a chair by the bedside, and sewing rings to new curtains. That woman was no other than Grace Poole.

There she sat, staid and taciturn-looking, as usual, in her brown stuff gown, her check apron, white handkerchief, and cap. She was intent on her work, in which her whole thoughts seemed absorbed: on her hard forehead, and in her commonplace features, was nothing either of the paleness or desperation one would have expected to see marking the countenance of a woman who had attempted murder; and whose intended victim had followed her last night to her lair, and (as I believed) charged her with the crime she wished to perpetrate. I was amazed — confounded. She looked up, while I still gazed at her: no start, no increase or failure of colour betrayed emotion, consciousness of guilt, or fear of detection. She said "Good morning, Miss," in her usual phlegmatic and brief manner; and taking up another ring and more tape, went on with her sewing.

"I will put her to some test," thought I: "such absolute impenetrability is past comprehension."

"Good morning, Grace," I said. "Has anything happened here? I thought I heard the servants all talking together a while ago."

"Only master had been reading in his bed last night; he fell asleep with his candle lit, and the curtains got on fire; but, fortunately, he awoke before the bed-clothes or the wood-work caught, and contrived to quench the flame with the water in the ewer."

"A strange affair!" I said, in a low voice: then, looking at her fixedly,—"Did Mr. Rochester wake nobody? Did no one hear him move?"

She again raised her eyes to me; and this time there was something of consciousness in their expression. She seemed to examine me warily; then she answered,—

"The servants sleep so far off, you know, Miss, they would not be likely to hear. Mrs. Fairfax's room and yours are the nearest to master's; but Mrs. Fairfax said she heard nothing: when people get elderly, they often sleep heavy." She paused, and then added, with a sort of assumed indifference, but still in a marked and significant tone, "But you are young, Miss; and I should say a light sleeper: perhaps you may have heard a noise?"

"I did," said I, dropping my voice, so that Leah, who was still polishing the panes, could not hear me, "and at first I thought it was Pilot: but Pilot cannot laugh; and I am certain I heard a laugh, and a strange one."

She took a new needleful of thread, waxed it carefully, threaded her needle with a steady hand, and then observed, with perfect composure,—

"It is hardly likely master would laugh, I should think, Miss, when he was in such danger: you must have been dreaming."

"I was not dreaming," I said, with some warmth, for her brazen coolness provoked me. Again she looked at me; and with the same scrutinising and conscious eye.

"Have you told master that you heard a laugh?" she inquired.

"I have not had the opportunity of speaking to him this morning."

"You did not think of opening your door and looking out into the gallery?" she further asked.

She appeared to be cross-questioning me; attempting to draw from me information unawares: the idea struck me that if she discovered I knew or suspected her guilt, she would be playing off some of her malignant pranks on me; I thought it advisable to be on my guard.

"On the contrary," said I, "I bolted my door."

"Then you are not in the habit of bolting your door every night before you get into bed?"

"Fiend! she wants to know my habits, that she may lay her plans accordingly!" Indignation again prevailed over prudence; I replied sharply, "Hitherto I have often omitted to fasten the bolt: I did not think it necessary. I was not aware any danger or annoyance was to be dreaded at Thornfield Hall: but in future" (and I laid marked stress on the words) "I shall take good care to make all secure before I venture to lie down."

"It will be wise so to do," was her answer: "this neighbourhood is as quiet as any I know, and I never heard of the hall being attempted by robbers since it was a house; though there are hundreds of pounds' worth of plate in the plate-closet, as is well known. And you see, for such a large house, there are very few servants, because master has never lived here much; and when he does come, being a bachelor, he needs little waiting on: but I always think it best to err on the safe side; a door is soon fastened, and it is as well to have a drawn bolt between one and any mischief that may be about. A deal of people, Miss, are for trusting all to Providence; but I say Providence will not dispense with the means, though he often blesses them when they are used discreetly." And here she closed her harangue: a long one for her, and uttered with the demureness of a Quakeress.

I still stood absolutely dumbfounded at what appeared to me her miraculous self-possession and most inscrutable hypocrisy, when the cook entered.

"Mrs. Poole," said she, addressing Grace, "the servants' dinner will soon be ready: will you come down?"

"No; just put my pint of porter and bit of pudding on a tray, and I'll carry it upstairs."

"You'll have some meat?"

"Just a morsel, and a taste of cheese, that's all."

"And the sago?"

"Never mind it, at present: I shall be coming down before teatime: I'll make it myself."

The cook here turned to me, saying that Mrs. Fairfax was waiting for me: so I departed.

I hardly heard Mrs. Fairfax's account of the curtain conflagration during dinner, so much was I occupied in puzzling my brains over the enigmatical character of Grace Poole; and still more in pondering the problem of her position at Thornfield: in questioning why she had not been given into custody that morning; or, at the very least, dismissed from her master's service. He had almost as much as declared his conviction of her criminality last night: what mysterious cause withheld him from accusing her? Why had he enjoined me, too, to secrecy? It was strange: a bold, vindictive, and haughty gentleman seemed somehow in the power of one of the meanest of his dependants; so much in her power, that even when she lifted her hand against his life, he dared not openly charge her with the attempt, much less punish her for it.

Had Grace been young and handsome, I should have been tempted to think that tenderer feelings than prudence or fear influenced Mr. Rochester in her behalf; but, hard-favoured and matronly as she was, the idea could not be admitted. "Yet," I reflected, "she has been young once; her youth would be contemporary with her master's: Mrs. Fairfax told me once, she had lived here many years, I don't think she can ever have been pretty; but, for aught I know, she may possess originality and strength of character to compensate for the want of personal advantages. Mr. Rochester is an amateur of the decided and eccentric: Grace is eccentric at least. What if a former caprice (a freak very possible to a nature so sudden and headstrong as his) has delivered him into her power, and she now exercises over his actions a secret influence, the result of his own indiscretion, which he cannot shake off, and dare not disregard?" But, having reached this point of conjecture, Mrs. Poole's square, flat figure, and uncomely, dry, even coarse face, recurred so distinctly to my mind's eye, that I thought, "No; impossible! my supposition cannot be correct. Yet," suggested the secret voice which talks to us in our hearts, "*you* are not beautiful either, and perhaps Mr. Rochester approves you: at any rate, you have often felt as if he did; and last night — remember his words; remember his look; remember his voice!"

I well remembered all: language, glance, and tone seemed at the moment vividly renewed. I was now in the school-room; Adèle was drawing; I bent over her and directed her pencil. She looked up with a sort of start.

"Qu'avez-vous, mademoiselle?" said she; "Vos doigts tremblent comme des cerises!"

"I am hot, Adèle, with stooping!" She went on sketching, I went on thinking.

I hastened to drive from my mind the hateful notion I had been conceiving respecting Grace Poole: it disgusted me. I compared myself with her, and found we were different. Bessie Leaven had said I was quite a lady; and she spoke truth: I was a lady. And now I looked much better than I did when Bessie saw me: I had more colour and more flesh; more life, more vivacity; because I had brighter hopes and keener enjoyments.

"Evening approaches," said I, as I looked towards the window. "I have never heard Mr. Rochester's voice or step in the house to-day; but surely I shall see him before night: I feared the meeting in the morning: now I desire it, because expectation has been so long baffled that it is grown impatient."

When dusk actually closed, and when Adèle left me to go and play in the nursery with Sophie, I did most keenly desire it. I listened for the bell to ring below; I listened for Leah coming up with a message; I fancied sometimes I heard Mr. Rochester's own tread, and I turned to the door, expecting it to open and admit him. The door remained shut: darkness only came in through the window. Still it was not late: he often sent for me at seven and eight o'clock, and it was yet but six. Surely I should not be wholly disappointed to-night, when I had so many things to say to him! I wanted again to introduce the subject of Grace Poole, and to hear what he would answer; I wanted to ask him plainly if he really believed it was she who had made last night's hideous attempt; and if so, why he kept her wickedness a secret. It little mattered whether my curiosity irritated him; I knew the pleasure of vexing and soothing him by turns; it was one I chiefly delighted in, and a sure instinct always prevented me from going too far: beyond the verge of provocation I never ventured; on the extreme brink I liked well to try my skill. Retaining every minute form of respect, every propriety of my station, I could still meet him in argument without fear of uneasy restraint: this suited both him and me.

A tread creaked on the stairs at last; Leah made her appearance; but it was only to intimate that tea was ready in Mrs. Fairfax's room. Thither I repaired, glad at least to go downstairs; for that brought me, I imagined, nearer to Mr. Rochester's presence.

"You must want your tea," said the good lady, as I joined her; "you ate so little at dinner. I am afraid," she continued, "you are not well to-day: you look flushed and feverish."

"Oh, quite well! I never felt better."

"Then you must prove it by evincing a good appetite; will you fill the tea-pot while I knit off this needle?" Having completed her task, she rose to draw down the blind which she had hitherto kept up; by way, I suppose, of making the most of daylight: though dusk was now fast deepening into total obscurity.

"It is fair to-night," said she, as she looked through the panes, "though not starlight; Mr. Rochester has, on the whole, had a favourable day for his journey."

"Journey! — Is Mr. Rochester gone anywhere? I did not know he was out."

"Oh, he set off the moment he had breakfasted! He is gone to the Leas; Mr. Eshton's place, ten miles on the other side Millcote; I believe there is quite a party assembled there; Lord Ingram, Sir George Lynn, Colonel Dent, and others."

"Do you expect him back to-night?"

"No — nor to-morrow either; I should think he is very likely to stay a week or more: when these fine, fashionable people get together, they are so surrounded by elegance and gaiety; so well provided with all that can please and entertain, they are in no hurry to separate. Gentlemen, especially, are often in request on such occasions; and Mr. Rochester is so talented and so lively in society, that I believe he is a general favourite: the ladies are very fond of him; though you would not think his appearance calculated to recommend him particularly in their eyes: but I suppose his acquirements and abilities, perhaps his wealth and good blood, make amends for any little fault of looks."

"Are there ladies at the Leas?"

"There are Mrs. Eshton and her three daughters — very elegant young ladies, indeed; and there are the Honourable Blanche and Mary Ingram; most beautiful women, I suppose: indeed I have seen Blanche, six or seven years since, when she was a girl of eighteen. She came here to a Christmas ball and party Mr. Rochester gave. You should have seen the dining-room that day — how richly it was decorated, how brilliantly lit up! I should think there were fifty ladies and gentlemen present — all of the first county-families; and Miss Ingram was considered the belle of the evening."

"You saw her, you say, Mrs. Fairfax: what was she like?"

"Yes, I saw her. The dining-room doors were thrown open; and, as it was Christmas-time, the servants were allowed to assemble in the hall, to hear some of the ladies sing and play. Mr. Rochester would have me to come in, and I sat down in a quiet corner and watched them. I never saw a more splendid scene: the ladies were magnificently dressed; most of them — at least most of the younger ones — looked handsome; but Miss Ingram was certainly the queen."

"And what was she like?"

"Tall, fine bust, sloping shoulders; long, graceful neck; olive complexion, dark and clear; noble features; eyes rather like Mr. Rochester's, large and black, and as brilliant as her jewels. And then she had such a fine head of hair; raven-black, and so becomingly arranged: a crown of thick plaits behind, and in front the longest, the glossiest curls I ever saw. She was dressed in pure white; an amber-coloured scarf was passed over her shoulder and across her breast, tied at the side, and descending in long, fringed ends below her knee. She wore an amber-coloured flower, too, in her hair: it contrasted well with the jetty mass of her curls."

"She was greatly admired of course?"

"Yes, indeed: and not only for her beauty, but for her accomplishments. She was one of the ladies who sang: a gentleman accompanied her on the piano. She and Mr. Rochester sang a duet."

"Mr. Rochester? I was not aware he could sing."

"Oh! he has a fine bass voice, and an excellent taste for music."

"And Miss Ingram: what sort of a voice had she?"

"A very rich and powerful one: she sang delightfully; it was a treat to listen to her; — and she played afterwards. I am no judge of music, but Mr. Rochester is; and I heard him say her execution was remarkably good."

"And this beautiful and accomplished lady is not yet married?"

"It appears not: I fancy neither she nor her sister have very large fortunes. Old Lord Ingram's estates were chiefly entailed, and the eldest son came in for everything almost."

"But I wonder no wealthy nobleman or gentleman has taken a fancy to her: Mr. Rochester, for instance. He is rich, is he not?"

"Oh! yes. But you see there is a considerable difference in age: Mr. Rochester is near forty; she is but twenty-five."

"What of that? More unequal matches are made every day."

"True: yet I should scarcely fancy Mr. Rochester would entertain an idea of the sort. But you eat nothing: you have scarcely tasted since you began tea."

"No: I am too thirsty to eat. Will you let me have another cup?"

I was about again to revert to the probability of a union between Mr. Rochester and the beautiful Blanche; but Adèle came in, and the conversation was turned into another channel.

When once more alone, I reviewed the information I had got; looked into my heart, examined its thoughts and feelings, and endeavoured to bring back with a strict hand such as had been straying through imagination's boundless and trackless waste, into the safe fold of common sense.

Arraigned at my own bar, Memory having given her evidence of the hopes, wishes, sentiments I had been cherishing since last night — of the general state of mind in which I had indulged for nearly a fortnight past; Reason having come forward and told, in her own quiet way, a plain, unvarnished tale, showing how I had rejected the real, and rabidly devoured the ideal; — I pronounced judgment to this effect: —

That a greater fool than Jane Eyre had never breathed the breath of life: that a more fantastic idiot had never surfeited herself on sweet lies, and swallowed poison as if it were nectar.

"*You,*" I said, "a favourite with Mr. Rochester? *You* gifted with the power of pleasing him? *You* of importance to him in any way? Go! your folly sickens me. And you have derived pleasure from occasional tokens of preference — equivocal tokens, shown by a gentleman of family, and a man of the world, to a dependant and a novice. How dared you? Poor stupid dupe! — Could not even self-interest make you wiser? You repeated to yourself this morning the brief scene of last night? — Cover your face and be ashamed! He said something in praise of your eyes, did he? Blind puppy! Open their bleared lids and look on your own accursed senselessness! It does good to no woman to be flattered by her superior, who cannot possibly intend to marry her; and it is madness in all women to let a secret love kindle within them, which, if unreturned and unknown, must devour the life that feeds it; and, if discovered and responded to, must lead, *ignis-fatuus*-like, into miry wilds whence there is no extrication.

"Listen, then, Jane Eyre, to your sentence: to-morrow, place the glass before you, and draw in chalk your own picture, faithfully; without softening one defect: omit no harsh line, smooth away no displeasing irregularity; write under it, 'Portrait of a Governess, disconnected, poor, and plain.'

"Afterwards, take a piece of smooth ivory — you have one prepared in your drawing-box: take your pallette, mix your freshest, finest, clearest tints; choose your most delicate camel-hair pencils; delineate carefully the loveliest face you can imagine; paint it in your softest shades and sweetest hues, according to the description given by Mrs. Fairfax of Blanche Ingram: remember the raven ringlets, the oriental eye; — what! you revert to Mr. Rochester as a model! Order! No snivel! — no sentiment! — no regret! I will endure only sense and resolution. Recall the august yet harmonious lineaments, the Grecian neck and bust: let the round and dazzling arm be visible, and the delicate hand; omit neither diamond ring nor gold bracelet; portray faithfully the attire, aërial lace and glistening satin, graceful scarf and golden rose: call it 'Blanche, an accomplished lady of rank.'

"Whenever, in future, you should chance to fancy Mr. Rochester thinks well of you, take out these two pictures and compare them: say, 'Mr. Rochester might probably win that noble lady's love, if he chose to strive for it; is it likely he would waste a serious thought on this indigent and insignificant plebeian?'"

"I'll do it," I resolved; and having framed this determination, I grew calm, and fell asleep.

I kept my word. An hour or two sufficed to sketch my own portrait in crayons; and in less than a fortnight I had completed an ivory miniature of an imaginary Blanche Ingram. It looked a lovely face enough, and when compared with the real head in chalk, the contrast was as great as self-control could desire. I derived benefit from the task: it had kept my head and hands employed, and had given force and fixedness to the new impressions I wished to stamp indelibly on my heart.

Ere long, I had reason to congratulate myself on the course of wholesome discipline to which I had thus forced my feelings to submit: thanks to it, I was able to meet subsequent occurrences with a decent calm; which, had they found me unprepared, I should probably have been unequal to maintain, even externally.

# CHAPTER XVII

A WEEK passed, and no news arrived of Mr. Rochester: ten days; and still he did not come. Mrs. Fairfax said she should not be surprised if he were to go straight from the Leas to London, and thence to the continent, and not show his face again at Thornfield for a year to come: he had not unfrequently quitted it in a manner quite as abrupt and unexpected. When I heard this I was beginning to feel a strange chill and failing at the heart. I was actually permitting myself to experience a sickening sense of disappointment: but rallying my wits, and recollecting my principles, I at once called my sensations to order; and it was wonderful how I got over the temporary blunder — how I cleared up the mistake of supposing Mr. Rochester's movements a matter in which I had any cause to take vital interest. Not that I humbled myself by a slavish notion of inferiority: on the contrary, I just said —

"You have nothing to do with the master of Thornfield, further than to receive the salary he gives you for teaching his protegée, and to be grateful for such respectful and kind treatment as, if you do your duty, you have a right to expect at his hands. Be sure that is the only tie he seriously acknowledges between you and him: so don't make him the object of your fine feelings, your raptures, agonies, and so forth. He is not of your order: keep to your caste; and be too self-respecting to lavish the love of the whole heart, soul, and strength, where such a gift is not wanted and would be despised."

I went on with my day's business tranquilly; but ever and anon vague suggestions kept wandering across my brain of reasons why I should quit Thornfield; and I kept involuntarily framing advertisements and pondering conjectures about new situations: these thoughts I did not think it necessary to check; they might germinate and bear fruit if they could.

Mr. Rochester had been absent upwards of a fortnight, when the post brought Mrs. Fairfax a letter.

"It was from the master," said she, as she looked at the direction. "Now I suppose we shall know whether we are to expect his return or not."

And while she broke the seal and perused the document, I went on taking my coffee (we were at breakfast): it was hot, and I attributed to that circumstance a fiery glow which suddenly rose to my face. Why my hand shook, and why I involuntarily spilt half the contents of my cup into my saucer, I did not choose to consider.

"Well — I sometimes think we are too quiet; but we run a chance of being busy enough now: for a little while at least," said Mrs. Fairfax, still holding the note before her spectacles.

Ere I permitted myself to request an explanation, I tied the string of Adéle's pinafore, which happened to be loose: having helped her also to another bun and refilled her mug with milk, I said, nonchalantly: —

"Mr. Rochester is not likely to return soon, I suppose?"

"Indeed, he is — in three days, he says; that will be next Thursday; and not alone either. I don't know how many of the fine people at the Leas are coming with him: he sends directions for all the best bed-rooms to be prepared; and the library and drawing-rooms are to be cleaned out; and I am to get more kitchen hands from the George Inn, at Millcote, and from wherever else I can; and the ladies will bring their maids and the gentlemen their valets: so we shall have a full house of it." And Mrs. Fairfax swallowed her breakfast and hastened away to commence operations.

The three days were, as she had foretold, busy enough. I had thought all the rooms at Thornfield beautifully clean and well arranged: but it appears I was mistaken. Three women were got to help; and such scrubbing, such brushing, such washing of paint and beating of carpets, such taking down and putting up of pictures, such polishing of mirrors and lustres, such lighting of fires in bed-rooms, such airing of sheets and feather-beds on hearths, I never beheld, either before or since. Adéle ran quite wild in the midst of it: the preparations for company and the prospect of their arrival, seemed to throw her into ecstasies. She would have Sophie to look over all her "toilettes," as she called frocks; to furbish up any that were "passées," and to air and arrange the new. For herself, she did nothing but caper about in the front chambers, jump on and off the bedsteads, and lie on the mattresses and piled-up bolsters and pillows before the enormous fires roaring in the chimneys. From school duties she was exonerated: Mrs. Fairfax had pressed me into her service, and I was all day in the store-room, helping (or hindering) her and the cook; learning to make custards and cheesecakes and French pastry, to truss game and garnish dessert-dishes.

The party were expected to arrive on Thursday afternoon, in time for dinner at six. During the intervening period I had no time to nurse chimeras; and I believe I was as active and gay as anybody — Adèle excepted. Still, now and then, I received a damping check to my cheerfulness; and was, in spite of myself, thrown back on the region of doubts and portents and dark conjectures. This was when I chanced to see the third story staircase door (which of late had always been kept locked) open slowly, and give passage to the form of Grace Poole, in prim cap, white apron, and handkerchief; when I watched her glide along the gallery, her quiet tread muffled in a list slipper; when I saw her look into the bustling, topsy-turvy bedrooms,— just say a word, perhaps, to the charwoman about the proper way to polish a grate, or clean a marble mantelpiece, or take stains from papered walls, and then pass on. She would thus descend to the kitchen once a day, eat her dinner, smoke a moderate pipe on the hearth, and go back, carrying her pot of porter with her, for her private solace, in her own gloomy upper haunt. Only one hour in the twenty-four did she pass with her fellow-servants below; all the rest of her time was spent in some low-ceiled, oaken chamber of the third story: there she sat and sewed — and probably laughed drearily to herself,— as companionless as a prisoner in his dungeon.

The strangest thing of all was, that not a soul in the house, except me, noticed her habits, or seemed to marvel at them; no one discussed her position or employment; no one pitied her solitude or isolation. I once, indeed, overheard part of a dialogue between Leah and one of the charwomen, of which Grace formed the subject. Leah had been saying something I had not caught, and the charwoman remarked: —

"She gets good wages, I guess?"

"Yes," said Leah; "I wish I had as good; not that mine are to complain of,— there's no stinginess at Thornfield; but they're not one-fifth of the sum Mrs. Poole receives. And she is laying by: she goes every quarter to the bank at Millcote. I should not wonder but she has saved enough to keep her independent if she liked to leave; but I suppose she's got used to the place; and then she's not forty yet, and strong and able for anything. It is too soon for her to give up business."

"She is a good hand, I daresay," said the charwoman.

"Ah! — she understands what she has to do,— nobody better," rejoined Leah significantly; "and it is not every one could fill her shoes; not for all the money she gets."

"That it is not!" was the reply. "I wonder whether master"—

The charwoman was going on; but here Leah turned and perceived me, and she instantly gave her companion a nudge.

"Doesn't she know?" I heard the woman whisper.

Leah shook her head, and the conversation was of course dropped. All I had gathered from it amounted to this,— that there was a mystery at Thornfield; and that from participation in that mystery, I was purposely excluded.

Thursday came: all work had been completed the previous evening; carpets were laid down, bed-hangings festooned, radiant white counterpanes spread, toilet tables arranged, furniture rubbed, flowers piled in vases: both chambers and saloons looked as fresh and bright as hands could make them. The hall, too, was scoured; and the great carved clock, as well as the steps and banisters of the staircase, were polished to the brightness of glass: in the dining-room, the side-board flashed resplendent with plate; in the drawing-room and boudoir, vases of exotics bloomed on all sides.

Afternoon arrived: Mrs. Fairfax assumed her best black satin gown, her gloves, and her gold watch; for it was her part to receive the company,— to conduct the ladies to their rooms, etc. Adèle, too, would be dressed: though I thought she had little chance of being introduced to the party that day at least. However, to please her, I allowed Sophie to apparel her in one of her short, full muslin frocks. For myself, I had no need to make any change; I should not be called upon to quit my sanctum of the school-room; for a sanctum it was now become to me,—"a very pleasant refuge in time of trouble."

It had been a mild, serene spring day; one of those days which, towards the end of March or the beginning of April, rise shining over the earth as heralds of summer. It was drawing to an end now; but the evening was even warm, and I sat at work in the school-room with the window open.

"It gets late," said Mrs. Fairfax, entering in rustling state. "I am glad I ordered dinner an hour after the time Mr. Rochester mentioned; for it is past six now. I have sent John down to the gates to see if there is anything on the road: one can see a long way from thence in the direction of Millcote." She went to the window. "Here he is!" said she. "Well, John" (leaning out), "any news?"

"They're coming, ma'am," was the answer. "They'll be here in ten minutes."

Adèle flew to the window. I followed; taking care to stand on one side, so that, screened by the curtain, I could see without being seen.

The ten minutes John had given seemed very long, but at last wheels were heard; four equestrians galloped up the drive, and after them came two open carriages. Fluttering veils and waving plumes filled the vehicles; two of the cavaliers were young, dashing-looking gentlemen; the third was Mr. Rochester, on his black horse, Mesrour; Pilot bounding before him: at his side rode a lady, and he and she were the first of the party. Her purple riding-habit almost swept the ground, her veil streamed long on the breeze; mingling with its transparent folds, and gleaming through them shone rich raven ringlets.

"Miss Ingram!" exclaimed Mrs. Fairfax, and away she hurried to her post below.

The cavalcade, following the sweep of the drive, quickly turned the angle of the house, and I lost sight of it. Adèle now petitioned to go down; but I took her on my knee and gave her to understand that she must not on any account think of venturing in sight of the ladies, either now or at any other time, unless expressly sent for: that Mr. Rochester would be very angry, etc. "Some natural tears she shed" on being told this; but as I began to look very grave, she consented at last to wipe them.

A joyous stir was now audible in the hall: gentlemen's deep tones, and ladies' silvery accents blent harmoniously together, and distinguishable above all, though not loud, was the sonorous voice of the master of Thornfield Hall, welcoming his fair and gallant guests under its roof. Then light steps ascended the stairs; and there was a tripping through the gallery, and soft cheerful laughs, and opening and closing doors, and, for a time, a hush.

"Elles changent de toilettes," said Adèle; who, listening attentively, had followed every movement; and she sighed.

"Chez maman," said she, "quand il y avait du monde, je le suivais partout, au salon et à leurs chambres; souvent je regardais les femmes de chambre coiffer et habiller les dames, et c'était si amusant: comme cela on apprend."

"Don't you feel hungry, Adèle?"

"Mais oui, mademoiselle: voilà cinq ou six heures que nous n'avons pas mangé."

"Well now, while the ladies are in their rooms, I will venture down and get you something to eat."

And issuing from my asylum with precaution, I sought a back-stairs which conducted directly to the kitchen. All in that region was fire and commotion; the soup and fish were in the last stage of projection, and the cook hung over her crucibles in a frame of mind and body threatening spontaneous combustion. In the servants' hall two coachmen and three gentlemen's gentlemen stood or sat round the fire; the Abigails, I suppose, were upstairs with their mistresses: the new servants that had been hired from Millcote, were bustling about everywhere. Threading this chaos, I at last reached the larder; there I took possession of a cold chicken, a roll of bread, some tarts, a plate or two and a knife and fork: with this booty I made a hasty retreat. I had regained the gallery, and was just shutting the back-door behind me, when an accelerated hum warned me that the ladies were about to issue from their chambers. I could not proceed to the school-room without passing some of their doors and running the risk of being surprised with my cargo of victualage; so I stood still at this end, which, being windowless, was dark: quite dark now, for the sun was set and twilight gathering.

Presently the chambers gave up their fair tenants one after another: each came out gaily and airily, with dress that gleamed lustrous through the dusk. For a moment they stood grouped together at the other extremity of the gallery, conversing in a key of sweet subdued vivacity: they then descended the staircase almost as noiselessly as a bright mist rolls down a hill. Their collective appearance had left on me an impression of high-born elegance, such as I had never before received.

I found Adèle peeping through the school-room door, which she held ajar. "What beautiful ladies!" cried she in English. "Oh,

I wish I might go to them! Do you think Mr. Rochester will send for us by-and-by, after dinner?"

"No, indeed, I don't; Mr. Rochester has something else to think about. Never mind the ladies to-night; perhaps you will see them to-morrow: here is your dinner."

She was really hungry, so the chicken and tarts served to divert her attention for a time. It was well I secured this forage; or both she, I and Sophie, to whom I conveyed a share of our repast, would have run a chance of getting no dinner at all: every one downstairs was too much engaged to think of us. The dessert was not carried out till after nine; and at ten, footmen were still running to and fro with trays and coffee-cups. I allowed Adèle to sit up much later than usual; for she declared she could not possibly go to sleep while the doors kept opening and shutting below, and people bustling about. Besides, she added, a message might possibly come from Mr. Rochester when she was undressed; "et alors quel dommage!"

I told her stories as long as she would listen to them; and then for a change I took her out into the gallery. The hall lamp was now lit, and it amused her to look over the balustrade and watch the servants passing backwards and forwards. When the evening was far advanced, a sound of music issued from the drawing-room, whither the piano had been removed; Adèle and I sat down on the top step of the stairs to listen. Presently a voice blent with the rich tones of the instrument; it was a lady who sang, and very sweet her notes were. The solo over, a duet followed, and then a glee: a joyous conversational murmur filled up the intervals. I listened long: suddenly I discovered that my ear was wholly intent on analysing the mingled sounds, and trying to discriminate amidst the confusion of accents those of Mr. Rochester; and when it caught them, which it soon did, it found a further task in framing the tones, rendered by distance inarticulate, into words.

The clock struck eleven. I looked at Adèle, whose head leant against my shoulder; her eyes were waxing heavy, so I took her up in my arms and carried her off to bed. It was near one before the gentlemen and ladies sought their chambers.

The next day was as fine as its predecessor; it was devoted by the party to an excursion to some site in the neighbourhood. They set out early in the afternoon, some on horseback, the rest in carriages; I witnessed both the departure and the return. Miss Ingram, as before, was the only lady equestrian; and, as before, Mr. Rochester galloped at her side; the two rode a little apart from the rest. I pointed out this circumstance to Mrs. Fairfax, who was standing at the window with me: —

"You said it was not likely they should think of being married," said I, "but you see Mr. Rochester evidently prefers her to any of the other ladies."

"Yes; I daresay: no doubt he admires her."

"And she him," I added; "look how she leans her head towards him as if she were conversing confidentially; I wish I could see her face; I have never had a glimpse of it yet."

"You will see her this evening," answered Mrs. Fairfax. "I happened to remark to Mr. Rochester how much Adèle wished to be introduced to the ladies, and he said: 'Oh! let her come into the drawing-room after dinner; and request Miss Eyre to accompany her.'"

"Yes — he said that from mere politeness: I need not go, I am sure," I answered.

"Well — I observed to him that as you were unused to company, I did not think you would like appearing before so gay a party — all strangers; and he replied, in his quick way: 'Nonsense! If she objects, tell her it is my particular wish; and if she resists, say I shall come and fetch her in case of contumacy.'"

"I will not give him that trouble," I answered. "I will go, if no better may be: but I don't like it. Shall you be there, Mrs. Fairfax?"

"No; I pleaded off, and he admitted my plea. I'll tell you how to manage so as to avoid the embarrassment of making a formal entrance, which is the most disagreeable part of the business. You must go into the drawing-room while it is empty, before the ladies leave the dinner-table; choose your seat in any quiet nook you like; you need not stay long after the gentlemen come in, unless you please: just let Mr. Rochester see you are there and then slip away — nobody will notice you."

"Will these people remain long, do you think?"

"Perhaps two or three weeks; certainly not more. After the Easter recess, Sir George Lynn, who was lately elected member for Millcote, will have to go up to town and take his seat; I daresay

Mr. Rochester will accompany him: it surprises me that he has already made so protracted a stay at Thornfield."

It was with some trepidation that I perceived the hour approach when I was to repair with my charge to the drawing-room. Adèle had been in a state of ecstasy all day, after hearing she was to be presented to the ladies in the evening; and it was not till Sophie commenced the operation of dressing her, that she sobered down. Then the importance of the process quickly steadied her; and by the time she had her curls arranged in well-smoothed, drooping clusters, her pink satin frock put on, her long sash tied, and her lace mittens adjusted, she looked as grave as any judge. No need to warn her not to disarrange her attire: when she was dressed, she sat demurely down in her little chair, taking care previously to lift up the satin skirt for fear she should crease it, and assured me she would not stir thence till I was ready. This I quickly was: my best dress (the silver-grey one, purchased for Miss Temple's wedding, and never worn since) was soon put on; my hair was soon smoothed; my sole ornament, the pearl brooch, soon assumed. We descended.

Fortunately there was another entrance to the drawing-room than that through the saloon where they were all seated at dinner. We found the apartment vacant; a large fire burning silently on the marble hearth, and wax candles shining in bright solitude, amid the exquisite flowers with which the tables were adorned. The crimson curtain hung before the arch: slight as was the separation this drapery formed from the party in the adjoining saloon, they spoke in so low a key that nothing of their conversation could be distinguished beyond a soothing murmur.

Adèle, who appeared to be still under the influence of a most solemnising impression, sat down, without a word, on the footstool I pointed out to her. I retired to a window-seat, and, taking a book from a table near, endeavoured to read. Adèle brought her stool to my feet; ere long she touched my knee.

"What is it, Adéle?"

"Est-ce que je ne puis pas prendre une seule de ces fleurs magnifiques, Mademoiselle? Seulement pour completer ma toilette."

"You think too much of your 'toilette,' Adèle: but you may have a flower." And I took a rose from a vase and fastened it in her sash. She sighed a sigh of ineffable satisfaction, as if her cup of happiness were now full. I turned my face away to conceal a smile I could not suppress: there was something ludicrous as well as painful in the little Parisienne's earnest and innate devotion to matters of dress.

A soft sound of rising now became audible; the curtain was swept back from the arch; through it appeared the dining-room, with its lit lustre pouring down light on the silver and glass of a magnificent dessert-service covering a long table; a band of ladies stood in the opening; they entered, and the curtain fell behind them.

There were but eight; yet somehow as they flocked in, they gave the impression of a much larger number. Some of them were very tall, many were dressed in white, and all had a sweeping amplitude of array that seemed to magnify their persons as a mist magnifies the moon. I rose and curtseyed to them: one or two bent their heads in return; the others only stared at me.

They dispersed about the room; reminding me, by the lightness and buoyancy of their movements, of a flock of white plumy birds. Some of them threw themselves in half-reclining positions on the sofas and ottomans: some bent over the tables and examined the flowers and books: the rest gathered in a group round the fire: all talked in a low but clear tone which seemed habitual to them. I knew their names afterwards, and may as well mention them now.

First, there was Mrs. Eshton and two of her daughters. She had evidently been a handsome woman, and was well preserved still. Of her daughters, the eldest, Amy, was rather little; naïve, and childlike in face and manner, and piquant in form: her white muslin dress and blue sash became her well. The second, Louisa, was taller and more elegant in figure; with a very pretty face, of that order the French term "minois chiffonné": both sisters were fair as lilies.

Lady Lynn was a large and stout personage of about forty; very erect, very haughty-looking, richly dressed in a satin robe of changeful sheen: her dark hair shone glossily under the shade of an azure plume, and within the circlet of a band of gems.

Mrs. Colonel Dent was less showy; but, I thought, more lady-like. She had a slight figure, a pale, gentle face, and fair hair. Her black satin dress, her scarf of rich foreign lace, and her pearl ornaments, pleased me better than the rainbow radiance of the titled dame.

But the three most distinguished — partly, perhaps, because the tallest figures of the band — were the Dowager Lady Ingram and her daughters, Blanche and Mary. They were all three of the loftiest stature of woman. The dowager might be between forty and fifty: her shape was still fine; her hair (by candlelight at least) still black; her teeth, too, were still apparently perfect. Most people would have termed her a splendid woman of her age: and so she was, no doubt, physically speaking; but then there was an expression of almost insupportable haughtiness in her bearing and countenance. She had Roman features and a double chin, disappearing into a throat like a pillar: these features appeared to me not only inflated and darkened, but even furrowed with pride; and the chin was sustained by the same principle, in a position of almost preternatural erectness. She had, likewise, a fierce and a hard eye: it reminded me of Mrs. Reed's; she mouthed her words in speaking; her voice was deep, its inflections very pompous, very dogmatical,— very intolerable, in short. A crimson velvet robe, and a shawl turban of some gold-wrought Indian fabric, invested her (I suppose she thought) with a truly imperial dignity.

Blanche and Mary were of equal stature,— straight and tall as poplars. Mary was too slim for her height; but Blanche was moulded like a Dian. I regarded her, of course, with special interest. First, I wished to see whether her appearance accorded with Mrs. Fairfax's description; secondly, whether it at all resembled the fancy miniature I had painted of her; and thirdly — it will out! — whether it were such as I should fancy likely to suit Mr. Rochester's taste.

As far as person went, she answered point for point, both to my picture and Mrs. Fairfax's description. The noble bust, the sloping shoulders, the graceful neck, the dark eyes and black ringlets were all there; — but her face? Her face was like her mother's; a youthful unfurrowed likeness: the same low brow, the same high features, the same pride. It was not, however, so saturnine a pride: she laughed continually; her laugh was satirical, and so was the habitual expression of her arched and haughty lip.

Genius is said to be self-conscious: I cannot tell whether Miss Ingram was a genius, but she was self-conscious — remarkably self-conscious indeed. She entered into a discourse on botany with the gentle Mrs. Dent. It seems Mrs. Dent had not studied that science: though, as she said, she liked flowers, "especially wild ones;" Miss

Ingram had, and she ran over its vocabulary with an air. I presently perceived she was (what is vernacularly termed) *trailing* Mrs. Dent; that is, playing on her ignorance: her *trail* might be clever, but it was decidedly not good-natured. She played: her execution was brilliant; she sang: her voice was fine; she talked French apart to her mama; and she talked it well, with fluency and with a good accent.

Mary had a milder and more open countenance than Blanche; softer features too, and a skin some shades fairer (Miss Ingram was dark as a Spaniard) — but Mary was deficient in life: her face lacked expression, her eye lustre; she had nothing to say, and having once taken her seat, remained fixed like a statue in its niche. The sisters were both attired in spotless white.

And did I now think Miss Ingram such a choice as Mr. Rochester would be likely to make? I could not tell — I did not know his taste in female beauty. If he liked the majestic, she was the very type of majesty: then she was accomplished, sprightly. Most gentlemen would admire her, I thought; and that he *did* admire her, I already seemed to have obtained proof: to remove the last shade of doubt, it remained but to see them together.

You are not to suppose, reader, that Adèle has all this time been sitting motionless on the stool at my feet: no; when the ladies entered, she rose, advanced to meet them, made a stately reverence, and said, with gravity,—

"Bon jour, mesdames."

And Miss Ingram had looked down at her with a mocking air, and exclaimed, "Oh, what a little puppet!"

Lady Lynn had remarked, "It is Mr. Rochester's ward, I suppose — the little French girl he was speaking of."

Mrs. Dent had kindly taken her hand, and given her a kiss. Amy and Louisa Eshton had cried out simultaneously —

"What a love of a child!"

And then they had called her to a sofa, where she now sat, ensconced between them, chattering alternately in French and broken English; absorbing not only the young ladies' attention, but that of Mrs. Eshton and Lady Lynn, and getting spoilt to her heart's content.

At last coffee is brought in, and the gentlemen are summoned. I sit in the shade — if any shade there be in this brilliantly-lit apartment; the window-curtain half hides me. Again the arch yawns: they come. The collective appearance of the gentlemen, like that of the ladies, is very imposing: they are all costumed in black; most of them are tall, some young. Henry and Frederick Lynn are very dashing sparks, indeed; and Colonel Dent is a fine soldierly man. Mr. Eshton, the magistrate of the district, is gentleman-like: his hair is quite white, his eyebrows and whiskers still dark, which gives him something of the appearance of a "père noble de théâtre." Lord Ingram, like his sisters, is very tall; like them, also, he is handsome; but he shares Mary's apathetic and listless look: he seems to have more length of limb than vivacity of blood or vigour of brain.

And where is Mr. Rochester?

He comes in last: I am not looking at the arch, yet I see him enter. I try to concentrate my attention on those netting-needles, on the meshes of the purse I am forming — I wish to think only of the work I have in my hands, to see only the silver beads and silk threads that lie in my lap; whereas, I distinctly behold his figure, and I inevitably recall the moment when I last saw it: just after I had rendered him, what he deemed, an essential service — and he, holding my hand, and looking down on my face, surveyed me with eyes that revealed a heart full and eager to overflow; in whose emotions I had a part. How near had I approached him at that moment! What had occurred since, calculated to change his and my relative positions? Yet now, how distant, how far estranged we were! So far estranged, that I did not expect him to come and speak to me. I did not wonder, when, without looking at me, he took a seat at the other side of the room, and began conversing with some of the ladies.

No sooner did I see that his attention was riveted on them, and that I might gaze without being observed, than my eyes were drawn involuntarily to his face: I could not keep their lids under control: they would rise and the irids would fix on him. I looked, and had an acute pleasure in looking,— a precious, yet poignant pleasure; pure gold, with a steely point of agony: a pleasure like what the thirst-perishing man might feel who knows the well to which he has crept is poisoned, yet stoops and drinks divine draughts nevertheless.

Most true it is that "beauty is in the eye of the gazer." My master's colourless, olive face, square, massive brow, broad and jetty eyebrows, deep eyes, strong features, firm, grim mouth,— all energy, decision, will,— were not beautiful, according to rule; but they were more than beautiful to me: they were full of an interest, an influence that quite mastered me,— that took my feelings from my own power and fettered them in his. I had not intended to love him: the reader knows I had wrought hard to extirpate from my soul the germs of love there detected; and now, at the first renewed view of him, they spontaneously revived, green and strong! He made me love him without looking at me.

I compared him with his guests. What was the gallant grace of the Lynns, the languid elegance of Lord Ingram,— even the military distinction of Colonel Dent, contrasted with his look of native pith and genuine power? I had no sympathy in their appearance, their expression: yet I could imagine that most observers would call them attractive, handsome, imposing; while they would pronounce Mr. Rochester at once harsh-featured and melancholy-looking. I saw them smile, laugh — it was nothing: the light of the candles had as much significance as their laugh. I saw Mr. Rochester smile: — his stern features softened; his eye grew both brilliant and gentle, its ray both searching and sweet. He was talking, at the moment, to Louisa and Amy Eshton. I wondered to see them receive with calm that look which seemed to me so penetrating: I expected their eyes to fall, their colour to rise under it; yet I was glad when I found they were in no sense moved. "He is not to them what he is to me," I thought: "he is not of their kind. I believe he is of mine; — I am sure he is,— I feel akin to him,— I understand the language of his countenance and movements: though rank and wealth sever us widely, I have something in my brain and heart, in my blood and nerves, that assimilates me mentally to him. Did I say, a few days since, that I had nothing to do with him but to receive my salary at his hands? Did I forbid myself to think of him in any other light than as a paymaster? Blasphemy against nature! Every good, true, vigorous feeling I have, gathers impulsively round him. I know I must conceal my sentiments: I must smother hope; I must remember that he cannot care much for me. For when I say that I am of his kind, I do not mean that I have his force to influence, and his spell to attract: I mean only that I have certain tastes and feelings in common with him. I must, then, repeat con-

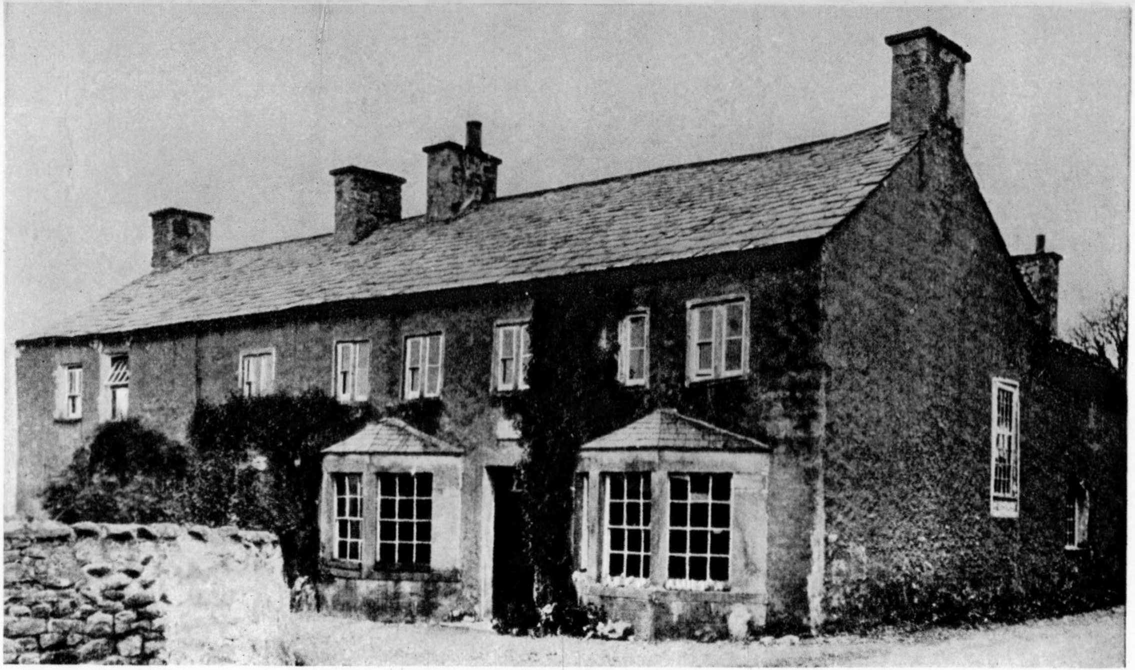

COWAN BRIDGE SCHOOL

In 1824, when she was eight years old, Charlotte with her three sisters was sent to the Clergy Daughters' School at Cowan Bridge, a school partly supported by charitable subscriptions, which she has drawn as "Lowood School." A tablet in the school now commemorates the fact that "Maria, Elizabeth, Charlotte, and Emily, daughters of the Rev. P. Brontë, were educated here." Both Maria and Elizabeth died young. Maria, as the eldest daughter in a motherless family, was the nurse of all the rest; Charlotte was devoted to her, and portrayed her as Jane's only friend at school, Helen Burns.

The school's records still have a report on Charlotte: "Entered school Aug. 10, 1824. Writes indifferently. Ciphers a little, and works neatly. Knows nothing of grammar, geography, history, or accomplishments. Altogether clever of her age, but knows nothing systematically. Left school June 1, 1835.

tinually that we are for ever sundered: — and yet, while I breathe and think I must love him."

Coffee is handed. The ladies, since the gentlemen entered, have become lively as larks; conversation waxes brisk and merry. Colonel Dent and Mr. Eshton argue on politics; their wives listen. The two proud dowagers, Lady Lynn and Lady Ingram, confabulate together. Sir George — whom, by-the-by, I have forgotten to describe, — a very big, and very fresh-looking country gentleman, stands before their sofa, coffee-cup in hand, and occasionally puts in a word. Mr. Frederick Lynn had taken a seat beside Mary Ingram, and is showing her the engravings of a splendid volume: she looks, smiles now and then, but apparently says little. The tall and phlegmatic Lord Ingram leans with folded arms on the chair-back of the little and lively Amy Eshton; she glances up at him, and chatters like a wren: she likes him better than she does Mr. Rochester. Henry Lynn has taken possession of an ottoman at the feet of Louisa; Adèle shares it with him: he is trying to talk French with her, and Louisa laughs at his blunders. With whom will Blanche Ingram pair? She is standing alone at the table, bending gracefully over an album. She seems waiting to be sought; but she will not wait too long: she herself selects a mate.

Mr. Rochester, having quitted the Eshtons, stands on the hearth as solitary as she stands by the table: she confronts him, taking her station on the opposite side of the mantelpiece.

"Mr. Rochester, I thought you were not fond of children?"

"Nor am I."

"Then, what induced you to take charge of such a little doll as that?" (pointing to Adèle). "Where did you pick her up?"

"I did not pick her up, she was left on my hands."

"You should have sent her to school."

"I could not afford it: schools are so dear."

"Why, I suppose you have a governess for her: I saw a person with her just now — is she gone? Oh, no! there she is still behind the window-curtain. You pay her, of course; I should think it quite as expensive, — more so; for you have them both to keep in addition."

I feared — or should I say, hoped? — the allusion to me would make Mr. Rochester glance my way; and I involuntarily shrank further into the shade: but he never turned his eyes.

"I have not considered the subject," said he indifferently, looking straight before him.

"No — you men never do consider economy and common-sense. You should hear mama on the chapter of governesses: Mary and I have had, I should think, a dozen at least in our day; half of them detestable and the rest ridiculous, and all incubi — were they not, mama?"

"Did you speak, my own?"

The young lady thus claimed as the dowager's special property, reiterated her question with an explanation.

"My dearest, don't mention governesses; the word makes me nervous. I have suffered a martyrdom from their incompetency and caprice; I thank Heaven I have now done with them!"

Mrs. Dent here bent over to the pious lady, and whispered something in her ear; I suppose from the answer elicited, it was a reminder that one of the anathematised race was present.

"Tant pis!" said her ladyship, "I hope it may do her good!" Then, in a lower tone, but still loud enough for me to hear, "I noticed her; I am a judge of physiognomy, and in hers I see all the faults of her class."

"What are they, madam?" inquired Mr. Rochester aloud.

"I will tell you in your private ear," replied she, wagging her turban three times with portentous significancy.

"But my curiosity will be past its appetite; it craves food now."

"Ask Blanche; she is nearer you than I."

"Oh, don't refer him to me, mama! I have just one word to say of the whole tribe; they are a nuisance. Not that I ever suffered much from them; I took care to turn the tables. What tricks Theodore and I used to play on our Miss Wilsons, and Mrs. Greys, and Madame Jouberts! Mary was always too sleepy to join in a plot with spirit. The best fun was with Madame Joubert: Miss Wilson was a poor sickly thing, lachrymose and low-spirited: not worth the trouble of vanquishing, in short; and Mrs. Grey was coarse and insensible: no blow took effect on her. But poor Madame Joubert! I see her yet in her raging passions, when we had driven her to extremities — spilt our tea, crumbled our bread and butter, tossed our books up to the ceiling, and played a charivari with the ruler and desk, the fender and fire-irons. Theodore, do you remember those merry days?"

"Yaas, to be sure I do," drawled Lord Ingram; "and the poor old stick used to cry out 'Oh you villains childs!'— and then we sermonised her on the presumption of attempting to teach such clever blades as we were, when she was herself so ignorant."

"We did; and Tedo, you know, I helped you in prosecuting (or persecuting) your tutor, whey-faced Mr. Vining — the parson in the pip, as we used to call him. He and Miss Wilson took the liberty of falling in love with each other — at least Tedo and I thought so; we surprised sundry tender glances and sighs which we interpreted as token of 'la belle passion,' and I promise you the public soon had the benefit of our discovery: we employed it as a sort of lever to hoist our dead-weights from the house. Dear mama, there, as soon as she got an inkling of the business, found out that it was of an immoral tendency. Did you not, my lady-mother?"

"Certainly, my best. And I was quite right; depend on that: there are a thousand reasons why liaisons between governesses and tutors should never be tolerated a moment in any well-regulated house; firstly"——

"Oh gracious, mama! Spare us the enumeration! Au reste, we all know them: danger of bad example to innocence of childhood; distractions and consequent neglect of duty on the part of the attached — mutual alliance and reliance; confidence thence resulting — insolence accompanying — mutiny and general blow-up. Am I right, Baroness Ingram, of Ingram Park?"

"My lily-flower, you are right now, as always."

"Then no more need be said: change the subject."

Amy Eshton, not hearing or not heeding this dictum, joined in with her soft, infantine tone: "Louisa and I used to quiz our governess too; but she was such a good creature, she would bear anything: nothing put her out. She was never cross with us; was she, Louisa?"

"No, never: we might do what we pleased; ransack her desk and her work-box, and turn her drawers inside out; and she was so good-natured, she would give us anything we asked for."

"I suppose, now," said Miss Ingram, curling her lip sarcastically, "we shall have an abstract of the memoirs of all the governesses extant: in order to avert such a visitation, I again move the introduction of a new topic. Mr. Rochester, do you second my motion?"

"Madam, I support you on this point as on every other."

"Then on me be the onus of bringing it forward. Signior Eduardo, are you in voice to-night?"

"Donna Bianca, if you command it, I will be."

"Then, signior, I lay on you my sovereign behest to furbish up your lungs and other vocal organs, as they will be wanted on my royal service."

"Who would not be the Rizzio of so divine a Mary?"

"A fig for Rizzio!" cried she, tossing her head with all its curls, as she moved to the piano. "It is my opinion the fiddler David must have been an insipid sort of fellow: I like black Bothwell better: to my mind a man is nothing without a spice of the devil in him; and history may say what it will of James Hepburn, but I have a notion he was just the sort of wild, fierce, bandit hero whom I could have consented to gift with my hand."

"Gentlemen, you hear! Now which of you most resembles Bothwell?" cried Mr. Rochester.

"I should say the preference lies with you," responded Colonel Dent.

"On my honour, I am much obliged to you," was the reply.

Miss Ingram, who had now seated herself with proud grace at the piano, spreading out her snowy robes in queenly amplitude, commenced a brilliant prelude; talking meantime. She appeared to be on her high horse to-night; both her words and her air seemed intended to excite not only the admiration but the amazement of her auditors: she was evidently bent on striking them as something very dashing and daring indeed.

"Oh, I am so sick of the young men of the present day!" exclaimed she, rattling away at the instrument. "Poor, puny things not fit to stir a step beyond papa's park-gates: nor to go even so far without mama's permission and guardianship! Creatures so absorbed in care about their pretty faces and their white hands, and their small feet; as if a man had anything to do with beauty! As if loveliness were not the special prerogative of woman — her legitimate appanage and heritage! I grant an ugly *woman* is a blot on the fair face of creation; but as to the *gentlemen,* let them be solicitous to possess only strength and valour: let their motto be: — Hunt, shoot, and fight: the rest is not worth a fillip. Such should be my device, were I a man.

"Whenever I marry," she continued after a pause which none

interrupted, "I am resolved my husband shall not be a rival, but a foil to me. I will suffer no competitor near the throne; I shall exact an undivided homage: his devotions shall not be shared between me and the shape he sees in his mirror. Mr. Rochester, now sing, and I will play for you."

"I am all obedience," was the response.

The divining party again laid their heads together: apparently and for the reason, sing it 'con spirito.'"

"Commands from Miss Ingram's lips would put spirit into a mug of milk and water."

"Take care, then: if you don't please me, I will shame you by showing how such things *should* be done."

"That is offering a premium on incapacity: I shall now endeavour to fail."

"Gardez-vous en bien! If you err wilfully, I shall devise a proportionate punishment."

"Miss Ingram ought to be clement, for she has it in her power to inflict a chastisement beyond mortal endurance."

"Ha! explain!" commanded the lady.

"Pardon me, madam: no need of explanation; your own fine sense must inform you that one of your frowns would be a sufficient substitute for capital punishment."

"Sing!" said she, and again touching the piano, she commenced an accompaniment in spirited style.

"Now is my time to slip away," thought I: but the tones that then severed the air arrested me. Mrs. Fairfax had said Mr. Rochester possessed a fine voice: he did — a mellow, powerful bass, into which he threw his own feeling, his own force; finding a way through the ear to the heart, and there waking sensation strangely. I waited till the last deep and full vibration had expired — till the tide of talk, checked an instant, had resumed its flow; I then quitted my sheltered corner and made my exit by the side-door, which was fortunately near. Thence a narrow passage led into the hall: in crossing it, I perceived my sandal was loose; I stopped to tie it, kneeling down for that purpose on the mat at the foot of the staircase. I heard the dining-room door unclose; a gentleman came out; rising hastily, I stood face to face with him: it was Mr. Rochester.

"How do you do?" he asked.

"I am very well, sir."

"Why did you not come and speak to me in the room?"

I thought I might have retorted the question on him who put it: but I would not take that freedom. I answered: —

"I did not wish to disturb you, as you seemed engaged, sir."

"What have you been doing during my absence?"

"Nothing particular; teaching Adèle as usual."

"And getting a good deal paler than you were — as I saw at first sight. What is the matter?"

"Nothing at all, sir."

"Did you take any cold that night you half drowned me?"

"Not the least."

"Return to the drawing-room: you are deserting too early."

"I am tired, sir."

He looked at me for a minute.

"And a little depressed," he said. "What about? Tell me."

"Nothing — nothing, sir. I am not depressed."

"But I affirm that you are: so much depressed that a few more words would bring tears to your eyes — indeed, they are there now, shining and swimming; and a bead has slipped from the lash and fallen on to the flag. If I had time, and was not in mortal dread of some prating prig of a servant passing, I would know what all this means. Well, to-night I excuse you; but understand that so long as my visitors stay, I expect you to appear in the drawing-room every evening; it is my wish; don't neglect it. Now go, and send Sophie for Adèle. Good-night, my"—— He stopped, bit his lip, and abruptly left me.

# CHAPTER XVIII

MERRY days were those at Thornfield Hall; and busy days too: how different from the first three months of stillness, monotony, and solitude I had passed beneath its roof! All sad feelings seemed now driven from the house, all gloomy associations forgotten: there was life everywhere, movement all day long. You could not now traverse the gallery, once so hushed, nor enter the front chambers, once so tenantless, without encountering a smart lady's maid or a dandy valet.

The kitchen, the butler's pantry, the servants' hall, the entrance hall, were equally alive; and the saloons were only left void and still, when the blue sky and halcyon sunshine of the genial spring weather called their occupants out into the grounds. Even when that weather was broken, and continuous rain set in for some days, no damp seemed cast over enjoyment: in-door amusements only became more lively and varied, in consequence of the stop put to out-door gaiety.

I wondered what they were going to do the first evening a change of entertainment was proposed: they spoke of "playing charades," but in my ignorance I did not understand the term. The servants were called in, the dining-room tables wheeled away, the lights otherwise disposed, the chairs placed in a semicircle opposite the arch. While Mr. Rochester and the other gentlemen directed these alterations, the ladies were running up and down stairs ringing for their maids. Mrs. Fairfax was summoned to give information respecting the resources of the house in shawls, dresses, draperies of any kind; and certain wardrobes of the third story were ransacked, and their contents, in the shape of brocaded and hooped petticoats, satin sacques, black modes, lace lappets, etc., were brought down in armfuls by the Abigails; then a selection was made, and such things as were chosen were carried to the boudoir within the drawing-room.

Meantime, Mr. Rochester had again summoned the ladies round him, and was selecting certain of their number to be of his party. "Miss Ingram is mine, of course," said he: afterwards he named the two Misses Eshton, and Mrs. Dent. He looked at me: I happened to be near him, as I had been fastening the clasp of Mrs. Dent's bracelet, which had got loose.

"Will you play?" he asked. I shook my head. He did not insist, which I rather feared he would have done: he allowed me to return quietly to my usual seat.

He and his aids now withdrew behind the curtain: the other party, which was headed by Colonel Dent, sat down on the crescent of chairs. One of the gentlemen, Mr. Eshton, observing me, seemed to propose that I should be asked to join them; but Lady Ingram instantly negatived the notion.

"No," I heard her say: "she looks too stupid for any game of the sort."

Ere long, a bell tinkled, and the curtain drew up. Within the arch, the bulky figure of Sir George Lynn, whom Mr. Rochester had likewise chosen, was seen enveloped in a white sheet: before him, on a table, lay open a large book; and at his side stood Amy Eshton, draped in Mr. Rochester's cloak, and holding a book in her hand. Somebody, unseen, rang the bell merrily; then Adèle (who had insisted on being one of her guardian's party), bounded forward, scattering round her the contents of a basket of flowers she carried on her arm. Then appeared the magnificent figure of Miss Ingram, clad in white, a long veil on her head, and a wreath of roses round her brow: by her side walked Mr. Rochester, and together they drew near the table. They knelt; while Mrs. Dent and Louisa Eshton, dressed also in white, took up their stations behind them. A ceremony followed, in dumb show, in which it was easy to recognise the pantomime of a marriage. At its termination, Colonel Dent and his party consulted in whispers for two minutes, then the colonel called out,—

"Bride!" Mr. Rochester bowed, and the curtain fell.

A considerable interval elapsed before it again rose. Its second rising displayed a more elaborately prepared scene than the last. The drawing-room, as I have before observed, was raised two steps above the dining-room, and on the top of the upper step, placed a yard or two back within the room, appeared a large marble basin, which I recognised as an ornament of the conservatory — where it usually stood, surrounded by exotics, and tenanted by gold-fish — and whence it must have been transported with some trouble, on account of its size and weight.

Seated on the carpet, by the side of this basin, was seen Mr. Rochester, costumed in shawls, with a turban on his head. His dark eyes and swarth skin and Paynim features suited the costume exactly: he looked the very model of an eastern emir; an agent or a victim of the bowstring. Presently advanced into view Miss Ingram. She, too, was attired in oriental fashion: a crimson scarf tied sash-like round the waist: an embroidered handkerchief knotted about her temples; her beautifully-moulded arms bare, one of them up-raised in the act of supporting a pitcher, poised gracefully on her head. Both her cast of form and feature, her complexion and her general air, suggested the idea of some Israelitish princess of the patriarchal days; and such was doubtless the character she intended to represent.

She approached the basin, and bent over it as if to fill her pitcher; she again lifted it to her head. The personage on the well-brink now seemed to accost her; to make some request:—"She hasted, let down her pitcher on her hand and gave him to drink." From the bosom of his robe, he then produced a casket, opened it and showed magnificent bracelets and earrings: she acted astonishment and admiration; kneeling, he laid the treasure at her feet; incredulity and delight were expressed by her looks and gestures; the stranger fastened the bracelets on her arms, and the rings in her ears. It was Eliezer and Rebecca: the camels only were wanting.

The divining party again laid their heads together: apparently they could not agree about the word or syllable this scene illustrated. Colonel Dent, their spokesman, demanded "the tableau of the Whole"; whereupon the curtain again descended.

On its third rising only a portion of the drawing-room was disclosed; the rest being concealed by a screen, hung with some sort of dark and coarse drapery. The marble basin was removed; in its place stood a deal table and a kitchen chair: these objects were visible by a very dim light proceeding from a horn lantern, the wax candles being all extinguished.

Amidst this sordid scene, sat a man with his clenched hands resting on his knees, and his eyes bent on the ground. I knew Mr. Rochester; though the begrimed face, the disordered dress (his coat hanging loose from one arm, as if it had been almost torn from his back in a scuffle), the desperate and scowling countenance, the rough, bristling hair might well have disguised him. As he moved, a chain clanked; to his wrists were attached fetters.

"Bridewell!" exclaimed Colonel Dent, and the charade was solved.

A sufficient interval having elapsed for the performers to assume their ordinary costume, they re-entered the dining-room. Mr. Rochester led in Miss Ingram; she was complimenting him on his acting.

"Do you know," said she, "that, of the three characters, I liked you in the last best? Oh, had you but lived a few years earlier, what a gallant gentleman-highwayman you would have made!"

"Is all the soot washed from my face?" he asked, turning it towards her.

"Alas, yes; the more's the pity! Nothing could be more becoming to your complexion than that ruffian's rouge."

"You would like a hero of the road then?"

"An English hero of the road would be the next best thing to an Italian bandit; and that could only be surpassed by a Levantine pirate."

"Well, whatever I am, remember you are my wife; we were married an hour since, in the presence of all these witnesses." She giggled, and her colour rose.

"Now, Dent," continued Mr. Rochester, "it is your turn." And as the other party withdrew, he and his band took the vacated seats. Miss Ingram placed herself at her leader's right hand; the other diviners filled the chairs on each side of him and her. I did not now watch the actors; I no longer waited with interest for the curtain to rise; my attention was absorbed by the spectators; my eyes, erewhile fixed on the arch, were now irresistibly attracted to the semicircle of chairs. What charade Colonel Dent and his party played, what word they chose, how they acquitted themselves, I no longer remember; but I still see the consultation which followed each scene: I see Mr. Rochester turn to Miss Ingram, and Miss Ingram to him; I see her incline her head towards him, till the jetty curls almost touch his shoulder and wave against his cheek; I hear the mutual whisperings; I recall their interchanged glances; and something even of the feeling roused by the spectacle returns in memory at this moment.

I have told you, reader, that I had learnt to love Mr. Rochester: I could not unlove him now, merely because I found that he had ceased to notice me — because I might pass hours in his presence, and he would never once turn his eyes in my direction — because I saw all his attentions appropriated by a great lady, who scorned to touch me with the hem of her robes as she passed; who, if ever her dark and imperious eye fell on me by chance, would withdraw it instantly as from an object too mean to merit observation. I could not unlove him, because I felt sure he would soon marry this very lady — because I read daily in her a proud security in his intentions respecting her — because I witnessed hourly in him a style of courtship which, if careless and choosing rather to be sought than to seek, was yet, in its very carelessness, captivating, and in its very pride, irresistible.

There was nothing to cool or banish love in these circumstances; though much to create despair. Much too, you will think, reader, to engender jealousy: if a woman, in my position, could presume to be jealous of a woman in Miss Ingram's. But I was not jealous: or very rarely; — the nature of the pain I suffered could not be explained by that word. Miss Ingram was a mark beneath jealousy: she was too inferior to excite the feeling. Pardon the seeming paradox: I mean what I say. She was very showy, but she was not genuine: she had a fine person, many brilliant attainments; but her mind was poor, her heart barren by nature: nothing bloomed spontaneously on that soil; no unforced natural fruit delighted by its freshness. She was not good; she was not original: she used to repeat sounding phrases from books: she never offered, nor had, an opinion of her own. She advocated a high tone of sentiment; but she did not know the sensations of sympathy and pity; tenderness and truth were not in her. Too often she betrayed this, by the undue vent she gave to a spiteful antipathy she had conceived against little Adèle: pushing her away with some contumelious epithet if she happened to approach her; sometimes ordering her from the room, and always treating her with coldness and acrimony. Other eyes besides mine watched these manifestations of character — watched them closely, keenly, shrewdly. Yes: the future bridegroom, Mr. Rochester himself, exercised over his intended a ceaseless surveillance: and it was from this sagacity — this guardedness of his — this perfect, clear consciousness of his fair one's defects — this obvious absence of passion in his sentiments towards her, that my ever-torturing pain arose.

I saw he was going to marry her, for family, perhaps political reasons; because her rank and connections suited him; I felt he had not given her his love, and that her qualifications were ill adapted to win from him that treasure. This was the point — this was where the nerve was touched and teased — this was where the fever was sustained and fed: *she could not charm him.*

If she had managed the victory at once, and he had yielded and sincerely laid his heart at her feet, I should have covered my face, turned to the wall, and (figuratively) have died to them. If Miss Ingram had been a good and noble woman, endowed with force, fervour, kindness, sense, I should have had one vital struggle with two tigers — jealousy and despair; then, my heart torn out and devoured, I should have admired her — acknowledged her excellence, and been quiet for the rest of my days: and the more absolute her superiority, the deeper would have been my admiration — the more truly tranquil my quiescence. But as matters really stood, to watch Miss Ingram's efforts at fascinating Mr. Rochester; to witness their repeated failure, herself unconscious that they did fail; vainly fancying that each shaft launched, hit the mark, and infatuatedly pluming herself on success, when her pride and self-complacency repelled further and further what she wished to allure — to witness *this,* was to be at once under ceaseless excitation and ruthless restraint.

Because, when she failed, I saw how she might have succeeded. Arrows that continually glanced off from Mr. Rochester's breast and fell harmless at his feet, might, I knew, if shot by a surer hand, have quivered keen in his proud heart — have called love into his eye, and softness into his sardonic face: or, better still, without weapons a silent conquest might have been won.

"Why can she not influence him more, when she is privileged to draw so near to him?" I asked myself. "Surely she cannot truly like him; or not like him with true affection! If she did, she need not coin her smiles so lavishly; flash her glances so unremittingly; manufacture airs so elaborate, graces so multitudinous. It seems to me, that she might, by merely sitting quietly at his side, saying little and looking less, get nigher his heart. I have seen in his face a far different expression from that which hardens it now while she is so vivaciously accosting him; but then it came of itself: it was not elicited by meretricious arts and calculated manœuvres; and one had but to accept it — to answer what he asked without pretension. to address him when needful without grimace — and it increased and grew kinder and more genial, and warmed one like a fostering sunbeam. How will she manage to please him when they are married? I do not think she will manage it; and yet it might be managed; and his wife might, I verily believe, be the happiest woman the sun shines on."

I have not yet said anything condemnatory of Mr. Rochester's project of marrying for interest and connections. It surprised me when I first discovered that such was his intention: I had thought him a man unlikely to be influenced by motives so commonplace in his choice of a wife; but the longer I considered the position, etc., of the parties, the less I felt justified in judging and blaming either him or Miss Ingram, for acting in conformity to ideas and principles instilled into them, doubtless, from their childhood. All their class held these principles: I supposed, then, they had reasons for holding them such as I could not fathom. It seemed to me that, were I a gentleman like him, I would take to my bosom only such a wife as I could love; but the very obviousness of the advantages to the husband's own happiness, offered by this plan, convinced me that there must be arguments against its general adoption of which I was quite ignorant: otherwise I felt sure all the world would act as I wished to act.

But in other points, as well as this, I was growing very lenient to my master: I was forgetting all his faults, for which I had once kept a sharp look-out. It had formerly been my endeavour to study all sides of his character: to take the bad with the good; and from the just weighing of both, to form an equitable judgment. Now I saw no bad. The sarcasm that had repelled, the harshness that had startled me once, were only like keen condiments in a choice dish: their presence was pungent, but their absence would be felt as comparatively insipid. And as for the vague something — was it a sinister or a sorrowful, a designing or a desponding expression? — that opened upon a careful observer, now and then, in his eye, and closed again before one could fathom the strange depth partially disclosed; that something which used to make me fear and shrink, as if I had been wandering amongst volcanic-looking hills, and had suddenly felt the ground quiver, and seen it gape: that something,

I, at intervals, beheld still; and with throbbing heart, but not with palsied nerves. Instead of wishing to shun, I longed only to dare — to divine it; and I thought Miss Ingram happy, because one day she might look into the abyss at her leisure, explore its secrets and analyse their nature.

Meantime, while I thought only of my master and his future bride — saw only them, heard only their discourse, and considered only their movements of importance — the rest of the party were occupied with their own separate interests and pleasures. The ladies Lynn and Ingram continued to consort in solemn conferences; where they nodded their two turbans at each other, and held up their four hands in confronting gestures of surprise, or mystery, or horror, according to the theme on which their gossip ran, like a pair of magnified puppets. Mild Mrs. Dent talked with good-natured Mrs. Eshton; and the two sometimes bestowed a courteous word or smile on me. Sir George Lynn, Colonel Dent, and Mr. Eshton discussed politics, or county affairs, or justice business. Lord Ingram flirted with Amy Eshton; Louisa played and sang to and with one of the Messrs. Lynn, and Mary Ingram listened languidly to the gallant speeches of the other. Sometimes all, as with one consent, suspended their by-play to observe and listen to the principal actors: for, after all, Mr. Rochester, and — because closely connected with him — Miss Ingram, were the life and soul of the party. If he were absent from the room an hour, a perceptible dulness seemed to steal over the spirits of his guests; and his re-entrance was sure to give a fresh impulse to the vivacity of conversation.

The want of his animating influence appeared to be peculiarly felt one day that he had been summoned to Millcote on business, and was not likely to return till late. The afternoon was wet: a walk the party had proposed to take to see a gipsy camp, lately pitched on a common beyond Hay, was consequently deferred. Some of the gentlemen were gone to the stables: the younger ones, together with the younger ladies, were playing billiards in the billiard-room. The dowagers Ingram and Lynn sought solace in a quiet game at cards. Blanche Ingram, after having repelled, by supercilious taciturnity, some efforts of Mrs. Dent and Mrs. Eshton to draw her into conversation, had first murmured over some sentimental tunes and airs on the piano, and then, having fetched a novel from the library, had flung herself in haughty listlessness on a sofa, and prepared to be guile, by the spell of fiction, the tedious hours of absence. The room and the house were silent: only now and then the merriment of the billiard players was heard from above.

It was verging on dusk, and the clock had already given warning of the hour to dress for dinner, when little Adèle, who knelt by me in the drawing-room window-seat, exclaimed: —

"Voilà Monsieur Rochester, qui revient!"

I turned, and Miss Ingram darted forwards from her sofa: the others, too, looked up from their several occupations; for at the same time a crunching of wheels, and a splashing tramp of horse-hoofs became audible on the wet gravel. A post-chaise was approaching.

"What can possess him to come home in that style?" said Miss Ingram. "He rode Mesrour (the black horse), did he not, when he went out? and Pilot was with him: — what has he done with the animals?"

As she said this, she approached her tall person and ample garments so near the window, that I was obliged to bend back almost to the breaking of my spine: in her eagerness she did not observe me at first, but when she did, she curled her lip and moved to another casement. The post-chaise stopped; the driver rang the door bell, and a gentleman alighted, attired in travelling garb; but it was not Mr. Rochester; it was a tall, fashionable-looking man, a stranger.

"Provoking!" exclaimed Miss Ingram: "you tiresome monkey!" (apostrophising Adèle) "who perched you up in the window to give false intelligence?" and she cast on me an angry glance, as if I were in fault.

Some parleying was audible in the hall, and soon the new comer entered. He bowed to Lady Ingram, as deeming her the eldest lady present.

"It appears I come at an inopportune time, madam," said he; "when my friend, Mr. Rochester, is from home; but I arrive from a very long journey, and I think I may presume so far on old and intimate acquaintance as to instal myself here till he returns."

His manner was polite; his accent, in speaking, struck me as being somewhat unusual,— not precisely foreign, but still not altogether English; his age might be about Mr. Rochester's,— between thirty and forty; his complexion was singularly sallow: otherwise he was a fine-looking man, at first sight especially. On closer examination, you detected something in his face that displeased; or rather, that failed to please. His features were regular, but too relaxed: his eye was large and well cut, but the life looking out of it was a tame, vacant life — at least so I thought.

The sound of the dressing-bell dispersed the party. It was not till after dinner that I saw him again: he then seemed quite at his ease. But I liked his physiognomy even less than before: it struck me as being, at the same time, unsettled, and inanimate. His eye wandered, and had no meaning in its wandering: this gave him an odd look, such as I never remembered to have seen. For a handsome and not an unamiable-looking man, he repelled me exceedingly: there was no power in that smooth-skinned face of a full oval shape; no firmness in that aquiline nose, and small, cherry mouth; there was no thought on the low, even forehead; no command in that blank, brown eye.

As I sat in my usual nook, and looked at him with the light of the girandoles on the mantelpiece beaming full over him — for he occupied an arm-chair, drawn close to the fire, and kept shrinking still nearer, as if he were cold — I compared him with Mr. Rochester. I think (with deference be it spoken) the contrast could not be much greater between a sleek gander and a fierce falcon: between a meek sheep and the rough-coated keen-eyed dog, its guardian.

He had spoken of Mr. Rochester as an old friend. A curious friendship theirs must have been: a pointed illustration indeed, of the old adage that "extremes meet."

Two or three of the gentlemen sat near him, and I caught at times scraps of their conversation across the room. At first I could not make much sense of what I heard; for the discourse of Louisa Eshton and Mary Ingram, who sat nearer to me, confused the fragmentary sentences that reached me at intervals. These last were discussing the stranger: they both called him "a beautiful man." Louisa said he was "a love of a creature," and she "adored him": and Mary instanced his "pretty little mouth, and nice nose," as her ideal of the charming.

"And what a sweet-tempered forehead he has!" cried Louisa,— "so smooth — none of those frowning irregularities I dislike so much: and such a placid eye and smile!"

And then, to my great relief, Mr. Henry Lynn summoned them to the other side of the room, to settle some point about the deferred excursion to Hay Common.

I was now able to concentrate my attention on the group by the fire, and I presently gathered that the new comer was called Mr. Mason: then I learned that he was but just arrived in England, and that he came from some hot country: which was the reason, doubtless, his face was so sallow, and that he sat so near the hearth, and wore a surtout in the house. Presently the words Jamaica, Kingston, Spanish Town, indicated the West Indies as his residence; and it was with no little surprise I gathered, ere long, that he had there first seen and become acquainted with Mr. Rochester. He spoke of his friend's dislike of the burning heats, the hurricanes, and rainy seasons of that region. I knew Mr. Rochester had been a traveller: Mrs. Fairfax had said so; but I thought the continent of Europe had bounded his wanderings: till now I had never heard a hint given of visits to more distant shores.

I was pondering these things, when an accident, and a somewhat unexpected one, broke the thread of my musings. Mr. Mason, shivering as some one chanced to open the door, asked for more coal to be put on the fire, which had burnt out its flame, though its mass of cinder still shone hot and red. The footman who brought the coal, in going out, stopped near Mr. Eshton's chair, and said something to him in a low voice, of which I heard only the words, "old woman," —"quite troublesome."

"Tell her she shall be put in the stocks if she does not take herself off," replied the magistrate.

"No — stop!" interrupted Colonel Dent. "Don't send her away, Eshton; we might turn the thing to account; better consult the ladies." And speaking aloud, he continued, "Ladies, you talked of going to Hay Common to visit the gipsy camp; Sam, here, says that one of the old Mother Bunches is in the servants' hall at this moment, and insists upon being brought in before 'the quality,' to tell them their fortunes. Would you like to see her?"

"Surely, colonel," cried Lady Ingram, "you would not encourage such a low impostor? Dismiss her, by all means, at once!"

"But I cannot persuade her to go away, my lady," said the footman; "nor can any of the servants: Mrs. Fairfax is with her just now, entreating her to be gone; but she has taken a chair in the chimney-corner, and says nothing shall stir her from it till she gets leave to come in here."

"What does she want?" asked Mrs. Eshton.

"'To tell the gentry their fortunes,' she says, ma'am; and she swears she must and will do it."

"What is she like?" inquired the Misses Eshton in a breath.

"A shockingly ugly old creature, miss; almost as black as a crock."

"Why, she's a real sorceress!" cried Frederick Lynn. "Let us have her in, of course."

"To be sure," rejoined his brother; "it would be a thousand pities to throw away such a chance of fun."

"My dear boys, what are you thinking about?" exclaimed Mrs. Lynn.

"I cannot possibly countenance any such inconsistent proceeding," chimed in the Dowager Ingram.

"Indeed, mama, but you can — and will," pronounced the haughty voice of Blanche, as she turned round on the piano-stool; where till now she had sat silent, apparently examining sundry sheets of music. "I have a curiosity to hear my fortune told: therefore, Sam, order the beldame forwards."

"My darling Blanche! recollect"—

"I do — I recollect all you can suggest; and I must have my will — quick, Sam!"

"Yes — yes — yes!" cried all the juveniles, both ladies and gentlemen. "Let her come — it will be excellent sport!"

The footman still lingered. "She looks such a rough one," said he.

"Go!" ejaculated Miss Ingram, and the man went.

Excitement instantly seized the whole party: a running fire of raillery and jests was proceeding when Sam returned.

"She won't come now," said he. "She says it's not her mission to appear before the 'vulgar herd' (them's her words). I must show her into a room by herself, and then those who wish to consult her must go to her one by one."

"You see now, my queenly Blanche," began Lady Ingram, "she encroaches. Be advised, my angel girl — and"—

"Show her into the library, of course," cut in the "angel girl."

"It is not my mission to listen to her before the vulgar herd either: I mean to have her all to myself. Is there a fire in the library?"

"Yes, ma'am — but she looks such a tinkler."

"Cease that chatter, blockhead! and do my bidding."

Again Sam vanished; and mystery, animation, expectation rose to full flow once more.

"She's ready now," said the footman, as he reappeared. "She wishes to know who will be her first visitor."

"I think I had better just look in upon her before any of the ladies go," said Colonel Dent.

"Tell her, Sam, a gentleman is coming."

Sam went and returned.

"She says, sir, that she'll have no gentlemen; they need not trouble themselves to come near her: nor," he added, with difficulty suppressing a titter, "any ladies either, except the young and single."

"By Jove, she has taste!" exclaimed Henry Lynn.

Miss Ingram rose solemnly: "I go first," she said, in a tone which might have befitted the leader of a forlorn hope, mounting a breach in the van of his men.

"Oh, my best! oh, my dearest! pause — reflect!" was her mama's cry; but she swept past her in stately silence, passed through the door which Colonel Dent held open, and we heard her enter the library.

A comparative silence ensued. Lady Ingram thought it "le cas" to wring her hands: which she did accordingly. Miss Mary declared she felt, for her part, she never dared venture. Amy and Louisa Eshton tittered under their breath, and looked a little frightened.

The minutes passed very slowly: fifteen were counted before the library-door again opened. Miss Ingram returned to us through the arch.

Would she laugh? Would she take it as a joke? All eyes met her with a glance of eager curiosity, and she met all eyes with one of rebuff and coldness: she looked neither flurried nor merry; she walked stiffly to her seat, and took it in silence.

"Well, Blanche?" said Lord Lngram.

"What did she say, sister?" asked Mary.

"What do you think? How do you feel? Is she a real fortune teller?" demanded the Misses Eshton.

"Now, now, good people," returned Miss Ingram, "don't press upon me. Really your organs of wonder and credulity are easily excited: you seem by the importance you all — my good mama included — ascribe to this matter — absolutely to believe we have a genuine witch in the house, who is in close alliance with the old gentleman. I have seen a gipsy vagabond; she has practised in hackneyed fashion the science of palmistry, and told me what such people usually tell. My whim is gratified; and now I think Mr. Eshton will do well to put the hag in the stocks to-morrow morning, as he threatened."

Miss Ingram took a book, leant back in her chair, and so declined further conversation. I watched her for nearly half an hour: during all that time she never turned a page, and her face grew momently darker, more dissatisfied, and more sourly expressive of disappointment. She had obviously not heard anything to her advantage: and it seemed to me, from her prolonged fit of gloom and taciturnity, that she herself, notwithstanding her professed indifference, attached undue importance to whatever revelations had been made her.

Meantime, Mary Ingram, Amy and Louisa Eshton, declared they dared not go alone; and yet they all wished to go. A negotiation was opened through the medium of the ambassador, Sam; and after much pacing to and fro, till, I think, the said Sam's calves must have ached with the exercise, permission was at last, with great difficulty, extorted from the rigorous Sybil, for the three to wait upon her in a body.

Their visit was not so still as Miss Ingram's had been: we heard hysterical giggling and little shrieks proceeding from the library; and at the end of about twenty minutes they burst the door open, and came running across the hall, as if they were half-scared out of their wits.

"I'm sure she is something not right!" they cried, one and all. "She told us such things! She knows all about us!" and they sank breathless into the various seats the gentlemen hastened to bring them.

Pressed for further explanation, they declared she had told them of things they had said and done when they were mere children; described books and ornaments they had in their boudoirs at home: keepsakes that different relations had presented to them. They affirmed that she had even divined their thoughts, and had whispered in the ear of each the name of the person she liked best in the world, and informed them of what they most wished for.

Here the gentlemen interposed with earnest petitions to be further enlightened on these two last-named points; but they got only blushes, ejaculations, tremors, and titters, in return for their importunity. The matrons, meantime, offered vinaigrettes and wielded fans; and again and again reiterated the expression of their concern that their warning had not been taken in time; and the elder gentlemen laughed, and the younger urged their services on the agitated fair ones.

In the midst of the tumult, and while my eyes and ears were fully engaged in the scene before me, I heard a hem close at my elbow: I turned, and saw Sam.

"If you please, Miss, the gipsy declares that there is another young single lady in the room who has not been to her yet, and she swears she will not go till she has seen all. I thought it must be you: there is no one else for it. What shall I tell her?"

"Oh, I will go by all means," I answered; and I was glad of the unexpected opportunity to gratify my much-excited curiosity. I slipped out of the room, unobserved by any eye—for the company were gathered in one mass about the trembling trio just returned—and I closed the door quietly behind me.

"If you like, miss," said Sam, "I'll wait in the hall for you; and if she frightens you, just call and I'll come in."

"No, Sam, return to the kitchen: I am not in the least afraid." Nor was I; but I was a good deal interested and excited.

## CHAPTER XIX

THE library looked tranquil enough as I entered it, and the Sybil — if Sybil she were — was seated snugly enough in an easy chair at the chimney-corner. She had on a red cloak and a black bonnet; or rather, a broad-brimmed gipsy hat, tied down with a striped handkerchief under the chin. An extinguished candle stood on the table; she was bending over the fire, and seemed reading in a little black book, like a prayer-book, by the light of the blaze; she muttered the words to herself, as most old women do, while she read; she did not desist immediately on my entrance: it appeared she wished to finish a paragraph.

I stood on the rug and warmed my hands, which were rather cold with sitting at a distance from the drawing-room fire. I felt now as composed as ever I did in my life: there was nothing indeed in the gipsy's appearance to trouble one's calm. She shut her book and slowly looked up; her hat-brim partially shaded her face, yet I could see, as she raised it, that it was a strange one. It looked all brown and black: elf-locks bristled out from beneath a white band which passed under her chin, and came half over her cheeks, or rather jaws; her eye confronted me at once, with a bold and direct gaze.

"Well, and you want your fortune told?" she said in a voice as decided as her glance, as harsh as her features.

"I don't care about it, mother; you may please yourself: but I ought to warn you, I have no faith."

"It's like your impudence to say so: I expected it of you; I heard it in your step as you crossed the threshold."

"Did you? You've a quick ear."

"I have; and a quick eye, and a quick brain."

"You need them all in your trade."

"I do; especially when I've customers like you to deal with. Why don't you tremble?"

"I'm not cold."

"Why don't you turn pale?"

"I'm not sick."

"Why don't you consult my art?"

"I'm not silly."

The old crone "nichered" a laugh under her bonnet and bandage: she then drew out a short black pipe, and lighting it began to smoke. Having indulged a while in this sedative, she raised her bent body, took the pipe from her lips, and while gazing steadily at the fire, said very deliberately: —

"You are cold; you are sick; and you are silly."

"Prove it," I rejoined.

"I will; in a few words. You are cold, because you are alone. no contact strikes the fire from you that is in you. You are sick: because the best of feelings, the highest and the sweetest given to man, keeps far away from you. You are silly, because, suffer as you may, you will not beckon it to approach; nor will you stir one step to meet it where it waits you."

She again put her short, black pipe to her lips, and renewed her smoking with vigour.

"You might say all that to almost any one who, you knew, lived as a solitary dependant in a great house."

"I might say it to almost any one; but would it be true of almost any one?"

"In my circumstances."

"Yes; just so, in *your* circumstances: but find me another precisely placed as you are."

"It would be easy to find you thousands."

"You could scarcely find me one. If you knew it, you are peculiarly situated: very near happiness; yes; within reach of it. The materials are all prepared; there only wants a movement to combine them. Chance laid them somewhat apart; let them be once approached and bliss results."

"I don't understand enigmas. I never could guess a riddle in my life."

"If you wish me to speak more plainly, show me your palm."

"And I must cross it with silver, I suppose?"

"To be sure."

I gave her a shilling: she put it into an old stocking-foot which she took out of her pocket, and having tied it round and returned it, she told me to hold out my hand. I did. She approached her face to the palm, and pored over it without touching it.

"It is too fine," said she. "I can make nothing of such a hand as that; almost without lines; besides, what is in a palm? Destiny is not written there."

"I believe you," said I.

"No," she continued, "it is in the face: on the forehead, about the eyes, in the eyes themselves, in the lines of the mouth. Kneel, and lift up your head."

"Ah! now you are coming to reality," I said as I obeyed her. "I shall begin to put some faith in you presently."

I knelt within half a yard of her. She stirred the fire, so that a ripple of light broke from the disturbed coal: the glare, however, as she sat, only threw her face into deeper shadow: mine, it illumined.

"I wonder with what feelings you came to me to-night," she said, when she had examined me a while. "I wonder what thoughts are busy in your heart during all the hours you sit in yonder room with the fine people flitting before you like shapes in a magic lantern: just as little sympathetic communion passing between you and them, as if they were really mere shadows of human forms, and not the actual substance."

"I feel tired often, sleepy sometimes; but seldom sad."

"Then you have some secret hope to buoy you up and please you with whispers of the future?"

"Not I. The utmost I hope is, to save money enough out of my earnings to set up a school some day in a little house rented by myself."

"A mean nutriment for the spirit to exist on: and sitting in that window-seat (you see I know your habits)"—

"You have learned them from the servants."

"Ah! you think yourself sharp. Well — perhaps I have: to speak truth, I have an acquaintance with one of them — Mrs. Poole"—

I started to my feet when I heard the name.

"You have — have you?" thought I; "there is diablerie in the business after all, then!"

"Don't be alarmed," continued the strange being; "she's a safe hand, is Mrs. Poole: close and quiet: any one may repose confidence in her. But, as I was saying: sitting in that window-seat, do you think of nothing but your future school? Have you no present interest in any of the company who occupy the sofas and chairs before you? Is there not one face you study? One figure whose movements you follow with, at least, curiosity?"

"I like to observe all the faces, and all the figures."

"But do you never single one from the rest — or it may be, two?"

"I do, frequently; when the gestures or looks of a pair seem telling a tale: it amuses me to watch them."

"What tale do you like best to hear?"

"Oh, I have not much choice! They generally run on the same theme — courtship; and promise to end in the same catastrophe — marriage."

"And do you like that monotonous theme?"

"Positively, I don't care about it: it is nothing to me."

"Nothing to you? When a lady, young and full of life and health, charming with beauty and endowed with the gifts of rank and fortune, sits and smiles in the eyes of a gentleman you"—

"I what?"

"You know — and, perhaps, think well of."

"I don't know the gentlemen here. I have scarcely interchanged a syllable with one of them; and as to thinking well of them, I consider some respectable and stately, and middle-aged, and others young, dashing, handsome and lively; but certainly they are all at liberty to be the recipients of whose smiles they please, without my feeling disposed to consider the transaction of any moment to me."

"You don't know the gentlemen here? You have not exchanged a syllable with one of them? Will you say that of the master of the house?"

"He is not at home."

"A profound remark! A most ingenious quibble! He went to Millcote this morning, and will be back here to-night, or to-morrow: does that circumstance exclude him from the list of your acquaintance — blot him, as it were, out of existence?"

"No: but I can scarcely see what Mr. Rochester has to do with the theme you had introduced."

"I was talking of ladies smiling in the eyes of gentlemen; and of late so many smiles have been shed into Mr. Rochester's eyes that they overflow like two cups filled above the brim: have you never remarked that?"

"Mr. Rochester has a right to enjoy the society of his guests."

"No question about his right: but have you never observed that, of all the tales told here about matrimony, Mr. Rochester has been favoured with the most lively and the most continuous?"

"The eagerness of a listener quickens the tongue of a narrator." I said this rather to myself than to the gipsy; whose strange talk, voice, manner, had by this time wrapped me in a kind of dream. One unexpected sentence came from her lips after another, till I got involved in a web of mystification; and wondered what unseen spirit had been sitting for weeks by my heart watching its workings, and taking record of every pulse.

"Eagerness of a listener!" repeated she: "yes; Mr. Rochester has sat by the hour, his ear inclined to the fascinating lips that took such delight in their task of communicating; and Mr. Rochester was so willing to receive and looked so grateful for the pastime given him: you have noticed this?"

"Grateful! I cannot remember detecting gratitude in his face."

"Detecting! You have analysed, then. And what did you detect, if not gratitude?"

I said nothing.

"You have seen love: have you not?—and, looking forward, you have seen him married, and beheld his bride happy?"

"Humph! Not exactly. Your witch's skill is rather at fault sometimes."

"What the devil have you seen, then?"

"Never mind: I came here to inquire, not to confess. Is it known that Mr. Rochester is to be married?"

"Yes; and to the beautiful Miss Ingram."

"Shortly?"

"Appearances would warrant that conclusion; and, no doubt (though, with an audacity that wants chastising out of you, you seem to question it), they will be a superlatively happy pair. He must love such a handsome, noble, witty, accomplished lady; and probably she loves him: or, if not his person, at least his purse. I know she considers the Rochester estate eligible to the last degree; though (God pardon me!) I told her something on that point about an hour ago, which made her look wondrous grave: the corners of her mouth fell half an inch. I would advise her black-aviced suitor to look out: if another comes, with a longer or clearer rent-roll,—he's dished"—

"But, mother, I did not come to hear Mr. Rochester's fortune: I came to hear my own; and you have told me nothing of it."

"Your fortune is yet doubtful: when I examined your face, one trait contradicted another. Chance has meted you a measure of happiness: that I know. I knew it before I came here this evening. She has laid it carefully on one side for you. I saw her do it. It depends on yourself to stretch out your hand, and take it up: but whether you will do so, is the problem I study. Kneel again on the rug."

"Don't keep me long; the fire scorches me."

I knelt. She did not stoop towards me, but only gazed, leaning back in her chair. She began muttering,—

"The flame flickers in the eye; the eye shines like dew; it looks soft and full of feeling; it smiles at my jargon: it is susceptible; impression follows impression through its clear sphere; where it ceases to smile, it is sad; an unconscious lassitude weighs on the lid: that signifies melancholy resulting from loneliness. It turns from me; it will not suffer farther scrutiny; it seems to deny, by a mocking glance, the truth of the discoveries I have already made,— to disown the charge both of sensibility and chagrin: its pride and reserve only confirm me in my opinion. The eye is favourable.

"As to the mouth, it delights at times in laughter; it is disposed to impart all that the brain conceives; though I daresay it would be silent on much the heart experiences. Mobile and flexible, it was never intended to be compressed in the eternal silence of solitude: it is a mouth which should speak much and smile often, and have human affection for its interlocutor. That feature too is propitious.

"I see no enemy to a fortunate issue but in the brow; and that brow professes to say,—'I can live alone, if self-respect and circumstances require me so to do. I need not sell my soul to buy bliss. I have an inward treasure, born with me, which can keep me alive if all extraneous delights should be withheld; or offered only at a price I cannot afford to give.' The forehead declares, 'Reason sits firm and holds the reins, and she will not let the feelings burst away and hurry her to wild chasms. The passions may rage furiously, like true heathens, as they are; and the desires may imagine all sorts of vain things: but judgment shall still have the last word in every argument, and the casting vote in every decision. Strong wind, earthquake-shock, and fire may pass by: but I shall follow the guiding of that still small voice which interprets the dictates of conscience.'

"Well said, forehead; your declaration shall be respected. I have formed my plans — right plans I deem them — and in them I have attended to the claims of conscience, the counsels of reason. I know how soon youth would fade and bloom perish, if, in the cup of bliss offered, but one dreg of shame, or one flavour of remorse were detected; and I do not want sacrifice, sorrow, dissolution — such is not my taste. I wish to foster, not to blight — to earn gratitude, not to wring tears of blood — no, nor of brine: my harvest must be in smiles, in endearments, in sweet — That will do. I think I rave in a kind of exquisite delirium. I should wish now to protract this moment *ad infinitum;* but I dare not. So far I have governed myself thoroughly. I have acted as I inwardly swore I would act; but farther might try me beyond my strength. Rise, Miss Eyre: leave me; 'the play is played out.'"

Where was I? Did I wake or sleep? Had I been dreaming? Did I dream still? The old woman's voice had changed: her accent, her gesture, and all were familiar to me as my own face in a glass — as the speech of my own tongue. I got up, but did not go. I looked; I stirred the fire, and I looked again: but she drew her bonnet and her bandage closer about her face, and again beckoned me to depart. The flame illuminated her hand stretched out; roused now, and on the alert for discoveries, I at once noticed that hand. It was no more the withered limb of eld than my own; it was a rounded supple member, with smooth fingers, symmetrically turned; a broad ring flashed on the little finger, and stooping forward, I looked at it, and saw a gem I had seen a hundred times before. Again I looked at the face; which was no longer turned from me — on the contrary, the bonnet was doffed, the bandage displaced, the head advanced.

"Well, Jane, do you know me?" asked the familiar voice.

"Only take off the red cloak, sir, and then"——

"But the string is in a knot — help me."

"Break it, sir."

"There, then —'Off, ye lendings!'" And Mr. Rochester stepped out of his disguise.

"Now, sir, what a strange idea!"

"But well carried out, eh? Don't you think so?"

"With the ladies you must have managed well."

"But not with you?"

"You did not act the character of a gipsy with me."

"What character did I act? My own?"

"No; some unaccountable one. In short, I believe you have been trying to draw me out — or in; you have been talking nonsense to make me talk nonsense. It is scarcely fair, sir."

"Do you forgive me, Jane?"

"I cannot tell till I have thought it all over. If, on reflection, I find I have fallen into no great absurdity, I shall try to forgive you; but it was not right."

"Oh! you have been very correct — very careful, very sensible."

I reflected, and thought, on the whole, I had. It was a comfort; but, indeed, I had been on my guard almost from the beginning of the interview. Something of masquerade I suspected. I knew gipsies and fortune-tellers did not express themselves as this seeming old woman had expressed herself; besides, I had noted her feigned voice, her anxiety to conceal her features. But my mind had been running on Grace Poole — that living enigma, that mystery of mysteries, as I considered her. I had never thought of Mr. Rochester.

"Well," said he, "what are you musing about? What does that grave smile signify?"

"Wonder and self-congratulation, sir. I have your permission to retire now, I suppose?"

"No; stay a moment; and tell me what the people in the drawing-room yonder are doing."

"Discussing the gipsy, I daresay."

"Sit down! — let me hear what they said about me."

"I had better not stay long, sir; it must be near eleven o'clock. Oh! are you aware, Mr. Rochester, that a stranger has arrived here since you left this morning?"

"A stranger! — no; who can it be? I expected no one; is he gone?"

"No; he said he had known you long, and that he could take the liberty of installing himself here till you returned."

"The devil he did! Did he give his name?"

"His name is Mason, sir; and he comes from the West Indies; from Spanish Town, in Jamaica, I think."

Mr. Rochester was standing near me; he had taken my hand, as if to lead me to a chair. As I spoke, he gave my wrist a convulsive grip; the smile on his lips froze: apparently a spasm caught his breath.

"Mason! — the West Indies!" he said, in the tone one might fancy a speaking automaton to enounce its single words; "Mason! — the West Indies!" he reiterated; and he went over the syllables three times, growing, in the intervals of speaking, whiter than ashes: he hardly seemed to know what he was doing.

"Do you feel ill, sir?" I inquired.

"Jane, I've got a blow; — I've got a blow, Jane!" He staggered.

"Oh! — lean on me, sir."

"Jane, you offered me your shoulder once before; let me have it now."

"Yes, sir, yes; and my arm."

He sat down, and made me sit beside him. Holding my hand in both his own, he chafed it; gazing on me, at the same time, with the most troubled and dreary look.

"My little friend!" said he, "I wish I were in a quiet island with only you; and trouble, and danger, and hideous recollections removed from me."

"Can I help you, sir? — I'd give my life to serve you."

"Jane, if aid is wanted, I'll seek it at your hands; I promise you that."

"Thank you, sir; tell me what to do, — I'll try, at least, to do it."

"Fetch me now, Jane, a glass of wine from the dining-room; they will be at supper there; and tell me if Mason is with them, and what he is doing."

I went. I found all the party in the dining-room at supper, as Mr. Rochester had said; they were not seated at table, — the supper was arranged on the side-board; each had taken what he chose, and they stood about here and there in groups, their plates and glasses in their hands. Every one seemed in high glee; laughter and conversation were general and animated. Mr. Mason stood near the fire, talking to Colonel and Mrs. Dent, and appeared as merry as any of them. I filled a wine-glass (I saw Miss Ingram watch me frowningly as I did so: she thought I was taking a liberty, I daresay), and I returned to the library.

Mr. Rochester's extreme pallor had disappeared, and he looked once more firm and stern. He took the glass from my hand.

"Here is to your health, ministrant spirit!" he said: he swallowed the contents and returned it to me. "What are they doing, Jane?"

"Laughing and talking, sir."

"They don't look grave and mysterious, as if they had heard something strange?"

"Not at all: — they are full of jests and gaiety."

"And Mason?"

"He was laughing too."

"If all these people came in a body and spat at me, what would you do, Jane?"

"Turn them out of the room, sir, if I could."

He half smiled. "But if I were to go to them, and they only looked at me coldly, and whispered sneeringly amongst each other, and then dropt off and left me one by one, what then? Would you go with them?"

"I rather think not, sir: I should have more pleasure in staying with you."

"To comfort me?"

"Yes, sir, to comfort you, as well as I could."

"And if they laid you under a ban for adhering to me?"

"I, probably, should know nothing about their ban; and if I did, I should care nothing about it."

"Then, you could dare censure for my sake?"

"I could dare it for the sake of any friend who deserved my adherence; as you, I am sure, do."

"Go back now into the room; step quietly up to Mason, and whisper in his ear that Mr. Rochester is come and wishes to see him: show him in here and then leave me."

"Yes, sir."

I did his behest. The company all stared at me as I passed straight among them. I sought Mr. Mason, delivered the message, and preceded him from the room: I ushered him into the library, and then I went upstairs.

At a late hour, after I had been in bed some time, I heard the visitors repair to their chambers: I distinguished Mr. Rochester's voice, and heard him say, "This way, Mason; this is your room."

He spoke cheerfully: the gay tones set my heart at ease. I was soon asleep.

## CHAPTER XX

I HAD forgotten to draw my curtain, which I usually did; and also to let down my window-blind. The consequence was, that when the moon, which was full and bright (for the night was fine), came in her course to that space in the sky opposite my casement, and looked in at me through the unveiled panes, her glorious gaze roused me. Awakening in the dead of night, I opened my eyes on her disk — silver-white and crystal-clear. It was beautiful, but too solemn: I half rose, and stretched my arm to draw the curtain.

Good God! What a cry!

The night — its silence — its rest, was rent in twain by a savage, a sharp, a shrilly sound that ran from end to end of Thornfield Hall.

My pulse stopped: my heart stood still; my stretched arm was paralysed. The cry died, and was not renewed. Indeed, whatever being uttered that fearful shriek could not soon repeat it: not the widest-winged condor on the Andes could, twice in succession, send out such a yell from the cloud shrouding his eyrie. The thing delivering such utterance must rest ere it could repeat the effort.

It came out of the third story; for it passed overhead. And overhead — yes, in the room just above my chamber-ceiling — I now heard a struggle: a deadly one it seemed from the noise; and a half-smothered voice shouted —

"Help! help! help!" three times rapidly.

"Will no one come?" it cried; and then, while the staggering and stamping went on wildly, I distinguished through plank and plaster: —

"Rochester! Rochester! for God's sake, come!"

A chamber-door opened: some one ran, or rushed, along the gallery. Another step stamped on the flooring above and something fell; and there was silence.

I put on some clothes, though horror shook all my limbs: I issued from my apartment. The sleepers were all aroused: ejaculations, terrified murmurs sounded in every room; door after door unclosed;

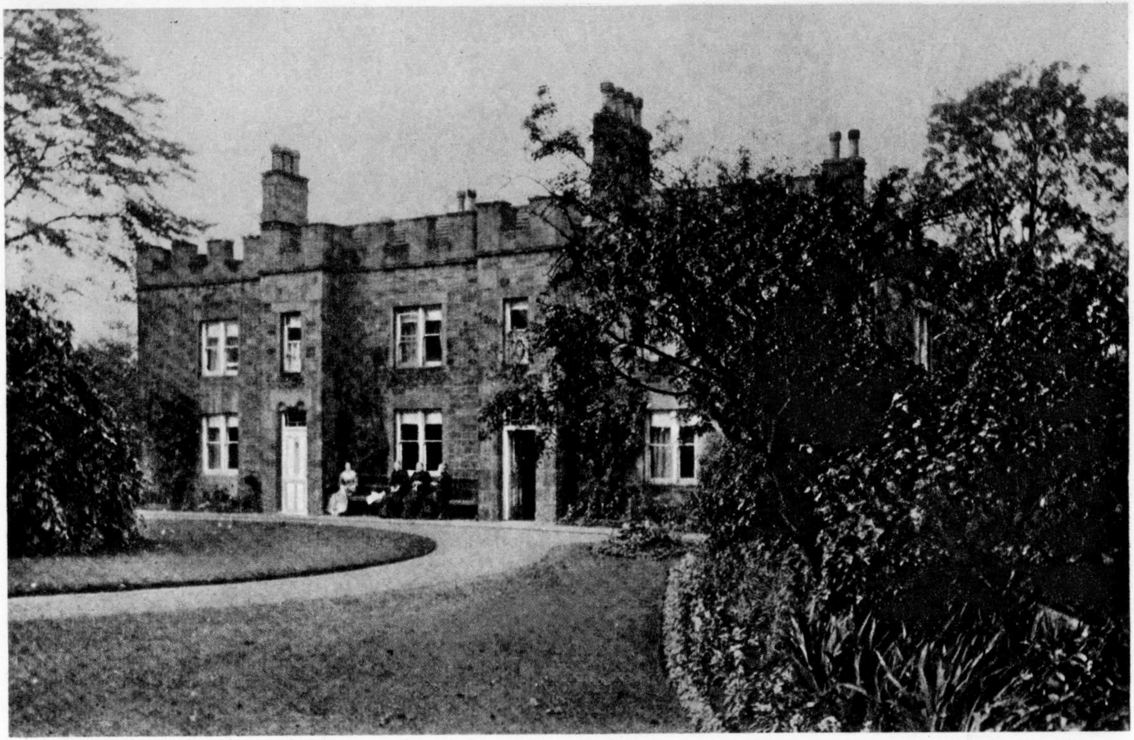

THE RYDINGS

The Rydings was the home of Charlotte Brontë's lifelong friend, Ellen Nussey, whom she visited there. "Thornfield," Mr. Rochester's seat in *Jane Eyre*, is in the main drawn from The Rydings, with some features taken from another house called Norton Conyers. "Thornfield," says Jane Eyre, "was three stories high, of proportions not vast though considerable: a gentleman's manor-house, not a nobleman's seat; battlements round the top gave it a picturesque look." Until recently, it was possible to see at The Rydings the lightning-struck tree of *Jane Eyre*, held together by iron hoops.

one looked out and another looked out; the gallery filled. Gentlemen and ladies alike had quitted their beds; and "Oh! what is it?" —"Who is hurt?"—"What has happened?"—"Fetch a light!" —"Is it fire?"—"Are there robbers?"—"Where shall we run?" was demanded confusedly on all hands. But for the moonlight they would have been in complete darkness. They ran to and fro; they crowded together: some sobbed, some stumbled: the confusion was inextricable.

"Where the devil is Rochester?" cried Colonel Dent. "I cannot find him in his bed."

"Here! here!" was shouted in return. "Be composed, all of you: I'm coming."

And the door at the end of the gallery opened, and Mr. Rochester advanced with a candle: he had just descended from the upper story. One of the ladies ran to him directly; she seized his arm: it was Miss Ingram.

"What awful event has taken place?" said she. "Speak! let us know the worst at once!"

"But don't pull me down or strangle me," he replied: for the Misses Eshton were clinging about him now; and the two dowagers, in vast white wrappers, were bearing down on him like ships in full sail.

"All's right! — all's right!" he cried. "It's a mere rehearsal of Much Ado About Nothing. Ladies, keep off; or I shall wax dangerous."

And dangerous he looked: his black eyes darted sparks. Calming himself by an effort, he added: —

"A servant has had the nightmare; that is all. She's an excitable, nervous person: she construed her dream into an apparition, or something of that sort, no doubt; and has taken a fit with fright. Now then, I must see you all back into your rooms; for, till the house is settled, she cannot be looked after. Gentlemen, have the goodness to set the ladies the example. Miss Ingram, I am sure you will not fail in evincing superiority to idle terrors. Amy and Louisa, return to your nests like a pair of doves, as you are. Mesdames" (to the dowagers), "you will take cold to a dead certainty, if you stay in this chill gallery any longer."

And so, by dint of alternate coaxing and commanding, he contrived to get them all once more enclosed in their separate dormitories.

I did not wait to be ordered back to mine; but retreated unnoticed: as unnoticed as I had left it.

Not, however, to go to bed: on the contrary, I began and dressed myself carefully. The sounds I had heard after the scream, and the words that had been uttered, had probably been heard only by me; for they had proceeded from the room above mine: but they assured me that it was not a servant's dream which had thus struck horror through the house; and that the explanation Mr. Rochester had given was merely an invention framed to pacify his guests. I dressed, then, to be ready for emergencies. When dressed, I sat a long time by the window, looking out over the silent grounds and silvered fields, and waiting for I knew not what. It seemed to me that some event must follow the strange cry, struggle, and call.

No: stillness returned: each murmur and movement ceased gradually, and in about an hour Thornfield Hall was again as hushed as a desert. It seemed that sleep and night had resumed their empire. Meantime the moon declined: she was about to set. Not liking to sit in the cold and darkness, I thought I would lie down on my bed, dressed as I was. I left the window, and moved with little noise across the carpet; as I stooped to take off my shoes, a cautious hand tapped low at the door.

"Am I wanted?" I asked.

"Are you up?" asked the voice I expected to hear, viz., my master's.

"Yes, sir."

"And dressed?"

"Yes."

"Come out, then, quietly."

I obeyed. Mr. Rochester stood in the gallery, holding a light.

"I want you," he said: "come this way: take your time, and make no noise."

My slippers were thin: I could walk the matted floor as softly as a cat. He glided up the gallery and up the stairs, and stopped in the dark, low corridor of the fateful third story: I had followed and stood at his side.

"Have you a sponge in your room?" he asked in a whisper.

"Yes, sir."

"Have you any salts—volatile salts?"

"Yes."

"Go back and fetch both."

I returned, sought the sponge on the wash-stand, the salts in my drawer, and once more retraced my steps. He still waited; he held a key in his hand: approaching one of the small, black doors, he put it in the lock; he paused and addressed me again.

"You don't turn sick at the sight of blood?"

"I think I shall not: I have never been tried yet."

I felt a thrill while I answered him; but no coldness, and no faintness.

"Just give me your hand," he said; "it will not do to risk a fainting fit."

I put my fingers into his. "Warm and steady," was his remark: he turned the key and opened the door.

I saw a room I remembered to have seen before; the day Mrs. Fairfax showed me over the house: it was hung with tapestry; but the tapestry was now looped up in one part, and there was a door apparent, which had then been concealed. This door was open; a light shone out of the room within: I heard thence a snarling, snatching sound, almost like a dog quarrelling. Mr. Rochester, putting down his candle, said to me, "Wait a minute," and he went forward to the inner apartment. A shout of laughter greeted his entrance; noisy at first, and terminating in Grace Poole's own goblin ha! ha! *She* then was there. He made some sort of arrangement, without speaking: though I heard a low voice address him: he came out and closed the door behind him.

"Here, Jane!" he said; and I walked round to the other side of a large bed, which with its drawn curtains concealed a considerable portion of the chamber. An easy-chair was near the bed-head: a man sat in it, dressed with the exception of his coat; he was still; his head leant back; his eyes were closed. Mr. Rochester held the candle over him; I recognised in his pale and seemingly lifeless face — the stranger, Mason: I saw too that his linen on one side, and one arm, was almost soaked in blood.

"Hold the candle," said Mr. Rochester, and I took it; he fetched a basin of water from the wash-stand: "Hold that," said he. I obeyed. He took the sponge, dipped it in and moistened the corpse-like face: he asked for my smelling-bottle, and applied it to the nostrils. Mr. Mason shortly unclosed his eyes; he groaned. Mr. Rochester opened the shirt of the wounded man, whose arm and shoulder were bandaged: he sponged away blood, trickling fast down.

"Is there immediate danger?" murmured Mr. Mason.

"Pooh! No — a mere scratch. Don't be so overcome, man: bear up! I'll fetch a surgeon for you now, myself: you'll be able to be removed by morning, I hope. Jane," he continued.

"Sir?"

"I shall have to leave you in this room with this gentleman, for an hour, or perhaps two hours; you will sponge the blood as I do when it returns: if he feels faint, you will put the glass of water on that stand to his lips, and your salts to his nose. You will not speak to him on any pretext — and — Richard — it will be at the peril of your life if you speak to her: open your lips — agitate yourself — and I'll not answer for the consequences."

Again the poor man groaned: he looked as if he dared not move: fear, either of death or of something else, appeared almost to paralyse him. Mr. Rochester put the now bloody sponge into my hand, and I proceeded to use it as he had done. He watched me a second, then saying, "Remember! — No conversation," he left the room. I experienced a strange feeling as the key grated in the lock, and the sound of his retreating step ceased to be heard.

Here then I was in the third story, fastened into one of its mystic cells; night around me; a pale and bloody spectacle under my eyes and hands; a murderess hardly separated from me by a single door: yes — that was appalling — the rest I could bear; but I shuddered at the thought of Grace Poole bursting out upon me.

I must keep to my post, however. I must watch this ghastly countenance — these blue, still lips forbidden to unclose — these eyes now shut, now opening, now wandering through the room, now fixing on me, and ever glazed with the dulness of horror. I must dip my hand again and again in the basin of blood and water, and wipe away the trickling gore. I must see the light of the unsnuffed candle wane on my employment; the shadows darken on the wrought, antique tapestry round me, and grow black, under the hangings of the vast old bed, and quiver strangely over the doors of a great cabinet opposite — whose front, divided into twelve panels, bore, in grim design, the heads of the twelve apostles, each inclosed in its separate panel as in a frame; while above them at the top rose an ebon crucifix and a dying Christ.

According as the shifting obscurity and flickering gleam hovered here or glanced there, it was now the bearded physician, Luke, that bent his brow; now St. John's long hair that waved; and anon the devilish face of Judas, that grew out of the panel, and seemed gathering life and threatening a revelation of the arch-traitor — of Satan himself — in his subordinate's form.

Amidst all this, I had to listen as well as watch: to listen for the movements of the wild beast or the fiend in yonder side den. But since Mr. Rochester's visit it seemed spell-bound: all the night I heard but three sounds at three long intervals,— a step creak, a momentary renewal of the snarling, canine noise, and a deep human groan.

Then my own thoughts worried me. What crime was this, that lived incarnate in this sequestered mansion, and could neither be expelled nor subdued by the owner? — What mystery, that broke out, now in fire and now in blood, at the deadest hours of night? What creature was it, that, masked in an ordinary woman's face and shape, uttered the voice, now of a mocking demon, and anon of a carrion-seeking bird of prey?

And this man I bent over — this commonplace, quiet stranger — how had he become involved in the web of horror? and why had the Fury flown at him? What made him seek this quarter of the house at an untimely season, when he should have been asleep in bed? I had heard Mr. Rochester assign him an apartment below — what brought him here? And why, now, was he so tame under the violence or treachery done him? Why did he so quietly submit to the concealment Mr. Rochester enforced? Why *did* Mr. Rochester enforce this concealment? His guest had been outraged, his own life on a former occasion had been hideously plotted against; and both attempts he smothered in secrecy and sank in oblivion! Lastly, I saw Mr. Mason was submissive to Mr. Rochester; that the impetuous will of the latter held complete sway over the inertness of the former: the few words which had passed between them assured me of this. It was evident that in their former intercourse, the passive disposition of the one had been habitually influenced by the active energy of the other: whence then had arisen Mr. Rochester's dismay when he heard of Mr. Mason's arrival? Why had the mere name of this unresisting individual — whom his word now sufficed to control like a child — fallen on him, a few hours since, as a thunderbolt might fall on an oak?

Oh! I could not forget his look and his paleness when he whispered: "Jane, I have got a blow — I have got a blow, Jane." I could not forget how the arm had trembled which he rested on my shoulder: and it was no light matter which could thus bow the resolute spirit and thrill the vigorous frame of Fairfax Rochester.

"When will he come? When will he come?" I cried inwardly, as the night lingered and lingered — as my bleeding patient drooped, moaned, sickened: and neither day nor aid arrived. I had, again and again, held the water to Mason's white lips; again and again offered him the stimulating salts: my efforts seemed ineffectual: either bodily or mental suffering, or loss of blood, or all three combined, were fast prostrating his strength. He moaned so, and looked so weak, wild, and lost, I feared he was dying; and I might not even speak to him!

The candle, wasted at last, went out; as it expired, I perceived streaks of grey light edging the window curtains; dawn was then approaching. Presently I heard Pilot bark far below, out of his distant kennel in the court-yard: hope revived. Nor was it unwarranted: in five minutes more the grating key, the yielding lock, warned me my watch was relieved. It could not have lasted more than two hours: many a week has seemed shorter.

Mr. Rochester entered, and with him the surgeon he had been to fetch.

"Now, Carter, be on the alert," he said to this last: "I give you but half an hour for dressing the wound, fastening the bandages, getting the patient downstairs and all."

"But is he fit to move, sir?"

"No doubt of it; it is nothing serious: he is nervous, his spirits must be kept up. Come, set to work."

Mr. Rochester drew back the thick curtain, drew up the holland blind, let in all the daylight he could; and I was surprised and cheered to see how far dawn was advanced: what rosy streaks were beginning to brighten the east. Then he approached Mason, whom the surgeon was already handling.

"Now, my good fellow, how are you?" he asked.

"She's done for me, I fear," was the faint reply.

"Not a whit! — courage! This day fortnight you'll hardly be a pin the worse of it: you've lost a little blood; that's all. Carter, assure him there's no danger."

"I can do that conscientiously," said Carter, who had now undone the bandages; "only I wish I could have got here sooner: he would not have bled so much — but how is this? The flesh on the shoulder is torn as well as cut. This wound was not done with a knife: there have been teeth here!"

"She bit me," he murmured. "She worried me like a tigress, when Rochester got the knife from her."

"You should not have yielded: you should have grappled with her at once," said Mr. Rochester.

"But under such circumstances what could one do?" returned Mason. "Oh, it was frightful!" he added, shuddering. "And I did not expect it: she looked so quiet at first."

"I warned you," was his friend's answer; "I said — be on your guard when you go near her. Besides, you might have waited till to-morrow, and had me with you: it was mere folly to attempt the interview to-night, and alone."

"I thought I could have done some good."

"You thought! you thought! Yes; it makes me impatient to hear you: but, however, you have suffered, and are likely to suffer enough for not taking my advice; so I'll say no more. Carter — hurry! — hurry! The sun will soon rise, and I must have him off."

"Directly, sir; the shoulder is just bandaged. I must look to this other wound in the arm: she has had her teeth here too, I think."

"She sucked the blood: she said she'd drain my heart," said Mason.

I saw Mr. Rochester shudder: a singularly marked expression of disgust, horror, hatred, warped his countenance almost to distortion; but he only said: —

"Come, be silent, Richard, and never mind her gibberish: don't repeat it."

"I wish I could forget it," was the answer.

"You will when you are out of the country: when you get back to Spanish Town, you may think of her as dead and buried — or rather, you need not think of her at all."

"Impossible to forget this night!"

"It is not impossible: have some energy, man. You thought you were as dead as a herring two hours since, and you are all alive and talking now. There! — Carter has done with you or nearly so; I'll make you decent in a trice. Jane" (he turned to me for the first time since his re-entrance) "take this key: go down into my bedroom, and walk straight forward into my dressing-room; open the the top drawer of the wardrobe and take out a clean shirt and neck-handkerchief: bring them here; and be nimble."

I went; sought the repository he had mentioned, found the articles named, and returned with them.

"Now," said he, "go to the other side of the bed while I order his toilet; but don't leave the room: you may be wanted again."

I retired as directed.

"Was anybody stirring below when you went down, Jane?" inquired Mr. Rochester, presently.

"No, sir; all was very still."

"We shall get you off cannily, Dick: and it will be better, both for your sake, and for that of the poor creature in yonder. I have striven long to avoid exposure, and I should not like it to come at last. Here, Carter, help him on with his waistcoat. Where did you leave your furred cloak? You can't travel a mile without that, I know, in this damned cold climate. In your room? — Jane, run down to Mr. Mason's room,— the one next mine,— and fetch a cloak you will see there."

Again I ran, and again returned, bearing an immense mantle lined and edged with fur.

"Now, I've another errand for you," said my untiring master; "you must away to my room again. What a mercy you are shod with velvet, Jane! — a clod-hopping messenger would never do at this juncture. You must open the middle drawer of my toilet-table and take out a little phial and a little glass you will find there,— quick!"

I flew thither and back, bringing the desired vessels.

"That's well! Now, doctor, I shall take the liberty of administering a dose myself; on my own responsibility. I got this cordial at Rome, of an Italian charlatan — a fellow you would have kicked, Carter. It is not a thing to be used indiscriminately, but it is good upon occasion: as now, for instance. Jane, a little water."

He held out the tiny glass, and I half filled it from the water bottle on the wash-stand.

"That will do: — now wet the lip of the phial."

I did so: he measured twelve drops of a crimson liquid, and presented it to Mason.

"Drink, Richard: it will give you the heart you lack, for an hour or so."

"But will it hurt me?"—is it inflammatory?"

"Drink! drink! drink!"

Mr. Mason obeyed, because it was evidently useless to resist. He was dressed now: he still looked pale, but he was no longer gory and sullied. Mr. Rochester let him sit three minutes after he had swallowed the liquid; he then took his arm:—

"Now I am sure you can get on your feet," he said:—"try."

The patient rose.

"Carter, take him under the other shoulder. Be of good cheer, Richard; step out:—that's it!"

"I do feel better," remarked Mr. Mason.

"I am sure you do. Now, Jane, trip on before us away to the backstairs; unbolt the side-passage door, and tell the driver of the post-chaise you will see in the yard—or just outside, for I told him not to drive his rattling wheels over the pavement—to be ready; we are coming: and, Jane, if any one is about, come to the foot of the stairs and hem."

It was by this time half-past five, and the sun was on the point of rising; but I found the kitchen still dark and silent. The side-passage door was fastened; I opened it with as little noise as possible: all the yard was quiet; but the gates stood wide open, and there was a post-chaise, with horses ready harnessed, and driver seated on the box, stationed outside. I approached him, and said the gentlemen were coming; he nodded: and then I looked carefully round and listened. The stillness of early morning slumbered everywhere; the curtains were yet drawn over the servants' chamber windows; little birds were just twittering in the blossom-blanched orchard trees, whose boughs drooped like white garlands over the wall enclosing one side of the yard; the carriage horses stamped from time to time in their closed stables: all else was still.

The gentlemen now appeared. Mason, supported by Mr. Rochester and the surgeon, seemed to walk with tolerable ease: they assisted him into the chaise; Carter followed.

"Take care of him," said Mr. Rochester to the latter, "and keep him at your house till he is quite well: I shall ride over in a day or two to see how he gets on. Richard, how is it with you?"

"The fresh air revives me, Fairfax."

"Leave the window open on his side, Carter; there is no wind—good-by, Dick."

"Fairfax"——

"Well, what is it?"

"Let her be taken care of; let her be treated as tenderly as may be: let her"—— he stopped and burst into tears.

"I do my best; and have done it, and will do it," was the answer: he shut up the chaise door, and the vehicle drove away.

"Yet would to God there was an end of all this!" added Mr. Rochester, as he closed and barred the heavy yard-gates. This done, he moved with slow step and abstracted air towards a door in the wall bordering the orchard. I, supposing he had done with me, prepared to return to the house; again, however, I heard him call "Jane!" He had opened the portal and stood at it, waiting for me.

"Come where there is some freshness, for a few moments," he said; "that house is a mere dungeon: don't you feel it so?"

"It seems to me a splendid mansion, sir."

"The glamour of inexperience is over your eyes," he answered; "and you see it through a charmed medium: you cannot discern that the gilding is slime and the silk draperies cobwebs; that the marble is sordid slate, and the polished woods mere refuse chips and scaly bark. Now *here* (he pointed to the leafy enclosure we had entered) all is real, sweet, and pure."

He strayed down a walk edged with box; with apple trees, pear trees, and cherry trees on one side, and a border on the other, full of all sorts of old-fashioned flowers, stocks, sweet-williams, primroses, pansies, mingled with southern-wood, sweet-briar, and various fragrant herbs. They were fresh now as a succession of April showers and gleams, followed by a lovely spring morning, could make them: the sun was just entering the dappled east, and his light illumined the wreathed and dewy orchard trees and shone down the quiet walks under them.

"Jane, will you have a flower?"

He gathered a half-blown rose, the first on the bush, and offered it to me.

"Thank you, sir."

"Do you like this sunrise, Jane? That sky with its high and light clouds which are sure to melt away as the day waxes warm — this placid and balmy atmosphere?"

"I do, very much."

"You have passed a strange night, Jane?"

"Yes, sir."

"And it has made you look pale — were you afraid when I left you alone with Mason?"

"I was afraid of some one coming out of the inner room."

"But I had fastened the door — I had the key in my pocket: I should have been a careless shepherd if I had left a lamb — my pet lamb — so near a wolf's den, unguarded: you were safe."

"Will Grace Poole live here still, sir?"

"Oh, yes! don't trouble your head about her — put the thing out of your thoughts."

"Yet it seems to me your life is hardly secure while she stays."

"Never fear — I will take care of myself."

"Is the danger you apprehended last night gone by now, sir?"

"I cannot vouch for that till Mason is out of England: nor even then. To live, for me, Jane, is to stand on a crater-crust which may crack and spue fire any day."

"But Mr. Mason seems a man easily led. Your influence, sir, is evidently potent with him: he will never set you at defiance, or wilfully injure you."

"Oh, no! Mason will not defy me; nor, knowing it, will he hurt me — but, unintentionally, he might in a moment, by one careless word, deprive me, if not of life, yet for ever of happiness."

"Tell him to be cautious, sir: let him know what you fear, and show him how to avert the danger."

He laughed sardonically, hastily took my hand, and as hastily threw it from him.

"If I could do that, simpleton, where would the danger be? Annihilated in a moment. Ever since I have known Mason, I have only had to say to him, 'Do that,' and the thing has been done. But I cannot give him orders in this case: I cannot say 'Beware of harming me, Richard;' for it is imperative that I should keep him ignorant that harm to me is possible. Now you look puzzled; and I will puzzle you farther. You are my little friend, are you not?"

"I like to serve you, sir, and to obey you in all that is right."

"Precisely: I see you do. I see genuine contentment in your gait, and mien, your eye and face, when you are helping me and pleasing me — working for me, and with me, in, as you characteristically say, *'all that is right,'* for if I bid you do what you thought wrong, there would be no light-footed running, no neat-handed alacrity, no lively glance and animated complexion. My friend would then turn to me, quiet and pale, and would say, 'No, sir; that is impossible: I cannot do it, because it is wrong;' and would become immutable as a fixed star. Well, you too have power over me, and may injure me: yet I dare not show you where I am vulnerable, lest, faithful and friendly as you are, you should transfix me at once."

"If you have no more to fear from Mr. Mason than you have from me, sir, you are very safe."

"God grant it may be so! Here, Jane, is an arbour; sit down."

The arbour was an arch in the wall, lined with ivy; it contained a rustic seat. Mr. Rochester took it, leaving room, however, for me: but I stood before him.

"Sit," he said; "the bench is long enough for two. You don't hesitate to take a place at my side, do you? Is that wrong, Jane?"

I answered him by assuming it: to refuse would, I felt, have been unwise.

"Now, my little friend, while the sun drinks the dew — while all the flowers in this old garden awake and expand, and the birds fetch their young ones' breakfast out of the Thornfield, and the early bees do their first spell of work — I'll put a case to you; which you must endeavour to suppose your own: but first, look at me, and tell me you are at ease, and not fearing that I err in detaining you, or that you err in staying."

"No, sir; I am content."

"Well, then, Jane, call to aid your fancy: — suppose you were no longer a girl well reared and disciplined, but a wild boy indulged from childhood upwards; imagine yourself in a remote foreign land; conceive that you there commit a capital error, no matter of what nature or from what motives, but one whose consequences must follow you through life and taint all your existence. Mind, I don't say a *crime;* I am not speaking of shedding of blood or any other guilty act, which might make the perpetrator amenable to the law: my word is *error.* The results of what you have done become in time to you utterly insupportable; you take measures to obtain relief: unusual measures, but neither unlawful nor culpable. Still you are miserable; for hope has quitted you on the very confines of life: your sun at noon darkens in an eclipse, which you feel will not leave it till the time of setting. Bitter and base associations have become the sole food of your memory: you wander here and there, seeking rest in exile: happiness in pleasure — I mean in heartless, sensual pleasure — such as dulls intellect and blights feeling. Heart-weary and soul-withered, you come home after years of voluntary banishment; you make a new acquaintance — how or where no matter: you find in this stranger much of the good and bright qualities which you have sought for twenty years, and never before encountered; and they are all fresh, healthy, without soil and without taint. Such society revives, regenerates: you feel better days come back — higher wishes, purer feelings; you desire to recommence your life, and to spend what remains to you of days in a way more worthy of an immortal being. To attain this end, are you justified in over-leaping an obstacle of custom — a mere conventional impediment, which neither your conscience sanctifies nor your judgment approves?"

He paused for an answer: and what was I to say? Oh, for some good spirit to suggest a judicious and satisfactory response! Vain aspiration! The west wind whispered in the ivy round me; but no gentle Ariel borrowed its breath as a medium of speech: the birds sang in the tree-tops; but their song, however sweet, was inarticulate.

Again Mr. Rochester propounded his query:

"Is the wandering and sinful, but now rest-seeking and repentant, man justified in daring the world's opinion, in order to attach to him for ever this gentle, gracious, genial stranger; thereby securing his own peace of mind and regeneration of life?"

"Sir," I answered, "a wanderer's repose or a sinner's reformation should never depend on a fellow-creature. Men and women die; philosophers falter in wisdom, and Christians in goodness: if any one you know suffered and erred, let him look higher than his equals for strength to amend, and solace to heal."

"But the instrument — the instrument! God, who does the work, ordains the instrument. I have myself — I tell it you without parable — been a worldly, dissipated, restless man; and I believe I have found the instrument for my cure, in"——

He paused: the birds went on carolling, the leaves lightly rustling.

I almost wondered they did not check their songs and whispers to catch the suspended revelation: but they would have had to wait many minutes — so long was the silence protracted. At last I looked up at the tardy speaker: he was looking eagerly at me.

"Little friend," said he, in quite a changed tone — while his face changed too; losing all its softness and gravity, and becoming harsh and sarcastic —"you have noticed my tender penchant for Miss Ingram: don't you think if I married her she would regenerate me with a vengeance?"

He got up instantly, went quite to the other end of the walk, and when he came back he was humming a tune.

"Jane, Jane," said he, stopping before me, "you are quite pale with your vigils: don't you curse me for disturbing your rest?"

"Curse you? No, sir."

"Shake hands in confirmation of the word. What cold fingers! They were warmer last night when I touched them at the door of the mysterious chamber. Jane, when will you watch with me again?"

"Whenever I can be useful, sir."

"For instance, the night before I am married! I am sure I shall not be able to sleep. Will you promise to sit up with me to bear me company? To you I can talk of my lovely one: for now you have seen her and know her."

"Yes, sir."

"She's a rare one, is she not, Jane?"

"Yes, sir."

"A strapper — a real strapper, Jane: big, brown, and buxom; with hair just such as the ladies of Carthage must have had. Bless me! there's Dent and Lynn in the stables! Go in by the shrubbery, through that wicket."

As I went one way, he went another, and I heard him in the yard, saying cheeringly: —

"Mason got the start of you all this morning; he was gone before sunrise: I rose at four to see him off."

## CHAPTER XXI

PRESENTIMENTS are strange things! and so are sympathies; and so are signs: and the three combined make one mystery to which humanity has not yet found the key. I never laughed at presentiments in my life; because I have had strange ones of my own. Sympathies, I believe, exist: (for instance, between far-distant, long-absent, wholly estranged relatives; asserting, notwithstanding their alienation, the unity of the source to which each traces his origin) whose workings baffle mortal comprehension. And signs, for aught we know, may be but the sympathies of Nature with man.

When I was a little girl, only six years old, I one night heard Bessie Leaven say to Martha Abbot that she had been dreaming about a little child; and that to dream of children was a sure sign of trouble, either to one's self or one's kin. The saying might have worn out of my memory, had not a circumstance immediately followed which served indelibly to fix it there. The next day Bessie was sent for home to the deathbed of her little sister.

Of late I had often recalled this saying and this incident; for during the past week scarcely a night had gone over my couch that had not brought with it a dream of an infant: which I sometimes hushed in my arms, sometimes dandled on my knee, sometimes watched playing with daisies on a lawn; or again, dabbling its hands in running water. It was a wailing child this night, and a laughing one the next: now it nestled close to me, and now it ran from me; but whatever mood the apparition evinced, whatever aspect it wore, it failed not for seven successive nights to meet me the moment I entered the land of slumber.

I did not like this iteration of one idea — this strange recurrence of one image; and I grew nervous as bedtime approached and the hour of the vision drew near. It was from companionship with this baby-phantom I had been roused on that moonlight night when I heard the cry; and it was on the afternoon of the day following I was summoned downstairs by a message that some one wanted me in Mrs. Fairfax's room. On repairing thither, I found a man waiting for me, having the appearance of a gentleman's servant: he was dressed in deep mourning, and the hat he held in his hand was surrounded with a crape band.

"I daresay you hardly remember me, miss," he said, rising as I entered; "but my name is Leaven; I lived coachman with Mrs. Reed when you were at Gateshead eight or nine years since, and I live there still."

"Oh, Robert! how do you do? I remember you very well: you used to give me a ride sometimes on Miss Georgiana's bay pony. And how is Bessie? You are married to Bessie?"

"Yes, miss: my wife is very hearty, thank you; she brought me another little one about two months since—we have three now—and both mother and child are thriving."

"And are the family well at the house, Robert?"

"I am sorry I can't give you better news of them, miss; they are very badly at present—in great trouble."

"I hope no one is dead," I said, glancing at his black dress. He too looked down at the crape round his hat and replied,—

"Mr. John died yesterday was a week, at his chambers in London."

"Mr. John?"

"Yes."

"And how does his mother bear it?"

"Why you see, Miss Eyre, it is not a common mishap: his life has been very wild: these last three years he gave himself up to strange ways; and his death was shocking."

"I heard from Bessie he was not doing well."

"Doing well! He could not do worse: he ruined his health and his estate amongst the worst men and the worst women. He got into debt and into jail: his mother helped him out twice, but as soon as he was free he returned to his old companions and habits. His head was not strong: the knaves he lived amongst fooled him beyond anything I ever heard. He came down to Gateshead about three weeks ago and wanted missis to give up all to him. Missis refused: her means have long been much reduced by his extravagance; so he went back again, and the next news was that he was dead. How he died, God knows!—they say he killed himself."

I was silent: the tidings were frightful. Robert Leaven resumed:—

"Missis had been out of health herself for some time: she had got very stout, but was not strong with it; and the loss of money and fear of poverty were quite breaking her down. The information about Mr. John's death and the manner of it came too suddenly: it brought on a stroke. She was three days without speaking; but last Tuesday she seemed rather better: she appeared as if she wanted to say something, and kept making signs to my wife and mumbling. It was only yesterday morning, however, that Bessie understood she was pronouncing your name; and at last she made out the words, 'Bring Jane — fetch Jane Eyre: I want to speak to her.' Bessie is not sure whether she is in her right mind, or means anything by the words; but she told Miss Reed and Miss Georgiana, and advised them to send for you. The young ladies put it off at first: but their mother grew so restless, and said, 'Jane, Jane,' so many times, that at last they consented. I left Gateshead yesterday; and if you can get ready, Miss, I should like to take you back with me early to-morrow morning."

"Yes, Robert, I shall be ready: it seems to me that I ought to go."

"I think so too, Miss. Bessie said she was sure you would not refuse: but I suppose you will have to ask leave before you can get off?"

"Yes; and I will do it now;" and having directed him to the servants' hall, and recommended him to the care of John's wife, and the attention of John himself, I went in search of Mr. Rochester.

He was not in any of the lower rooms; he was not in the yard, the stables, or the grounds. I asked Mrs. Fairfax if she had seen him; —yes: she believed he was playing billiards with Miss Ingram. To the billiard-room I hastened: the click of balls and the hum of voices resounded thence; Mr. Rochester, Miss Ingram, the two Misses Eshton, and their admirers, were all busied in the game. It required some courage to disturb so interesting a party; my errand, however, was one I could not defer, so I approached the master where he stood at Miss Ingram's side. She turned as I drew near, and looked at me haughtily: her eyes seemed to demand, "What can the creeping creature want now?" and when I said, in a low voice, "Mr. Rochester," she made a movement as if tempted to order me away. I remember her appearance at the moment,— it was very graceful and very striking: she wore a morning robe of sky-blue crape; a gauzy azure scarf was twisted in her hair. She had been all animation with the game, and irritated pride did not lower the expression of her haughty lineaments.

"Does that person want you?" she inquired of Mr. Rochester; and Mr. Rochester turned to see who the "person" was. He made a curious grimace,— one of his strange and equivocal demonstrations — threw down his cue and followed me from the room.

"Well, Jane?" he said, as he rested his back against the schoolroom door, which he had shut.

"If you please, sir, I want leave of absence for a week or two."

"What to do? — Where to go?"

"To seek a sick lady who has sent for me."

"What sick lady? — Where does she live?"

"At Gateshead, in —— shire."

"——shire? That is a hundred miles off! Who may she be that sends for people to see her that distance?"

"Her name is Reed, sir,— Mrs. Reed."

"Reed of Gateshead? There was a Reed of Gateshead, a magistrate."

"It is his widow, sir."

"And what have you to do with her? How do you know her?"

"Mr. Reed was my uncle,— my mother's brother."

"The deuce he was! You never told me that before: you always said you had no relations."

"None that would own me, sir. Mr. Reed is dead, and his wife cast me off."

"Why?"

"Because I was poor, and burdensome, and she disliked me."

"But Reed left children? — you must have cousins? Sir George Lynn was talking of a Reed of Gateshead, yesterday — who, he said, was one of the veriest rascals on town; and Ingram was mentioning a Georgiana Reed of the same place, who was much admired for her beauty, a season or two ago, in London."

"John Reed is dead, too, sir: he ruined himself and half-ruined his family, and is supposed to have committed suicide. The news so shocked his mother that it brought on an apoplectic attack."

"And what good can you do her? Nonsense, Jane! I would never think of running a hundred miles to see an old lady who will, perhaps, be dead before you reach her: besides, you say she cast you off."

"Yes, sir, but that is long ago; and when her circumstances were very different: I could not be easy to neglect her wishes now."

"How long will you stay?"

"As short a time as possible, sir."

"Promise me only to stay a week"——

"I had better not pass my word: I might be obliged to break it."

"At all events you *will* come back: you will not be induced under any pretext to take up a permanent residence with her?"

"Oh no! I shall certainly return if all be well."

"And who goes with you? You don't travel a hundred miles alone."

"No, sir, she has sent her coachman."

"A person to be trusted?"

"Yes, sir, he has lived ten years in the family."

Mr. Rochester meditated. "When do you wish to go?"

"Early to-morrow morning, sir."

"Well, you must have some money; you can't travel without money, and I daresay you have not much: I have given you no salary yet. How much have you in the world, Jane?" he asked, smiling.

I drew out my purse; a meagre thing it was. "Five shillings, sir." He took the purse, poured the hoard into his palm and chuckled over it as if its scantiness pleased him. Soon he produced his pocket-book: "Here," said he, offering me a note: it was fifty pounds, and he owed me but fifteen. I told him I had no change.

"I don't want change: you know that. Take your wages."

I declined accepting more than was my due. He scowled at first; then, as if recollecting something, he said:—

"Right, right! Better not give you all now: you would, perhaps, stay away three months if you had fifty pounds. There are ten: is it not plenty?"

"Yes, sir, but now you owe five."

"Come back for it then: I am your banker for forty pounds."

"Mr. Rochester, I may as well mention another matter of business to you while I have the opportunity."

"Matter of business? I'm curious to hear it."

"You have as good as informed me, sir, that you are going shortly to be married?"

"Yes: what then?"

"In that case, sir, Adèle ought to go to school: I am sure you will perceive the necessity of it."

"To get her out of my bride's way; who might otherwise walk over her rather too emphatically. There's sense in the suggestion; not a doubt of it: Adèle, as you say, must go to school; and you, of course must march straight to — the devil?"

"I hope not, sir: but I must seek another situation somewhere."

"In course!" he exclaimed, with a twang of voice and a distortion of features equally fantastic and ludicrous. He looked at me some minutes.

"And old Madam Reed, or the Misses, her daughters, will be solicited by you to seek a place, I suppose?"

"No, sir; I am not on such terms with my relatives as would justify me in asking favours of them — but I shall advertise."

"You shall walk up the pyramids of Egypt!" he growled. "At your peril you advertise! I wish I had only offered you a sovereign instead of ten pounds. Give me back nine pounds, Jane; I've use for it."

"And so have I, sir," I returned, putting my hands and my purse behind me. "I could not spare the money on any account."

"Little niggard!" said he, "refusing me a pecuniary request! Give me five pounds, Jane."

"Not five shillings, sir; nor five pence."

"Just let me look at the cash."

"No, sir; you are not to be trusted."

"Jane!"

"Sir?"

"Promise me one thing."

"I'll promise you anything, sir, that I think I am likely to perform."

"Not to advertise: and to trust this quest of a situation to me. I'll find you one in time."

"I shall be glad so to do, sir, if you, in your turn will promise that I and Adèle shall be both safe out of the house before your bride enters it."

"Very well! very well! I'll pledge my word on it. You go to-morrow, then?"

"Yes, sir; early."

"Shall you come down to the drawing-room after dinner?"

"No, sir, I must prepare for the journey."

"Then you and I must bid good-bye for a little while?"

"I suppose so, sir."

"And how do people perform that ceremony of parting, Jane? Teach me; I'm not quite up to it."

"They say, Farewell; or any other form they prefer."

"Then say it."

"Farewell, Mr. Rochester, for the present."

"What must I say?"

"The same, if you like, sir."

"Farewell, Miss Eyre, for the present: is that all?"

"Yes."

"It seems stingy, to my notions, and dry, and unfriendly. I should like something else: a little addition to the rite. If one shook hands, for instance; but no,— that would not content me either. So you'll do no more than say Farewell, Jane?"

"It is enough, sir: as much good-will may be conveyed in one hearty word as in many."

"Very likely; but it is blank and cool—'farewell.'"

"How long is he going to stand with his back against that door?" I asked myself; "I want to commence my packing." The dinner-bell rang, and suddenly away he bolted, without another syllable: I saw him no more during the day, and was off before he had risen in the morning.

I reached the lodge at Gateshead about five o'clock in the afternoon of the first of May: I stepped in there before going up to the hall. It was very clean and neat: the ornamental windows were hung with little white curtains; the floor was spotless; the grate and fire-irons were burnished bright, and the fire burnt clear. Bessie sat on the hearth, nursing her last-born, and Robert and his sister played quietly in a corner.

"Bless you!—I knew you would come!" exclaimed Mrs. Leaven, as I entered.

"Yes, Bessie," said I, after I had kissed her; "and I trust I am not too late. How is Mrs. Reed?—Alive still, I hope."

"Yes, she is alive; and more sensible and collected than she was. The doctor says she may linger a week or two yet; but he hardly thinks she will finally recover."

"Has she mentioned me lately?"

"She was talking of you only this morning, and wishing you would come: but she is sleeping now; or was ten minutes ago, when I was up at the house. She generally lies in a kind of lethargy all the afternoon, and wakes up about six or seven. Will you rest yourself here an hour, miss, and then I will go up with you?"

Robert here entered, and Bessie laid her sleeping child in the cradle and went to welcome him: afterwards she insisted on my taking off my bonnet and having some tea; for she said I looked pale and tired. I was glad to accept her hospitality; and I submitted to be relieved of my travelling garb just as passively as I used to let her undress me when a child.

Old times crowded fast back on me as I watched her bustling about — setting out the tea-tray with her best china, cutting bread and butter, toasting a tea-cake, and, between whiles, giving little Robert or Jane an occasional tap or push, just as she used to give me in former days. Bessie had retained her quick temper as well as her light foot and good looks.

Tea ready, I was going to approach the table; but she desired me to sit still, quite in her old, peremptory tones. I must be served at the fireside, she said; and she placed before me a little round stand with my cup and a plate of toast, absolutely as she used to accommodate me with some privately purloined dainty on a nursery chair: and I smiled and obeyed her as in bygone days.

She wanted to know if I was happy at Thornfield Hall, and what sort of a person the mistress was; and when I told her there was only a master, whether he was a nice gentleman, and if I liked him. I told her he was rather an ugly man, but quite a gentleman; and that he treated me kindly, and I was content. Then I went on to describe to her the gay company that had lately been staying at the house; and to these details Bessie listened with interest: they were precisely of the kind she relished.

In such conversation an hour was soon gone: Bessie restored to me my bonnet, etc., and, accompanied by her, I quitted the lodge for the hall. It was also accompanied by her that I had, nearly nine years ago, walked down the path I was now ascending. On a dark, misty, raw morning in January, I had left a hostile roof with a desperate and embittered heart — a sense of outlawry and almost of reprobation — to seek the chilly harbourage of Lowood: that bourne so far away and unexplored. The same hostile roof now again rose before me: my prospects were doubtful yet; and I had yet an aching heart. I still felt as a wanderer on the face of the earth; but I experienced firmer trust in myself and my own powers, and less withering dread of oppression. The gaping wound of my wrongs, too, was now quite healed; and the flame of resentment extinguished.

"You shall go into the breakfast-room first," said Bessie, as she preceded me through the hall; "the young ladies will be there."

In another moment I was within that apartment. There was every article of furniture looking just as it did on the morning I was first introduced to Mr. Brocklehurst: the very rug he had stood upon still covered the hearth. Glancing at the book-cases, I thought I could distinguish the two volumes of Bewick's British Birds occupying their old place on the third shelf, and Gulliver's Travels and the Arabian Nights ranged just above. The inanimate objects were not changed: but the livings things had altered past recognition.

Two young ladies appeared before me; one very tall, almost as tall as Miss Ingram,— very thin too, with a sallow face and severe mien. There was something ascetic in her look, which was augmented by the extreme plainness of a straight-skirted, black stuff dress, a starched linen collar, hair combed away from the temples, and the nun-like ornament of a string of ebony beads and a crucifix: This I felt sure was Eliza, though I could trace little resemblance to her former self in that elongated and colourless visage.

The other was as certainly Georgiana: but not the Georgiana I remembered — the slim and fairylike girl of eleven. This was a full-blown, very plump damsel, fair as waxwork; with handsome and regular features, languishing blue eyes, and ringleted yellow hair. The hue of her dress was black too; but its fashion was so different from her sister's — so much more flowing and becoming — it looked as stylish as the other's looked puritanical.

In each of the sisters there was one trait of the mother — and only one: the thin and pallid elder daughter had her parent's Cairngorm eye: the blooming and luxuriant younger girl had her contour of jaw and chin,— perhaps a little softened, but still imparting an indescribable hardness to the countenance, otherwise so voluptuous and buxom.

Both ladies, as I advanced, rose to welcome me, and both addressed me by the name of "Miss Eyre." Eliza's greeting was delivered in a short, abrupt voice, without a smile; and then she sat down again, fixed her eyes on the fire, and seemed to forget me. Georgiana added to her "How d'ye do?" several commonplaces about my journey, the weather and so on, uttered in rather a drawling tone: and accompanied by sundry side-glances that measured me from head to foot — now traversing the folds of my drab merino pelisse, and now lingering on the plain trimming of my cottage bonnet. Young ladies have a remarkable way of letting you know that they think you a "quiz," without actually saying the words. A certain superciliousness of look, coolness of manner, nonchalance of tone, express fully their sentiments on the point, without committing them by any positive rudeness in word or deed.

A sneer, however, whether covert or open, had now no longer that power over me it once possessed: as I sat between my cousins, I was surprised to find how easy I felt under the total neglect of the one and the semi-sarcastic attentions of the other — Eliza did not mortify, nor Georgiana ruffle me. The fact was, I had other things to think about; within the last few months feelings had been stirred in me so much more potent than any they could raise — pains and pleasures so much more acute and exquisite had been excited, than any it was in their power to inflict or bestow — that their airs gave me no concern either for good or bad.

"How is Mrs. Reed?" I asked soon, looking calmly at Georgiana; who thought fit to bridle at the direct address, as if it were an unexpected liberty.

"Mrs. Reed? Ah! mama you mean; she is extremely poorly: I doubt if you can see her to-night."

"If," said I, "you would just step upstairs and tell her I am come, I should be much obliged to you."

Georgiana almost started, and she opened her blue eyes wild and wide. "I know she had a particular wish to see me," I added, "and I would not defer attending to her desire longer than is absolutely necessary."

"Mama dislikes being disturbed in an evening," remarked Eliza.

I soon rose, quietly took off my bonnet and gloves, uninvited, and said I would just step out to Bessie — who was, I dared say, in the kitchen — and ask her to ascertain whether Mrs. Reed was disposed to receive me or not to-night. I went, and having found Bessie and despatched her on my errand, I proceeded to take further measures. It had heretofore been my habit always to shrink from arrogance: received as I had been to-day, I should, a year ago, have resolved to quit Gateshead the very next morning; now, it was disclosed to me all at once, that that would be a foolish plan. I had taken a journey of a hundred miles to see my aunt, and I must stay with her till she was better — or dead: as to her daughters' pride and folly, I must put it on one side; make myself independent of it. So I addressed the housekeeper; asked her to show me a room, told her I should probably be a visitor for a week or two, had my trunk conveyed to my chamber, and followed it thither myself. I met Bessie on the landing.

"Missis is awake," said she; "I have told her you are here: come and let us see if she will know you."

I did not need to be guided to the well-known room: to which I had so often been summoned for chastisement or reprimand in former days. I hastened before Bessie, I softly opened the door: a shaded light stood on the table, for it was now getting dark. There was the great fourpost bed with amber hangings as of old; there the toilet-table, the armchair, and the foot-stool: at which I had a hundred times been sentenced to kneel, to ask pardon for offences, by me, uncommitted. I looked into a certain corner near, half-expecting to see the slim outline of a once-dreaded switch; which used to lurk there, waiting to leap out imp-like and lace my quivering palms or shrinking neck. I approached the bed; I opened the curtains and leant over the high-piled pillows.

Well did I remember Mrs. Reed's face, and I eagerly sought the familiar image. It is a happy thing that time quells the longings of vengeance, and hushes the promptings of rage and aversion: I had left this woman in bitterness and hate, and I came back to her now with no other emotion than a sort of ruth for her great sufferings, and a strong yearning to forget and forgive all injuries — to be reconciled and clasp hands in amity.

The well-known face was there: stern, relentless as ever — there was that peculiar eye which nothing could melt; and the somewhat raised, imperious, despotic eyebrow. How often had it lowered on me menace and hate! and how the recollection of childhood's terrors and sorrows revived as I traced its harsh line now! And yet I stooped down and kissed her: she looked at me.

"Is this Jane Eyre?" she said.

"Yes, aunt Reed. How are you, dear aunt?"

I had once vowed that I would never call her aunt again: I thought it no sin to forget and break that vow now. My fingers had fastened on her hand which lay outside the sheet: had she pressed mine kindly, I should at that moment have experienced true pleasure. But unimpressionable natures are not so soon softened, nor are natural antipathies so readily eradicated: Mrs. Reed took her hand away, and, turning her face rather from me, she remarked that the night was warm. Again she regarded me, so icily, I felt at once that her opinion of me — her feeling towards me — was unchanged, and unchangeable. I knew by her stony eye — opaque to tenderness, indissoluble to tears — that she was resolved to consider me bad to the last; because to believe me good, would give her no generous pleasure: only a sense of mortification.

I felt pain, and then I felt ire; and then I felt a determination to subdue her — to be her mistress in spite both of her nature and her will. My tears had risen, just as in childhood: I ordered them back to their source. I brought a chair to the bed-head: I sat down and leaned over the pillow.

"You sent for me," I said, "and I am here; and it is my intention to stay till I see how you get on."

"Oh, of course! You have seen my daughters?"

"Yes."

"Well, you may tell them I wish you to stay till I can talk some things over with you I have on my mind: to-night it is too late, and I have a difficulty in recalling them. But there was something I wished to say — let me see" —

The wandering look and changed utterance told what wreck had taken place in her once-vigorous frame. Turning restlessly, she drew the bed-clothes round her; my elbow, resting on a corner of the quilt, fixed it down: she was at once irritated.

"Sit up!" said she; "don't annoy me with holding the clothes fast — are you Jane Eyre?"

"I am Jane Eyre."

"I have had more trouble with that child than any one would believe. Such a burden to be left on my hands — and so much annoyance as she caused me, daily and hourly, with her incomprehensible disposition, and her sudden starts of temper, and her continual, unnatural watchings of one's movements! I declare she talked to me once like something mad, or like a fiend — no child ever spoke or looked as she did; I was glad to get her away from the house. What did they do with her at Lowood? The fever broke out there, and many of the pupils died. She, however, did not die: but I said she did — I wish she had died!"

"A strange wish, Mrs. Reed: why do you hate her so?"

"I had a dislike to her mother always; for she was my husband's only sister, and a great favourite with him: he opposed the family's disowning her when she made her low marriage, and when news came of her death, he wept like a simpleton. He would send for the baby; though I entreated him rather to put it out to nurse and pay for its maintenance. I hated it the first time I set my eyes on it — a sickly, whining, pining thing! It would wail in its cradle all night long — not screaming heartily like any other child, but whimpering and moaning. Reed pitied it; and he used to nurse it and notice it as if it had been his own: more, indeed, than he ever noticed his own at that age. He would try to make my children friendly to the little beggar: the darlings could not bear it, and he was angry with them when they showed their dislike. In his last illness, he had it brought continually to his bedside; and but an hour before he died, he bound me by vow to keep the creature. I would as soon have been charged with a pauper brat out of a workhouse: but he was weak, naturally weak. John does not at all resemble his father, and I'm glad of it: John is like me and like my brothers — he is quite a Gibson. Oh, I wish he would cease tormenting me with letters for money! I have no more money to give him: we are getting poor. I must send away half the servants and shut up part of the house; or let it off. I can never submit to do that — yet how are we to get on? Two-thirds of my income goes in paying the interest of mortgages. John gambles dreadfully, and always loses — poor boy! He is beset by sharpers: John is sunk and degraded — his look is frightful — I feel ashamed for him when I see him."

She was getting much excited. "I think I had better leave

her now," said I to Bessie, who stood on the other side of the bed.

"Perhaps you had, Miss: but she often talks in this way towards night — in the morning she is calmer."

I rose. "Stop!" exclaimed Mrs. Reed, "There is another thing I wished to say. He threatens me — he continually threatens me with his own death, or mine: and I dream sometimes that I see him laid out with a great wound in his throat, or with a swollen and blackened face. I am come to a strange pass: I have heavy troubles. What is to be done? How is the money to be had?"

Bessie now endeavoured to persuade her to take a sedative draught: she succeeded with difficulty. Soon after, Mrs. Reed grew more composed, and sank into a dozing state. I then left her.

More than ten days elapsed before I had again any conversation with her. She continued either delirious or lethargic; and the doctor forbade everything which could painfully excite her. Meantime, I got on as well as I could with Georgiana and Eliza. They were very cold, indeed, at first. Eliza would sit half the day sewing, reading, or writing, and scarcely utter a word either to me or her sister. Georgiana would chatter nonsense to her canary bird by the hour, and take no notice of me. But I was determined not to seem at a loss for occupation or amusement: I had brought my drawing materials with me, and they served me for both.

Provided with a case of pencils, and some sheets of paper, I used to take a seat apart from them, near the window, and busy myself in sketching fancy vignettes, representing any scene that happened momentarily to shape itself in the ever-shifting kaleidoscope of imagination: a glimpse of sea between two rocks; the rising moon, and a ship crossing its disk; a group of reeds and water-flags, and a naiad's head, crowned with lotus-flowers, rising out of them; an elf sitting in a hedge-sparrow's nest, under a wreath of hawthorn-bloom.

One morning I fell to sketching a face: what sort of a face it was to be, I did not care or know. I took a soft black pencil, gave it a broad point, and worked away. Soon I had traced on the paper a broad and prominent forehead, and a square lower outline of visage: that contour gave me pleasure; my fingers proceeded actively to fill it with features. Strongly-marked horizontal eyebrows must be traced under that brow; then followed, naturally, a well-defined nose, with a straight ridge and full nostrils; then a flexible-looking mouth, by no means narrow; then a firm chin, with a decided cleft down the middle of it: of course, some black whiskers were wanted, and some jetty hair, tufted on the temples, and waved above the forehead. Now for the eyes: I had left them to the last, because they required the most careful working. I drew them large; I shaped them well: the eyelashes I traced long and sombre; the irids lustrous and large. "Good! but not quite the thing," I thought, as I surveyed the effect: "They want more force and spirit;" and I wrought the shades blacker, that the lights might flash more brilliantly — a happy touch or two secured success. There, I had a friend's face under my gaze; and what did it signify that those young ladies turned their backs on me? I looked at it; I smiled at the speaking likeness: I was absorbed and content.

"Is that a portrait of some one you know?" asked Eliza, who had approached me unnoticed. I responded that it was merely a fancy head, and hurried it beneath the other sheets. Of course, I lied: it was, in fact, a very faithful representation of Mr. Rochester. But what was that to her, or to any one but myself? Georgiana also advanced to look. The other drawings pleased her much, but she called that "an ugly man." They both seemed surprised at my skill. I offered to sketch their portraits; and each, in turn, sat for a pencil outline. Then Georgiana produced her album. I promised to contribute a water-colour drawing: this put her at once into good humour. She proposed a walk in the grounds. Before we had been out two hours, we were deep in a confidential conversation: she had favoured me with a description of the brilliant winter she had spent in London two seasons ago — of the admiration she had there excited — the attention she had received; and I even got hints of the titled conquest she had made. In the course of the afternoon and evening these hints were enlarged on: various soft conversations were reported, and sentimental scenes represented; and, in short, a volume of a novel of fashionable life was that day improvised by her for my benefit. The communications were renewed from day to day: they always ran on the same theme — herself, her loves, and woes. It was strange she never once adverted either to her mother's illness, or her brother's death, or the present gloomy state of the family prospects. Her mind seemed wholly taken up with reminiscences of past gaiety, and aspirations after dissipations to come. She passed about five minutes each day in her mother's sick-room and no more.

Eliza still spoke little: she had evidently no time to talk. I never saw a busier person than she seemed to be; yet it was difficult to say what she did: or rather, to discover any result of her diligence. She had an alarum to call her up early. I know not how she occupied herself before breakfast, but after that meal she divided her time into regular portions; and each hour had its allotted task. Three times a day she studied a little book, which I found, on inspection, was a Common Prayer Book. I asked her once what was the great attraction of that volume, and she said "the Rubric." Three hours she gave to stitching, with gold thread, the border of a square crimson cloth, almost large enough for a carpet. In answer to my inquiries after the use of this article, she informed me it was a covering for the altar of a new church lately erected near Gateshead. Two hours she devoted to her diary; two to working by herself in the kitchen-garden; and one to the regulation of her accounts. She seemed to want no company; no conversation. I believe she was happy in her way: this routine sufficed to her; and nothing annoyed her so much as the occurrence of any incident which forced her to vary its clock-work regularity.

She told me one evening, when more disposed to be communicative than usual, that John's conduct, and the threatened ruin of the family, had been a source of profound affliction to her: but she had now, she said, settled her mind, and formed her resolution. Her own fortune she had taken care to secure; and when her mother died,— and it was wholly improbable, she tranquilly remarked, that she should either recover or linger long,— she would execute a long-cherished project: seek a retirement where punctual habits would be permanently secured from disturbance, and place safe barriers between herself and a frivolous world. I asked if Georgiana would accompany her.

"Of course not. Georgiana and she had nothing in common: they never had had. She would not be burdened with her society for any consideration. Georgiana should take her own course; and she, Eliza, would take hers."

Georgiana, when not unburdening her heart to me, spent most of her time in lying on the sofa, fretting about the dullness of the house, and wishing over and over again that her aunt Gibson would send her an invitation up to town. "It would be so much better," she said, "if she could only get out of the way for a month or two, till all was over." I did not ask what she meant by "all being over," but I suppose she referred to the expected decease of her mother and the gloomy sequel of funeral rites. Eliza generally took no more notice of her sister's indolence and complaints than if no such murmuring, lounging object had been before her. One day, however, as she put away her account-book, and unfolded her embroidery, she suddenly took her up thus: —

"Georgiana, a more vain and absurd animal than you, was certainly never allowed to cumber the earth. You had no right to be born; for you make no use of life. Instead of living for, in, and with yourself, as a reasonable being ought, you seek only to fasten your feebleness on some other person's strength: if no one can be found willing to burden her or himself with such a fat, weak, puffy, useless thing, you cry out that you are ill-treated, neglected, miserable. Then, too, existence for you must be a scene of continual change and excitement, or else the world is a dungeon: you must be admired, you must be courted, you must be flattered — you must have music, dancing, and society — or you languish, you die away. Have you no sense to devise a system which will make you independent of all efforts, and all wills, but your own? Take one day; share it into sections; to each section apportion its task: leave no stray unemployed quarters of an hour, ten minutes, five minutes, include all; do each piece of business in its turn with method, with rigid regularity. The day will close almost before you are aware it has begun; and you are indebted to no one for helping you to get rid of one vacant moment: you have had to seek no one's company, conversation, sympathy, forbearance; you have lived, in short, as an independent being ought to do. Take this advice: the first and last I shall offer you; then you will not want me or any one else, happen what may. Neglect it — go on as heretofore, craving, whining, and idling — and suffer the results of your idiocy, however bad and insufferable they may be. I tell you this plainly; and listen: for though I shall no more repeat what I am now about to say, I shall steadily act on it. After my mother's death, I wash my hands of you: from the day her coffin is carried to the vault in Gateshead Church, you and I will be as separate as if we had never known each other. You need not think that because we chanced to be born of the same parents, I shall suffer you to fasten me down by even the feeblest claim: I can tell you this — if the whole human race, ourselves excepted, were swept away, and we two stood alone on the earth, I would leave you in the old world, and betake myself to the new."

She closed her lips.

"You might have spared yourself the trouble of delivering that tirade," answered Georgiana. "Everybody knows you are the most selfish heartless creature in existence: and *I* know your spiteful hatred towards me: I have had a specimen of it before in the trick you played me about Lord Edwin Vere: you could not bear me to be raised above you, to have a title, to be received into circles where you dare not show your face, and so you acted the spy and informer, and ruined my prospects for ever." Georgiana took out her handkerchief and blew her nose for an hour afterwards; Eliza sat cold, impassible, and assiduously industrious.

True, generous feeling is made small account of by some; but here were two natures rendered, the one intolerably acrid, the other despicably savourless for the want of it. Feeling without judgment is a washy draught indeed; but judgment untempered by feeling is too bitter and husky a morsel for human deglutition.

It was a wet and windy afternoon: Georgiana had fallen asleep on the sofa over the perusal of a novel; Eliza was gone to attend a saint's-day service at the new church — for in matters of religion she was a rigid formalist: no weather ever prevented the punctual discharge of what she considered her devotional duties; fair or foul, she went to church thrice every Sunday, and as often on week-days as there were prayers.

I bethought myself to go upstairs and see how the dying woman sped, who lay there almost unheeded: the very servants paid her but a remittent attention: the hired nurse, being little looked after, would slip out of the room whenever she could. Bessie was faithful; but she had her own family to mind, and could only come occasionally to the hall. I found the sick-room unwatched, as I had expected: no nurse was there; the patient lay still, and seemingly lethargic; her livid face sunk in the pillows: the fire was dying in the grate. I renewed the fuel, re-arranged the bed-clothes, gazed awhile on her who could not now gaze on me, and then I moved away to the window.

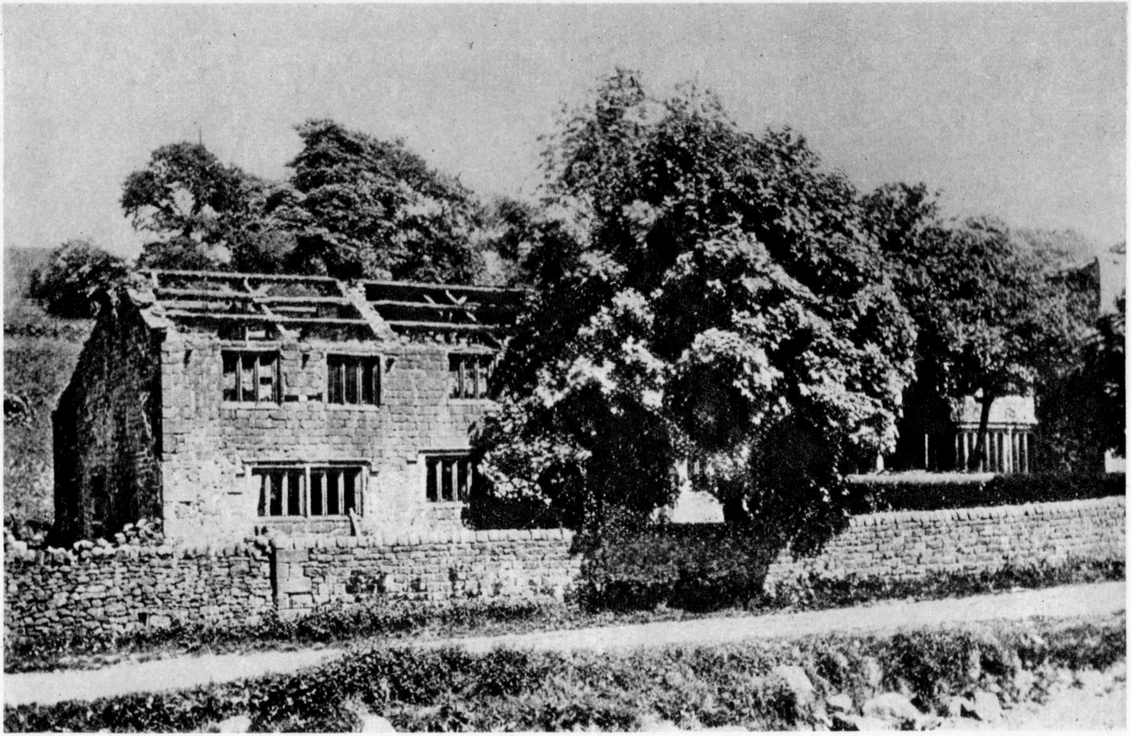

WYCOLLER DEAN

Wycoller Dean is the house on which Charlotte Brontë drew for the gloomy Ferndean Manor—"A building of considerable antiquity, moderate size, and no architectural pretension, deep buried in a wood." This is the place of which Rochester says, "I possess an old house, Ferndean Manor, even more retired and hidden than this, where I could have lodged her safely enough, had not a scruple about the unhealthiness of the situation, in the heart of a wood, made my conscience recoil from such an arrangement."

The rain beat strongly against the panes, the wind blew tempestuously: "One lies there," I thought, "who will soon be beyond the war of earthly elements. Whither will that spirit — now struggling to quit its material tenement — flit when at length released?"

In pondering the great mystery, I thought of Helen Burns: recalled her dying words — her faith — her doctrine of the equality of disembodied souls. I was still listening in thought to her well-remembered tones — still picturing her pale and spiritual aspect, her wasted face and sublime gaze, as she lay on her placid deathbed, and whispered her longing to be restored to her divine Father's bosom — when a feeble voice murmured from the couch behind: "Who is that?"

I knew Mrs. Reed had not spoken for days: was she reviving? I went up to her.

"It is I, aunt Reed."

"Who — I?" was her answer. "Who are you?" looking at me with surprise and a sort of alarm, but still not wildly. "You are quite a stranger to me — where is Bessie?"

"She is at the lodge, aunt."

"Aunt," she repeated. "Who calls me Aunt? You are not one of the Gibsons; and yet I know you — that face, and the eyes and forehead are quite familiar to me: you are like — why, you are like Jane Eyre!"

I said nothing: I was afraid of occasioning some shock by declaring my identity.

"Yet," said she, "I am afraid it is a mistake: my thoughts deceive me. I wished to see Jane Eyre, and I fancy a likeness where none exists: besides, in eight years she must be so changed." I now gently assured her that I was the person she supposed and desired me to be: and seeing that I was understood, and that her senses were quite collected, I explained how Bessie had sent her husband to fetch me from Thornfield.

"I am very ill, I know," she said ere long. "I was trying to turn myself a few minutes since, and find I cannot move a limb. It is as well I should ease my mind before I die: what we think little of in health, burdens us at such an hour as the present is to me. Is the nurse here? or is there no one in the room but you?"

I assured her we were alone.

"Well, I have twice done you a wrong which I regret now. One was in breaking the promise which I gave my husband to bring you up as my own child; the other"— she stopped. "After all, it is of no great importance, perhaps," she murmured to herself: "and then I may get better; and to humble myself so to her is painful."

She made an effort to alter her position, but failed: her face changed; she seemed to experience some inward sensation — the precursor, perhaps, of the last pang.

"Well: I must get it over. Eternity is before me: I had better tell her.— Go to my dressing-case, open it, and take out a letter you will see there."

I obeyed her directions. "Read the letter," she said. It was short, and thus conceived: —

"MADAM,

"Will you have the goodness to send me the address of my niece, Jane Eyre, and to tell me how she is: it is my intention to write shortly and desire her to come to me at Madeira. Providence has blessed my endeavours to secure a competency; and as I am unmarried and childless, I wish to adopt her during my life, and bequeath her at my death whatever I may have to leave.

"I am, Madam, etc., etc.

"JOHN EYRE, Madeira."

It was dated three years back.

"Why did I never hear of this?" I asked.

"Because I disliked you too fixedly and thoroughly ever to lend a hand in lifting you to prosperity. I could not forget your conduct to me, Jane — the fury with which you once turned on me; the tone in which you declared you abhorred me the worst of anybody in the world; the unchildlike look and voice with which you affirmed that the very thought of me made you sick, and asserted that I had treated you with miserable cruelty. I could not forget my own sensations when you thus started up and poured out the venom of your mind: I felt fear, as if an animal that I had struck or pushed had looked up at me with human eyes and cursed me in a man's voice.— Bring me some water! Oh! make haste!"

"Dear Mrs. Reed," said I, as I offered her the draught she

required, "think no more of all this, let it pass away from your mind. Forgive me for my passionate language: I was a child then; eight, nine years have passed since that day."

She heeded nothing of what I said; but when she had tasted the water and drawn breath, she went on thus: —

"I tell you I could not forget it; and I took my revenge: for you to be adopted by your uncle, and placed in a state of ease and comfort, was what I could not endure. I wrote to him; I said I was sorry for his disappointment, but Jane Eyre was dead: she had died of typhus fever at Lowood. Now act as you please: write and contradict my assertion — expose my falsehood as soon as you like. You were born, I think, to be my torment: my last hour is racked by the recollection of a deed, which, but for you, I should never have been tempted to commit."

"If you could but be persuaded to think no more of it, aunt, and to regard me with kindness and forgiveness"—

"You have a very bad disposition," said she, "and one to this day I feel it impossible to understand: how for nine years you could be patient and quiescent under any treatment, and in the tenth break out all fire and violence, I can never comprehend."

"My disposition is not so bad as you think: I am passionate, but not vindictive. Many a time, as a little child, I should have been glad to love you if you would have let me; and I long earnestly to be reconciled to you now: kiss me, aunt."

I approached my cheek to her lips: she would not touch it. She said I oppressed her by leaning over the bed; and again demanded water. As I laid her down — for I raised her and supported her on my arm while she drank — I covered her ice-cold and clammy hand with mine: the feeble fingers shrank from my touch — the glazing eyes shunned my gaze.

"Love me, then, or hate me, as you will," I said at last, "you have my full and free forgiveness: ask now for God's; and be at peace."

Poor, suffering woman! it was too late for her to make now the effort to change her habitual frame of mind: living, she had ever hated me — dying, she must hate me still.

The nurse now entered, and Bessie followed. I yet lingered half an hour longer, hoping to see some sign of amity: but she gave none. She was fast relapsing into stupor; nor did her mind again rally: at twelve o'clock that night she died. I was not present to close her eyes; nor were either of her daughters. They came to tell us the next morning that all was over. She was by that time laid out. Eliza and I went to look at her: Georgiana, who had burst out into loud weeping, said she dared not go. There was stretched Sarah Reed's once robust and active frame, rigid and still: her eye of flint was covered with its cold lid; her brow and strong traits wore yet the impress of her inexorable soul. A strange and solemn object was that corpse to me. I gazed on it with gloom and pain: nothing soft, nothing sweet, nothing pitying, or hopeful, or subduing, did it inspire; only a grating anguish for *her* woes — not *my* loss — and a sombre tearless dismay at the fearfulness of death in such a form.

Eliza surveyed her parent calmly. After a silence of some minutes she observed,—

"With her constitution she should have lived to a good old age: her life was shortened by trouble." And then a spasm constricted her mouth for an instant: as it passed away she turned and left the room, and did I. Neither of us had dropt a tear.

## CHAPTER XXII

MR. ROCHESTER had given me but one week's leave of absence: yet a month elapsed before I quitted Gateshead. I wished to leave immediately after the funeral; but Georgiana entreated me to stay till she could get off to London: whither she was now at last invited by her uncle, Mr. Gibson; who had come down to direct his sister's interment, and settle the family affairs. Georgiana said she dreaded being left alone with Eliza; from her she got neither sympathy in her dejection, support in her fears, nor aid in her preparations; so I bore with her feeble-minded quailings, and selfish lamentations, as well as I could, and did my best in sewing for her and packing her dresses. It is true, that while I worked, she would idle; and I thought to myself, "If you and I were destined to live always together, cousin, we would commence matters on a different footing. I should not settle tamely down into being the forbearing party; I should assign you your share of labour, and compel you to accomplish it, or else it should be left undone: I should insist, also, on your keeping some of those drawling, half-insincere complaints hushed in your own breast. It is only because our connection happens to be very transitory, and comes at a peculiarly mournful season, that I consent thus to render it so patient and compliant on my part."

At last I saw Georgiana off; but now it was Eliza's turn to request me to stay another week. Her plans required all her time and attention, she said: she was about to depart for some unknown bourne; and all day long she stayed in her own room, her door bolted within, filling trunks, emptying drawers, burning papers, and holding no communication with any one. She wished me to look after the house, to see callers, and answer notes of condolence.

One morning, she told me I was at liberty. "And," she added, "I am obliged to you for your valuable services and discreet conduct! There is some difference between living with such a one as you, and with Georgiana: you perform your own part in life, and burden no one. To-morrow," she continued, "I set out for the Continent. I shall take up my abode in a religious house, near

Lisle — a nunnery you would call it: there I shall be quiet and unmolested. I shall devote myself for a time to the examination of the Roman Catholic dogmas, and to a careful study of the workings of their system; if I find it to be, as I half suspect it is, the one best calculated to ensure the doing of all things decently and in order, I shall embrace the tenets of Rome and probably take the veil."

I neither expressed surprise at this resolution nor attempted to dissuade her from it. "The vocation will fit you to a hair," I thought: "much good may it do you!"

When we parted, she said: "Good-bye, cousin Jane Eyre; I wish you well: you have some sense."

I then returned: "You are not without sense, cousin Eliza; but what you have, I suppose in another year will be walled up alive in a French convent. However, it is not my business, and so it suits you — I don't much care."

"You are in the right," said she: and with these words we each went our separate way. As I shall not have occasion to refer either tc her or her sister again, I may as well mention here, that Georgiana made an advantageous match with a wealthy worn-out man of fashion; and that Eliza actually took the veil, and is at this day superior of the convent where she passed the period of her novitiate: and which she endowed with her fortune.

How people feel when they are returning home from an absence, long or short, I did not know: I had never experienced the sensation. I had known what it was to come back to Gateshead when a child, after a long walk — to be scolded for looking cold or gloomy; and later, what it was to come back from church to Lowood — to long for a plenteous meal and a good fire, and to be unable to get either. Neither of these returnings were very pleasant or desirable: no magnet drew me to a given point, increasing in its strength of attraction the nearer I came. The return to Thornfield was yet to be tried.

My journey seemed tedious — very tedious: fifty miles one day, a night spent at an inn; fifty miles the next day. During the first twelve hours I thought of Mrs. Reed in her last moments: I saw her disfigured and discoloured face, and heard her strangely altered voice. I mused on the funeral day, the coffin, the hearse, the black train of tenants and servants — few was the number of relatives — the gaping vault, the silent church, the solemn service. Then I thought of Eliza and Georgiana: I beheld one the cynosure of a ball-room, the other the inmate of a convent cell; and I dwelt on and analysed their separate peculiarities of person and character. The evening arrival at the great town of —— scattered these thoughts; night gave them quite another turn: laid down on my traveller's bed, I left reminiscence for anticipation.

I was going back to Thornfield: but how long was I to stay there? Not long; of that I was sure. I had heard from Mrs. Fairfax in the interim of my absence: the party at the hall was dispersed; Mr. Rochester had left for London three weeks ago, but he was then expected to return in a fortnight. Mrs. Fairfax surmised that he was gone to make arrangements for his wedding, as he had talked of purchasing a new carriage: she said the idea of his marrying Miss Ingram still seemed strange to her; but from what everybody said, and from what she had herself seen, she could no longer doubt that the event would shortly take place. "You would be strangely incredulous if you did doubt it," was my mental comment. "I don't doubt it."

The question followed, "Where was I to go?" I dreamt of Miss Ingram all the night: in a vivid morning dream I saw her closing the gates of Thornfield against me and pointing me out another road; and Mr. Rochester looked on with his arms folded — smiling sardonically, as it seemed, at both her and me.

I had not notified to Mrs. Fairfax the exact day of my return; for I did not wish either car or carriage to meet me at Millcote. I proposed to walk the distance quietly by myself; and very quietly, after leaving my box in the ostler's care, did I slip away from the George Inn, about six o'clock of a June evening, and take the old road to Thornfield: a road which lay chiefly through fields, and was now little frequented.

It was not a bright or splendid summer evening, though fair and soft: the haymakers were at work all along the road; and the sky, though far from cloudless, was such as promised well for the future: its blue — where blue was visible — was mild and settled, and its cloud strata high and thin. The west, too, was warm: no watery gleam chilled it — it seemed as if there was a fire lit, an altar burning behind its screen of marbled vapour, and out of apertures shone a golden redness.

I felt glad as the road shortened before me: so glad that I stopped once to ask myself what that joy meant: and to remind reason that it was not to my home I was going, or to a permanent resting-place, or to a place where fond friends looked out for me and waited my arrival. "Mrs. Fairfax will smile you a calm welcome, to be sure," said I; "and little Adèle will clap her hands and jump to see you: but you know very well you are thinking of another than they; and that he is not thinking of you."

But what is so headstrong as youth? What so blind as inexperience? These affirmed that it was pleasure enough to have the privilege of again looking on Mr. Rochester, whether he looked on me or not; and they added—"Hasten! hasten! be with him while you may: but a few more days or weeks at most, and you are parted with him for ever!" And then I strangled a new-born agony—a deformed thing which I could not persuade myself to own and rear—and ran on.

They are making hay, too, in Thornfield meadows; or rather, the labourers are just quitting their work, and returning home with their rakes on their shoulders: now, at the hour I arrive. I have but a field or two to traverse, and then I shall cross the road and reach the gates. How full the hedges are of roses! But I have no time to gather any; I want to be at the house. I passed a tall briar, shooting leafy and flowery branches across the path; I see the narrow stile with stone steps; and I see—Mr. Rochester sitting there, a book and a pencil in his hand: he is writing.

Well, he is not a ghost; yet every nerve I have is unstrung: for a moment I am beyond my own mastery. What does it mean? I did not think I should tremble in this way when I saw him—or lose my voice or the power of motion in his presence. I will go back as soon as I can stir: I need not make an absolute fool of myself. I know another way to the house. It does not signify if I knew twenty ways; for he has seen me.

"Hello!" he cries; and he puts up his book and his pencil. "There you are! Come on, if you please."

I suppose I do come on; though in what fashion I know not: being scarcely cognisant of my movements, and solicitous only to appear calm; and, above all, to control the working muscles of my face—which I feel rebel insolently against my will, and struggle to express what I had resolved to conceal. But I have a veil—it is down: I make shift yet to behave with decent composure.

"And this is Jane Eyre? Are you coming from Millcote, and on foot? Yes — just one of your tricks: not to send for a carriage, and come clattering over street and road like a common mortal, but to steal into the vicinage of your home along with twilight, just as if you were a dream or a shade. What the deuce have you done with yourself this last month?"

"I have been with my aunt, sir, who is dead."

"A true Janian reply! Good angels be my guard! She comes from the other world — from the abode of people who are dead; and tells me so when she meets me alone here in the gloaming! If I dared I'd touch you to see if you are substance or shadow, you elf! — but I'd as soon offer to take hold of a blue *ignis fatuus* light in a marsh. Truant! truant!" he added, when he had paused an instant. "Absent from me a whole month: and forgetting me quite, I'll be sworn!"

I knew there would be pleasure in meeting my master again; even though broken by the fear that he was so soon to cease to be my master, and by the knowledge that I was nothing to him: but there was ever in Mr. Rochester (so at least I thought) such a wealth of the power of communicating happiness, that to taste but of the crumbs he scattered to stray and stranger birds like me, was to feast genially. His last words were balm: they seemed to imply that it imported something to him whether I forgot him or not. And he had spoken of Thornfield as my home — would that it were my home!

He did not leave the stile, and I hardly liked to ask to go by. I inquired soon if he had not been to London.

"Yes: I suppose you found that out by second-sight?"

"Mrs. Fairfax told me in a letter."

"And did she inform you what I went to do?"

"Oh, yes, sir! Everybody knew your errand."

"You must see the carriage, Jane, and tell me if you don't think it will suit Mrs. Rochester exactly; and whether she won't look like Queen Boadicea, leaning back against those purple cushions. I wish, Jane, I were a trifle better adapted to match with her externally. Tell me, now, fairy as you are,— can't you give me a charm, or a philter, or something of that sort, to make me a handsome man?"

"It would be past the power of magic, sir;" and, in thought,

I added, "a loving eye is all the charm needed: to such you are handsome enough; or rather, your sternness has a power beyond beauty."

Mr. Rochester had sometimes read my unspoken thoughts with an acumen to me incomprehensible: in the present instance he took no notice of my abrupt vocal response; but he smiled at me with a certain smile he had of his own, and which he used but on rare occasions. He seemed to think it too good for common purposes: it was the real sunshine of feeling — he shed it over me now.

"Pass, Janet," said he, making room for me to cross the stile: "go up home, and stay your weary little wandering feet at a friend's threshold."

All I had now to do was to obey him in silence: no need for me to colloquise further. I got over the stile without a word, and meant to leave him calmly. An impulse held me fast,— a force turned me round. I said — or something in me said for me, and in spite of me: —

"Thank you, Mr. Rochester, for your great kindness. I am strangely glad to get back again to you; and wherever you are is my home — my only home."

I walked on so fast that even he could hardly have overtaken me had he tried. Little Adèle was half wild with delight when she saw me. Mrs. Fairfax received me with her usual plain friendliness. Leah smiled; and even Sophie bid me "bon soir" with glee. This was very pleasant: there is no happiness like that of being loved by your fellow-creatures, and feeling that your presence is an addition to their comfort.

I, that evening, shut my eyes resolutely against the future: I stopped my ears against the voice that kept warning me of near separation and coming grief. When tea was over and Mrs. Fairfax had taken her knitting, and I had assumed a low seat near her, and Adèle, kneeling on the carpet, had nestled close up to me, and a sense of mutual affection seemed to surround us with a ring of golden peace, I uttered a silent prayer that we might not be parted far or soon; but when, as we thus sat, Mr. Rochester entered, unannounced, and looking at us, seemed to take pleasure in the spectacle of a group so amicable — when he said he supposed the old lady was all right now that she had got her adopted daughter back again, and added that he saw Adèle was "prête à croquer sa petite maman

Anglaise"— I half ventured to hope that he would, even after his marriage, keep us together somewhere under the shelter of his protection, and not quite exiled from the sunshine of his presence.

A fortnight of dubious calm succeeded my return to Thornfield Hall. Nothing was said of the master's marriage, and I saw no preparation going on for such an event. Almost every day I asked Mrs. Fairfax if she had yet heard anything decided: her answer was always in the negative. Once, she said, she had actually put the question to Mr. Rochester as to when he was going to bring his bride home; but he had answered her only by a joke, and one of his queer looks, and she could not tell what to make of him.

One thing specially surprised me, and that was, there were no journeyings backward and forward, no visits to Ingram Park: to be sure it was twenty miles off, on the borders of another county; but what was that distance to an ardent lover? To so practised and indefatigable a horseman as Mr. Rochester, it would be but a morning's ride. I began to cherish hopes I had no right to conceive: that the match was broken off; that rumour had been mistaken; that one or both parties had changed their minds. I used to look at my master's face to see if it were sad or fierce; but I could not remember the time when it had been so uniformly clear of clouds or evil feelings. If, in the moments I and my pupil spent with him, I lacked spirits and sank into inevitable dejection, he became even gay. Never had he called me more frequently to his presence; never been kinder to me when there — and, alas! never had I loved him so well.

# CHAPTER XXIII

A SPLENDID Midsummer shone over England: skies so pure, suns so radiant as were then seen in long succession, seldom favour, even singly, our wave-girt land. It was as if a band of Italian days had come from the South, like a flock of glorious passenger birds, and lighted to rest them on the cliffs of Albion. The hay was all got in; the fields round Thornfield were green and shorn; the roads white and baked; the trees were in their dark prime; hedge and wood, full-leaved and deeply tinted, contrasted well with the sunny hue of the clear meadows between.

One Midsummer-eve, Adèle, weary with gathering wild strawberries in Hay Lane half the day, had gone to bed with the sun. I watched her drop asleep, and when I left her I sought the garden.

It was now the sweetest hour of the twenty-four:— "Day its fervid fires had wasted," and dew fell cool on panting plain and scorched summit. Where the sun had gone down in simple state — pure of the pomp of clouds — spread a solemn purple, burning with the light of red jewel and furnace flame at one point, on one hill-peak, and extending high and wide, soft and still softer, over half heaven. The east had its own charm of fine, deep blue, and its own modest gem, a rising and solitary star: soon it would boast the moon; but she was yet beneath the horizon.

I walked a while on the pavement; but a subtle, well-known scent — that of a cigar — stole from some window; I saw the library casement open a hand-breadth; I knew I might be watched thence; so I went apart into the orchard. No nook in the grounds more sheltered and more Eden-like; it was full of trees, it bloomed with flowers: a very high wall shut it out from the court, on one side; on the other, a beech avenue screened it from the lawn. At the bottom was a sunk fence, its sole separation from lonely fields: a winding walk, bordered with laurels and terminating in a giant horse-chestnut, circled at the base by a seat, led down to the fence. Here one could wander unseen. While such honey-dew fell, such silence reigned, such gloaming gathered, I felt as if I could haunt such shade for ever: but in threading the flower and fruit-parterres at the upper part of the inclosure, enticed there by the light the now-rising moon casts on this more open quarter, my step is stayed — not by sound, not by sight, but once more by a warning fragrance.

Sweet briar and southern wood, jasmine, pink, and rose, have long been yielding their evening sacrifice of incense: this new scent is neither of shrub nor flower; it is — I know it well — it is Mr. Rochester's cigar. I look round and I listen. I see trees laden with ripening fruit. I hear a nightingale warbling in a wood half a mile off; no moving form is visible, no coming step audible; but that perfume increases: I must flee. I make for the wicket leading to the shrubbery, and I see Mr. Rochester entering. I step aside into the ivy recess, he will not stay long: he will soon return whence he came, and if I sit still he will never see me.

But no — eventide is as pleasant to him as to me, and this antique garden as attractive; and he strolls on, now lifting the gooseberry-tree branches to look at the fruit, large as plums, with which they are laden; now taking a ripe cherry from the wall; now stooping towards a knot of flowers, either to inhale their fragrance or to admire the dew-beads on their petals. A great moth goes humming by me; it alights on a plant at Mr. Rochester's foot: he sees it, and bends to examine it.

"Now, he has his back towards me," thought I, "and he is occupied too; perhaps, if I walk softly, I can slip away unnoticed."

I trode on an edging of turf that the crackle of the pebbly gravel might not betray me: he was standing among the beds at a yard or two distant from where I had to pass; the moth apparently engaged him. "I shall get by very well," I meditated. As I crossed his shadow, thrown long over the garden by the moon, not yet risen high, he said quietly without turning: —

"Jane, come and look at this fellow."

I had made no noise: he had not eyes behind — could his shadow feel? I started at first, and then I approached him.

"Look at his wings," said he, "he reminds me rather of a West Indian insect; one does not often see so large and gay a night-rover in England: there! he is flown."

The moth roamed away. I was sheepishly retreating also; but Mr. Rochester followed me, and when we reached the wicket, he said: —

"Turn back: on so lovely a night it is a shame to sit in the house; and surely no one can wish to go to bed while sunset is thus at meeting with moonrise."

It is one of my faults, that though my tongue is sometimes prompt enough at an answer, there are times when it sadly fails me in framing an excuse; and always the lapse occurs at some crisis, when a facile word or plausible pretext is specially wanted to get me out of painful embarrassment. I did not like to walk at this hour alone with Mr. Rochester in the shadowy orchard; but I could not find a reason to allege for leaving him. I followed with lagging step, and thoughts busily bent on discovering a means of extrication; but he himself looked so composed and so grave also, I became ashamed of feeling any confusion: the evil — if evil existent or prospective there was — seemed to lie with me only; his mind was unconscious and quiet.

"Jane," he recommenced, as we entered the laurel walk, and slowly strayed down in the direction of the sunk fence and the horse-chestnut, "Thornfield is a pleasant place in summer, is it not?"

"Yes, sir."

"You must have become in some degree attached to the house, — you, who have an eye for natural beauties, and a good deal of the organ of Adhesiveness?"

"I am attached to it, indeed."

"And though I don't comprehend how it is, I perceive you have acquired a degree of regard for that foolish little child Adèle, too; and even for simple dame Fairfax?"

"Yes, sir; in different ways, I have an affection for both."

"And would be sorry to part with them?"

"Yes."

"Pity!" he said, and sighed and paused. "It is always the way of events in this life," he continued presently: "no sooner have you got settled in a pleasant resting-place, than a voice calls out to you to rise and move on, for the hour of repose is expired."

"Must I move on, sir?" I asked. "Must I leave Thornfield?"

"I believe you must, Jane. I am sorry, Janet, but I believe indeed you must."

This was a blow: but I did not let it prostrate me.

"Well, sir, I shall be ready when the order to march comes."

"It is come now — I must give it to-night."

"Then you are going to be married, sir?"

"Ex-act-ly — pre-cise-ly: with your usual acuteness, you have hit the nail straight on the head."

"Soon, sir?"

"Very soon, my —— that is, Miss Eyre: and you'll remember, Jane, the first time I, or Rumour, plainly intimated to you that it was my intention to put my old bachelor's neck into the sacred noose, to enter into the holy estate of matrimony — to take Miss Ingram to my bosom, in short (she's an extensive armful: but that's not to the point — one can't have too much of such a very excellent thing as my beautiful Blanche): well, as I was saying — listen to me, Jane! You're not turning your head to look after more moths, are you? That was only a lady-clock, child, 'flying away home.' I wish to remind you that it was you who first said to me, with that discretion I respect in you — with that foresight, prudence and humility which befit your responsible and dependent position — that in case I married Miss Ingram — both you and little Adèle had better trot forthwith. I pass over the sort of slur conveyed in this suggestion on the character of my beloved; indeed, when you are far away, Janet, I'll try to forget it: I shall notice only its wisdom; which is such that I have made it my law of action. Adèle must go to school; and you, Miss Eyre, must get a new situation."

"Yes, sir, I will advertise immediately: and meantime, I suppose" —— I was going to say, "I suppose I may stay here, till I find another shelter to betake myself to:" but I stopped, feeling it would not do to risk a long sentence, for my voice was not quite under command.

"In about a month I hope to be a bridegroom," continued Mr. Rochester; "and in the interim I shall myself look out for employment and an asylum for you."

"Thank you, sir; I am sorry to give" ——

"Oh, no need to apologise! I consider that when a dependant does her duty as well as you have done yours, she has a sort of claim upon her employer for any little assistance he can conveniently render her; indeed I have already, through my future mother-in-law, heard of a place that I think will suit: it is to undertake the education of the five daughters of Mrs. Dionysius O'Gall of Bitternutt

Lodge, Connaught, Ireland. You'll like Ireland, I think: they're such warm-hearted people there, they say."

"It is a long way off, sir."

"No matter — a girl of your sense will not object to the voyage or the distance."

"Not the voyage, but the distance: and then the sea is a barrier"——

"From what, Jane?"

"From England and from Thornfield: and"——

"Well?"

"From *you,* sir."

I said this almost involuntarily; and, with as little sanction of free will, my tears gushed out. I did not cry so as to be heard, however; I avoided sobbing. The thought of Mrs. O'Gall and Bitternutt Lodge struck cold to my heart; and colder the thought of all the brine and foam, destined, as it seemed, to rush between me and the master at whose side I now walked; and coldest the remembrance of the wider ocean — wealth, caste, custom intervened between me and what I naturally and inevitably loved.

"It is a long way," I again said.

"It is, to be sure; and when you get to Bitternutt Lodge, Connaught, Ireland, I shall never see you again, Jane: that's morally certain. I never go over to Ireland, not having myself much of a fancy for the country. We have been good friends, Jane; have we not?"

"Yes, sir."

"And when friends are on the eve of separation, they like to spend the little time that remains to them close to each other. Come — we'll talk over the voyage and the parting quietly, half an hour or so, while the stars enter into their shining life up in heaven yonder: here is the chestnut tree: here is the bench at its old roots. Come, we will sit there in peace to-night, though we should never more be destined to sit there together." He seated me and himself.

"It is a long way to Ireland, Janet, and I am sorry to send my little friend on such weary travels: but if I can't do better, how is it to be helped? Are you anything akin to me, do you think, Jane?"

I could risk no sort of answer by this time: my heart was full.

"Because," he said, "I sometimes have a queer feeling with regard to you — especially when you are near me, as now: it is as it I had a string somewhere under my left ribs, tightly and inextricably knotted to a similar string situated in the corresponding quarter of your little frame. And if that boisterous channel, and two hundred miles or so of land come broad between us, I am afraid that cord of communion will be snapt; and then I've a nervous notion I should take to bleeding inwardly. As for you,— you'd forget me."

"That I *never* should, sir: you know"—— impossible to proceed.

"Jane, do you hear that nightingale singing in the wood? Listen!"

In listening, I sobbed convulsively; for I could repress what I endured no longer; I was obliged to yield, and I was shaken from head to foot with acute distress. When I did speak, it was only to express an impetuous wish that I had never been born, or never come to Thornfield.

"Because you are sorry to leave it?"

The vehemence of emotion, stirred by grief and love within me, was claiming mastery, and struggling for full sway; and asserting a right to predominate: to overcome, to live, rise, and reign at last; yes,— and to speak.

"I grieve to leave Thornfield: I love Thornfield: — I love it, because I have lived in it a full and delightful life,— momentarily at least. I have not been trampled on. I have not been petrified. I have not been buried with inferior minds, and excluded from every glimpse of communion with what is bright and energetic, and high. I have talked, face to face, with what I reverence; with what I delight in,— with an original, a vigorous, an expanded mind. I have known you, Mr. Rochester; and it strikes me with terror and anguish to feel I absolutely must be torn from you for ever. I see the necessity of departure; and it is like looking on the necessity of death."

"Where do you see the necessity?" he asked, suddenly.

"Where? You, sir, have placed it before me."

"In what shape?"

"In the shape of Miss Ingram; a noble and beautiful woman,— your bride."

"My bride! What bride? I have no bride!"

"But you will have."

"Yes:—I will!—I will!" He set his teeth.

"Then I must go:—you have said it yourself."

"No: you must stay! I swear it—and the oath shall be kept."

"I tell you I must go!" I retorted, roused to something like passion. "Do you think I can stay to become nothing to you? Do you think I am an automaton?—a machine without feelings? and can bear to have my morsel of bread snatched from my lips, and my drop of living water dashed from my cup? Do you think, because I am poor, obscure, plain, and little, I am soulless and heartless? You think wrong!—I have as much soul as you,—and full as much heart! And if God had gifted me with some beauty, and much wealth, I should have made it as hard for you to leave me, as it is now for me to leave you. I am not talking to you now through the medium of custom, conventionalities, or even of mortal flesh:—it is my spirit that addresses your spirit; just as if both had passed through the grave, and we stood at God's feet, equal,—as we are!"

"As we are!" repeated Mr. Rochester—"so," he added, enclosing me in his arms, gathering me to his breast, pressing his lips on my lips: "so, Jane!"

"Yes, so, sir," I rejoined: "and yet not so; for you are a married man—or as good as a married man, and wed to one inferior to you—to one with whom you have no sympathy—whom I do not believe you truly love; for I have seen and heard you sneer at her. I would scorn such a union: therefore I am better than you—let me go!"

"Where, Jane? To Ireland?"

"Yes—to Ireland. I have spoken my mind, and can go anywhere now."

"Jane, be still; don't struggle so, like a wild, frantic bird that is rending its own plumage in its desperation."

"I am no bird; and no net ensnares me; I am a free human being with an independent will; which I now exert to leave you."

Another effort set me at liberty, and I stood erect before him.

"And your will shall decide your destiny," he said: "I offer you my hand, my heart, and a share of all my possessions."

"You play a farce, which I merely laugh at."

"I ask you to pass through life at my side—to be my second self and best earthly companion."

"For that fate you have already made your choice, and must abide by it."

"Jane, be still a few moments: you are over-excited: I will be still too."

A waft of wind came sweeping down the laurel-walk, and trembled through the boughs of the chestnut: it wandered away—away to an indefinite distance — it died. The nightingale's song was then the only voice of the hour: in listening to it, I again wept. Mr. Rochester sat quiet, looking at me gently and seriously. Some time passed before he spoke: he at last said: —

"Come to my side, Jane, and let us explain and understand one another."

"I will never again come to your side: I am torn away now, and cannot return."

"But, Jane, I summon you as my wife: it is you only I intend to marry."

I was silent: I thought he mocked me.

"Come, Jane — come hither."

"Your bride stands between us."

He rose, and with a stride reached me.

"My bride is here," he said, again drawing me to him, "because my equal is here, and my likeness. Jane, will you marry me?"

Still I did not answer, and still I writhed myself from his grasp: for I was still incredulous.

"Do you doubt me, Jane?"

"Entirely."

"You have no faith in me?"

"Not a whit."

"Am I a liar in your eyes?" he asked passionately. "Little sceptic, you *shall* be convinced. What love have I for Miss Ingram? None: and that you know. What love has she for me? None: as I have taken pains to prove: I caused a rumour to reach her that my fortune was not a third of what was supposed, and after that I presented myself to see the result; it was coldness both from her and her mother. I would not — I could not — marry Miss Ingram. You — you strange — you almost unearthly thing! — I love as my own flesh. You — poor and obscure, and small and plain as you are — I entreat to accept me as a husband."

"What, me!" I ejaculated: beginning in his earnestness — and especially in his incivility — to credit his sincerity: "me who have not a friend in the world but you — if you are my friend: not a shilling but what you have given me?"

"You, Jane. I must have you for my own — entirely my own. Will you be mine? Say yes, quickly."

"Mr. Rochester, let me look at your face: turn to the moonlight."

"Why?"

"Because I want to read your countenance; turn!"

"There: you will find it scarcely more legible than a crumpled, scratched page. Read on: only make haste, for I suffer."

His face was very much agitated and very much flushed, and there were strong workings in the features, and strange gleams in the eyes.

"Oh, Jane, you torture me!" he exclaimed. "With that searching and yet faithful and generous look, you torture me!"

"How can I do that? If you are true and your offer real, my only feelings to you must be gratitude and devotion — they cannot torture."

"Gratitude!" he ejaculated; and added wildly —"Jane, accept me quickly. Say Edward — give me my name — Edward — I will marry you."

"Are you in earnest? — Do you truly love me? — Do you sincerely wish me to be your wife?"

"I do; and if an oath is necessary to satisfy you, I swear it."

"Then, sir, I will marry you."

"Edward — my little wife!"

"Dear Edward!"

"Come to me — come to me entirely now," said he: and added, in his deepest tone, speaking in my ear as his cheek was laid on mine, "Make my happiness — I will make yours."

"God pardon me!" he subjoined ere long, "and man meddle not with me: I have her, and will hold her."

"There is no one to meddle, sir. I have no kindred to interfere."

"No — that is the best of it," he said. And if I had loved him less I should have thought his accent and look of exultation savage: but sitting by him, roused from the nightmare of parting — called to the paradise of union — I thought only of the bliss given me to drink in so abundant a flow. Again and again he said, "Are you happy, Jane?" And again and again I answered, "Yes." After which he murmured, "It will atone — it will atone. Have I not found her friendless, and cold, and comfortless? Will I not guard, and cherish, and solace her? Is there not love in my heart, and constancy in my resolves? It will expiate at God's tribunal. I know my Maker sanctions what I do. For the world's judgment — I wash my hands thereof. For man's opinion — I defy it."

But what had befallen the night? The moon was not yet set, and we were all in shadow: I could scarcely see my master's face, near as I was. And what ailed the chestnut tree? it writhed and groaned; while wind roared in the laurel walk, and came sweeping over us.

"We must go in," said Mr. Rochester: "the weather changes. I could have sat with thee till morning, Jane."

"And so," thought I, "could I with you." I should have said so, perhaps, but a livid, vivid spark leapt out of a cloud at which I was looking, and there was a crack, a crash, and a close rattling peal; and I thought only of hiding my dazzled eyes against Mr. Rochester's shoulder.

The rain rushed down. He hurried me up the walk, through the grounds, and into the house; but we were quite wet before we could pass the threshold. He was taking off my shawl in the hall, and shaking the water out of my loosened hair, when Mrs. Fairfax emerged from her room. I did not observe her at first, nor did Mr. Rochester. The lamp was lit. The clock was on the stroke of twelve.

"Hasten to take off your wet things," said he: "and before you go, good-night — good-night, my darling!"

He kissed me repeatedly. When I looked up, on leaving his arms, there stood the widow, pale, grave, and amazed. I only smiled at her, and ran upstairs. "Explanation will do for another time," thought I. Still, when I reached my chamber, I felt a pang at the idea she should even temporarily misconstrue what she had seen. But joy soon effaced every other feeling; and loud as the wind blew, near and deep as the thunder crashed, fierce and frequent as the lightning gleamed, cataract-like as the rain fell during a storm of two hours' duration, I experienced no fear, and little awe. Mr.

Rochester came thrice to my door in the course of it, to ask if I was safe and tranquil: and that was comfort, that was strength for anything.

Before I left my bed in the morning, little Adèle came running in to tell me that the great horse-chestnut at the bottom of the orchard had been struck by lightning in the night, and half of it split away.

## CHAPTER XXIV

As I rose and dressed, I thought over what had happened, and wondered if it were a dream. I could not be certain of the reality till I had seen Mr. Rochester again, and heard him renew his words of love and promise.

While arranging my hair, I looked at my face in the glass, and felt it was no longer plain: there was hope in its aspect, and life in its colour: and my eyes seemed as if they had beheld the fount of fruition, and borrowed beams from the lustrous ripple. I had often been unwilling to look at my master, because I feared he could not be pleased at my look; but I was sure I might lift my face to his now, and not cool his affection by its expression. I took a plain but clean and light summer dress from my drawer and put it on: it seemed no attire had ever so well become me; because none had I ever worn in so blissful a mood.

I was not surprised, when I ran down into the hall, to see that a brilliant June morning had succeeded to the tempest of the night: and to feel, through the open glass door, the breathing of a fresh and fragrant breeze. Nature must be gladsome when I was so happy. A beggar-woman and her little boy — pale, ragged objects both — were coming up the walk, and I ran down and gave them all the money I happened to have in my purse — some three or four shillings: good or bad, they must partake of my jubilee. The rooks cawed, and blither birds sang; but nothing was so merry or so musical as my own rejoicing heart.

Mrs. Fairfax surprised me by looking out of the window with a sad countenance, and saying gravely: — "Miss Eyre, will you come to breakfast?" During the meal she was quiet and cool: but I could not undeceive her then. I must wait for my master to give explanations; and so must she. I ate what I could, and then I hastened upstairs. I met Adèle leaving the school-room.

"Where are you going? It is time for lessons."

"Mr. Rochester has sent me away to the nursery."

"Where is he?"

"In there," pointing to the apartment she had left; and I went in, and there he stood.

"Come and bid me good-morning," said he. I gladly advanced; and it was not merely a cold word now, or even a shake of the hand that I received, but an embrace and a kiss. It seemed natural: it seemed genial to be so well-loved, so caressed by him.

"Jane, you look blooming, and smiling, and pretty," said he: "truly pretty this morning. Is this my pale little elf? Is this my mustard-seed? This little sunny-faced girl with the dimpled cheek and rosy lips; the satin-smooth hazel hair, and the radiant hazel eyes?" (I had green eyes, reader; but you must excuse the mistake: for him they were new-dyed, I suppose.)

"It is Jane Eyre, sir."

"Soon to be Jane Rochester," he added: "in four weeks, Janet; not a day more. Do you hear that?"

I did, and I could not quite comprehend it: it made me giddy. The feeling the announcement sent through me was something stronger than was consistent with joy — something that smote and stunned: it was, I think, almost fear.

"You blushed, and now you are white, Jane: what is that for?"

"Because you gave me a new name — Jane Rochester; and it seems so strange."

"Yes; Mrs. Rochester," said he; "young Mrs. Rochester — Fairfax Rochester's girl-bride."

"It can never be, sir; it does not sound likely. Human beings never enjoy complete happiness in this world. I was not born for a different destiny to the rest of my species; to imagine such a lot befalling me is a fairy tale — a day-dream."

"Which I can and will realise. I shall begin to-day. This morning I wrote to my banker in London to send me certain jewels he has in his keeping,— heirlooms for the ladies of Thornfield. In a day or two I hope to pour them into your lap: for every privilege, every attention shall be yours, that I would accord a peer's daughter if about to marry her."

"Oh, sir! — never mind jewels! I don't like to hear them spoken of. Jewels for Jane Eyre sounds unnatural and strange: I would rather not have them."

"I will myself put the diamond chain round your neck, and the circlet on your forehead,— which it will become: for nature, at least, has stamped her patent of nobility on this brow, Jane; and I will clasp the bracelets on these fine wrists, and load these fairy-like fingers with rings."

"No, no, sir! think of other subjects, and speak of other things, and in another strain. Don't address me as if I were a beauty; I am your plain, Quakerish governess."

"You are a beauty, in my eyes; and a beauty just after the desire of my heart,—delicate and aërial."

"Puny and insignificant, you mean. You are dreaming, sir,—or you are sneering. For God's sake, don't be ironical!"

"I will make the world acknowledge you a beauty, too," he went on, while I really became uneasy at the strain he had adopted; because I felt he was either deluding himself, or trying to delude me. "I will attire my Jane in satin and lace, and she shall have roses in her hair; and I will cover the head I love best with a priceless veil."

"And then you won't know me, sir; and I shall not be your Jane Eyre any longer, but an ape in a harlequin's jacket,—a jay in borrowed plumes. I would as soon see you, Mr. Rochester, tricked out in stage-trappings, as myself clad in a court-lady's robe; and I don't call you handsome, sir, though I love you most dearly: far too dearly to flatter you. Don't flatter me."

He pursued his theme, however, without noticing my deprecation. "This very day I shall take you in the carriage to Millcote, and you must choose some dresses for yourself. I told you we shall be married in four weeks. The wedding is to take place quietly, in the church down below yonder; and then I shall waft you away at once to town. After a brief stay there, I shall bear my treasure to regions nearer the sun: to French vineyards and Italian plains; and she shall see whatever is famous in old story and in modern record: she shall taste, too, of the life of cities; and she shall learn to value herself by just comparison with others."

"Shall I travel?—and with you, sir?"

"You shall sojourn at Paris, Rome, and Naples: at Florence, Venice, and Vienna: all the ground I have wandered over shall be re-trodden by you: wherever I stamped my hoof, your sylph's foot shall step also. Ten years since, I flew through Europe half mad; with disgust, hate, and rage, as my companions: now I shall revisit it healed and cleansed, with a very angel as my comforter."

I laughed at him as he said this. "I am not an angel," I asserted; "and I will not be one till I die: I will be myself, Mr. Rochester, you must neither expect nor exact anything celestial of me — for you will not get it, any more than I shall get it of you: which I do not at all anticipate."

"What do you anticipate of me?"

"For a little while you will perhaps be as you are now,—a very little while; and then you will turn cool; and then you will be capricious; and then you will be stern, and I shall have much ado to please you: but when you get well used to me, you will perhaps like me again,—*like* me, I say, not *love* me. I suppose your love will effervesce in six months, or less. I have observed in books written by men, that period assigned as the farthest to which a husband's ardour extends. Yet, after all, as a friend and companion, I hope never to become quite distasteful to my dear master."

"Distasteful! and like you again! I think I shall like you again and yet again: and I will make you confess I do not only *like*, but *love* you — with truth, fervour, constancy."

"Yet are you not capricious, sir?"

"To women who please me only by their faces, I am the very devil when I find out they have neither souls nor hearts — when they open to me a perspective of flatness, triviality, and perhaps imbecility, coarseness, and ill-temper: but to the clear eye and eloquent tongue, to the soul made of fire, and the character that bends but does not break — at once supple and stable, tractable and consistent — I am ever tender and true."

"Had you ever experience of such a character, sir? Did you ever love such a one?"

"I love it now."

"But before me: if I, indeed, in any respect come up to your difficult standard?"

"I never met your likeness. Jane: you please me, and you master me — you seem to submit, and I like the sense of pliancy you impart; and while I am twining the soft, silken skein round my finger, it sends a thrill up my arm to my heart. I am influenced —conquered; and the influence is sweeter than I can express; and the conquest I undergo has a witchery beyond any triumph *I* can win. Why do you smile, Jane? What does that inexplicable, that uncanny turn of countenance mean?"

"I was thinking, sir (you will excuse the idea; it was involuntary), I was thinking of Hercules and Samson with their charmers"——

"You were, you little elfish"——

"Hush, sir! You don't talk very wisely just now; any more than those gentlemen acted very wisely. However, had they been married, they would no doubt by their severity as husbands have made up for their softness as suitors; and so will you, I fear. I wonder how you will answer me a year hence, should I ask a favour it does not suit your convenience or pleasure to grant."

"Ask me something now, Janet — the least thing: I desire to be entreated"——

"Indeed, I will, sir; I have my petition all ready."

"Speak! But if you look up and smile with that countenance, I shall swear concession before I know to what, and that will make a fool of me."

"Not at all, sir; I ask only this: don't send for the jewels, and don't crown me with roses: you might as well put a border of gold lace round that plain pocket handkerchief you have there."

"I might as well 'gild refined gold.' I know it: your request is granted then — for the time. I will remand the order I despatched to my banker. But you have not yet asked for anything: you have prayed a gift to be withdrawn: try again."

"Well, then, sir, have the goodness to gratify my curiosity, which is much piqued on one point."

He looked disturbed. "What? what?" he said hastily. "Curiosity is a dangerous petition: it is well I have not taken a vow to accord every request"——

"But there can be no danger in complying with this, sir."

"Utter it, Jane: but I wish that instead of a mere inquiry into, perhaps, a secret, it was a wish for half my estate."

"Now, king Ahasuerus! What do I want with half your estate? Do you think I am a Jew-usurer, seeking good investment in land? I would much rather have all your confidence. You will not exclude me from your confidence, if you admit me to your heart?"

"You are welcome to all my confidence that is worth having, Jane: but for God's sake, don't desire a useless burden! Don't long for poison — don't turn out a downright Eve on my hands!"

"Why not, sir? You have just been telling me how much you liked to be conquered, and how pleasant over-persuasion is to you.

Don't you think I had better take advantage of the confession, and begin and coax and entreat — even cry and be sulky if necessary — for the sake of a mere essay of my power?"

"I dare you to any such experiment. Encroach, presume, and the game is up."

"Is it, sir? You soon give in. How stern you look now! Your eyebrows have become as thick as my finger, and your forehead resembles, what, in some very astonishing poetry, I once saw styled, 'a blue-piled thunderloft.' That will be your married look, sir, I suppose?"

"If that will be *your* married look, I, as a Christian, will soon give up the notion of consorting with a mere sprite or salamander. But what had you to ask, thing? — out with it!"

"There, you are less than civil now; and I like rudeness a great deal better than flattery. I had rather be a *thing* than an angel. This is what I have to ask,—Why did you take such pains to make me believe you wished to marry Miss Ingram?"

"Is that all! Thank God, it is no worse!" And now he unknit his black brows; looked down, smiling at me, and stroked my hair, as well pleased at seeing a danger averted. "I think I may confess," he continued, "even although I should make you a little indignant, Jane — and I have seen what a fire-spirit you can be when you are indignant. You glowed in the cool moonlight last night, when you mutinied against fate, and claimed your rank as my equal. Janet, by-the-by, it was you who made me the offer."

"Of course, I did. But to the point if you please, sir — Miss Ingram?"

"Well, I feigned courtship of Miss Ingram, because I wished to render you as madly in love with me as I was with you; and I knew jealousy would be the best ally I could call in for the furtherance of that end."

"Excellent! — Now you are small — not one whit bigger than the end of my little finger. It was a burning shame, and a scandalous disgrace to act in that way. Did you think nothing of Miss Ingram's feelings, sir!"

"Her feelings are concentrated in one — pride; and that needs humbling. Were you jealous, Jane?"

"Never mind, Mr. Rochester: it is in no way interesting to you tc know that Answer me truly once more. Do you think Miss

Ingram will not suffer from your dishonest coquetry? Won't she feel forsaken and deserted?"

"Impossible! — when I told you how she, on the contrary, deserted me: the idea of my insolvency cooled, or rather extinguished, her flame in a moment."

"You have a curious, designing mind, Mr. Rochester. I am afraid your principles on some points are eccentric."

"My principles were never trained, Jane: they may have grown a little awry for want of attention."

"Once again, seriously; may I enjoy the great good that has been vouchsafed to me, without fearing that any one else is suffering the bitter pain I myself felt a while ago?"

"That you may, my good little girl: there is not another being in the world has the same pure love for me as yourself — for I lay that pleasant unction to my soul, Jane, a belief in your affection."

I turned my lips to the hand that lay on my shoulder. I loved him very much — more than I could trust myself to say — more than words had power to express.

"Ask something more," he said presently; "it is my delight to be entreated, and to yield."

I was again ready with my request. "Communicate your intentions to Mrs. Fairfax, sir: she saw me with you last night in the hall, and she was shocked. Give her some explanation before I see her again. It pains me to be misjudged by so good a woman."

"Go to your room, and put on your bonnet," he replied. "I mean you to accompany me to Millcote this morning; and while you prepare for the drive, I will enlighten the old lady's understanding. Did she think, Janet, you had given the world for love, and considered it well lost?"

"I believe she thought I had forgotten my station, and yours, sir."

"Station! station! — your station is in my heart, and on the necks of those who would insult you, now or hereafter. — Go."

I was soon dressed; and when I heard Mr. Rochester quit Mrs. Fairfax's parlour, I hurried down to it. The old lady had been reading her morning portion of Scripture — the lesson for the day; her Bible lay open before her, and her spectacles were upon it. Her occupation, suspended by Mr. Rochester's announcement, seemed now forgotten: her eyes, fixed on the blank wall opposite, expressed the surprise of a quiet mind, stirred by unwonted tidings. Seeing me, she roused herself: she made a sort of effort to smile, and framed a few words of congratulation; but the smile expired, and the sentence was abandoned unfinished. She put up her spectacles, shut the Bible, and pushed her chair back from the table.

"I feel so astonished," she began, "I hardly know what to say to you, Miss Eyre. I have surely not been dreaming, have I? Sometimes I half fall asleep when I am sitting alone, and fancy things that have never happened. It has seemed to me more than once when I have been in a doze, that my dear husband, who died fifteen years since, has come in and sat down beside me; and that I have even heard him call me by my name, Alice, as he used to do. Now, can you tell me whether it is actually true that Mr. Rochester has asked you to marry him? Don't laugh at me. But I really thought he came in here five minutes ago, and said, that in a month you would be his wife."

"He has said the same thing to me," I replied.

"He has! Do you believe him? Have you accepted him?"

"Yes." She looked at me bewildered.

"I could never have thought it. He is a proud man: all the Rochesters were proud: and his father, at least, liked money. He, too, has always been called careful. He means to marry you?"

"He tells me so."

She surveyed my whole person: in her eyes I read that they had there found no charm powerful enough to solve the enigma.

"It passes me!" she continued: "but no doubt it is true since you say so. How it will answer, I cannot tell: I really don't know. Equality of position and fortune is often advisable in such cases; and there are twenty years of difference in your ages. He might almost be your father."

"No, indeed, Mrs. Fairfax!" exclaimed I, nettled: "he is nothing like my father! No one, who saw us together, would suppose it for an instant. Mr. Rochester looks as young, and is as young as some men at five-and-twenty."

"Is it really for love he is going to marry you?" she asked.

I was so hurt by her coldness and scepticism, that the tears rose to my eyes.

"I am sorry to grieve you," pursued the widow; "but you are

so young, and so little acquainted with men, I wished to put you on your guard. It is an old saying that 'all is not gold that glitters'; and in this case I do fear there will be something found to be different to what either you or I expect."

"Why! — am I a monster?" I said: "is it impossible that Mr. Rochester should have a sincere affection for me?"

"No: you are very well; and much improved of late; and Mr. Rochester, I daresay, is fond of you. I have always noticed that you were a sort of pet of his. There are times when, for your sake, I have been a little uneasy at his marked preference, and have wished to put you on your guard: but I did not like to suggest even the possibility of wrong. I knew such an idea would shock, perhaps offend you; and you were so discreet, and so thoroughly modest and sensible, I hoped you might be trusted to protect yourself. Last night I cannot tell you what I suffered when I sought all over the house, and could find you nowhere, nor the master either; and then, at twelve o'clock, saw you come in with him."

"Well, never mind that now," I interrupted impatiently: "it is enough that all was right."

"I hope all will be right in the end," she said: "but believe me, you cannot be too careful. Try and keep Mr. Rochester at a distance: distrust yourself as well as him. Gentlemen in his station are not accustomed to marry their governesses."

I was growing truly irritated: happily, Adèle ran in.

"Let me go,— let me go to Millcote too!" she cried. "Mr. Rochester won't; though there is so much room in the new carriage. Beg him to let me go, mademoiselle."

"That I will, Adèle;" and I hastened away with her, glad to quit my gloomy monitress. The carriage was ready; they were bringing it round to the front, and master was pacing the pavement, Pilot following him backwards and forwards.

"Adèle may accompany us, may she not, sir?"

"I told her no. I'll have no brats! — I'll have only you."

"Do let her go, Mr. Rochester, if you please: it would be better."

"Not it: she will be a restraint."

He was quite peremptory, both in look and voice. The chill of Mrs. Fairfax's warnings, and the damp of her doubts were upon me: something of unsubstantiality and uncertainty had beset my hopes. I half lost the sense of power over him. I was about mechanically to obey him, without further remonstrance: but as he helped me into the carriage, he looked at my face.

"What is the matter?" he asked; "all the sunshine is gone. Do you really wish the bairn to go? Will it annoy you if she is left behind?"

"I would far rather she went, sir."

"Then off for your bonnet, and back, like a flash of lightning!" cried he to Adèle.

She obeyed him with what speed she might.

"After all, a single morning's interruption will not matter much," said he, "when I mean shortly to claim you — your thoughts, conversation, and company — for life."

Adèle, when lifted in, commenced kissing me, by way of expressing her gratitude for my intercession; she was instantly stowed away into a corner on the other side of him. She then peeped round to where I sat; so stern a neighbour was too restrictive: to him, in his present fractious mood, she dared whisper no observations, nor ask of him any information.

"Let her come to me," I entreated: "she will, perhaps, trouble you, sir: there is plenty of room on this side."

He handed her over as if she had been a lap-dog: "I'll send her to school yet," he said, but now he was smiling.

Adèle heard him, and asked if she was to go to school "sans mademoiselle?"

"Yes," he replied, "absolutely sans mademoiselle; for I am to take mademoiselle to the moon, and there I shall seek a cave in one of the white valleys among the volcano-tops, and mademoiselle shall live with me there and only me."

"She will have nothing to eat: you will starve her," observed Adèle.

"I shall gather manna for her morning and night: the plains and hill-sides in the moon are bleached with manna, Adèle."

"She will want to warm herself: what will she do for a fire?"

"Fire rises out of the lunar mountains: when she is cold, I'll carry her up to a peak and lay her down on the edge of a crater."

"Oh, qu'elle y sera ma! — comfortable! And her clothes, they will wear out: how can she get new ones?"

Mr. Rochester professed to be puzzled. "Hem!" said he.

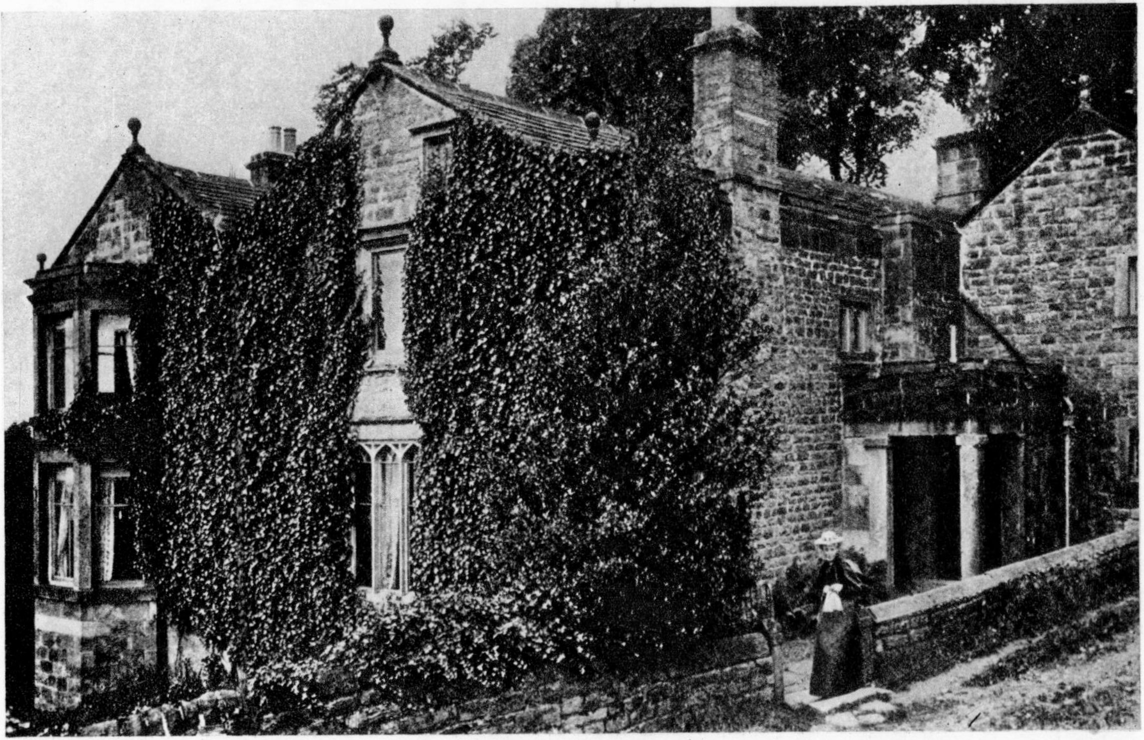

MOORSEATS, HATHERSAGE

Moorseats at Hathersage is the house which appears in *Jane Eyre* as Moor House at Morton. The steps in the picture are those on which Jane fainted when she reached the end of her strength.

"What would you do, Adèle? Cudgel your brains for an expedient. How would a white or pink cloud answer for a gown, do you think? And one could cut a pretty enough scarf out of a rainbow."

" She is far better as she is," concluded Adèle, after musing some time: " besides, she would get tired of living with only you in the moon. If I were mademoiselle, I would never consent to go with you."

" She has consented: she has pledged her word."

" But you can't get her there: there is no road to the moon: it is all air; and neither you nor she can fly."

" Adèle, look at that field." We were now outside Thornfield gates, and bowling lightly along the smooth road to Millcote, where the dust was well laid by the thunder-storm, and where the low hedges and lofty timber trees on each side glistened green, and rain-refreshed.

" In that field, Adèle, I was walking late one evening about a fortnight since — the evening of the day you helped me to make hay in the orchard meadows; and as I was tired with raking swaths, I sat down to rest me on a stile; and there I took out a little book and a pencil, and began to write about a misfortune that befell me long ago, and a wish I had for happy days to come: I was writing away very fast, though daylight was fading from the leaf, when something came up the path and stopped two yards off me. I looked at it. It was a little thing with a veil of gossamer on its head. I beckoned it to come near me: it stood soon at my knee. I never spoke to it, and it never spoke to me in words: but I read its eyes, and it read mine; and our speechless colloquy was to this effect: —

" It was a fairy, and come from Elf-land, it said; and its errand was to make me happy: I must go with it out of the common world to a lonely place — such as the moon, for instance — and it nodded its head towards her horn, rising over Hay-hill: it told me of the alabaster cave and silver vale where we might live. I said I should like to go: but reminded it, as you did me, that I had no wings to fly."

" 'Oh,' returned the fairy, 'that does not signify! Here is a talisman will remove all difficulties;' and she held out a pretty gold ring. 'Put it,' she said, 'on the fourth finger of my left hand, and I am yours, and you are mine; and we shall leave earth, and make our own heaven yonder.' She nodded again at the moon. The ring, Adèle, is in my breeches-pocket, under the disguise of a sovereign: but I mean soon to change it to a ring again."

"But what has mademoiselle to do with it? I don't care for the fairy: you said it was mademoiselle you would take to the moon?"——

"Mademoiselle is a fairy," he said, whispering mysteriously. Whereupon I told her not to mind his badinage; and she, on her part, evinced a fund of genuine French scepticism: denominating Mr. Rochester "un crai menteur," and assuring him that she made no account whatever of his "Contes de fée," and that "du reste, il n'y avait pas de fées, et quand même il y en avait:" she was sure they would never appear to him, nor ever give him rings, or offer to live with him in the moon.

The hour spent at Millcote was a somewhat harassing one to me. Mr. Rochester obliged me to go to a certain silk warehouse: there I was ordered to choose half a dozen dresses. I hated the business, I begged leave to defer it: no — it should be gone through with now. By dint of entreaties expressed in energetic whispers, I reduced the half-dozen to two: these, however, he vowed he would select himself. With anxiety I watched his eye rove over the gay stores: he fixed on a rich silk of the most brilliant amethyst dye, and a superb pink satin. I told him in a new series of whispers, that he might as well buy me a gold gown and a silver bonnet at once: I should certainly never venture to wear his choice. With infinite difficulty, for he was stubborn as a stone, I persuaded him to make an exchange in favour of a sober black satin and pearl-grey silk. "It might pass for the present," he said; "but he would yet see me glittering like a parterre."

Glad was I to get him out of the silk warehouse, and then out of a jeweller's shop: the more he bought me, the more my cheek burned with a sense of annoyance and degradation. As we reentered the carriage, and I sat back feverish and fagged, I remembered what in the hurry of events, dark and bright, I had wholly forgotten — the letter of my uncle, John Eyre, to Mrs. Reed: his intention to adopt me and make me his legatee. "It would, indeed, be a relief," I thought, "if I had ever so small an independency; I never can bear being dressed like a doll by Mr. Rochester, or sitting like a second Danaë with the golden shower falling daily round me. I will write to Madeira the moment I get home, and tell my uncle John I am going to be married, and to whom: if I had but a prospect of one day bringing Mr. Rochester an accession of fortune, I could better endure to be kept by him now." And somewhat relieved by this idea (which I failed not to execute that day), I ventured once more to meet my master's and lover's eye; which most pertinaciously sought mine, though I averted both face and gaze. He smiled; and I thought his smile was such as a sultan might, in a blissful and fond moment, bestow on a slave his gold and gems had enriched: I crushed his hand, which was ever hunting mine, vigorously, and thrust it back to him red with the passionate pressure —

"You need not look that way," I said: "if you do, I'll wear nothing but my old Lowood frocks to the end of the chapter. I'll be married in this lilac gingham — you may make a dressing-gown for yourself out of the pearl-grey silk, and an infinite series of waistcoats out of the black satin."

He chuckled; he rubbed his hands: "Oh, it is rich to see and hear her!" he exclaimed. "Is she original? Is she piquant? I would not exchange this one little English girl for the grand Turk's whole seraglio; gazelle-eyes, houri forms and all!"

The eastern allusion bit me again: "I'll not stand you an inch in the stead of a seraglio," I said; "so don't consider me an equivalent for one; if you have a fancy for anything in that line, away with you, sir, to the bazaars of Stamboul without delay; and lay out in extensive slave-purchases some of that spare cash you seem at a loss to spend satisfactorily here."

"And what will you do, Janet, while I am bargaining for so many tons of flesh and such an assortment of black eyes?"

"I'll be preparing myself to go out as a missionary to preach liberty to them that are enslaved — your harem inmates amongst the rest. I'll get admitted there, and I'll stir up mutiny; and you, three-tailed bashaw as you are, sir, shall in a trice find yourself fettered amongst our hands: nor will I, for one, consent to cut your bonds till you have signed a charter, the most liberal that despot ever yet conferred."

"I would consent to be at your mercy, Jane."

"I would have no mercy, Mr. Rochester, if you supplicated for it with an eye like that. While you looked so, I should be certain that whatever charter you might grant under coercion, your first act, when released, would be to violate its conditions."

"Why, Jane, what would you have? I fear you will compel me to go through a private marriage ceremony, besides that performed at the altar. You will stipulate, I see, for peculiar terms — what will they be?"

"I only want an easy mind, sir; not crushed by crowded obligations. Do you remember what you said of Céline Varens? — of the diamonds, the cashmeres you gave her? I will not be your English Céline Varens. I shall continue to act as Adèle's governess; by that I shall earn my board and lodging, and thirty pounds a year besides. I'll furnish my own wardrobe out of that money, and you shall give me nothing but"——

"Well, but what?"

"Your regard: and if I give you mine in return, that debt will be quit."

"Well, for cool native impudence, and pure innate pride, you haven't your equal," said he. We were now approaching Thornfield. "Will it please you to dine with me to-day?" he asked, as we re-entered the gates.

"No, thank you, sir."

"And what for 'no, thank you'? if one may inquire."

"I never have dined with you, sir: and I see no reason why I should now: till"——

"Till what? You delight in half-phrases."

"Till I can't help it."

"Do you suppose I eat like an ogre, or a ghoul, that you dread being the companion of my repast?"

"I have formed no supposition on the subject, sir; but I want to go on as usual for another month."

"You will give up your governessing slavery at once."

"Indeed! begging your pardon, sir, I shall not. I shall just go on with it as usual. I shall keep out of your way all day, as I have been accustomed to do: you may send for me in the evening, when you feel disposed to see me, and I'll come then, but at no other time."

"I want a smoke, Jane, or a pinch of snuff, to comfort me under all this 'pour me donner une contenance,' as Adèle would say; and unfortunately I have neither my cigar-case, nor my snuff-box.

But listen — whisper — it is your time now, little tyrant, but it will be mine presently: and when once I have fairly seized you, to have and to hold, I'll just — figuratively speaking — attach you to a chain like this" (touching his watch-guard). "Yes, bonny wee thing, I'll wear you in my bosom, lest my jewel I should tyne."

He said this as he helped me to alight from the carriage: and while he afterwards lifted out Adèle. I entered the house, and made good my retreat upstairs.

He duly summoned me to his presence in the evening. I had prepared an occupation for him; for I was determined not to spend the whole time in a *tête-à-tête* conversation. I remembered his fine voice: I knew he liked to sing — good singers generally do. I was no vocalist myself, and, in his fastidious judgment, no musician, either; but I delighted in listening when the performance was good. No sooner had twilight, that hour of romance, begun to lower her blue and starry banner over the lattice, than I rose, opened the piano, and entreated him, for the love of heaven, to give me a song. He said I was a capricious witch, and that he would rather sing another time; but I averred that no time was like the present.

"Did I like his voice?" he asked.

"Very much." I was not fond of pampering that susceptible vanity of his; but for once, and from motives of expediency, I would e'en soothe and stimulate it.

"Then, Jane, you must play the accompaniment."

"Very well, sir, I will try."

I did try, but was presently swept off the stool and denominated, "a little bungler." Being pushed unceremoniously to one side — which was precisely what I wished — he usurped my place, and proceeded to accompany himself: for he could play as well as sing. I hied me to the window-recess; and while I sat there and looked out on the still trees and dim lawn, to a sweet air was sung in mellow tones the following strain: —

The truest love that ever heart
　Felt at its kindled core
Did through each vein, in quickened start,
　The tide of being pour.

Her coming was my hope each day,
　Her parting was my pain;

The chance that did her steps delay
  Was ice in every vein.

I dreamed it would be nameless bliss,
  As I loved, loved to be;
And to this object did I press
  As blind as eagerly.

But wide as pathless was the space
  That lay, our lives between,
And dangerous as the foamy race
  Of ocean-surges green.

And haunted as a robber path
  Through wilderness or wood;
For Might and Right, and Woe and Wrath,
  Between our spirits stood.

I dangers dared; I hind'rance scorned;
  I omens did defy;
Whatever menaced, harassed, warned,
  I passed impetuous by.

On sped my rainbow, fast as light;
  I flew as in a dream;
For glorious rose upon my sight
  That child of Shower and Gleam.

Still bright on clouds of suffering dim
  Shines that soft, solemn joy;
Nor care I now, how dense and grim
  Disasters gather nigh.

I care not in this moment sweet,
  Though all I have rushed o'er
Should come on pinion, strong and fleet,
  Proclaiming vengeance sore:

Though haughty Hate should strike me down,
  Right, bar approach to me,
And grinding Might, with furious frown,
  Swear endless enmity.

My love has placed her little hand
  With noble faith in mine,
And vowed that wedlock's sacred band
  Our nature shall entwine.

My love has sworn, with sealing kiss,
With me to live — to die;
I have at last my nameless bliss:
As I love — loved am I!

He rose and came towards me, and I saw his face all kindled, and his full falcon-eye flashing, and tenderness and passion in every lineament. I quailed momentarily — then I rallied. Soft scene, daring demonstration, I would not have; and I stood in peril of both: a weapon of defence must be prepared — I whetted my tongue; as he reached me, I asked with asperity, "whom he was going to marry now?"

"That was a strange question to be put by his darling Jane."

"Indeed! I considered it a very natural and necessary one: he had talked of his future wife dying with him. What did he mean by such a pagan idea? *I* had no intention of dying with him — he might depend on that."

"Oh, all he longed, all he prayed for, was that I might live with him! Death was not for such as I."

"Indeed it was: I had as good a right to die when my time came as he had: but I should bide that time, and not be hurried away in a suttee."

"Would I forgive him for the selfish idea, and prove my pardon by a reconciling kiss?"

"No: I would rather be excused."

Here I heard myself apostrophised as a "hard little thing"; and it was added, "any other woman would have been melted to marrow at hearing such stanzas crooned in her praise."

I assured him I was naturally hard — very flinty, and that he would often find me so; and that, moreover, I was determined to show him divers rugged points in my character before the ensuing four weeks elapsed: he should know fully what sort of a bargain he had made, while there was yet time to rescind it.

"Would I be quiet, and talk rationally?"

"I would be quiet if he liked; and as to talking rationally, I flattered myself I was doing that now."

He fretted, pished, and pshawed. "Very good," I thought; "you may fume and fidget as you please: but this is the best plan to pursue with you, I am certain. I like you more than I can say;

but I'll not sink into a bathos of sentiment; and with this needle of repartee I'll keep you from the edge of the gulf too; and, moreover, maintain by its pungent aid that distance between you and myself most conducive to our real mutual advantage."

From less to more, I worked him up to considerable irritation; then, after he had retired, in dudgeon, quite to the other end of the room, and I got up, saying, "I wish you good-night, sir," in my natural and wonted respectful manner, I slipped out by the side-door and got away.

The system thus entered on, I pursued during the whole season of probation; and with the best success. He was kept, to be sure, rather cross and crusty: but on the whole I could see he was excellently entertained; and that a lamb-like submission and turtle-dove sensibility, while fostering his despotism more, would have pleased his judgment, satisfied his common-sense, and even suited his taste, less.

In other people's presence I was, as formerly, deferential and quiet; any other line of conduct being uncalled for: it was only in the evening conferences I thus thwarted and afflicted him. He continued to send for me punctually the moment the clock struck seven; though when I appeared before him now, he had no such honeyed terms as "love" and "darling" on his lips: the best words at my service were "provoking puppet," "malicious elf," "sprite," "changeling," etc. For caresses, too, I now got grimaces; for a pressure of the hand, a pinch on the arm; for a kiss on the cheek, a severe tweak of the ear. It was all right: at present I decidedly preferred these fierce favours to anything more tender. Mrs. Fairfax, I saw, approved me: her anxiety on my account vanished; therefore I was certain I did well. Meantime, Mr. Rochester affirmed I was wearing him to skin and bone, and threatened awful vengeance for my present conduct at some period fast coming. I laughed in my sleeve at his menaces: "I can keep you in reasonable check now," I reflected; "and I don't doubt to be able to do it hereafter: if one expedient loses its virtue, another must be devised."

Yet after all my task was not an easy one; often I would rather have pleased than teased him. My future husband was becoming to me my whole world; and more than the world: almost my hope of heaven. He stood between me and every thought of religion, as an eclipse intervenes between man and the broad sun. I could not, in those days, see God for his creature: of whom I had made an idol.

# CHAPTER XXV

THE month of courtship had wasted: its very last hours were being numbered. There was no putting off the day that advanced — the bridal day; and all preparations for its arrival were complete. *I*, at least, had nothing more to do: there were my trunks, packed, locked, corded, ranged in a row along the wall of my little chamber; to-morrow, at this time, they would be far on their road to London: and so should I (D. V.),— or rather, not I, but one Jane Rochester, a person whom as yet I knew not. The cards of address alone remained to nail on: they lay, four little squares on the drawer. Mr. Rochester had himself written the direction, "Mrs. Rochester,—— Hotel, London," on each: I could not persuade myself to affix them, or to have them affixed. Mrs. Rochester! She did not exist: she would not be born till to-morrow, some time after eight o'clock A. M.: and I would wait to be assured she had come into the world alive, before I assigned to her all that property. It was enough that in yonder closet, opposite my dressing-table, garments said to be hers had already displaced my black stuff Lowood frock and straw bonnet: for not to me appertained that suit of wedding raiment; the pearl-coloured robe, the vapoury veil, pendent from the usurped portmanteau. I shut the closet, to conceal the strange, wraith-like apparel it contained; which, at this evening hour — nine o'clock — gave out certainly a most ghostly shimmer through the shadow of my apartment. "I will leave you by yourself, white dream," I said. "I am feverish: I heard the wind blowing: I will go out of doors and feel it."

It was not only the hurry of preparation that made me feverish; not only the anticipation of the great change — the new life which was to commence to-morrow; both these circumstances had their share, doubtless, in producing that restless, excited mood which hurried me forth at this late hour into the darkening grounds: but a third cause influenced my mind more than they.

I had at heart a strange and anxious thought. Something had

happened which I could not comprehend; no one knew of or had seen the event but myself: it had taken place the preceding night. Mr. Rochester that night was absent from home; nor was he yet returned: business had called him to a small estate of two or three farms he possessed thirty miles off — business it was requisite he should settle in person, previously to his meditated departure from England. I waited now his return; eager to disburthen my mind, and to seek of him the solution of the enigma that perplexed me. Stay till he comes, reader; and, when I disclose my secret to him, you shall share the confidence.

I sought the orchard: driven to its shelter by the wind, which all day had blown strong and full from the south; without, however, bringing a speck of rain. Instead of subsiding as night drew on, it seemed to augment its rush and deepen its roar: the trees blew stedfastly one way, never writhing round, and scarcely tossing back their boughs once in an hour; so continuous was the strain bending their branchy heads northward — the clouds drifted from pole to pole, fast following, mass on mass: no glimpse of blue sky had been visible that July day.

It was not without a certain wild pleasure I ran before the wind delivering my trouble of mind to the measureless air-torrent thundering through space. Descending the laurel walk, I faced the wreck of the chestnut-tree; it stood up, black and riven: the trunk, split down the centre, gasped ghastly. The cloven halves were not broken from each other, for the firm base and strong roots kept them unsundered below; though community of vitality was destroyed — the sap could flow no more: their great boughs on each side were dead, and next winter's tempests would be sure to fell one or both to earth: as yet, however, they might be said to form one tree — a ruin, but an entire ruin.

"You did right to hold fast to each other," I said: as if the monster-splinters were living things, and could hear me. "I think, scathed as you look, and charred and scorched, there must be a little sense of life in you yet: rising out of that adhesion at the faithful, honest roots: you will never have green leaves more — never more see birds making nests and singing idylls in your boughs; the time of pleasure and love is over with you: but you are not desolate: each of you has a comrade to sympathise with him in his decay." As I looked up at them, the moon appeared momentarily in that part of the sky which filled their fissure; her disk was blood-red, and half overcast; she seemed to throw on me one bewildered, dreary glance, and buried herself again instantly in the deep drift of cloud. The wind fell, for a second, round Thornfield; but far away over wood and water, poured a wild, melancholy wail: it was sad to listen to, and I ran off again.

Here and there I strayed through the orchard, gathered up the apples with which the grass round the tree roots was thickly strewn: then I employed myself in dividing the ripe from the unripe; I carried them into the house and put them away in the store-room. Then I repaired to the library to ascertain whether the fire was lit; for, though summer, I knew on such a gloomy evening, Mr. Rochester would like to see a cheerful hearth when he came in: yes, the fire had been kindled some time, and burnt well. I placed his arm-chair by the chimney-corner: I wheeled the table near it: I let down the curtain, and had the candles brought in ready for lighting. More restless than ever, when I had completed these arrangements I could not sit still, nor even remain in the house: a little time-piece in the room and the old clock in the hall simultaneously struck ten.

"How late it grows!" I said: "I will run down to the gates: it is moonlight at intervals: I can see a good way on the road. He may be coming now, and to meet him will save some minutes of suspense."

The wind roared high in the great trees which embowered the gates; but the road as far as I could see, to the right hand and the left, was all still and solitary: save for the shadows of clouds crossing it at intervals, as the moon looked out, it was but a long pale line, unvaried by one moving speck.

A puerile tear dimmed my eye while I looked — a tear of disappointment and impatience: ashamed of it, I wiped it away. I lingered; the moon shut herself wholly within her chamber, and drew close her curtain of dense cloud: the night grew dark; rain came driving fast on the gale.

"I wish he would come! I wish he would come!" I exclaimed, seized with hypochondriac foreboding. I had expected his arrival before tea; now it was dark: what could keep him? Had an accident happened? The event of last night again recurred to me. I interpreted it as a warning of disaster. I feared my hopes were too bright to be realised; and I had enjoyed so much bliss lately that

I imagined my fortune had passed its meridian, and must now decline.

"Well, I cannot return to the house," I thought; "I cannot sit by the fireside, while he is abroad in inclement weather: better tire my limbs than strain my heart; I will go forward and meet him."

I set out; I walked fast, but not far: ere I had measured a quarter of a mile, I heard the tramp of hoofs; a horseman came on, full gallop; a dog ran by his side. Away with evil presentiment! It was he: here he was, mounted on Mesrour, followed by Pilot. He saw me; for the moon had opened a blue field in the sky, and rode in it watery bright: he took his hat off, and waved it round his head. I now ran to meet him.

"There!" he exclaimed, as he stretched out his hand and bent from the saddle: "You can't do without me, that is evident. Step on my boot-toe; give me both hands: mount!"

I obeyed; joy made me agile: I sprang up before him. A hearty kissing I got for a welcome; and some boastful triumph, which I swallowed as well as I could. He checked himself in his exultation to demand, "But is there anything the matter, Janet, that you come to meet me at such an hour: Is there anything wrong?"

"No; but I thought you would never come. I could not bear to wait in the house for you, especially with this rain and wind."

"Rain and wind, indeed! Yes, you are dripping like a mermaid; pull my cloak round you: but I think you are feverish, Jane: both your cheek and hand are burning hot. I ask again, is there anything the matter?"

"Nothing, now: I am neither afraid nor unhappy."

"Then you have been both?"

"Rather: but I'll tell you all about it by-and-by, sir; and I daresay you will only laugh at me for my pains."

"I'll laugh at you heartily when to-morrow is past; till then I dare not: my prize is not certain. This is you; who have been as slippery as an eel this last month, and as thorny as a briar-rose? I could not lay a finger anywhere but I was pricked; and now I seem to have gathered up a stray lamb in my arms: you wandered out of the fold to seek your shepherd, did you, Jane?"

"I wanted you, but don't boast. Here we are at Thornfield: now let me get down."

He landed me on the pavement. As John took his horse, and

he followed me into the hall, he told me to make haste and put something dry on, and then return to him in the library; and he stopped me, as I made for the staircase, to extort a promise that I would not be long: nor was I long; in five minutes I rejoined him. I found him at supper.

"Take a seat and bear me company, Jane: please God, it is the last meal but one you will eat at Thornfield Hall for a long time."

I sat down near him; but told him I could not eat.

"Is it because you have the prospect of a journey before you, Jane? Is it the thoughts of going to London that takes away your appetite?"

"I cannot see my prospects clearly to-night, sir: and I hardly know what thoughts I have in my head. Everything in life seems unreal."

"Except me: I am substantial enough: — touch me."

"You, sir, are the most phantom-like of all: you are a mere dream."

He held out his hand, laughing: "Is that a dream?" said he, placing it close to my eyes. He had a rounded, muscular, and vigorous hand, as well as a long, strong arm.

"Yes; though I touch it, it is a dream," said I, as I put it down from before my face. "Sir, have you finished supper?"

"Yes, Jane."

I rang the bell, and ordered away the tray. When we were again alone, I stirred the fire, and then took a low seat at my master's knee.

"It is near midnight," I said.

"Yes: but remember, Jane, you promised to wake with me the night before my wedding."

"I did; and I will keep my promise, for an hour or two at least; I have no wish to go to bed."

"Are all your arrangements complete?"

"All, sir."

"And on my part, likewise," he returned, "I have settled everything; and we leave Thornfield to-morrow, within half an hour after our return from church."

"Very well, sir."

"With what an extraordinary smile you uttered that word —

'very well,' Jane! What a bright spot of colour you have on each cheek! and how strangely your eyes glitter! Are you well?"

"I believe I am."

"Believe! What is the matter?—Tell me what you feel."

"I could not, sir: no words could tell you what I feel. I wish this present hour would never end: who knows with what fate the next may come charged?"

"This is hypochondria, Jane. You have been over-excited or over-fatigued."

"Do you, sir, feel calm and happy?"

"Calm?—no: but happy—to the heart's core."

I looked up at him to read the signs of bliss in his face: it was ardent and flushed.

"Give me your confidence, Jane," he said: "relieve your mind of any weight that oppresses it, by imparting it to me. What do you fear?—that I shall not prove a good husband?"

"It is the idea farthest from my thoughts."

"Are you apprehensive of the new sphere you are about to enter?—of the new life into which you are passing?"

"No."

"You puzzle me, Jane: your look and tone of sorrowful audacity perplex and pain me. I want an explanation."

"Then, sir,—listen. You were from home last night?"

"I was:—I know that; and you hinted a while ago at something which had happened in my absence:—nothing, probably, of consequence; but, in short, it has disturbed you. Let me hear it. Mrs. Fairfax has said something, perhaps? or you have overheard the servants talk?—your sensitive self-respect has been wounded?"

"No, sir." It struck twelve—I waited till the time-piece had concluded its silver chime, and the clock its hoarse, vibrating stroke, and then I proceeded.

"All day, yesterday, I was very busy, and very happy in my ceaseless bustle; for I am not, as you seem to think, troubled by any haunting fears about the new sphere, et cetera: I think it a glorious thing to have the hope of living with you, because I love you. No, sir, don't caress me now—let me talk undisturbed. Yesterday I trusted well in Providence, and believed that events were working together for your good and mine: it was a fine day, if you recollect — the calmness of the air and sky forbade apprehensions regarding your safety or comfort on your journey. I walked a little while on the pavement after tea, thinking of you; and I beheld you in imagination so near me, I scarcely missed your actual presence. I thought of the life that lay before me — *your* life, sir — an existence more expansive and stirring than my own: as much more so as the depths of the sea to which the brook runs, are than the shallows of its own strait channel. I wondered why moralists call this world a dreary wilderness: for me it blossomed like a rose. Just at sunset, the air turned cold and the sky cloudy: I went in. Sophie called me upstairs to look at my wedding-dress, which they had just brought; and under it in the box I found your present — the veil which, in your princely extravagance, you sent for from London: resolved, I suppose, since I would not have jewels, to cheat me into accepting something as costly. I smiled as I unfolded it, and devised how I would tease you about your aristocratic tastes, and your efforts to masque your plebeian bride in the attributes of a peeress. I thought how I would carry down to you the square of unembroidered blond I had myself prepared as a covering for my low-born head, and ask if that was not good enough for a woman who could bring her husband neither fortune, beauty, nor connections. I saw plainly how you would look; and heard your impetuous republican answers, and your haughty disavowal of any necessity on your part to augment your wealth, or elevate your standing, by marrying either a purse or a coronet."

"How well you read me, you witch!" interposed Mr. Rochester: "but what did you find in the veil besides its embroidery? Did you find poison or a dagger that you look so mournful now?"

"No, no, sir; besides the delicacy and richness of the fabric, I found nothing save Fairfax Rochester's pride; and that did not scare me, because I am used to the sight of the demon. But, sir, as it grew dark, the wind rose: it blew yesterday evening, not as it blows now — wild and high — but 'with a sullen, moaning sound' far more eerie. I wished you were at home. I came into this room, and the sight of the empty chair and fireless hearth chilled me. For some time after I went to bed, I could not sleep — a sense of anxious excitement distressed me. The gale still rising, seemed to my ear to muffle a mournful under-sound; whether in the house or abroad I could not at first tell, but it recurred, doubtful yet doleful at every lull: at last I made out it must be some dog howling at a distance. I was glad when it ceased. On sleeping, I continued in dreams the idea of a dark and gusty night. I continued also the wish to be with you, and experienced a strange, regretful consciousness, of some barrier dividing us. During all my first sleep, I was following the windings of an unknown road; total obscurity environed me; rain pelted me; I was burdened with the charge of a little child: a very small creature, too young and feeble to walk, and which shivered in my cold arms, and wailed piteously in my ear. I thought, sir, that you were on the road a long way before me; and I strained every nerve to overtake you, and made effort on effort to utter your name and entreat you to stop — but my movements were fettered; and my voice still died away inarticulate; while you, I felt, withdrew farther and farther every moment."

"And these dreams weigh on your spirits now, Jane, when I am close to you? Little nervous subject! Forget visionary woe, and think only of real happiness! You say you love me, Janet: yes — I will not forget that; and you cannot deny it. *Those* words did not die inarticulate on your lips. I heard them clear and soft: a thought too solemn perhaps, but sweet as music —'I think it is a glorious thing to have the hope of living with you, Edward, because I love you.'— Do you love me, Janet? repeat it."

"I do, sir.— I do, with my whole heart."

"Well," he said, after some minutes' silence, "it is strange; but that sentence has penetrated my breast painfully. Why? I think because you said it with such an earnest, religious energy; and because your upward gaze at me now is the very sublime of faith, truth, and devotion: it is too much as if some spirit were near me. Look wicked, Jane; as you know well how to look: coin one of your wild, shy, provoking smiles; tell me you hate me — tease me, vex me: do anything but move me: I would rather be incensed than saddened."

"I will tease you and vex you to your heart's content, when I have finished my tale: but hear me to the end."

"I thought, Jane, you had told me all. I thought I had found the source of your melancholy in a dream!"

I shook my head. "What! is there more? But I will not believe it to be anything important. I warn you of incredulity beforehand. Go on."

The disquietude of his air, the somewhat apprehensive impatience of his manner, surprised me: but I proceeded.

"I dreamt another dream, sir: that Thornfield Hall was a dreary ruin, the retreat of bats and owls. I thought that of all the stately front nothing remained but a shell-like wall, very high, and very fragile-looking. I wandered, on a moonlight night, through the gress-grown enclosure within: here I stumbled over a marble hearth, and there over a fallen fragment of cornice. Wrapped up in a shawl, I still carried the unknown little child: I might not lay it down anywhere, however tired were my arms — however much its weight impeded my progress, I must retain it. I heard the gallop of a horse at a distance on the road: I was sure it was you; and you were departing for many years, and for a distant country. I climbed the thin wall with frantic perilous haste, eager to catch one glimpse of you from the top: the stones rolled from under my feet, the ivy branches I grasped gave way, the child clung round my neck in terror, and almost strangled me: at last I gained the summit. I saw you like a speck on a white track, lessening every moment. The blast blew so strong I could not stand. I sat down on the narrow ledge; I hushed the scared infant in my lap: you turned an angle in the road; I bent forward to take a last look; the wall crumbled; I was shaken; the child rolled from my knee, I lost my balance, fell, and woke."

"Now, Jane, that is all."

"All the preface, sir; the tale is yet to come. On waking, a gleam dazzled my eyes: I thought — oh, it is daylight! But I was mistaken: it was only candle-light. Sophie, I supposed, had come in. There was a light on the dressing-table, and the door of the closet, where, before going to bed, I had hung my wedding dress and veil, stood open: I heard a rustling there. I asked, 'Sophie, what are you doing?' No one answered; but a form emerged from the closet: it took the light, held it aloft and surveyed the garments pendent from the portmanteau. 'Sophie! Sophie!' I again cried: and still it was silent. I had risen up in bed, I bent forward: first, surprise, then bewilderment, came over me; and then my blood crept cold through my veins. Mr. Rochester, this was not Sophie, it was not Leah, it was not Mrs. Fairfax: it was not — no, I was sure of it, and am still — it was not even that strange woman, Grace Poole."

"It must have been one of them," interrupted my master.

"No, sir, I solemnly assure you to the contrary. The shape standing before me had never crossed my eyes within the precincts of Thornfield Hall before; the height, the contour were new to me."

"Describe it, Jane."

"It seemed, sir, a woman, tall and large, with thick and dark hair hanging long down her back. I know not what dress she had on: it was white and straight; but whether gown, sheet, or shroud, I cannot tell."

"Did you see her face?"

"Not at first. But presently she took my veil from its place; she held it up; gazed at it long, and then she threw it over her own head, and turned to the mirror. At that moment I saw the reflection of the visage and features quite distinctly in the dark oblong glass."

"And how were they?"

"Fearful and ghastly to me — oh, sir, I never saw a face like it! It was a discoloured face — it was a savage face. I wish I could forget the roll of the red eyes and the fearful blackened inflation of the lineaments!"

"Ghosts are usually pale, Jane."

"This, sir, was purple: the lips were swelled and dark; the brow furrowed; the black eyebrows widely raised over the blood-shot eyes. Shall I tell you of what it reminded me?"

"You may."

"Of the foul German spectre — the Vampyre."

"Ah! — what did it do?"

"Sir, it removed my veil from its gaunt head, rent it in two parts, and flinging both on the floor, trampled on them."

"Afterwards?"

"It drew aside the window-curtain and looked out: perhaps it saw dawn approaching, for, taking the candle, it retreated to the door. Just at my bedside the figure stopped: the fiery eye glared upon me — she thrust up her candle close to my face, and extinguished it under my eyes. I was aware her lurid visage flamed over mine, and I lost consciousness: for the second time in my life — only the second time — I became insensible from terror."

"Who was with you when you revived?"

"No one, sir; but the broad day. I rose, bathed my head and

face in water, drank a long draught; felt that though enfeebled I was not ill, and determined that to none but you would I impart this vision. Now, sir, tell me who and what that woman was?"

"The creature of an over-stimulated brain; that is certain. I must be careful of you, my treasure: nerves like yours were not made for rough handling."

"Sir, depend upon it, my nerves were not in fault; the thing was real: the transaction actually took place."

"And your previous dreams: were they real too? Is Thornfield Hall a ruin? Am I severed from you by insuperable obstacles? Am I leaving you without a tear — without a kiss — without a word?"

"Not yet."

"Am I about to do it? — Why, the day is already commenced which is to bind us indissolubly; and when we are once united, there shall be no recurrence of these mental terrors: I guarantee that."

"Mental terrors, sir! I wish I could believe them to be only such: I wish it more than ever; since even you cannot explain to me the mystery of that awful visitant."

"And since I cannot do it, Jane, it must have been unreal."

"But, sir, when I said so to myself on rising this morning, and when I looked round the room to gather courage and comfort from the cheerful aspect of each familiar object in full daylight, there — on the carpet — I saw what gave the distinct lie to my hypothesis,— the veil, torn from top to bottom in two halves!"

I felt Mr. Rochester start and shudder; he hastily flung his arms round me: "Thank God!" he exclaimed, "that if anything malignant did come near you last night, it was only the veil that was harmed.— Oh, to think what might have happened!"

He drew his breath short, and strained me so close to him, I could scarcely pant. After some minutes' silence, he continued, cheerily: —

"Now, Janet, I'll explain to you all about it. It was half dream, half reality: a woman did, I doubt not, enter your room: and that woman was — must have been — Grace Poole. You call her a strange being yourself: from all you know, you have reason so to call her — what did she do to me? what to Mason? In a state between sleeping and waking, you noticed her entrance and her actions; but feverish, almost delirious as you were, you ascribed to her a goblin appearance different from her own: the long dishevelled hair, the swelled black face, the exaggerated stature, were figments of imagination; results of nightmare: the spiteful tearing of the veil was real: and it is like her. I see you would ask why I keep such a woman in my house: when we have been married a year and a day, I will tell you: but not now. Are you satisfied, Jane? Do you accept my solution of the mystery?"

I reflected, and in truth it appeared to me the only possible one: satisfied I was not, but to please him I endeavoured to appear so — relieved, I certainly did feel; so I answered him with a contented smile. And now, as it was long past one, I prepared to leave him.

"Does not Sophie sleep with Adèle in the nursery?" he asked, as I lit my candle.

"Yes, sir."

"And there is room enough in Adèle's little bed for you. You must share it with her to-night, Jane: it is no wonder that the incident you have related should make you nervous, and I would rather you did not sleep alone: promise me to go to the nursery."

"I shall be very glad to do so, sir."

"And fasten the door securely on the inside. Wake Sophie when you go upstairs, under pretence of requesting her to rouse you in good time to-morrow; for you must be dressed and have finished breakfast before eight. And now, no more sombre thoughts: chase dull care away, Janet. Don't you hear to what soft whispers the wind has fallen? and there is no more beating of rain against the window-panes: look here" (he lifted up the curtain) —"it is a lovely night!"

It was. Half heaven was pure and stainless: the clouds, now trooping before the wind, which had shifted to the west, were filing off eastward, in long, silvered columns. The moon shone peacefully.

"Well," said Mr. Rochester, gazing inquiringly into my eyes, "how is my Janet now?"

"The night is serene, sir; and so am I."

"And you will not dream of separation and sorrow to-night; but of happy love and blissful union."

This prediction was but half fulfilled: I did not indeed dream of sorrow, but as little did I dream of joy; for I never slept at all. With little Adèle in my arms, I watched the slumber of childhood — so tranquil, so passionless, so innocent — and waited for the coming day: all my life was awake and astir in my frame: and as soon as the sun rose I rose too. I remember Adèle clung to me as I left her: I remember I kissed her as I loosened her little hands from my neck; and I cried over her with strange emotion, and quitted her because I feared my sobs would break her still sound repose. She seemed the emblem of my past life; and he, I was now to array myself to meet, the dread, but adored, type of my unknown future day.

## CHAPTER XXVI

SOPHIE came at seven to dress me; she was very long indeed in accomplishing her task; so long that Mr. Rochester, grown, I suppose, impatient of my delay, sent up to ask why I did not come. She was just fastening my veil (the plain square of blond after all) to my hair with a brooch; I hurried from under her hands as soon as I could.

"Stop!" she cried in French. "Look at yourself in the mirror: you have not taken one peep."

So I turned at the door: I saw a robed and veiled figure, so unlike my usual self that it seemed almost the image of a stranger. "Jane!" called a voice, and I hastened down. I was received at the foot of the stairs by Mr. Rochester.

"Lingerer," he said, "my brain is on fire with impatience; and you tarry so long!"

He took me into the dining-room, surveyed me keenly all over, pronounced me "fair as a lily, and not only the pride of his life, but the desire of his eyes," and then telling me he would give me but ten minutes to eat some breakfast, he rang the bell. One of his lately hired servants, a footman, answered it.

"Is John getting the carriage ready?"

"Yes, sir."

"Is the luggage brought down?"

"They are bringing it down, sir."

"Go you to the church: see if Mr. Wood (the clergyman) and the clerk are there: return and tell me."

The church, as the reader knows, was but just beyond the gates; the footman soon returned.

"Mr. Wood is in the vestry, sir, putting on his surplice."

"And the carriage?"

"The horses are harnessing."

"We shall not want it to go to church; but it must be ready the moment we return: all the boxes and luggage arranged and strapped on, and the coachman in his seat."

"Yes, sir."

"Jane, are you ready?"

I rose. There were no groomsmen, no bridesmaids, no relatives to wait for or marshal: none but Mr. Rochester and I. Mrs. Fairfax stood in the hall as we passed. I would fain have spoken to her, but my hand was held by a grasp of iron: I was hurried along by a stride I could hardly follow; and to look at Mr. Rochester's face was to feel that not a second of delay would be tolerated for any purpose. I wonder what other bridegroom ever looked as he did — so bent up to a purpose, so grimly resolute: or who, under such stedfast brows, ever revealed such flaming and flashing eyes.

I know not whether the day was fair or foul; in descending the drive, I gazed neither on sky nor earth: my heart was with my eyes; and both seemed migrated into Mr. Rochester's frame. I wanted to see the invisible thing on which, as we went along, he appeared to fasten a glance fierce and fell. I wanted to feel the thoughts whose force he seemed breasting and resisting.

At the churchyard wicket he stopped: he discovered I was quite out of breath. "Am I cruel in my love?" he said. "Delay an instant: lean on me, Jane."

And now I can recall the picture of the grey old house of God rising calm before me, of a rook wheeling round the steeple, of a ruddy morning sky beyond. I remember something, too, of the green grave-mounds; and I have not forgotten, either, two figures of strangers, straying amongst the low hillocks, and reading the mementoes graven on the few mossy head-stones. I noticed them, because, as they saw us, they passed round to the back of the church; and I doubted not they were going to enter by the side-aisle door, and witness the ceremony. By Mr. Rochester they were not observed; he was earnestly looking at my face, from which the blood had, I daresay, momentarily fled: for I felt my forehead dewy, and my cheeks and lips cold. When I rallied, which I soon did, he walked gently with me up the path to the porch.

We entered the quiet and humble temple; the priest waited in his white surplice at the lowly altar, the clerk beside him. All was still: two shadows only moved in a remote corner. My conjecture had been correct: the strangers had slipped in before us, and they now stood by the vault of the Rochesters, their backs towards us, viewing through the rails the old time-stained marble tomb, where a kneeling angel guarded the remains of Damer de Rochester, slain at Marston Moor in the time of the civil wars; and of Elizabeth, his wife.

Our place was taken at the communion rails. Hearing a cautious step behind me, I glanced over my shoulder: one of the strangers — a gentleman, evidently — was advancing up the chancel. The service began. The explanation of the intent of matrimony was gone through; and then the clergyman came a step further forward, and, bending slightly towards Mr. Rochester, went on.

"I require and charge you both (as ye will answer at the dreadful day of judgment, when the secrets of all hearts shall be disclosed), that if either of you know any impediment why ye may not lawfully be joined together in matrimony, ye do now confess it; for be ye well assured that so many as are coupled together otherwise than God's word doth allow, are not joined together by God, neither is their matrimony lawful."

He paused, as the custom is. When is the pause after that sentence ever broken by reply? Not, perhaps, once in a hundred years. And the clergyman, who had not lifted his eyes from his book, and had held his breath but for a moment, was proceeding: his hand was already stretched towards Mr. Rochester, as his lips unclosed to ask, "Wilt thou have this woman for thy wedded wife?" — when a distinct and near voice said: —

"The marriage cannot go on: I declare the existence of an impediment."

The clergyman looked up at the speaker, and stood mute; the clerk did the same; Mr. Rochester moved slightly, as if an earthquake had rolled under his feet: taking a firmer footing, and not turning his head or eyes, he said, "Proceed."

Profound silence fell when he had uttered that word, with deep but low intonation. Presently Mr. Wood said: —

"I cannot proceed without some investigation into what has been asserted, and evidence of its truth or falsehood."

"The ceremony is quite broken off," subjoined the voice behind us. "I am in a condition to prove my allegation: an insuperable impediment to this marriage exists."

Mr. Rochester heard, but heeded not: he stood stubborn and rigid: making no movement, but to possess himself of my hand. What a hot and strong grasp he had! — and how like quarried marble was his pale, firm, massive front at this moment! How his eye shone, still, watchful, and yet wild beneath!

Mr. Wood seemed at a loss. "What is the nature of the impediment?" he asked. "Perhaps it may be got over — explained away?"

"Hardly," was the answer: "I have called it insuperable, and I speak advisedly."

The speaker came forwards, and leaned on the rails. He continued, uttering each word distinctly, calmly, steadily, but not loudly.

"It simply consists in the existence of a previous marriage. Mr. Rochester has a wife now living."

My nerves vibrated to those low-spoken words as they had never vibrated to thunder — my blood felt their subtle violence as it had never felt frost or fire: but I was collected, and in no danger of swooning. I looked at Mr. Rochester: I made him look at me. His whole face was colourless rock: his eye was both spark and flint. He disavowed nothing; he seemed as if he would defy all things. Without speaking; without smiling; without seeming to recognise in me a human being, he only twined my waist with his arm, and riveted me to his side.

"Who are you?" he asked of the intruder.

"My name is Briggs — a solicitor of —— Street, London."

"And you would thrust on me a wife?"

"I would remind you of your lady's existence, sir; which the law recognises, if you do not."

"Favour me with an account of her — with her name, her parentage, her place of abode."

"Certainly." Mr. Briggs calmly took a paper from his pocket, and read out in a sort of official, nasal voice: —

"'I affirm and can prove that on the 20th of October, A. D., ——, (a date of fifteen years back) Edward Fairfax Rochester, of Thornfield Hall, in the county of ——, and of Ferndean Manor, in ——shire, England, was married to my sister, Bertha Antoinetta Mason, daughter of Jonas Mason, merchant, and of Antoinetta his wife, a Creole — at —— church, Spanish Town, Jamaica. The record of the marriage will be found in the register of that church — a copy of it is now in my possession. Signed, Richard Mason.'"

"That — if a genuine document — may prove I have been

married, but it does not prove that the woman mentioned therein as my wife is still living."

"She was still living three months ago," returned the lawyer.

"How do you know?"

"I have a witness to the fact; whose testimony even you, sir, will scarcely controvert."

"Produce him — or go to hell."

"I will produce him first — he is on the spot: Mr. Mason, have the goodness to step forward."

Mr. Rochester, on hearing the name, set his teeth; he experienced, too, a sort of strong convulsive quiver; near to him as I was, I felt the spasmodic movement of fury or despair run through his frame. The second stranger, who had hitherto lingered in the background, now drew near; a pale face looked over the solicitor's shoulder — yes, it was Mason himself. Mr. Rochester turned and glared at him. His eye, as I have often said, was a black eye: it had now a tawny, nay a bloody light in its gloom; and his face flushed — olive cheek, and hueless forehead received a glow, as from spreading, ascending heart-fire: and he stirred, lifted his strong arm — he could have struck Mason — dashed him on the church-floor — shocked by ruthless blow the breath from his body — but Mason shrank away, and cried faintly, "Good God!" Contempt fell cool on Mr. Rochester — his passion died as if a blight had shrivelled it up: he only asked, "What have *you* to say?"

An inaudible reply escaped Mason's white lips.

"The devil is in it if you cannot answer distinctly. I again demand, what have *you* to say?"

"Sir — sir" — interrupted the clergyman, "do not forget you are in a sacred place." Then addressing Mason, he inquired gently, "Are you aware, sir, whether or not this gentleman's wife is still living?"

"Courage," urged the lawyer, — "speak out."

"She is now living at Thornfield Hall," said Mason, in more articulate tones: "I saw her there last April. I am her brother."

"At Thornfield Hall!" ejaculated the clergyman. "Impossible! I am an old resident in this neighbourhood, sir, and I never heard of a Mrs. Rochester at Thornfield Hall."

I saw a grim smile contort Mr. Rochester's lip, and he muttered: —

"No — by God! I took care that none should hear of it — or of her under that name." He mused — for ten minutes he held counsel with himself: he formed his resolve, and announced it: —

"Enough — all shall bolt out at once, like the bullet from the barrel.— Wood, close your book, and take off your surplice; John Green (to the clerk), leave the church: there will be no wedding to-day:" the man obeyed.

Mr. Rochester continued, hardily and recklessly: "Bigamy is an ugly word! — I meant, however, to be a bigamist: but fate has out-manœuvred me; or Providence has checked me,— perhaps the last. I am little better than a devil at this moment; and, as my pastor there would tell me, deserve no doubt the sternest judgments of God, — even to the quenchless fire and deathless worm. Gentlemen, my plan is broken up! — what this lawyer and his client say is true: I have been married: and the woman to whom I was married lives! You say you never heard of a Mrs. Rochester at the house up yonder, Wood: but I daresay you have many a time inclined your ear to gossip about the mysterious lunatic kept there under watch and ward. Some have whispered to you that she is my bastard half-sister: some, my cast-off mistress; I now inform you that she is my wife, whom I married fifteen years ago,— Bertha Mason by name; sister of this resolute personage, who is now, with his quivering limbs and white cheeks, showing you what a stout heart men may bear. Cheer up, Dick! — never fear me! — I'd almost as soon strike a woman as you. Bertha Mason is mad; and she came of a mad family; — idiots and maniacs through three generations! Her mother, the Creole, was both a mad woman and a drunkard! — as I found out after I had wed the daughter: for they were silent on family secrets before. Bertha, like a dutiful child, copied her parent in both points. I had a charming partner — pure, wise, modest: you can fancy I was a happy man.— I went through rich scenes! Oh! my experience has been heavenly, if you only knew it! But I owe you no further explanation. Briggs, Wood, Mason,— I invite you all to come up to the house and visit Mrs. Poole's patient, and *my wife!* — You shall see what sort of a being I was cheated into espousing, and judge whether or not I had a right to break the compact, and seek sympathy with something at least human. This girl," he continued, looking at me, "knew no more than you, Wood, of the disgusting secret: she thought all was fair and legal; and never dreamt she was going to be entrapped into a feigned union with a defrauded wretch, already bound to a bad, mad, and embruted partner! Come all of you, follow!"

Still holding me fast, he left the church: the three gentlemen came after. At the front door of the hall we found the carriage.

"Take it back to the coach-house, John," said Mr. Rochester, coolly; "it will not be wanted to-day."

At our entrance, Mrs. Fairfax, Adèle, Sophie, Leah, advanced to meet and greet us.

"To the right about — every soul!" cried the master: "away with your congratulations! Who wants them? — Not I! — they are fifteen years too late!"

He passed on and ascended the stairs, still holding my hand, and still beckoning the gentlemen to follow him; which they did. We mounted the first staircase, passed up the gallery, proceeded to the third story: the low, black door, opened by Mr. Rochester's master key, admitted us to the tapestried room, with its great bed, and its pictorial cabinet.

"You know this place, Mason," said our guide; "she bit and stabbed you here."

He lifted the hangings from the wall, uncovering the second door: this, too, he opened. In a room without a window, there burnt a fire, guarded by a high and strong fender, and a lamp suspended from the ceiling by a chain. Grace Poole bent over the fire, apparently cooking something in a saucepan. In the deep shade, at the further end of the room, a figure ran backwards and forwards. What it was, whether beast or human being, one could not, at first sight, tell: it grovelled, seemingly, on all fours; it snatched and growled like some strange wild animal: but it was covered with clothing; and a quantity of dark, grizzled hair, wild as a mane, hid its head and face.

"Good-morrow, Mrs. Poole!" said Mr. Rochester. "How are you? and how is your charge to-day?"

"We're tolerable, sir, I thank you," replied Grace, lifting the boiling mess carefully on to the hob: "rather snappish, but not 'rageous."

A fierce cry seemed to give the lie to her favourable report: the clothed hyena rose up, and stood tall on its hind feet.

"Ah, sir, she sees you!" exclaimed Grace: "you'd better not stay."

"Only a few moments, Grace: you must allow me a few moments."

"Take care then, sir! — for God's sake, take care!"

The maniac bellowed: she parted her shaggy locks from her visage, and gazed wildly at her visitors. I recognised well that purple face,— those bloated features. Mrs. Poole advanced.

"Keep out of the way," said Mr. Rochester, thrusting her aside: "she has no knife, now, I suppose? and I'm on my guard."

"One never knows what she has, sir: she is so cunning: it is not in mortal discretion to fathom her craft."

"We had better leave her," whispered Mason.

"Go to the devil!" was his brother-in-law's recommendation.

"Ware!" cried Grace. The three gentlemen retreated simultaneously. Mr. Rochester flung me behind him: the lunatic sprang and grappled his throat viciously, and laid her teeth to his cheek: they struggled. She was a big woman, in stature almost equalling her husband, and corpulent besides: she showed virile force in the contest — more than once she almost throttled him, athletic as he was. He could have settled her with a well-planted blow; but he would not strike: he would only wrestle. At last he mastered her arms; Grace Poole gave him a cord, and he pinioned them behind her: with more rope, which was at hand, he bound her to a chair. The operation was performed amidst the fiercest yells, and the most convulsive plunges. Mr. Rochester then turned to the spectators: he looked at them with a smile both acrid and desolate.

"That is *my wife,"* said her. "Such is the sole conjugal embrace I am ever to know — such are the endearments which are to solace my leisure hours! And *this* is what I wished to have" (laying his hand on my shoulder): "this young girl, who stands so grave and quiet at the mouth of hell, looking collectedly at the gambols of a demon. I wanted her just as a change after that fierce ragout. Wood and Briggs, look at the difference! Compare these clear eyes with the red balls yonder — this face with that mask — this form with that bulk; then judge me, priest of the gospel and man of the law, and remember, with what judgment ye judge ye shall be judged! Off with you now. I must shut up my prize."

We all withdrew. Mr. Rochester stayed a moment behind us, to give some further order to Grace Poole. The solicitor addressed me as he descended the stair.

"You, madam," said he, "are cleared from all blame: your uncle will be glad to hear it — if, indeed, he should be still living — when Mr. Mason returns to Madeira."

"My uncle! What of him? Do you know him?"

"Mr. Mason does: Mr. Eyre has been the Funchal correspondent of his house for some years. When your uncle received your letter intimating the contemplated union between yourself and Mr. Rochester, Mr. Mason, who was staying at Madeira to recruit his health, on his way back to Jamaica, happened to be with him. Mr. Eyre mentioned the intelligence; for he knew that my client here was acquainted with a gentleman of the name of Rochester. Mr. Mason, astonished and distressed as you may suppose, revealed the real state of matters. Your uncle, I am sorry to say, is now on a sick bed; from which, considering the nature of his disease — decline — and the stage it has reached, it is unlikely he will ever rise. He could not then hasten to England himself, to extricate you from the snare into which you had fallen, but he implored Mr. Mason to lose no time in taking steps to prevent the false marriage. He referred him to me for assistance. I used all despatch, and am thankful I was not too late: as you, doubtless, must be also. Were I not morally certain that your uncle will be dead ere you reach Madeira, I would advise you to accompany Mr. Mason back: but as it is, I think you had better remain in England till you can hear further, either from or of Mr. Eyre. Have we anything else to stay for?" he inquired of Mr. Mason.

"No, no — let us be gone," was the anxious reply; and without waiting to take leave of Mr. Rochester, they made their exit at the hall door. The clergyman stayed to exchange a few sentences, either of admonition or reproof, with his haughty parishioner; this duty done, he too departed.

I heard him go as I stood at the half-open door of my own room, to which I had now withdrawn. The house cleared, I shut myself in, fastened the bolt that none might intrude, and proceeded — not to weep, not to mourn, I was yet too calm for that, but — mechanically to take off the wedding dress, and replace it by the stuff gown I had worn yesterday, as I thought for the last time. I then sat down: I felt weak and tired. I leaned my arms on a table, and my head dropped on them. And now I thought: till now I had only heard, seen, moved — followed up and down where I was led or dragged — watched event rush on event, disclosure open beyond disclosure: but *now, I thought.*

The morning had been a quiet morning enough — all except the brief scene with the lunatic: the transaction in the church had not been noisy; there was no explosion of passion, no loud altercation, no dispute, no defiance or challenge, no tears, no sobs: a few words had been spoken, a calmly pronounced objection to the marriage made; some stern short questions put by Mr. Rochester; answers, explanations given, evidence adduced; an open admission of the truth had been uttered by my master; then the living proof had been seen: the intruders were gone, and all was over.

I was in my own room as usual — just myself, without obvious change: nothing had smitten me, or scathed me, or maimed me. And yet where was the Jane Eyre of yesterday? — where was her life? — where were her prospects?

Jane Eyre, who had been an ardent, expectant woman — almost a bride — was a cold, solitary girl again: her life was pale, her prospects were desolate. A Christmas frost had come at midsummer; a white December storm had whirled over June; ice glazed the ripe apples, drifts crushed the blowing roses; on hay-field and corn-field lay a frozen shroud: lanes which last night blushed full of flowers, to-day were pathless with untrodden snow; and the woods which twelve hours since waved leafy and fragrant as groves between the tropics, now spread, waste, wild and white as pine-forests in wintry Norway. My hopes were all dead — struck with a subtle doom, such as, in one night, fell on all the first-born in the land of Egypt. I looked on my cherished wishes, yesterday so blooming and glowing; they lay stark, chill, livid corpses, that could never revive. I looked at my love: that feeling which was my master's — which he had created; it shivered in my heart, like a suffering child in a cold cradle; sickness and anguish had seized it; it could not seek Mr. Rochester's arms — it could not derive warmth from his breast. Oh, never more could it turn to him; for faith was blighted — confidence destroyed! Mr. Rochester was not to me what he had been; for he was not what I had thought him. I would not ascribe vice to him; I would not say he had betrayed me: but

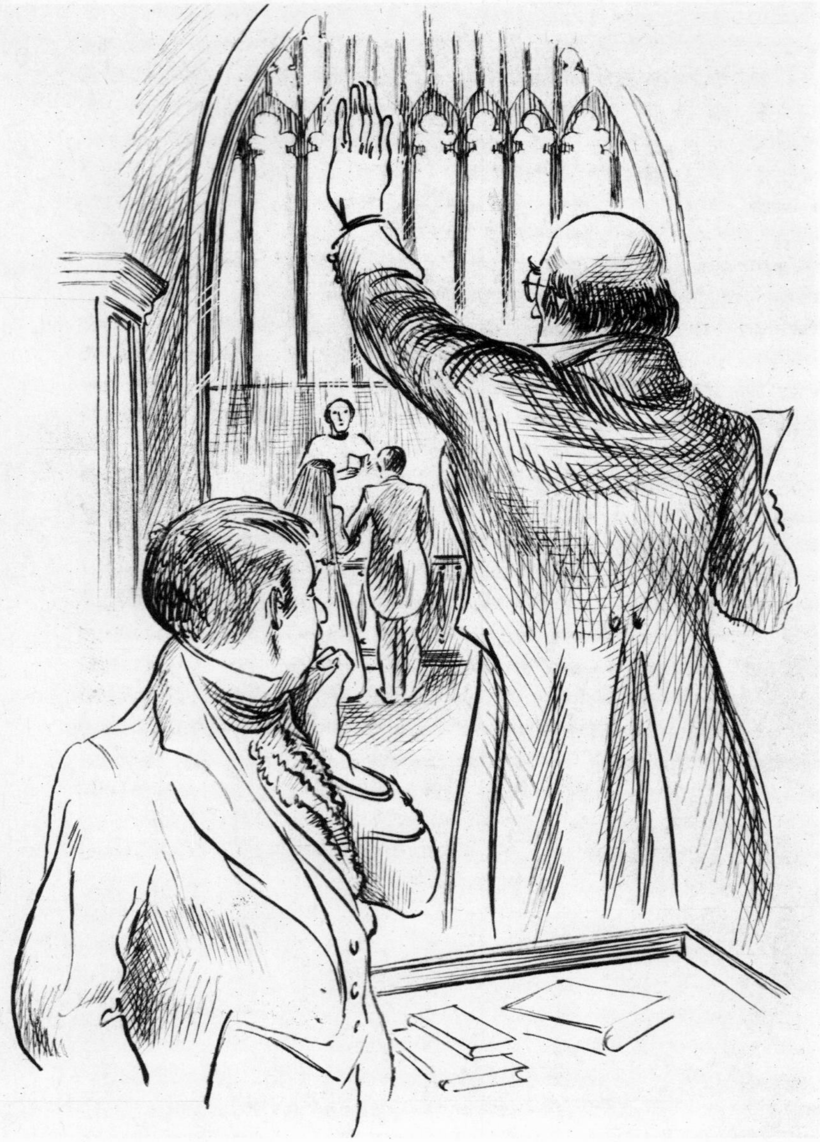

"The marriage cannot go on; I declare the existence of an impediment!"

the attribute of stainless truth was gone from his idea; and from his presence I must go: *that* I perceived well. When — how — whither, I could not yet discern: but he himself, I doubted not, would hurry me from Thornfield. Real affection, it seemed, he could not have for me; it had been only fitful passion, that was balked; he would want me no more. I should fear even to cross his path now: my view must be hateful to him. Oh, how blind had been my eyes! How weak my conduct!

My eyes were covered and closed: eddying darkness seemed to swim round me, and reflection came in as black and confused a flow. Self-abandoned, relaxed, and effortless, I seemed to have laid me down in the dried-up bed of a great river; I heard a flood loosened in remote mountains, and felt the torrent come: to rise I had no will, to flee I had no strength. I lay faint; longing to be dead. One idea only still throbbed life-like within me — a remembrance of God: it begot a muttered prayer: these words went wandering up and down in my rayless mind, as something that should be whispered; but no energy was found to express them: —

" Be not far from me, for trouble is near: there is none to help."

It was near: and as I had lifted no petition to Heaven to avert it — as I had neither joined my hands, nor bent my knees, nor moved my lips — it came: in full, heavy swing the torrent poured over me. The whole consciousness of my life lorn, my love lost, my hope quenched, my faith death-struck, swayed full and mighty above me in one sullen mass. That bitter hour cannot be described: in truth, " the waters came into my soul; I sank in deep mire: I felt no standing; I came into deep waters; the floods overflowed me."

## CHAPTER XXVII

SOME time in the afternoon I raised my head, and looking round and seeing the western sun gilding the sign of its decline on the wall, I asked, "What am I to do?"

But the answer my mind gave—"Leave Thornfield at once"—was so prompt, so dread, that I stopped my ears: I said, I could not bear such words now. "That I am not Edward Rochester's bride is the least part of my woe," I alleged: "that I have wakened out of most glorious dreams, and found them all void and vain, is a horror I could bear and master; but that I must leave him decidedly, instantly, entirely, is intolerable. I cannot do it."

But, then, a voice within me averred that I could do it; and foretold that I should do it. I wrestled with my own resolution: I wanted to be weak that I might avoid the awful passage of further suffering I saw laid out for me; and conscience, turned tyrant, held passion by the throat, told her tauntingly, she had yet but dipped her dainty foot in the slough, and swore that with that arm of iron, he would thrust her down to unsounded depths of agony.

"Let me be torn away, then!" I cried. "Let another help me!"

"No; you shall tear yourself away, none shall help you: you shall, yourself, pluck out your right eye: yourself cut off your right hand: your heart shall be the victim; and you, the priest, to transfix it."

I rose up suddenly, terror-struck at the solitude which so ruthless a judge haunted,—at the silence which so awful a voice filled. My head swam as I stood erect: I perceived that I was sickening from excitement and inanition; neither meat nor drink had passed my lips that day, for I had taken no breakfast. And, with a strange pang, I now reflected that, long as I had been shut up here, no message had been sent to ask how I was, or to invite me to come down: not even little Adèle had tapped at the door; not even Mrs. Fairfax had sought me. "Friends always forget those whom fortune forsakes," I murmured, as I undrew the bolt and passed out. I stumbled over an obstacle: my head was still dizzy, my sight was dim, and my limbs were feeble. I could not soon recover myself. I fell, but not on the ground: an out-stretched arm caught me; I looked up — I was supported by Mr. Rochester, who sat in a chair across my chamber threshold.

"You have come out at last," he said. "Well, I have been waiting for you long, and listening: yet not one movement have I heard, nor one sob: five minutes more of that death-like hush, and I should have forced the lock like a burglar. So, you shun me? — you shut yourself up and grieve alone! I would rather you had come and upbraided me with vehemence. You are passionate: I expected a scene of some kind. I was prepared for the hot rain of tears; only I wanted them to be shed on my breast: now a senseless floor has received them, or your drenched handkerchief. But I err: you have not wept at all! I see a white cheek and a faded eye, but no trace of tears. I suppose, then, your heart has been weeping blood?

"Well, Jane; not a word of reproach? Nothing bitter — nothing poignant? Nothing to cut a feeling or sting a passion? You sit quietly where I have placed you, and regard me with a weary, passive look.

"Jane, I never meant to wound you thus. If the man who had but one little ewe lamb that was dear to him as a daughter, that ate of his bread and drank of his cup, and lay in his bosom, had by some mistake slaughtered it at the shambles, he would not have rued his bloody blunder more than I now rue mine. Will you ever forgive me?"

Reader! — I forgave him at the moment, and on the spot. There was such deep remorse in his eye, such true pity in his tone, such manly energy in his manner; and, besides, there was such unchanged love in his whole look and mien — I forgave him all: yet not in words, not outwardly; only at my heart's core.

"You know I am a scoundrel, Jane?" ere long he inquired wistfully — wondering, I suppose, at my continued silence and tameness: the result rather of weakness than or will.

"Yes, sir."

"Then tell me so roundly and sharply — don't spare me."

"I cannot: I am tired and sick. I want some water." He

heaved a sort of shuddering sigh, and taking me in his arms, carried me downstairs. At first I did not know to what room he had borne me; all was cloudy to my glazed sight: presently I felt the reviving warmth of a fire; for, summer as it was, I had become icy cold in my chamber. He put wine to my lips; I tasted it and revived; then I ate something he offered me, and was soon myself. I was in the library — sitting in his chair — he was quite near. "If I could go out of life now, without too sharp a pang, it would be well for me," I thought; "then I should not have to make the effort of cracking my heart-strings in rending them from among Mr. Rochester's. I must leave him, it appears. I do not want to leave him — I cannot leave him."

"How are you now, Jane?"

"Much better, sir: I shall be well soon."

"Taste the wine again, Jane."

I obeyed him; then he put the glass on the table, stood before me, and looked at me attentively. Suddenly he turned away, with an inarticulate exclamation, full of passionate emotion of some kind; he walked fast through the room and came back: he stooped towards me as if to kiss me; but I remembered caresses were now forbidden. I turned my face away, and put his aside.

"What! — how is this?" he exclaimed hastily. "Oh, I know! you won't kiss the husband of Bertha Mason? You consider my arms filled, and my embraces appropriated?"

"At any rate, there is neither room nor claim for me, sir."

"Why, Jane? I will spare you the trouble of much talking: I will answer for you — because I have a wife already, you would reply.— I guess rightly?"

"Yes."

"If you think so, you must have a strange opinion of me; you must regard me as a plotting profligate — a base and low rake who has been simulating disinterested love in order to draw you into a snare deliberately laid, and strip you of honour, and rob you of self-respect. What do you say to that? I see you can say nothing: in the first place, you are faint, still, and have enough to do to draw your breath; in the second place, you cannot yet accustom yourself to accuse and revile me; and, besides, the flood-gates of tears are opened, and they would rush out if you spoke much; and you have no desire to expostulate, to upbraid, to make a scene: you are thinking how *to act* — *talking*, you consider, is of no use. I know you — I am on my guard."

"Sir, I do not wish to act against you," I said; and my unsteady voice warned me to curtail my sentence.

"Not in *your* sense of the word but in *mine*, you are scheming to destroy me. You have as good as said that I am a married man — as a married man you will shun me, keep out of my way: just now you have refused to kiss me. You intend to make yourself a complete stranger to me; to live under this roof only as Adèle's governess; if ever I say a friendly word to you; if ever a friendly feeling inclines you again to me, you will say,—'That man had nearly made me his mistress: I must be ice and rock to him;' and ice and rock you will accordingly become."

I cleared and steadied my voice to reply: "All is changed about me, sir; I must change too — there is no doubt of that: and to avoid fluctuations of feeling, and continual combats with recollections and associations, there is only one way — Adèle must have a new governess, sir."

"Oh, Adèle will go to school — I have settled that already; nor do I mean to torment you with the hideous associations and recollections of Thornfield Hall — this accursed place — this tent of Achan — this insolent vault, offering the ghastliness of living death to the light of the open sky — this narrow stone hell, with its one real fiend, worse than a legion of such as we imagine.— Jane, you shall not stay here, nor will I. I was wrong ever to bring you to Thornfield Hall, knowing as I did how it was haunted. I charged them to conceal from you, before I ever saw you, all knowledge of the curse of the place; merely because I feared Adèle never would have a governess to stay if she knew with what inmate she was housed, and my plans would not permit me to remove the maniac elsewhere — though I possess an old house, Ferndean Manor, even more retired and hidden than this, where I could have lodged her safely enough, had not a scruple about the unhealthiness of the situation, in the heart of a wood, made my conscience recoil from the arrangement. Probably those damp walls would soon have eased me of her charge: but to each villain his own vice; and mine is not a tendency to indirect assassination, even of what I most hate.

"Concealing the mad-woman's neighbourhood, from you, however, was something like covering a child with a cloak, and laying it down near a upas-tree: that demon's vicinage is poisoned, and always was. But I'll shut up Thornfield Hall: I'll nail up the front door, and board the lower windows; I'll give Mrs. Poole two hundred a year to live here with *my wife,* as you term that fearful hag: Grace will do much for money, and she shall have her son, the keeper at Grimsby Retreat, to bear her company and be at hand to give her aid, in the paroxysms, when *my wife* is prompted by her familiar to burn people in their beds at night, to stab them, to bite their flesh from their bones, and so on"—

"Sir," I interrupted him, "you are inexorable for that unfortunate lady: you speak of her with hate — with vindictive antipathy. It is cruel — she cannot help being mad."

"Jane, my little darling (so I will call you, for so you are), you don't know what you are talking about; you misjudge me again: it is not because she is mad I hate her. If you were mad, do you think I should hate you?"

"I do indeed, sir."

"Then you are mistaken, and you know nothing about me, and nothing about the sort of love of which I am capable. Every atom of your flesh is as dear to me as my own: in pain and sickness it would still be dear. Your mind is my treasure, and if it were broken, it would be my treasure still: if you raved, my arms should confine you, and not a strait waistcoat — your grasp, even in fury, would have a charm for me: if you flew at me as wildly as that woman did this morning, I should receive you in an embrace, at least as fond as it would be restrictive. I should not shrink from you with disgust as I did from her: in your quiet moments you should have no watcher and no nurse but me; and I could hang over you with untiring tenderness, though you gave me no smile in return; and never weary of gazing into your eyes, though they had no longer a ray of recognition for me.—But why do I follow that train of ideas? I was talking of removing you from Thornfield. All, you know, is prepared for prompt departure: to-morrow you shall go. I only ask you to endure one more night under this roof, Jane: and then, farewell to its miseries and terrors for ever! I have a place to repair to, which will be a secure sanctuary from hateful reminiscences, from unwelcome intrusion — even from falsehood and slander."

"And take Adèle with you, sir," I interrupted; "she will be a companion for you."

"What do you mean, Jane? I told you I would send Adèle to school: and what do I want with a child for a companion? and not my own child,— a French dancer's bastard. Why do you importune me about her? I say, why do you assign Adèle to me for a companion?"

"You spoke of a retirement, sir; and retirement and solitude are dull: too dull for you."

"Solitude! solitude!" he reiterated, with irritation. "I see I must come to an explanation. I don't know what sphynx-like expression is forming in your countenance. *You* are to share my solitude. Do you understand?"

I shook my head: it required a degree of courage, excited as he was becoming, even to risk that mute sign of dissent. He had been walking fast about the room, and he stopped, as if suddenly rooted to one spot. He looked at me long and hard: I turned my eyes from him, fixed them on the fire, and tried to assume and maintain a quiet, collected aspect.

"Now for the hitch in Jane's character," he said at last, speaking more calmly than from his look I had expected him to speak. "The reel of silk has run smoothly enough so far; but I always knew there would come a knot and a puzzle: here it is. Now for vexation, and exasperation, and endless trouble! By God! I long to exert a fraction of Samson's strength, and break the entanglement like tow!"

He recommenced his walk: but soon again stopped, and this time just before me.

"Jane! will you hear reason?" (he stooped and approached his lips to my ear) "because, if you won't, I'll try violence." His voice was hoarse; his look that of a man who is just about to burst an insufferable bond and plunge headlong into wild licence. I saw that in another moment, and with one impetus of frenzy more, I should be able to do nothing with him. The present — the passing second of time — was all I had in which to control and restrain him: a movement of repulsion, flight, fear, would have sealed my doom,— and his. But I was not afraid: not in the least. I felt an inward power; a sense of influence, which supported me. The crisis was perilous; but not without its charm: such as the Indian, perhaps, feels when he slips over the rapid in his canoe. I took hold of his clenched hand; loosened the contorted fingers; and said to him, soothingly,—

"Sit down; I'll talk to you as long as you like, and hear all you have to say, whether reasonable or unreasonable."

He sat down: but he did not get leave to speak directly. I had been struggling with tears for some time: I had taken great pains to repress them, because I knew he would not like to see me weep. Now, however, I considered it well to let them flow as freely and as long as they liked. If the flood annoyed him, so much the better. So I gave way and cried heartily.

Soon I heard him earnestly entreating me to be composed. I said I could not while he was in such a passion.

"But I am not angry, Jane: I only love you too well; and you had steeled your little pale face with such a resolute, frozen look, I could not endure it. Hush, now, and wipe your eyes."

His softened voice announced that he was subdued; so I, in my turn, became calm. Now he made an effort to rest his head on my shoulder: but I would not permit it. Then he would draw me to him: no.

"Jane! Jane!" he said — in such an accent of bitter sadness it thrilled along every nerve I had; "you don't love me, then? It was only my station, and the rank of my wife, that you valued? Now that you think me disqualified to become your husband, you recoil from my touch as if I were some toad or ape."

These words cut me: yet what could I do or say? I ought probably to have done or said nothing: but I was so tortured by a sense of remorse at thus hurting his feelings, I could not control the wish to drop balm where I had wounded.

"I *do* love you," I said, "more than ever: but I must not show or indulge the feeling: and this is the last time I must express it."

"The last time, Jane! What! do you think you can live with me, and see me daily, and yet, if you still love me, be always cold and distant?"

"No, sir; that I am certain I could not; and therefore I see there is but one way: but you will be furious if I mention it."

"Oh, mention it! If I storm, you have the art of weeping."

"Mr. Rochester, I must leave you."

"For how long, Jane? For a few minutes, while you smooth you hair — which is somewhat dishevelled; and bathe your face — which looks feverish?"

"I must leave Adèle and Thornfield. I must part with you for my whole life: I must begin a new existence amongst strange faces and strange scenes."

"Of course: I told you you should. I pass over the madness about parting from me. You mean you must become a part of me. As to the new existence, it is all right: you shall yet be my wife: I am not married. You shall be Mrs. Rochester — both virtually and nominally. I shall keep only to you so long as you and I live. You shall go to a place I have in the south of France: a white-washed villa on the shores of the Mediterranean. There you shall live a happy, and guarded, and most innocent life. Never fear that I wish to lure you into error — to make you my mistress. Why do you shake your head? Jane, you must be reasonable; or in truth I shall again become frantic."

His voice and hand quivered: his large nostrils dilated: his eyes blazed: still I dared to speak: —

"Sir, your wife is living: that is a fact acknowledged this morning by yourself. If I lived with you as you desire, I should then be your mistress: to say otherwise is sophistical — is false."

"Jane, I am not a gentle-tempered man — you forget that: I am not long-enduring; I am not cool and dispassionate. Out of pity to me and yourself, put your finger on my pulse, feel how it throbs, and — beware!"

He bared his wrist, and offered it to me: the blood was forsaking his check and lips, they were growing livid; I was distressed on all hands. To agitate him thus deeply, by a resistance he so abhorred, was cruel: to yield was out of the question. I did what human beings do instinctively when they are driven to utter extremity — looked for aid to one higher than man: the words "God help me!" burst involuntarily from my lips.

"I am a fool!" cried Mr. Rochester, suddenly. "I keep telling her I am not married, and do not explain to her why. I forget she knows nothing of the character of that woman, or of the circumstances attending my infernal union with her. Oh, I am certain Jane will agree with me in opinion, when she knows all that I know! Just put your hand in mine, Janet — that I may have the evidence of touch as well as sight, to prove you are near me — and I will in a few words show you the real state of the case. Can you listen to me?"

"Yes, sir; for hours if you will."

"I ask only minutes. Jane, did you ever hear, or know that I was not the eldest son of my house: that I had once a brother older than I?"

"I remember Mrs. Fairfax told me so once."

"And did you ever hear that my father was an avaricious, grasping man?"

"I have understood something to that effect."

"Well, Jane, being so, it was his resolution to keep the property together; he could not bear the idea of dividing his estate and leaving me a fair portion: all, he resolved, should go to my brother, Rowland. Yet as little could he endure that a son of his should be a poor man. I must be provided for by a wealthy marriage. He sought me a partner betimes. Mr. Mason, a West India planter and merchant, was his old acquaintance. He was certain his possessions were real and vast: he made inquiries. Mr. Mason, he found, had a son and daughter; and he learned from him that he could and would give the latter a fortune of thirty thousand pounds: that sufficed. When I left college, I was sent out to Jamaica, to espouse a bride already courted for me. My father said nothing about her money; but he told me Miss Mason was the boast of Spanish Town for her beauty: and this was no lie. I found her a fine woman, in the style of Blanche Ingram; tall, dark, majestic. Her family wished to secure me because I was of a good race; and so did she. They showed her to me in parties, splendidly dressed. I seldom saw her alone, and had very little private conversation with her. She flattered me, and lavishly displayed for my pleasure her charms and accomplishments. All the men in her circle seemed to admire her and envy me. I was dazzled, stimulated: my senses were excited; and being ignorant, raw, and inexperienced, I thought I loved her. There is no folly so besotted that the idiotic rivalries of society, the prurience, the rashness, the blindness of youth, will not hurry a man to its commission. Her relatives encouraged me; competitors piqued me; she allured me: a marriage was achieved almost before I knew where I was. Oh, I have no respect for myself when I think of that act! — an agony of inward contempt masters me. I never loved, I never esteemed, I did not even know her. I was not sure of the existence of one virtue in her nature: I had marked neither modesty, nor benevolence, nor candour, nor refinement in her mind or manners — and, I married her: — gross, grovelling, mole-eyed blockhead that I was! With less sin I might have — but let me remember to whom I am speaking.

"My bride's mother I had never seen: I understood she was dead. The honey-moon over, I learned my mistake; she was only mad, and shut up in a lunatic asylum. There was a younger brother, too; a complete dumb idiot. The elder one, whom you have seen (and whom I cannot hate, whilst I abhor all his kindred, because he has some grains of affection in his feeble mind; shown in the continued interest he takes in his wretched sister and also in a dog-like attachment he once bore me), will probably be in the same state one day. My father and my brother Rowland, knew all this; but they thought only of the thirty thousand pounds, and joined in the plot against me.

"These were vile discoveries; but, except for the treachery of concealment, I should have made them no subject of reproach to my wife: even when I found her nature wholly alien to mine; her tastes obnoxious to me; her cast of mind common, low, narrow, and singularly incapable of being led to anything higher, expanded to anything larger — when I found that I could not pass a single evening nor a single hour of the day with her in comfort; that kindly conversation could not be sustained between us, because whatever topic I started, immediately received from her a turn at once coarse and trite, perverse and imbecile — when I perceived that I should never have a quiet or settled household, because no servant would bear the continued outbreaks of her violent and unreasonable temper, or the vexations of her absurd, contradictory, exacting orders — even then I restrained myself: I eschewed upbraiding, I curtailed remonstrance; I tried to devour my repentance and disgust in secret; I repressed the deep antipathy I felt.

"Jane, I will not trouble you with abominable details: some strong words shall express what I have to say. I lived with that woman upstairs four years, and before that time she had tried me indeed: her character ripened and developed with frightful rapidity; her vices sprang up fast and rank: they were so strong, only cruelty could check them; and I would not use cruelty. What a pigmy intellect she had — and what giant propensities! How fearful were the curses those propensities entailed on me! Bertha Mason,— the true daughter of an infamous mother,— dragged me through all the hideous and degrading agonies which must attend a man bound to a wife at once intemperate and unchaste.

"My brother in the interval was dead; and at the end of the four years my father died too. I was rich enough now — yet poor to hideous indigence: a nature the most gross, impure, depraved I ever saw, was associated with mine, and called by the law and by society a part of me. And I could not rid myself of it by any legal proceedings: for the doctors now discovered that *my wife* was mad — her excesses had prematurely developed the germs of insanity: — Jane, you don't like my narrative; you look almost sick — shall I defer the rest to another day?"

"No, sir, finish it now: I pity you — I do earnestly pity you."

"Pity, Jane, from some people is a noxious and insulting sort of tribute, which one is justified in hurling back in the teeth of those who offer it; but that is a sort of pity native to callous, selfish hearts: it is a hybrid, egotistical pain at hearing of woes, crossed with ignorant contempt for those who have endured them. But that is not your pity, Jane: it is not the feeling of which your whole face is full at this moment — with which your eyes are now almost overflowing — with which your heart is heaving — with which your hand is trembling in mine. Your pity, my darling, is the suffering mother of love: its anguish is the very natal pang of the divine passion. I accept it, Jane; let the daughter have free advent — my arms wait to receive her."

"Now, sir, proceed: what did you do when you found she was mad?"

"Jane — I approached the verge of despair: a remnant of self-respect was all that intervened between me and the gulf. In the eyes of the world, I was doubtless covered with grimy dishonour: but I resolved to be clean in my own sight — and to the last I repudiated the contamination of her crimes, and wrenched myself from connection with her mental defects. Still, society associated my name and person with hers; I yet saw her and heard her daily: something of her breath (faugh!) mixed with the air I breathed; and, besides, I remembered I had once been her husband — that recollection was then, and is now, inexpressibly odious to me; moreover,

I knew that while she lived I could never be the husband of another and better wife; and, though five years my senior (her family and her father had lied to me even in the particular of her age), she was likely to live as long as I, being as robust in frame as she was infirm in mind. Thus, at the age of twenty-six, I was hopeless.

"One night I had been awakened by her yells — (since the medical men had pronounced her mad, she had of course been shut up) — it was a fiery West Indian night; one of the description that frequently precedes the hurricanes of those climates; being unable to sleep in bed, I got up and opened the window. The air was like sulphur-steams — I could find no refreshment anywhere. Mosquitoes came buzzing in and hummed sullenly round the room; the sea, which I could hear from thence, rumbled dull like an earthquake — black clouds were casting up over it; the moon was setting in the waves, broad and red, like a hot cannon-ball — she threw her last bloody glance over a world quivering with the ferment of tempest. I was physically influenced by the atmosphere and scene, and my ears were filled with the curses the maniac still shrieked out; wherein she momentarily mingled my name with such a tone of demon-hate, with such language! — no professed harlot ever had a fouler vocabulary than she: though two rooms off, I heard every word — the thin partitions of the West India house opposing but slight obstruction to her wolfish cries.

"'This life,' said I at last, 'is hell! this is the air — those are the sounds of the bottomless pit! I have a right to deliver myself from it if I can. The sufferings of this mortal state will leave me with the heavy flesh that now cumbers my soul. Of the fanatic's burning eternity I have no fear: there is not a future state worse than this present one — let me break away and go home to God!'

"I said this whilst I knelt down at, and unlocked a trunk which contained a brace of loaded pistols: I meant to shoot myself. I only entertained the intention for a moment; for, not being insane, the crisis of exquisite and unalloyed despair which had originated the wish and design of self-destruction, was past in a second.

"A wind fresh from Europe blew over the ocean and rushed through the open casement: the storm broke, streamed, thundered, blazed, and the air grew pure. I then framed and fixed a resolution. While I walked under the dripping orange-trees of my wet garden, and amongst its drenched pomegranates and pine-apples, and while the refulgent dawn of the tropics kindled round me — I reasoned thus, Jane: — and now listen; for it was true Wisdom that consoled me in that hour, and showed me the right path to follow.

"The sweet wind from Europe was still whispering in the refreshed leaves, and the Atlantic was thundering in glorious liberty; my heart, dried up and scorched for a long time, swelled to the tone, and filled with living blood — my being longed for renewal — my soul thirsted for a pure draught. I saw Hope revive — and felt Regeneration possible. From a flowery arch at the bottom of my garden I gazed over the sea — bluer than the sky; the old world was beyond; clear prospects opened thus: —

"'Go,' said Hope, 'and live again in Europe: there it is not known what a sullied name you bear, nor what a filthy burden is bound to you. You may take the maniac with you to England; confine her with due attendance and precautions at Thornfield: then travel yourself to what clime you will, and form what new tie you like. That woman, who has so abused your long-suffering — so sullied your name; so outraged your honour; so blighted your youth — is not your wife; nor are you her husband. See that she is cared for as her condition demands, and you have done all that God and Humanity require of you. Let her identity, her connection with yourself, be buried in oblivion: you are about to impart them to no living being. Place her in safety and comfort: shelter her degradation with secrecy, and leave her.'

"I acted precisely on this suggestion. My father and brother had not made my marriage known to their acquaintance; because, in the very first letter I wrote to apprise them of the union — having already begun to experience extreme disgust of its consequences; and from the family character and constitution, seeing a hideous future opening to me — I added an urgent charge to keep it secret: and very soon, the infamous conduct of the wife my father had selected for me, was such as to make him blush to own her as his daughter-in-law. Far from desiring to publish the connection, he became as anxious to conceal it as myself.

"To England, then, I conveyed her; a fearful voyage I had with such a monster in the vessel. Glad was I when I at last got her to Thornfield, and saw her safely lodged in that third story room, of whose secret inner cabinet she has now for ten years made a wild beast's den — a goblin's cell. I had some trouble in finding an attendant for her: as it was necessary to select one on whose fidelity dependence could be placed; for her ravings would inevitably betray my secret: besides, she had lucid intervals of days — sometimes weeks — which she filled up with abuse of me. At last I hired Grace Poole, from the Grimsby Retreat. She and the surgeon, Carter (who dressed Mason's wounds that night he was stabbed and worried), are the only two I have ever admitted to my confidence. Mrs. Fairfax may indeed have suspected something; but she could have gained no precise knowledge as to facts. Grace has, on the whole, proved a good keeper; though, owing partly to a fault of her own, of which it appears nothing can cure her, and which is incident to her harassing profession, her vigilance has been more than once lulled and baffled. The lunatic is both cunning and malignant; she has never failed to take advantage of her guardian's temporary lapses; once to secrete the knife with which she stabbed her brother, and twice to possess herself of the key of her cell, and issue therefrom in the night-time. On the first of these occasions, she perpetrated the attempt to burn me in my bed; on the second she paid that ghastly visit to you. I thank Providence, who watched over you, that she spent her fury on your wedding apparel; which perhaps brought back vague reminiscences of her own bridal days: but on what might have happened, I cannot endure to reflect. When I think of the thing which flew at my throat this morning, hanging its black and scarlet visage over the nest of my dove, my blood curdles"——

"And what, sir," I asked, while he paused, "did you do when you had settled her here? Where did you go?"

"What did I do, Jane? I transformed myself into a Will-o'-the-wisp. Where did I go? I pursued wanderings as wild as those of the March-spirit. I sought the Continent, and went devious through all its lands. My fixed desire was to seek and find a good and intelligent woman, whom I could love: a contrast to the fury I left at Thornfield"——

"But you could not marry, sir."

"I had determined, and was convinced that I could and ought. It was not my original intention to deceive, as I have deceived you. I meant to tell my tale plainly, and make my proposals openly: and as it appeared to me so absolutely rational that I should be considered free to love and be loved, I never doubted some woman might be found willing and able to understand my case and accept me, in spite of the curse with which I was burdened."

"Well, sir?"

"When you are inquisitive, Jane, you always make me smile. You open your eyes like an eager bird, and make every now and then a restless movement; as if answers in speech did not flow fast enough for you, and you wanted to read the tablet of one's heart. But before I go on, tell me what you mean by your 'Well, sir?' It is a small phrase very frequent with you; and which many a time has drawn me on and on through interminable talk: I don't very well know why."

"I mean,— What next? How did you proceed? What came of such an event?"

"Precisely: and what do you wish to know now?"

"Whether you found any one you liked: whether you asked her to marry you; and what she said."

"I can tell you whether I found any one I liked, and whether I asked her to marry me: but what she said is yet to be recorded in the book of Fate. For ten long years I roved about, living first in one capital, then another: sometimes in St. Petersburgh; oftener in Paris; occasionally in Rome, Naples, and Florence. Provided with plenty of money, and the passport of an old name, I could choose my own society: no circles were closed against me. I sought my ideal of a woman amongst English ladies, French countesses, Italian signoras, and German gräfinnen. I could not find her. Sometimes, for a fleeting moment, I thought I caught a glance, heard a tone, beheld a form, which announced the realisation of my dream: but I was presently undeceived. You are not to suppose that I desired perfection, either of mind or person. I longed only for what suited me — for the antipodes of the Creole: and I longed vainly. Amongst them all I found not one, whom, had I been ever so free, I — warned as I was of the risks, the horrors, the loathings of incongruous unions — would have asked to marry me. Disappointment made me reckless. I tried dissipation — never debauchery: that I hated, and hate. That was my Indian Messalina's attribute: rooted disgust at it and her restrained me much, even in pleasure. Any enjoyment that bordered on riot seemed to approach me to her and her vices, and I eschewed it.

"Yet I could not live alone; so I tried the companionship of mistresses. The first I chose was Céline Varens — another of those steps which make a man spurn himself when he recalls them. You already know what she was, and how my liaison with her terminated. She had two successors: an Italian, Giacinta, and a German, Clara; both considered singularly handsome. What was their beauty to me in a few weeks? Giacinta was unprincipled and violent: I tired of her in three months. Clara was honest and quiet; but heavy, mindless, unimpressible: not one whit to my taste. I was glad to give her a sufficient sum to set her up in a good line of business, and so get decently rid of her. But, Jane, I see by your face you are not forming a very favourable opinion of me just now. You think me an unfeeling, loose-principled rake: don't you?"

"I don't like you so well as I have done sometimes, indeed, sir. Did it not seem to you in the least wrong to live in that way: first with one mistress and then another? You talk of it as a mere matter of course."

"It was with me; and I did not like it. It was a grovelling fashion of existence: I should never like to return to it. Hiring a mistress is the next worst thing to buying a slave: both are often by nature, and always by position, inferior: and to live familiarly with inferiors is degrading. I now hate the recollection of the time I passed with Céline, Giacinta, and Clara."

I felt the truth of these words; and I drew from them the certain inference, that if I were so far to forget myself and all the teaching that had ever been instilled into me, as — under any pretext — with any justification — through any temptation — to become the successor of these poor girls, he would one day regard me with the same feeling which now in his mind desecrated their memory. I did not give utterance to this conviction: it was enough to feel it. I impressed it on my heart, that it might remain there to serve me as aid in the time of trial.

"Now, Jane, why don't you say 'Well, sir?' I have not done. You are looking grave. You disapprove of me still, I see. But let me come to the point. Last January, rid of all mistresses — in a harsh, bitter frame of mind, the result of a useless, roving, lonely life — corroded with disappointment, sourly disposed against all men, and especially against all *woman*kind (for I began to regard the notion of an intellectual, faithful, loving woman as a mere dream), recalled by business, I came back to England.

"On a frosty winter afternoon, I rode in sight of Thornfield Hall. Abhorred spot! I expected no peace — no pleasure there. On a stile in Hay Lane I saw a quiet little figure sitting by itself. I passed it as negligently as I did the pollard willow opposite to it: I had no presentiment of what it would be to me; no inward warning that the arbitress of my life — my genius for good or evil — waited there in humble guise. I did not know it, even when, on the occasion of Mesrour's accident, it came up and gravely offered me help. Childish and slender creature! It seemed as if a linnet had hopped to my foot and proposed to bear me on its tiny wing. I was surly; but the thing would not go: it stood by me with strange perseverance, and looked and spoke with a sort of authority. I must be aided, and by that hand: and aided I was.

"When once I had pressed the frail shoulder, something new — a fresh sap and sense — stole into my frame. It was well I had learnt that this elf must return to me — that it belonged to my house down below — or I could not have felt it pass away from under my hand, and seen it vanish behind the dim hedge, without singular regret. I heard you come home that night, Jane: though probably you were not aware that I thought of you, or watched for you. The next day I observed you — myself unseen — for half an hour, while you played with Adèle in the gallery. It was a snowy day, I recollect, and you could not go out of doors. I was in my room; the door was ajar: I could both listen and watch. Adèle claimed your outward attention for a while; yet I fancied your thoughts were elsewhere: but you were very patient with her, my little Jane; you talked to her and amused her a long time. When at last she left you, you lapsed at once into deep reverie: you betook yourself slowly to pace the gallery. Now and then, in passing a casement, you glanced out at the thick-falling snow; you listened to the sobbing wind, and again you paced gently on and dreamed. I think those day visions were not dark: there was a pleasurable illumination in your eye occasionally, a soft excitement in your aspect, which told of no bitter, bilious, hypochondriac brooding: your look revealed rather the sweet musings of youth, when its spirit follows on willing wings the flight of Hope, up and on to an ideal heaven. The voice of Mrs. Fairfax, speaking to a servant in the hall, wakened you: and how curiously you smiled to and at yourself, Jane! There was much sense in your smile: it was very shrewd, and seemed to make light of your own abstraction. It seemed to say—'My fine visions are all very well, but I must not forget they are absolutely unreal. I have a rosy sky, and a green flowery Eden in my brain; but without, I am perfectly aware, lies at my feet a rough tract to travel, and around me gather black tempests to encounter.' You ran downstairs and demanded of Mrs. Fairfax some occupation: the weekly house accounts to make up, or something of that sort, I think it was. I was vexed with you for getting out of my sight.

"Impatiently I waited for evening, when I might summon you to my presence. An unusual — to me — a perfectly new character I suspected was yours: I desired to search it deeper, and know it better. You entered the room with a look and air at once shy and independent: you were quaintly dressed — much as you are now. I made you talk: ere long I found you full of strange contrasts. Your garb and manner were restricted by rule; your air was often diffident, and altogether that of one refined by nature, but absolutely unused to society, and a good deal afraid of making herself disadvantageously conspicuous by some solecism or blunder; yet when addressed, you lifted a keen, a daring, and a glowing eye to your interlocutor's face: there was penetration and power in each glance you gave: when plied by close questions, you found ready and round answers. Very soon, you seemed to get used to me: I believe you felt the existence of sympathy between you and your grim and cross master, Jane; for it was astonishing to see how quickly a certain pleasant ease tranquillised your manner: snarl as I would, you showed no surprise, fear, annoyance, or displeasure at my moroseness; you watched me, and now and then smiled at me with a simple yet sagacious grace I cannot describe. I was at once content and stimulated with what I saw: I liked what I had seen, and wished to see more. Yet, for a long time, I treated you distantly, and sought your company rarely. I was an intellectual epicure, and wished to prolong the gratification of making this novel and piquant acquaintance: besides, I was for a while troubled with a haunting fear that if I handled the flower freely its bloom would fade — the sweet charm of freshness would leave it. I did not then know that it was no transitory blossom; but rather the radiant resemblance of one, cut in an indestructible gem. Moreover, I wished to see whether you would seek me if I shunned you — but you did not; you kept in the school-room as still as your own desk and easel; if by chance I met you, you passed me as soon, and with as little token of recognition, as was consistent with respect. Your habitual expression in those days, Jane, was a thoughtful look; not despondent, for you were not sickly; but not buoyant, for you had little hope, and no actual pleasure. I wondered what you thought of me — or if you ever thought of me; to find this out, I resumed my notice of you. There was something glad in your glance, and genial in your manner, when you conversed: I saw you had a social heart; it was the silent school-room — it was the tedium of your life — that made you mournful. I permitted myself the delight of being kind to you; kindness stirred emotion soon: your face became soft in expression, your tones gentle: I liked my name pronounced by your lips in a grateful happy accent. I used to enjoy a chance meeting with you, Jane, at this time: there was a curious hesitation in your manner: you glanced at me with a slight trouble — a hovering doubt: you did not know what my caprice might be — whether I was going to play the master and be stern, or the friend and be benignant. I was now too fond of you often to simulate the first whim; and, when I stretched my hand out cordially, such bloom and light and bliss rose to your young, wistful features, I had much ado often to avoid straining you then and there to my heart."

"Don't talk any more of those days, sir," I interrupted, furtively dashing away some tears from my eyes; his language was torture to me; for I knew what I must do — and do soon — and all these reminiscences, and these revelations of his feelings only made my work more difficult.

"No, Jane," he returned: "what necessity is there to dwell on the Past, when the Present is so much surer — the Future so much brighter?"

I shuddered to hear the infatuated assertion.

"You see now how the case stands — do you not?" he continued. "After a youth and manhood passed half in unutterable misery and half in dreary solitude, I have for the first time found what I can truly love — I have found *you*. You are my sympathy — my better self — my good angel — I am bound to you with a strong attachment. I think you good, gifted, lovely: a fervent, a solemn passion is conceived in my heart; it leans to you, draws you to my centre and spring of life, wraps my existence about you — and, kindling in pure, powerful flame, fuses you and me in one.

"It was because I felt and knew this, that I resolved to marry you. To tell me that I had already a wife is empty mockery: you know now that I had but a hideous demon. I was wrong to attempt to deceive you; but I feared a stubbornness that exists in your character. I feared early instilled prejudice: I wanted to have you safe before hazarding confidences. This was cowardly: I should have appealed to your nobleness and magnanimity at first, as I do now — opened to you plainly my life of agony — described to you my hunger and thirst after a higher and worthier existence — shown to you, not my *resolution* (that word is weak), but my resistless *bent* to love faithfully and well, where I am faithfully and well loved in return. Then I should have asked you to accept my pledge of fidelity, and to give me yours: Jane — give it me now."

A pause.

"Why are you silent, Jane?"

I was experiencing an ordeal: a hand of fiery iron grasped my vitals. Terrible moment: full of struggle, blackness, burning! Not a human being that ever lived could wish to be loved better than I was loved; and him who thus loved me I absolutely worshipped: and I must renounce love and idol. One drear word comprised my intolerable duty — "Depart!"

"Jane, you understand what I want of you? Just this promise — 'I will be yours, Mr. Rochester.'"

"Mr. Rochester, I will *not* be yours."

Another long silence.

"Jane!" recommenced he, with a gentleness that broke me down with grief, and turned me stone-cold with ominous terror — for this still voice was the pant of a lion rising — "Jane, do you mean to go one way in the world, and to let me go another?"

"I do."

"Jane" (bending towards and embracing me), "do you mean it now?"

"I do."

"And now?" softly kissing my forehead and cheek.

"I do" — extricating myself from restraint rapidly and completely.

"Oh, Jane, this is bitter! This — this is wicked. It would not be wicked to love me."

"It would to obey you."

A wild look raised his brows — crossed his features: he rose; but he forbore yet. I laid my hand on the back of a chair for support: I shook, I feared — but I resolved.

"One instant, Jane. Give one glance to my horrible life when you are gone. All happiness will be torn away with you. What then is left? For a wife I have but the maniac upstairs: as well might you refer me to some corpse in yonder churchyard. What shall I do, Jane? Where turn for a companion, and for some hope?"

"Do as I do: trust in God and yourself. Believe in heaven. Hope to meet again there."

"Then you will not yield?"

"No."

"Then you condemn me to live wretched, and to die accursed?" His voice rose.

"I advise you to live sinless: and I wish you to die tranquil."

"Then you snatch love and innocence from me? You fling me back on lust for a passion — vice for an occupation?"

"Mr. Rochester, I no more assign this fate to you than I grasp at it for myself. We were born to strive and endure — you as well as I: do so. You will forget me before I forget you."

"You make me a liar by such language: you sully my honour. I declare I could not change: you tell me to my face I shall change soon. And what a distortion in your judgment, what a perversity in your ideas, is proved by your conduct! Is it better to drive a fellow-creature to despair than to transgress a mere human law — no man being injured by the breach? for you have neither relatives nor acquaintances whom you need fear to offend by living with me."

This was true: and while he spoke my very conscience and reason turned traitors against me, and charged me with crime in resisting him. They spoke almost as loud as Feeling: and that clamoured wildly. "Oh, comply!" it said. "Think of his misery; think of his danger — look at his state when left alone; remember his headlong nature; consider the recklessness following on despair — soothe him; save him; love him; tell him you love him and will be his

Who in the world cares for *you?* or who will be injured by what you do?"

Still indomitable was the reply —"*I* care for myself. The more solitary, the more friendless, the more unsustained I am, the more I will respect myself. I will keep the law given by God; sanctioned by man. I will hold to the principles received by me when I was sane, and not mad — as I am now. Laws and principles are not for the times when there is no temptation: they are for such moments as this, when body and soul rise in mutiny against their rigour; stringent are they; inviolate they shall be. If at my individual convenience I might break them, what would be their worth? They have a worth — so I have always believed; and if I cannot believe it now, it is because I am insane — quite insane: with my veins running fire, and my heart beating faster than I can count its throbs. Preconceived opinions, foregone determinations, are all I have at this hour to stand by: there I plant my foot."

I did. Mr. Rochester, reading my countenance, saw I had done so. His fury was wrought to the highest: he must yield to it for a moment, whatever followed; he crossed the floor and seized my arm, and grasped my waist. He seemed to devour me with his flaming glance: physically, I felt, at the moment, powerless as stubble exposed to the draught and glow of a furnace — mentally, I still possessed my soul, and with it the certainty of ultimate safety. The soul, fortunately, has an interpreter — often an unconscious, but still a truthful interpreter — in the eye. My eye rose to his; and while I looked in his fierce face, I gave an involuntary sigh: his grip was painful, and my over-tasked strength almost exhausted.

"Never," said he, as he ground his teeth, "never was anything at once so frail and so indomitable. A mere reed she feels in my hand!" (And he shook me with the force of his hold.) "I could bend her with my finger and thumb: and what good would it do if I bent, if I uptore, if I crushed her? Consider that eye: consider the resolute, wild, free thing looking out of it, defying me, with more than courage — with a stern triumph. Whatever I do with its cage, I cannot get at it — the savage, beautiful creature! If I tear, if I rend the slight prison, my outrage will only let the captive loose. Conqueror I might be of the house; but the inmate would escape to heaven before I could call myself possessor of its clay dwelling-place. And it is you, spirit — with will and energy, and virtue and purity — that I want: not alone your brittle frame. Of yourself, you could come with soft flight and nestle against my heart, if you would: seized against your will you will elude the grasp like an essence — you will vanish ere I inhale your fragrance. Oh! come, Jane, come!"

As he said this, he released me from his clutch, and only looked at me. The look was far worse to resist than the frantic strain: only an idiot, however, would have succumbed now. I had dared and baffled his fury; I must elude his sorrow: I retired to the door.

"You are going, Jane?"

"I am going, sir."

"You are leaving me?"

"Yes."

"You will not come? — You will not be my comforter, my rescuer? — My deep love, my wild woe, my frantic prayer, are all nothing to you?"

What unutterable pathos was in his voice! How hard it was to reiterate firmly, "I am going."

"Jane!"

"Mr. Rochester!"

"Withdraw, then, — I consent — but remember, you leave me here in anguish. Go up to your own room; think over all I have said, Jane, cast a glance on my sufferings — think of me."

He turned away; he threw himself on his face on the sofa. "Oh, Jane! my hope — my love — my life!" broke in anguish from his lips. Then came a deep, strong sob.

I had already gained the door: but, reader, I walked back — walked back as determinedly as I had retreated. I knelt down by him; I turned his face from the cushion to me; I kissed his cheek; I smoothed his hair with my hand.

"God bless you, my dear master!" I said. "God keep you from harm and wrong — direct you, solace you — reward you well for your past kindness to me."

"Little Jane's love would have been my best reward," he answered: "without it, my heart is broken. But Jane will give me her love: yes — nobly, generously."

Up the blood rushed to his face; forth flashed the fire from his eyes; erect he sprang; he held his arms out; but I evaded the embrace, and at once quitted the room.

"Farewell!" was the cry of my heart as I left him. Despair added, "Farewell, for ever!"

. . . . . . . . .

That night I never thought to sleep; but a slumber fell on me as soon as I lay down in bed. I was transported in thought to the scenes of childhood: I dreamt I lay in the red-room at Gateshead; that the night was dark, and my mind impressed with strange fears. The light that long ago had struck me into syncope, recalled in this vision, seemed glidingly to mount the wall, and tremblingly to pause in the centre of the obscured ceiling. I lifted up my head to look: the roof resolved to clouds, high and dim; the gleam was such as the moon imparts to vapours she is about to sever. I watched her come — watched with the strangest anticipation; as though some word of doom were to be written on her disk. She broke forth as never moon yet burst from cloud: a hand first penetrated the sable folds and waved them away; then, not a moon, but a white human form shone in the azure, inclining a glorious brow earthward. It gazed and gazed on me. It spoke to my spirit: immeasurably distant was the tone, yet so near, it whispered in my heart —

"My daughter, flee temptation!"

"Mother, I will."

So I answered after I had waked from the trance-like dream. It was yet night, but July nights are short: soon after midnight, dawn comes. "It cannot be too early to commence the task I have to fulfil," thought I. I rose: I was dressed; for I had taken off nothing but my shoes. I knew where to find in my drawers some linen, a locket, a ring. In seeking these articles, I encountered the beads of a pearl necklace Mr. Rochester had forced me to accept a few days ago. I left that; it was not mine: it was the visionary bride's, who had melted in air. The other articles I made up in a parcel; my purse, containing twenty shillings (it was all I had), I put in my pocket: I tried on my straw bonnet, pinned my shawl, took the parcel and my slippers, which I would not put on yet, and stole from my room.

"Farewell, kind Mrs. Fairfax!" I whispered, as I glided past her door. "Farewell, my darling Adèle!" I said as I glanced towards the nursery. No thought could be admitted of entering to embrace her. I had to deceive a fine ear: for aught I knew, it might now be listening.

I would have got past Mr. Rochester's chamber without a pause; but my heart momentarily stopping its beat at that threshold, my foot was forced to stop also. No sleep was there: the inmate was walking restlessly from wall to wall; and again and again he sighed while I listened. There was a heaven — a temporary heaven — in this room for me, if I chose: I had but to go in and to say —

"Mr. Rochester, I will love you and live with you through life till death," and a fount of rapture would spring to my lips. I thought of this.

That kind master, who could not sleep now, was waiting with impatience for day. He would send for me in the morning; I should be gone. He would have me sought for: vainly. He would feel himself forsaken; his love rejected: he would suffer; perhaps grow desperate. I thought of this too. My hand moved towards the lock: I caught it back, and glided on.

Drearily I wound my way downstairs: I knew what I had to do, and I did it mechanically. I sought the key of the side-door in the kitchen; I sought, too, a phial of oil and a feather; I oiled the key and the lock. I got some water, I got some bread: for perhaps I should have to walk far; and my strength, sorely shaken of late, must not break down. All this I did without one sound. I opened the door, passed out, shut it softly. Dim dawn glimmered in the yard. The great gates were closed and locked; but a wicket in one of them was only latched. Through that I departed: it, too, I shut; and now I was out of Thornfield.

A mile off, beyond the fields, lay a road which stretched in the contrary direction to Millcote; a road I had never travelled, but often noticed, and wondered where it led: thither I bent my steps. No reflection was to be allowed now: not one glance was to be cast back; not even one forward. Not one thought was to be given either to the past or the future. The first was a page so heavenly sweet — so deadly sad — that to read one line of it would dissolve my courage and break down my energy. The last was an awful blank: something like the world when the deluge was gone by.

I skirted fields, and hedges, and lanes, till after sunrise. I believe it was a lovely summer morning: I know my shoes, which I had put on when I left the house, were soon wet with dew. But I looked neither to rising sun, nor smiling sky, nor wakening nature. He who is taken out to pass through a fair scene to the scaffold, thinks not of the flowers that smile on his road, but of the block and axe-edge; of the disseverment of bone and vein; of the grave gaping at the end: and I thought of drear flight and homeless wandering — and, oh! with agony I thought of what I left. I could not help it. I thought of him now — in his room — watching the sunrise; hoping I should soon come to say I would stay with him, and be his. I longed to be his; I panted to return: it was not too late; I could yet spare him the bitter pang of bereavement. As yet my flight, I was sure, was undiscovered. I could go back and be his comforter — his pride; his redeemer from misery; perhaps from ruin. Oh, that fear of his self-abandonment — far worse than my abandonment — how it goaded me! It was a barbed arrow-head in my breast; it tore me when I tried to extract it; it sickened me when remembrance thrust it further in. Birds began singing in brake and copse: birds were faithful to their mates; birds were emblems of love. What was I? In the midst of my pain of heart, and frantic effort of principle, I abhorred myself. I had no solace from self-approbation: none even from self-respect. I had injured — wounded — left my master. I was hateful in my own eyes. Still I could not turn, nor retrace one step. God must have led me on. As to my own will or conscience, impassioned grief had trampled one and stifled the other. I was weeping wildly as I walked along my solitary way: fast, fast I went like one delirious. A weakness, beginning inwardly, extending to the limbs, seized me, and I fell: I lay on the ground some minutes, pressing my face to the wet turf. I had some fear — or hope — that here I should die: but I was soon up; crawling forwards on my hands and knees, and then again raised to my feet — as eager and as determined as ever to reach the road.

When I got there I was forced to sit to rest me under the hedge; and while I sat, I heard wheels, and saw a coach come on. I stood up and lifted my hand; it stopped. I asked where it was going: the driver named a place a long way off, and where I was sure Mr. Rochester had no connections. I asked for what sum he would take me there; he said thirty shillings; I answered I had but twenty; well, he would try to make it do. He further gave me leave to get into the inside, as the vehicle was empty: I entered, was shut in, and it rolled on its way.

Gentle reader, may you never feel what I then felt! May your eyes never shed such stormy, scalding, heart-wrung tears as poured from mine. May you never appeal to Heaven in prayers so hopeless and so agonised as in that hour left my lips: for never may you, like me, dread to be the instrument of evil to what you wholly love.

## CHAPTER XXVIII

TWO days are passed. It is a summer evening; the coachman has set me down at a place called Whitcross; he could take me no farther for the sum I had given, and I was not possessed of another shilling in the world. The coach is a mile off by this time; I am alone. At this moment I discover that I forgot to take my parcel out of the pocket of the coach, where I had placed it for safety; there it remains, there it must remain; and now, I am absolutely destitute.

Whitcross is no town, nor even a hamlet; it is but a stone pillar set up where four roads meet: white-washed, I suppose, to be more obvious at a distance and in darkness. Four arms spring from its summit: the nearest town to which these point is, according to the inscription, distant ten miles; the farthest, above twenty. From the well-known names of these towns I learn in what county I have lighted; a north-midland shire, dusk with moorland, ridged with mountain: this I see. There are great moors behind and on each hand of me; there are waves of mountains far beyond that deep valley at my feet. The population here must be thin, and I see no passengers on these roads: they stretch out east, west, north, and south — white, broad, lonely; they are all cut in the moor, and the heather grows deep and wild to their very verge. Yet a chance traveller might pass by; and I wish no eye to see me now: strangers would wonder what I am doing, lingering here at the sign-post, evidently objectless and lost. I might be questioned: I could give no answer but what would sound incredible, and excite suspicion. Not a tie holds me to human society at this moment — not a charm or hope calls me where my fellow-creatures are — none that saw me would have a kind thought or good wish for me. I have no relative but the universal mother, Nature: I will seek her breast and ask repose.

I struck straight into the heath; I held on to a hollow I saw deeply furrowing the brown moorside; I waded knee-deep in its dark growth; I turned with its turnings, and finding a moss-blackened granite crag in a hidden angle, I sat down under it. High banks of moor were about me; the crag protected my head: the sky was over that.

Some time passed before I felt tranquil even here: I had a vague dread that wild cattle might be near, or that some sportsman or poacher might discover me. If a gust of wind swept the waste, I looked up, fearing it was the rush of a bull; if a plover whistled, I imagined it a man. Finding my apprehensions unfounded, however, and calmed by the deep silence that reigned as evening declined at nightfall, I took confidence. As yet I had not thought; I had only listened, watched, dreaded; now I regained the faculty of reflection.

What was I to do? Where to go? Oh, intolerable questions, when I could do nothing and go nowhere! — when a long way must yet be measured by my weary, trembling limbs, before I could reach human habitation — when cold charity must be entreated before I could get a lodging: reluctant sympathy importuned: almost certain repulse incurred: before my tale could be listened to, or one of my wants relieved!

I touched the heath: it was dry, and yet warm with the heat of the summer-day. I looked at the sky; it was pure: a kindly star twinkled just above the chasm ridge. The dew fell, but with propitious softness; no breeze whispered. Nature seemed to me benign and good; I thought she loved me, outcast as I was; and I, who from man could anticipate only mistrust, rejection, insult, clung to her with filial fondness. To-night, at least, I would be her guest — as I was her child: my mother would lodge me without money and without price. I had one morsel of bread yet: the remnant of a roll I had bought in a town we passed through at noon with a stray penny — my last coin. I saw ripe bilberries gleaming here and there, like jet beads in the heath: I gathered a handful and ate them with the bread. My hunger, sharp before, was, if not satisfied, appeased by this hermit's meal. I said my evening prayers at its conclusion, and then chose my couch.

Beside the crag, the heath was very deep: when I lay down my feet were buried in it; rising high on each side, it left only a narrow space for the night-air to invade. I folded my shawl double, and spread it over me for a coverlet; a low, mossy swell was my pillow. Thus lodged, I was not, at least at the commencement of the night, cold.

My rest might have been blissful enough, only a sad heart broke it. It plained of its gaping wounds, its inward bleeding, its riven chords. It trembled for Mr. Rochester and his doom: it bemoaned him with bitter pity; it demanded him with ceaseless longing: and, impotent as a bird with both wings broken, it still quivered its shattered pinions in vain attempts to seek him.

Worn out with this torture of thought, I rose to my knees. Night was come, and her planets were risen: a safe, still night; too serene for the companionship of fear. We know that God is everywhere; but certainly we feel His presence most when His works are on the grandest scale spread before us: and it is in the unclouded night-sky, where His worlds wheel their silent course, that we read clearest His infinitude, His omnipotence, His omnipresence. I had risen to my knees to pray for Mr. Rochester. Looking up, I, with tear-dimmed eyes, saw the mighty Milky-way. Remembering what it was — what countless systems there swept space like a soft trace of light — I felt the might and strength of God. Sure was I of His efficiency to save what He had made: convinced I grew that neither earth should perish, nor one of the souls it treasured. I turned my prayer to thanksgiving: the Source of Life was also the Saviour of spirits. Mr. Rochester was safe: he was God's and by God would he be guarded. I again nestled to the breast of the hill; and ere long, in sleep, forgot sorrow.

But next day, Want came to me, pale and bare. Long after the little birds had left their nests; long after bees had come in the sweet prime of day to gather the heath honey before the dew was dried — when the long morning shadows were curtailed, and the sunfilled earth and sky — I got up, and I looked round me.

What a still, hot, perfect day! What a golden desert this spreading moor! Everywhere sunshine. I wished I could live in it and on it. I saw a lizard run over the crag; I saw a bee busy among the sweet bilberries. I would fain at the moment have become bee or lizard, that I might have found fitting nutriment, permanent shelter here. But I was a human being, and had a human being's wants: I must not linger where there was nothing to supply them. I rose; I looked back at the bed I had left. Hopeless of the future, I wished but this — that my Maker had that night thought good to require my soul of me while I slept; and that this weary frame, absolved by death from further conflict with fate, had now but to decay quietly, and mingle in peace with the soil of this wilderness. Life, however, was yet in my possession: with all its requirements, and pains, and responsibilities. The burden must be carried; the want provided for; the suffering endured; the responsibility fulfilled. I set out.

Whitcross regained, I followed a road which led from the sun, now fervent and high. By no other circumstance had I will to decide my choice. I walked a long time, and when I thought I had nearly done enough, and might conscientiously yield to the fatigue that almost overpowered me — might relax this forced action, and, sitting down on a stone I saw near, submit resistlessly to the apathy that clogged heart and limb — I heard a bell chime — a church bell.

I turned in the direction of the sound, and there, amongst the romantic hills, whose changes and aspect I had ceased to note an hour ago, I saw a hamlet and a spire. All the valley at my right hand was full of pasture-fields, and corn-fields, and wood; and a glittering stream ran zig-zag through the varied shades of green, the mellowing grain, the sombre wood-land, the clear and sunny lea. Recalled by the rumbling of wheels to the road before me, I saw a heavily-laden waggon labouring up the hill; and not far beyond were two cows and their drover. Human life and human labour were near. I must struggle on: strive to live and bend to toil like the rest.

About two o'clock, P. M., I entered the village. At the bottom of its one street, there was a little shop with some cakes of bread in the window. I coveted a cake of bread. With that refreshment I could perhaps regain a degree of energy; without it, it would be difficult to proceed. The wish to have some strength and some vigour returned to me as soon as I was amongst my fellow-beings. I felt it would be degrading to faint with hunger on the causeway of a hamlet. Had I nothing about me I could offer in exchange for one of these rolls? I considered. I had a small silk handkerchief tied round my throat; I had my gloves. I could hardly tell how men and women in extremities of destitution proceeded. I did not know whether either of these articles would be accepted: probably they would not; but I must try.

I entered the shop: a woman was there. Seeing a respectably-dressed person, a lady as she supposed, she came forward with

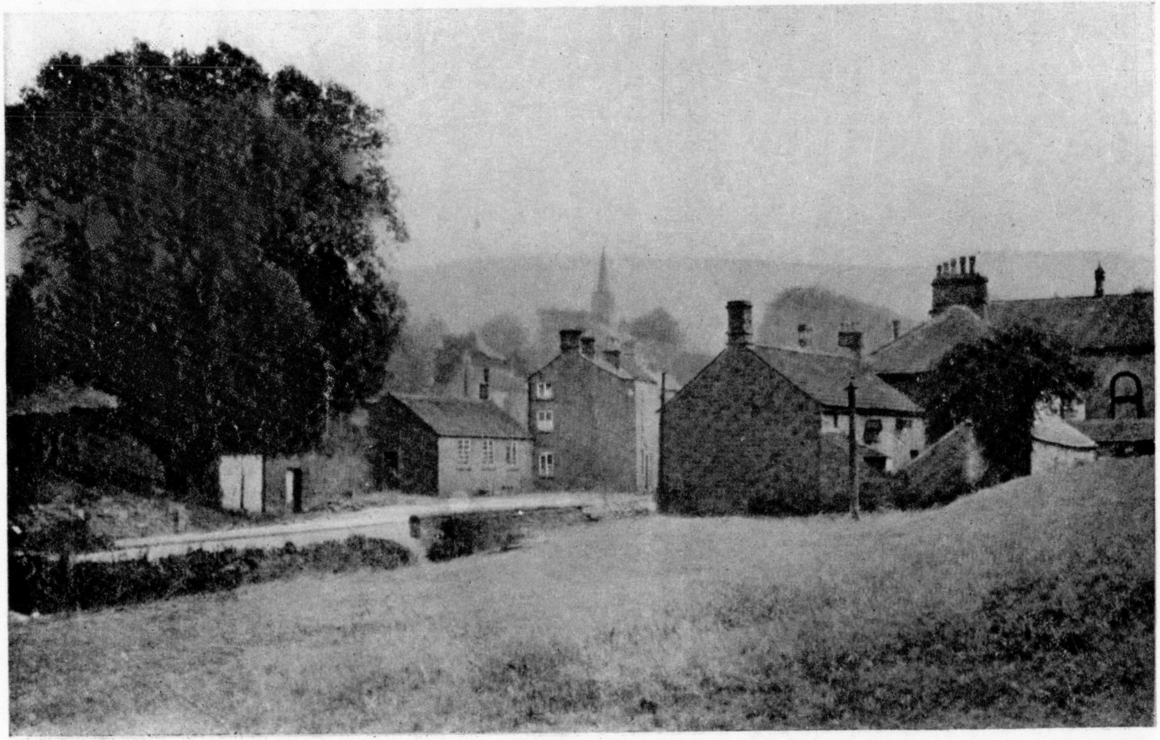

HATHERSAGE

Charlotte's friend Ellen Nussey had a brother who was a clergyman at Hathersage in Derbyshire, where Charlotte visited her. In *Jane Eyre,* she described the village as "Morton." Hathersage Church contains a monument to Robert Eyre, who fought at Agincourt, and his wife Joanna Eyre, where no doubt Charlotte got the name of her heroine. The churchyard also contains the grave of John Nailor, better known as Robin Hood's man Little John.

civility. How could she serve me? I was seized with shame: my tongue would not utter the request I had prepared. I dared not offer her the half-worn gloves, the creased handkerchief: besides, I felt it would be absurd. I only begged permission to sit down a moment, as I was tired. Disappointed in the expectation of a customer, she coolly acceded to my request. She pointed to a seat; I sank into it. I felt sorely urged to weep; but conscious how unseasonable such a manifestation would be, I restrained it. Soon I asked her, "if there were any dressmaker or plain-work-woman in the village?"

"Yes; two or three. Quite as many as there was employment for."

I reflected. I was driven to the point now. I was brought face to face with Necessity. I stood in the position of one without a resource: without a friend; without a coin. I must do something. What? I must apply somewhere. Where?

"Did she know of any place in the neighbourhood where a servant was wanted?"

"Nay; she couldn't say."

"What was the chief trade in this place? What did most of the people do?"

"Some were farm labourers; a good deal worked at Mr. Oliver's needle-factory, and at the foundry."

"Did Mr. Oliver employ women?"

"Nay; it was men's work."

"And what do the women do?"

"I knawn't," was the answer. "Some does one thing, and some another. Poor folk mun get on as they can."

She seemed to be tired of my questions: and, indeed, what claim had I to importune her? A neighbour or two came in; my chair was evidently wanted. I took leave.

I passed up the street, looking as I went at all the houses to the right hand and to the left: but I could discover no pretext, nor see an inducement, to enter any. I rambled round the hamlet, going sometimes to a little distance and returning again, for an hour or more. Much exhausted, and suffering greatly now for want of food, I turned aside into a lane and sat down under the hedge. Ere many minutes had elapsed, I was again on my feet, however, and again searching something — a resource, or at least an informant. A pretty little house stood at the top of the lane, with a garden before it; exquisitely neat, and brilliantly blooming. I stopped at it. What business had I to approach the white door, or touch the glittering knocker? In what way could it possibly be the interest of the inhabitants of that dwelling to serve me? Yet I drew near and knocked. A mild-looking, cleanly-attired young woman opened the door. In such a voice as might be expected from a hopeless heart and fainting frame — a voice wretchedly low and faltering — I asked if a servant was wanted here?

"No," said she; "we do not keep a servant."

"Can you tell me where I could get employment of any kind?" I continued. "I am a stranger, without acquaintance, in this place. I want some work: no matter what."

But it was not her business to think for me, or to seek a place for me: besides, in her eyes, how doubtful must have appeared my character, position, tale. She shook her head, she "was sorry she could give me no information," and the white door closed, quite gently and civilly: but it shut me out. If she had held it open a little longer, I believe I should have begged a piece of bread; for I was now brought low.

I could not bear to return to the sordid village; where, besides, no prospect of aid was visible. I should have longed rather to deviate to a wood I saw not far off, which appeared in its thick shade to offer inviting shelter; but I was so sick, so weak, so gnawed with nature's cravings, instinct kept me roaming round abodes where there was a chance of food. Solitude would be no solitude — rest no rest — while the vulture, hunger, thus sank beak and talons in my side.

I drew near houses; I left them, and came back again, and again I wandered away: always repelled by the consciousness of having no claim to ask — no right to expect interest in my isolated lot. Meantime, the afternoon advanced, while I thus wandered about like a lost and starving dog. In crossing a field, I saw the church spire before me: I hastened towards it. Near the churchyard, and in the middle of a garden, stood a well-built though small house, which I had no doubt was the parsonage. I remembered that strangers who arrive at a place where they have no friends, and who want employment, sometimes apply to the clergyman for introduction and aid. It is the clergyman's function to help — at least with advice — those who wished to help themselves. I seemed to have something like a right to seek counsel here. Renewing then, my courage, and gathering my feeble remains of strength, I pushed on. I reached the house, and knocked at the kitchen-door. An old woman opened: I asked was this the parsonage?

"Yes."

"Was the clergyman in?"

"No."

"Would he be in soon?"

"No, he was gone from home."

"To a distance?"

"Not so far — happen three mile. He had been called away by the sudden death of his father: he was at Marsh End now, and would very likely stay there a fortnight longer."

"Was there any lady of the house?"

"Nay, there was naught but her, and she was housekeeper;" and of her, reader, I could not bear to ask the relief for want of which I was sinking; I could not yet beg; and again I crawled away.

Once more I took off my handkerchief — once more I thought of the cakes of bread in the little shop. Oh, for but a crust! for but one mouthful to allay the pang of famine! Instinctively I turned my face again to the village; I found the shop again, and I went in; and though others were there besides the woman, I ventured the request: "Would she give me a roll for this handkerchief?"

She looked at me with evident suspicion: "Nay, she never sold stuff i' that way."

Almost desperate, I asked for half a cake; she again refused. "How could she tell where I had got the handkerchief," she said.

"Would she take my gloves?"

"No! what could she do with them?"

Reader, it is not pleasant to dwell on these details. Some say there is enjoyment in looking back to painful experience past; but at this day I can scarcely bear to review the times to which I allude: the moral degradation, blent with the physical suffering, form too distressing a recollection ever to be willingly dwelt on. I blamed none of those who repulsed me. I felt it was what was to be expected, and what could not be helped: an ordinary beggar is frequently an object of suspicion; a well-dressed beggar inevitably so. To be sure what I begged was employment: but whose business was it to provide me with employment? Not, certainly, that of persons who saw me then for the first time, and who knew nothing about my character. And as to the woman who would not take my handkerchief in exchange for her bread, why, she was right; if the offer appeared to her sinister, or the exchange unprofitable. Let me condense now. I am sick of the subject.

A little before dark I passed a farm-house, at the open door of which the farmer was sitting, eating his supper of bread and cheese; I stopped, and said: —

"Will you give me a piece of bread? for I am very hungry." He cast on me a glance of surprise; but without answering, he cut a thick slice from his loaf, and gave it to me. I imagine he did not think I was a beggar, but only an eccentric sort of lady, who had taken a fancy to his brown loaf. As soon as I was out of sight of his house, I sat down and ate it.

I could not hope to get a lodging under a roof, and sought it in the wood I have before alluded to. But my night was wretched, my rest broken: the ground was damp, the air cold: besides, intruders passed near me more than once, and I had again and again to change my quarters: no sense of safety or tranquillity befriended me. Towards morning it rained; the whole of the following day was wet. Do not ask me, reader, to give a minute account of that day; as before, I sought work; as before, I was repulsed; as before, I starved; but once did food pass my lips. At the door of a cottage I saw a little girl about to throw a mess of cold porridge into a pig trough. "Will you give me that?" I asked.

She stared at me. "Mother!" she exclaimed; "there is a woman wants me to give her these porridge."

"Well, lass," replied a voice within, "give it her if she's a beggar. T' pig doesn't want it."

The girl emptied the stiffened mould into my hand, and I devoured it ravenously.

As the wet twilight deepened, I stopped in a solitary bridle-path, which I had been pursuing an hour or more.

"My strength is quite failing me," I said, in soliloquy. "I feel I cannot go much further. Shall I be an outcast again this night? While the rain descends so, must I lay my head on the cold, drenched ground! I fear I cannot do otherwise: for who will receive me?

But it will be very dreadful: with this feeling of hunger, faintness, chill, and this sense of desolation — this total prostration of hope. In all likelihood, though, I should die before morning. And why cannot I reconcile myself to the prospect of death? Why do I struggle to retain a valueless life? Because I know, or believe, Mr. Rochester is still living: and then, to die of want and cold, is a fate to which nature cannot submit passively. Oh, Providence! sustain me a little longer! Aid — direct me!"

My glazed eye wandered over the dim and misty landscape. I saw I had strayed far from the village: it was quite out of sight. The very cultivation surrounding it had disappeared; I had, by cross-ways and by-paths, once more drawn near the tract of moorland; and now only a few fields, almost as wild and unproductive as the heath from which they were scarcely reclaimed, lay between me and the dusky hill.

"Well, I would rather die yonder than in a street, or on a frequented road," I reflected. "And far better that crows and ravens — if any ravens there be in these regions — should pick my flesh from my bones, than that they should be prisoned in a work-house coffin and moulder in a pauper's grave."

To the hill, then, I turned. I reached it. It remained now only to find a hollow where I could lie down, and feel at least hidden, if not secure: but all the surface of the waste looked level. It showed no variation but of tint: green, where rush and moss over-grew the marshes; black, where the dry soil bore only heath. Dark as it was getting, I could still see these changes: though but as mere alterations of light and shade: for colour had faded with the daylight.

My eye still roved over the sullen swell, and along the moor-edge, vanishing amidst the wildest scenery; when at one dim point, far in among the marshes and the ridges, a light sprang up. "That is an *ignis fatuus*," was my first thought; and I expected it would soon vanish. It burnt on, however, quite steadily; neither receding nor advancing. "Is it, then, a bonfire just kindled?" I questioned. I watched to see whether it would spread: but no; as it did not diminish, so it did not enlarge. "It may be a candle in a house," I then conjectured: "but if so, I can never reach it. It is much too far away: and were it within a yard of me, what would it avail? I should but knock at the door to have it shut in my face."

And I sank down where I stood, and hid my face against the ground. I lay still a while: the night-wind swept over the hill and over me, and died moaning in the distance; the rain fell fast, wetting me afresh to the skin. Could I but have stiffened to the still frost — the friendly numbness of death — it might have pelted on: I should not have felt it; but my yet living flesh shuddered to its chilling influence. I rose ere long.

The light was yet there: shining dim, but constant, through the rain. I tried to walk again: I dragged my exhausted limbs slowly towards it. It led me aslant over the hill, through a wide bog; which would have been impassable in winter, and was splashy and shaking even now, in the height of summer. Here I fell twice; but as often I rose and rallied my faculties. This light was my forlorn hope: I must gain it.

Having crossed the marsh, I saw a trace of white over the moor. I approached it; it was a road or a track: it led straight up to the light, which now beamed from a sort of knoll, amidst a clump of trees — firs, apparently, from what I could distinguish of the character of their forms and foliage through the gloom. My star vanished as I drew near: some obstacle had intervened between me and it. I put out my hand to feel the dark mass before me; I discriminated the rough stones of a low wall — above it, something like palisades, and within, a high and prickly hedge. I groped on. Again a whitish object gleamed before me: it was a gate — a wicket; it moved on its hinges as I touched it. On each side stood a sable bush — holly or yew.

Entering the gate and passing the shrubs, the silhouette of a house rose to view; black, low, and rather long; but the guiding light shone nowhere. All was obscurity. Were the inmates retired to rest? I feared it must be so. In seeking the door, I turned an angle: there shot out the friendly gleam again, from the lozenged panes of a very small latticed window, within a foot of the ground; made still smaller by the growth of ivy or some other creeping plant, whose leaves clustered thick over the portion of the house wall in which it was set. The aperture was so screened and narrow, that curtain or shutter had been deemed unnecessary; and when I stooped down and put aside the spray of foliage shooting over it, I could see all within. I could see clearly a room with a sanded floor, clean scoured; a dresser of walnut, with pewter plates ranged in rows, reflecting the redness and radiance of a glowing peat-fire. I could see a clock, a white deal table, some chairs. The candle, whose ray had been my beacon, burnt on the table; and by its light an elderly woman, somewhat rough-looking, but scrupulously clean, like all about her, was knitting a stocking.

I noted these objects cursorily only — in them there was nothing extraordinary. A group of more interest appeared near the hearth, sitting still amidst the rosy peace and warmth suffusing it. Two young, graceful women — ladies in every point — sat, one on a low rocking-chair, the other on a lower stool; both wore deep mourning of crape and bombazeen, which sombre garb singularly set off very fair necks and faces: a large old pointer dog rested its massive head on the knee of one girl — in the lap of the other was cushioned a black cat.

A strange place was this humble kitchen for such occupants! Who were they? They could not be the daughters of the elderly person at the table; for she looked like a rustic, and they were all delicacy and cultivation. I had nowhere seen such faces as theirs: and yet, as I gazed on them, I seemed intimate with every lineament. I cannot call them handsome — they were too pale and grave for the word: as they each bent over a book, they looked thoughtful almost to severity. A stand between them supported a second candle and two great volumes, to which they frequently referred; comparing them seemingly with the smaller books they held in their hands, like people consulting a dictionary to aid them in the task of translation. This scene was as silent as if all the figures had been shadows, and the firelit apartment a picture: so hushed was it, I could hear the cinders fall from the grate, the clock tick in its obscure corner; and I even fancied I could distinguish the click-click of the woman's knitting-needles. When, therefore, a voice broke the strange stillness at last, it was audible enough to me.

"Listen, Diana," said one of the absorbed students: "Franz and old Daniel are together in the night-time, and Franz is telling a dream from which he has awakened in terror — listen!" And in a low voice she read something, of which not one word was intelligible to me; for it was in an unknown tongue — neither French nor Latin. Whether it were Greek or German I could not tell.

"That is strong," she said, when she had finished: "I relish it." The other girl, who had lifted her head to listen to her sister, repeated, while she gazed at the fire, a line of what had been read. At a later day, I knew the language and the book; therefore I will here quote the line: though when I first heard it, it was only like a stroke on sounding brass to me — conveying no meaning: —

"'Da trat hervor Einer, anzusehen wie die Sternen Nacht.' Good! good!" she exclaimed, while her dark and deep eyes sparkled. "There you have a dim and mighty archangel, fitly set before you! The line is worth a hundred pages of fustian. 'Ich wäge die Gedanken in der Schale meines Zornes und die Werke mit dem Gewichte meines Grimms.' I like it!"

Both were again silent.

"Is there ony country where they talk i' that way?" asked the old woman, looking up from her knitting.

"Yes, Hannah — a far larger country than England; where they talk in no other way."

"Well, for sure case, I knawn't how they can understand t' one t' other: and if either o' ye went there, ye could tell what they said, I guess?"

"We could probably tell something of what they said, but not all — for we are not as clever as you think us, Hannah. We don't speak German, and we cannot read it without a dictionary to help us."

"And what good does it do you?"

"We mean to teach it some time — or at least the elements, as they say; and then we shall get more money than we do now."

"Varry like: but give ower studying: ye've done enough for to-night."

"I think we have: at least I'm tired. Mary, are you?"

"Mortally: after all, it's tough work fagging away at a language with no master but a lexicon."

"It is: especially such a language as this crabbed but glorious Deutsch. I wonder when St. John will come home."

"Surely he will not be long now: it is just ten" (looking at a little gold watch she drew from her girdle). "It rains fast. Hannah, will you have the goodness to look at the fire in the parlour?"

The woman rose: she opened a door, through which I dimly saw a passage: soon I heard her stir a fire in an inner room; she presently came back.

"Ah, childer!" said she, "it fair troubles me to go into yond' room now; it looks so lonesome wi' the chair empty and set back in a corner."

She wiped her eyes with her apron: the two girls, grave before, looked sad now.

"But he is in a better place," continued Hannah: "we shouldn't wish him here again. And then, nobody need to have a quieter death nor he had."

"You say he never mentioned us?" inquired one of the ladies.

"He hadn't time, bairn: he was gone in a minute — your father. He had been a bit ailing like the day before, but naught to signify; and when Mr. St. John asked if he would like either o' ye to be sent for, he fair laughed at him. He began again with a bit of a heaviness in his head the next day — that is, a fortnight sin' — and he went to sleep and niver wakened; he wor a'most stark when your brother went into t' chamber and fand him. Ah, childer! that's t' last o' t' old stock — for ye and Mr. St. John is like of a different soart to them 'at's gone; for all your mother wor mich i' your way; and a'most as book-learned. She wor the pictur' o' ye, Mary: Diana is more like your father."

I thought them so similar I could not tell where the old servant (for such I now concluded her to be) saw the difference. Both were fair complexioned and slenderly made; both possessed faces full of distinction and intelligence. One, to be sure, had hair a shade darker than the other, and there was a difference in their style of wearing it: Mary's pale brown locks were parted and braided smooth; Diana's duskier tresses covered her neck with thick curls. The clock struck ten.

"You'll want your supper, I am sure," observed Hannah; "and so will Mr. St. John when he comes in."

And she proceeded to prepare the meal. The ladies rose; they seemed about to withdraw to the parlour. Till this moment, I had been so intent on watching them, their appearance and conversation had excited in me so keen an interest, I had half-forgotten my own wretched position: now it recurred to me. More desolate, more desperate than ever, it seemed from contrast. And how impossible did it appear to touch the inmates of this house with concern on my behalf; to make them believe in the truth of my wants and woes — to induce them to vouchsafe a rest for my wanderings! As I groped out the door, and knocked at it hesitatingly, I felt that last idea to be a mere chimera. Hannah opened.

"What do you want?" she inquired, in a voice of surprise, as she surveyed me by the light of the candle she held.

"May I speak to your mistresses?" I said.

"You had better tell me what you have to say to them. Where do you come from?"

"I am a stranger."

"What is your business here at this hour?"

"I want a night's shelter in an out-house or anywhere, and a morsel of bread to eat."

Distrust, the very feeling I dreaded, appeared in Hannah's face. "I'll give you a piece of bread," she said, after a pause; "but we can't take in a vagrant to lodge. It isn't likely."

"Do let me speak to your mistresses."

"No; not I. What can they do for you? You should not be roving about now; it looks very ill."

"But where shall I go if you drive me away? What shall I do?"

"Oh, I'll warrant you know where to go, and what to do. Mind you don't do wrong, that's all. Here is a penny; now go"——

"A penny cannot feed me, and I have no strength to go farther. Don't shut the door: — oh, don't, for God's sake!"

"I must; the rain is driving in"——

"Tell the young ladies.— Let me see them"——

"Indeed, I will not. You are not what you ought to be, or you wouldn't make such a noise. Move off."

"But I must die if I am turned away."

"Not you. I'm fear'd you have some ill plans agate, that bring you about folk's houses at this time o' night. If you've any followers — housebreakers or such like — anywhere near, you may tell them we are not by ourselves in the house; we have a gentleman, and dogs, and guns." Here the honest but inflexible servant clapped the door to and bolted it within.

This was the climax. A pang of exquisite suffering — a throe of true despair — rent and heaved my heart. Worn out, indeed, I was; not another step could I stir. I sank on the wet door-step: I groaned — I wrung my hands — I wept in utter anguish. Oh, this spectre of death! Oh, this last hour, approaching in such horror! Alas, this isolation — this banishment from my kind!

Not only the anchor of home, but the footing of fortitude was gone — at least for a moment: but the last I soon endeavoured to regain.

"I can but die," I said, "and I believed in God. Let me try to wait His will in silence."

These words I not only thought, but uttered; and thrusting back all my misery into my heart, I made an effort to compel it to remain there — dumb and still.

"All men must die," said a voice quite close at hand; "but all are not condemned to meet a lingering and premature doom, such as yours would be if you perished here of want."

"Who or what speaks?" I asked, terrified at the unexpected sound, and incapable now of deriving from any occurrence a hope of aid. A form was near — what form, the pitch-dark night and my enfeebled vision prevented me from distinguishing. With a loud long knock, the new comer appealed to the door.

"Is it you, Mr. St. John?" cried Hannah.

"Yes — yes; open quickly."

"Well, how wet and cold you must be, such a wild night as it is! Come in — your sisters are quite uneasy about you, and I believe there are bad folks about. There has been a beggar-woman — I declare she is not gone yet! — laid down there. Get up! for shame! Move off, I say!"

"Hush, Hannah! I have a word to say to the woman. You have done your duty in excluding, now let me do mine in admitting her. I was near, and listened to both you and her. I think this is a peculiar case — I must at least examine into it. Young woman, rise, and pass before me into the house."

With difficulty I obeyed him. Presently I stood within that clean, bright kitchen — on the very hearth — trembling, sickening; conscious of an aspect in the last degree ghastly, wild, and weather-beaten. The two ladies, their brother, Mr. St. John, the old servant, were all gazing at me.

"St. John, who is it?" I heard one ask.

"I cannot tell: I found her at the door," was the reply.

"She does look white," said Hannah.

"As white as clay or death," was responded. "She will fall: let her sit."

And indeed my head swam: I dropped; but a chair received me. I still possessed my senses; though just now I could not speak.

"Perhaps a little water would restore her. Hannah, fetch some. But she is worn to nothing. How very thin, and how very bloodless!"

"A mere spectre!"

"Is she ill, or only famished?"

"Famished, I think. Hannah, is that milk? Give it me, and a piece of bread."

Diana (I knew her by the long curls which I saw drooping between me and the fire as she bent over me) broke some bread, dipped it in milk, and put it to my lips. Her face was near mine: I saw there was pity in it, and I felt sympathy in her hurried breathing. In her simple words, too, the same balm-like emotion spoke: "Try to eat."

"Yes — try," repeated Mary gently; and Mary's hand removed my sodden bonnet and lifted my head. I tasted what they offered me: feebly at first, eagerly soon.

"Not too much at first — restrain her," said the brother; "she has had enough." And he withdrew the cup of milk and the plate of bread.

"A little more, St. John — look at the avidity in her eyes."

"No more at present, sister. Try if she can speak now — ask her her name."

I felt I could speak, and I answered — "My name is Jane Elliot." Anxious as ever to avoid discovery, I had before resolved to assume an *alias*.

"And where do you live? Where are your friends?"

I was silent.

"Can we send for any one you know?"

I shook my head.

"What account can you give of yourself?"

Somehow, now that I had once crossed the threshold of this house, and once was brought face to face with its owners, I felt no longer outcast, vagrant, and disowned by the wide world. I dared to put off the mendicant — to resume my natural manner and character. I began once more to know myself; and when Mr. St. John demanded an account — which at present I was far too weak to render — I said after a brief pause,—

"Sir, I can give you no details to-night."

"But what, then," said he, "do you expect me to do for you?"

"Nothing," I replied. My strength sufficed for but short answers. Diana took the word: —

"Do you mean," she asked, "that we have now given you what aid you require? and that we may dismiss you to the moor and the rainy night?"

I looked at her. She had, I thought, a remarkable countenance; instinct both with power and goodness. I took sudden courage. Answering her compassionate gaze with a smile, I said: "I will trust you. If I were a masterless and stray dog, I know that you would not turn me from your hearth to-night: as it is, I really have no fear. Do with me and for me as you like; but excuse me from much discourse — my breath is short — I feel a spasm when I speak." All three surveyed me, and all three were silent.

"Hannah," said Mr. St. John, at last, "let her sit there at present, and ask her no questions; in ten minutes more, give her the remainder of that milk and bread. Mary and Diana, let us go into the parlour and talk the matter over."

They withdrew. Very soon one of the ladies returned — I could not tell which. A kind of pleasant stupor was stealing over me as I sat by the genial fire. In an undertone she gave some directions to Hannah. Ere long, with the servant's aid, I contrived to mount a staircase; my dripping clothes were removed; soon, a warm, dry bed received me. I thanked God — experienced amidst unutterable exhaustion a glow of grateful joy — and slept.

## CHAPTER XXIX

THE recollection of about three days and nights succeeding this is very dim in my mind. I can recall some sensations felt in the interval; but few thoughts framed, and no actions performed. I knew I was in a small room, and in a narrow bed. To that bed I seemed to have grown; I lay on it motionless as a stone; and to have torn me from it would have been almost to kill me. I took no note of the lapse of time — of the change from morning to noon, from noon to evening. I observed when any one entered or left the apartment; I could even tell who they were; I could understand what was said when the speaker stood near to me; but I could not answer; to open my lips or move my limbs was equally impossible. Hannah, the servant, was my most frequent visitor. Her coming disturbed me. I had a feeling that she wished me away: that she did not understand me or my circumstances: that she was prejudiced against me. Diana and Mary appeared in the chamber once or twice a day. They would whisper sentences of this sort at my bedside: —

"It is very well we took her in."

"Yes; she would certainly have been found dead at the door in the morning, had she been left out all night. I wonder what she has gone through?"

"Strange hardships, I imagine — poor, emaciated, pallid wanderer!"

"She is not an uneducated person, I should think, by her manner of speaking; her accent was quite pure; and the clothes she took off, though splashed and wet, were little worn and fine."

"She has a peculiar face; fleshless and haggard as it is, I rather like it; and when in good health and animated, I can fancy her physiognomy would be agreeable."

Never once in their dialogues did I hear a syllable of regret at the hospitality they had extended to me; or of suspicion of, or aversion to, myself. I was comforted.

Mr. St. John came but once: he looked at me, and said my state of lethargy was the result of reaction from excessive and protracted fatigue. He pronounced it needless to send for a doctor: nature, he was sure, would manage best, left to herself. He said every nerve had been overstrained in some way, and the whole system must sleep torpid a while. There was no disease. He imagined my recovery would be rapid enough when once commenced. These opinions he delivered in a few words, in a quiet, low voice; and added, after a pause, in the tone of a man little accustomed to expansive comment, "rather an unusual physiognomy; certainly, not indicative of vulgarity or degradation."

"Far otherwise," responded Diana. "To speak truth, St. John, my heart rather warms to the poor little soul. I wish we may be able to benefit her permanently."

"That is hardly likely," was the reply. "You will find she is some young lady who has had a misunderstanding with her friends and has probably injudiciously left them. We may, perhaps, succeed in restoring her to them, if she is not obstinate: but I trace lines of force in her face which make me sceptical of her tractability." He stood considering me some minutes; then added, "She looks sensible, but not at all handsome."

"She is so ill, St. John."

"Ill or well, she would always be plain. The grace and harmony of beauty are quite wanting in those features."

On the third day, I was better; on the fourth, I could speak, move, rise in bed, and turn. Hannah had brought me some gruel and dry toast, about, as I supposed, the dinner hour. I had eaten with relish: the food was good — void of the feverish flavour which had hitherto poisoned what I had swallowed. When she left me, I felt comparatively strong and revived: ere long satiety of repose, and desire for action stirred me. I wished to rise; but what could I put on? Only my damp and bemired apparel; in which I had slept on the ground and fallen in the marsh. I felt ashamed to appear before my benefactors so clad. I was spared the humiliation.

On a chair by the bedside were all my own things, clean and dry. My black silk frock hung against the wall. The traces of the bog were removed from it; the creases left by the wet smoothed out: it was quite decent. My very shoes and stockings were purified and rendered presentable. There were the means of washing in the room, and a comb and brush to smooth my hair. After a weary process, and resting every five minutes, I succeeded in dressing myself. My clothes hung loose on me; for I was much wasted, but I covered deficiencies with a shawl, and once more, clean and respectable-looking — no speck of the dirt, no trace of the disorder I so hated, and which seemed so to degrade me, left — I crept down a stone staircase with the aid of the banisters, to a narrow low passage, and found my way presently to the kitchen.

It was full of the fragrance of new bread, and the warmth of a generous fire. Hannah was baking. Prejudices, it is well known, are most difficult to eradicate from the heart whose soil has never been loosened or fertilised by education: they grow there, firm as weeds among stones. Hannah had been cold and stiff, indeed, at the first: latterly she had begun to relent a little; and when she saw me come in tidy and well-dressed, she even smiled.

"What, you have got up?" she said. "You are better, then. You may sit you down in my chair on the hearthstone, if you will."

She pointed to the rocking chair: I took it. She bustled about, examining me every now and then with the corner of her eye. Turning to me, as she took some loaves from the oven, she asked, bluntly —

"Did you ever go a-begging afore you came here?"

I was indignant for a moment; but remembering that anger was out of the question, and that I had indeed appeared as a beggar to her, I answered quietly; but still not without a certain marked firmness —

"You are mistaken in supposing me a beggar. I am no beggar; any more than yourself or your young ladies."

After a pause, she said, "I dunnut understand that: you've like no house, nor no brass, I guess?"

"The want of house or brass (by which I suppose you mean money) does not make a beggar in your sense of the word."

"Are you book-learned?" she inquired, presently.

"Yes, very."

"But you've never been to a boarding-school!"

"I was at a boarding-school eight years."

She opened her eyes wide. "Whatever cannot ye keep yourself for, then?"

"I have kept myself; and, I trust, shall keep myself again. What are you going to do with these gooseberries?" I inquired, as she brought out a basket of the fruit.

"Mak'em into pies."

"Give them to me and I'll pick them."

"Nay; I dunnut want ye to do nought."

"But I must do something. Let me have them."

She consented; and she even brought me a clean towel to spread over my dress, "lest," as she said, "I should mucky it."

"Ye've not been used to sarvant's wark, I see by your hands," she remarked. "Happen ye've been a dressmaker."

"No, you are wrong. And, now, never mind what I have been: don't trouble your head further about me; but tell me the name of the house where we are."

"Some calls it Marsh End, and some calls it Moor House."

"And the gentleman who lives here is called Mr. St. John?"

"Nay; he doesn't live here: he is only staying a while. When he is at home, he is in his own parish at Morton."

"That village a few miles off?"

"Aye."

"And what is he?"

"He is a parson."

I remembered the answer of the old housekeeper at the parsonage, when I had asked to see the clergyman. "This, then, was his father's residence?"

"Aye; old Mr. Rivers lived here, and his father, and grandfather, and gurt (great) grandfather afore him."

"The name, then, of that gentleman, is Mr. St. John Rivers?"

"Aye; St. John is like his kirstened name."

"And his sisters are called Diana and Mary Rivers?"

"Yes."

"Their father is dead?"

"Dead three weeks sin' of a stroke."

"They have no mother?"

"The mistress has been dead this mony a year."

"Have you lived with the family long?"

"I've lived here thirty year. I nursed them all three."

"That proves you must have been an honest and faithful servant. I will say so much for you, though you have had the incivility to call me a beggar."

She again regarded me with a surprised stare. "I believe," she said, "I was quite mista'en in my thoughts of you: but there is so mony cheats goes about, you mun forgie me."

"And though," I continued, rather severely, "you wished to turn me from the door, on a night when you should not have shut out a dog."

"Well, it was hard: but what can a body do? I thought more o' th' childer nor of mysel: poor things! They've like nobody to tak' care on 'em but me. I'm like to look sharpish."

I maintained a grave silence for some minutes.

"You munnut think too hardly of me," she again remarked.

"But I do think hardly of you," I said; "and I'll tell you why — not so much because you refused to give me shelter, or regarded me as an impostor, as because you just now made it a species of reproach that I had no 'brass,' and no house. Some of the best people that ever lived have been as destitute as I am; and if you are a Christian, you ought not to consider poverty a crime."

"No more I ought," said she: "Mr. St. John tells me so too; and I see I wor wrang — but I've clear a different notion on you now to what I had. You look a raight down dacent little crater."

"That will do — I forgive you now. Shake hands."

She put her floury and horny hand into mine; another and heartier smile illumined her rough face; and from that moment we were friends.

Hannah was evidently fond of talking. While I picked the fruit, and she made the paste for the pies, she proceeded to give me sundry details about her deceased master and mistress, and "the childer," as she called the young people.

Old Mr. Rivers, she said, was a plain man enough; but a gentleman, and of as ancient a family as could be found. Marsh End had belonged to the Rivers' ever since it was a house: and it was, she affirmed, "aboon two hundred year old — for all it looked but a small, humble place, naught to compare wi' Mr. Oliver's grand hall down i' Morton Vale. But she could remember Bill Oliver's father, a journeyman needle-maker; and th' Rivers wor gentry i' th' owd days o' th' Henrys, as onybody might see by looking into th' registers i' Morton Church vestry." Still, she allowed, "the owd maister was like other folk — naught mich out o' t' common way: stark mad o' shooting, and farming, and sich like." The mistress was different. She was a great reader, and studied a deal; and the "bairns" had taken after her. There was nothing like them in these parts, nor ever had been; they had liked learning, all three, almost from the time they could speak; and they had always been "of a mak' of their own." Mr. St. John, when he grew up, would go to college and be a parson; and the girls, as soon as they left school, would seek places as governesses: for they had told her their father had some years ago lost a great deal of money, by a man he had trusted turning bankrupt; and as he was now not rich enough to give them fortunes, they must provide for themselves. They had lived very little at home for a long while, and were only come now to stay a few weeks on account of their father's death: but they did so like Marsh End and Morton, and all these moors and hills about. They had been in London, and many other grand towns; but they always said there was no place like home; and then they were so agreeable with each other — never fell out nor "threaped." She did not know where there was such a family for being united.

Having finished my task of gooseberry picking, I asked where the two ladies and their brother were now.

"Gone over to Morton for a walk; but they would be back in half an hour to tea."

They returned within the time Hannah had allotted them: they entered by the kitchen door. Mr. St. John, when he saw me, merely bowed and passed through; the two ladies stopped: Mary, in a few words, kindly and calmly expressed the pleasure she felt in seeing me well enough to be able to come down; Diana took my hand: she shook her head at me.

"You should have waited for my leave to descend," she said. "You still look very pale — and so thin! Poor child! — poor girl!"

Diana had a voice toned, to my ear, like the cooing of a dove. She possessed eyes whose gaze I delighted to encounter. Her whole face seemed to me full of charm. Mary's countenance was equally intelligent — her features equally pretty: but her expression was more reserved; and her manners, though gentle, more distant. Diana looked and spoke with a certain authority: she had a will, evidently. It was my nature to feel pleasure in yielding to authority supported like hers; and to bend, where my conscience and self-respect permitted, to an active will.

"And what business have you here?" she continued. "It is not your place. Mary and I sit in the kitchen sometimes, because at home we like to be free, even to licence — but you are a visitor, and must go into the parlour."

"I am very well here."

"Not at all — with Hannah bustling about and covering you with flour."

"Besides, the fire is too hot for you," interposed Mary.

"To be sure," added her sister. "Come, you must be obedient." And still holding my hand she made me rise, and led me into the inner room.

"Sit there," she said, placing me on the sofa, "while we take our things off and get the tea ready; it is another privilege we exercise in our little moorland home — to prepare our own meals when we are so inclined; or when Hannah is baking, brewing, washing, or ironing."

She closed the door, leaving me solus with Mr. St. John, who sat opposite; a book or newspaper in his hand. I examined, first, the parlour, and then its occupant.

The parlour was rather a small room, very plainly furnished; yet comfortable, because clean and neat. The old-fashioned chairs were very bright, and the walnut-wood table was like a looking-glass. A few strange, antique portraits of the men and women of other days decorated the stained walls; a cupboard with glass doors contained some books and an ancient set of china. There was no superfluous ornament in the room — not one modern piece of furniture, save a brace of work-boxes and a lady's desk in rosewood, which stood on a side-table: everything — including the carpet and curtains — looked at once well worn and well saved.

Mr. St. John — sitting as still as one of the dusky pictures on the walls; keeping his eyes fixed on the page he perused and his lips mutely sealed — was easy enough to examine. Had he been a statue instead of a man, he could not have been easier. He was young — perhaps from twenty-eight to thirty — tall, slender; his face riveted the eye; it was like a Greek face, very pure in outline: quite a straight, classic nose; quite an Athenian mouth and chin. It is seldom, indeed, an English face comes so near the antique models as did his. He might well be a little shocked at the irregularity of my lineaments, his own being so harmonious. His eyes were large and blue, with brown lashes; his high forehead, colourless as ivory, was partially streaked over by careless locks of fair hair.

This is a gentle delineation, it is not, reader? Yet he whom it describes scarcely impressed one with the idea of a gentle, a yielding, an impressible, or even of a placid nature. Quiescent as he now sat, there was something about his nostril, his mouth, his brow, which, to my perceptions, indicated elements within either restless, or hard, or eager. He did not speak to me one word nor even direct to me one glance, till his sisters returned. Diana, as she passed in and out, in the course of preparing tea, brought me a little cake, baked on the top of the oven.

"Eat that now," she said: "you must be hungry. Hannah says you have had nothing but some gruel since breakfast."

I did not refuse it, for my appetite was awakened and keen. Mr. Rivers now closed his book, approached the table, and, as he took a seat, fixed his blue pictorial-looking eyes full on me. There was an unceremonious directness, a searching, decided steadfastness in his gaze now, which told that intention, and not diffidence, had hitherto kept it averted from the stranger.

"You are very hungry," he said.

"I am, sir." It is my way — it always was my way, by instinct — ever to meet the brief with brevity, the direct with plainness.

"It is well for you that a low fever has forced you to abstain for the last three days: there would have been danger in yielding to the cravings of your appetite at first. Now you may eat; though still not immoderately."

"I trust I shall not eat long at your expense, sir," was my very clumsily-contrived, unpolished answer.

"No," he said, coolly: "when you have indicated to us the residence of your friends, we can write to them, and you may be restored to home."

"That, I must plainly tell you, is out of my power to do; being absolutely without home and friends."

The three looked at me; but not distrustfully; I felt there was no suspicion in their glances: there was more of curiosity. I speak particularly of the young ladies. St. John's eyes, though clear enough in a literal sense, in a figurative one were difficult to fathom. He seemed to use them rather as instruments to search other people's thoughts, than as agents to reveal his own: the which combination of keenness and reserve was considerably more calculated to embarrass than to encourage.

"Do you mean to say," he asked, "that you are completely isolated from every connection?"

"I do. Not a tie links me to any living thing: not a claim do I possess to admittance under any roof in England."

"A most singular position at your age!"

Here I saw his glance directed to my hands, which were folded on the table before me. I wondered what he sought there: his words soon explained the quest.

"You have never been married? You are a spinster?"

Diana laughed. "Why, she can't be above seventeen or eighteen years old, St. John," she said.

"I am near nineteen: but I am not married. No."

I felt a burning glow mount to my face; for bitter and agitating recollections were awakened by the allusion to marriage. They all saw the embarrassment, and the emotion. Diana and Mary relieved me by turning their eyes elsewhere than to my crimsoned visage; but the colder and sterner brother continued to gaze, till the trouble he had excited forced out tears as well as colour.

"Where did you last reside?" he now asked.

"You are too inquisitive, St. John," murmured Mary, in a low voice; but he leaned over the table and required an answer, by a second firm and piercing look.

"The name of the place where, and of the person with whom I lived, is my secret," I replied, concisely.

"Which, if you like, you have, in my opinion, a right to keep, both from St. John and every other questioner," remarked Diana.

"Yet if I know nothing about you or your history, I cannot help you," he said. "And you need help: do you not?"

"I need it, and I seek it; so far, sir, that some true philanthropist will put me in the way of getting work which I can do, and the remuneration for which will keep me: if but in the barest necessaries of life."

"I know not whether I am a true philanthropist; yet I am willing to aid you to the utmost of my power, in a purpose so honest. First, then, tell me what you have been accustomed to do, and what you *can* do."

I had now swallowed my tea. I was mightily refreshed by the

beverage; as much so as a giant with wine: it gave new tone to my unstrung nerves, and enabled me to address this penetrating young judge steadily.

"Mr. Rivers," I said, turning to him, and looking at him, as he looked at me, openly and without diffidence, "you and your sisters have done me a great service — the greatest man can do his fellow-being; you have rescued me, by your noble hospitality, from death. This benefit conferred gives you an unlimited claim on my gratitude; and a claim, to a certain extent, on my confidence. I will tell you as much of the history of the wanderer you have harboured, as I can tell without compromising my own peace of mind — my own security, moral and physical, and that of others.

"I am an orphan; the daughter of a clergyman. My parents died before I could know them. I was brought up a dependant; educated in a charitable institution. I will even tell you the name of the establishment, where I passed six years as a pupil, and two as a teacher — Lowood Orphan Asylum, ——shire: you will have heard of it, Mr. Rivers? — the Rev. Robert Brocklehurst is the treasurer."

"I have heard of Mr. Brocklehurst, and I have seen the school."

"I left Lowood nearly a year since to become a private governess. I obtained a good situation, and was happy. This place I was obliged to leave four days before I came here. The reason of my departure I cannot and ought not to explain: it would be useless — dangerous; and would sound incredible. No blame attached to me: I am as free from culpability as any one of you three. Miserable I am, and must be for a time; for the catastrophe which drove me from the house I had found a paradise was of a strange and direful nature. I observed but two points in planning my departure — speed, secrecy: to secure these, I had to leave behind me everything I possessed except a small parcel; which, in my hurry and trouble of mind, I forgot to take out of the coach that brought me to Whitcross. To this neighbourhood, then, I came, quite destitute. I slept two nights in the open air, and wandered about two days without crossing a threshold: but twice in that space of time did I taste food; and it was when brought by hunger, exhaustion, and despair, almost to the last gasp, that you, Mr. Rivers, forbade me to perish of want at your door, and took me under the shelter of your roof. I know all your sisters have done for me since — for I have not been insensible during my seeming torpor — and I owe to their spontaneous, genuine, genial compassion as large a debt as to your evangelical charity."

"Don't make her talk any more now, St. John," said Diana, as I paused; "she is evidently not yet fit for excitement. Come to the sofa, and sit down now, Miss Elliott."

I gave an involuntary half-start at hearing the *alias:* I had forgotten my new name. Mr. Rivers, whom nothing seemed to escape, noticed it at once.

"You said your name was Jane Elliott?" he observed.

"I did say so; and it is the name by which I think it expedient to be called at present: but it is not my real name, and when I hear it, it sounds strange to me."

"Your real name you will not give?"

"No: I fear discovery above all things; and whatever disclosure would lead to it, I avoid."

"You are quite right, I am sure," said Diana. "Now do, brother, let her be at peace awhile."

But when St. John had mused a few moments, he recommenced, as imperturbably, and with as much acumen as ever.

"You would not like to be long dependent on our hospitality — you would wish, I see, to dispense as soon as may be with my sisters' compassion; and, above all, with my *charity* (I am quite sensible of the distinction drawn, nor do I resent it — it is just): you desire to be independent of us?"

"I do: I have already said so. Show me how to work, or how to seek work: that is all I now ask; then let me go, if it be but to the meanest cottage — but *till then,* allow me to stay here: I dread another essay of the horrors of homeless destitution."

"Indeed, you *shall* stay here," said Diana, putting her white hand on my head. "You *shall,*" repeated Mary, in the tone of undemonstrative sincerity, which seemed natural to her.

"My sisters, you see, have a pleasure in keeping you," said Mr. St. John, "as they would have a pleasure in keeping and cherishing a half-frozen bird, some wintry wind might have driven through their casement. *I* feel more inclination to put you in the way of keeping yourself: and shall endeavour to do so: but observe, my sphere is narrow. I am but the incumbent of a poor country parish: my aid must be of the humblest sort. And if you are inclined to despise the day of small things, seek some more efficient succour than such as I can offer."

"She has already said that she is willing to do anything honest she *can* do," answered Diana, for me; "and you know, St. John, she has no choice of helpers: she is forced to put up with such crusty people as you."

"I will be a dressmaker: I will be a plain work-woman; I will be a servant, a nurse-girl, if I can be no better," I answered.

"Right," said Mr. St. John, quite coolly. "If such is your spirit, I promise to aid you; in my own time and way."

He now resumed the book with which he had been occupied before tea. I soon withdrew; for I had talked as much, and sat up as long, as my present strength would permit.

## CHAPTER XXX

THE more I knew of the inmates of Moor House, the better I liked them. In a few days I had so far recovered my health that I could sit up all day, and walk out sometimes. I could join with Diana and Mary in all their occupations; converse with them as much as they wished, and aid them when and where they would allow me. There was a reviving pleasure in this intercourse, of a kind now tasted by me for the first time — the pleasure arising from perfect congeniality of tastes, sentiments, and principles.

I liked to read what they liked to read: what they enjoyed, delighted me; what they approved, I reverenced. They loved their sequestered home. I, too, in the grey, small, antique structure, with its low roof, its latticed casements, its mouldering walls, its avenue of aged firs — all grown aslant under the stress of mountain winds; its garden, dark with yew and holly — and where no flowers but of the hardiest species would bloom — found a charm both potent and permanent. They clung to the purple moors behind and around their dwelling — to the hollow vale into which the pebbly bridle-path leading from their gate descended; and which wound between fern-banks first, and then amongst a few of the wildest little pasture-fields that ever bordered a wilderness of heath, or gave sustenance to a flock of grey moorland sheep, with their little mossy-faced lamps: — they clung to this scene, I say, with a perfect enthusiasm of attachment. I could comprehend the feeling, and share both its strength and truth. I saw the fascination of the locality. I felt the consecration of its loneliness: my eye feasted on the outline of sweil and sweep — on the wild colouring communicated to ridge and dell, by moss, by heath-bell, by flower-sprinkled turf, by brilliant bracken, and mellow granite crag. These details were just to me what they were to them — so many pure and sweet sources of pleasure. The strong blast and the soft breeze; the rough and the halcyon day; the hours of sunrise and sunset; the moonlight and the clouded night, developed for me, in these regions, the same attraction as for them — wound round my faculties the same spell that entranced theirs.

In-doors we agreed equally well. They were both more accomplished and better read than I was: but with eagerness I followed in the path of knowledge they had trodden before me. I devoured the books they lent me: then it was full satisfaction to discuss with them in the evening what I had perused during the day. Thought fitted thought; opinion met opinion: we coincided, in short, perfectly.

If in our trio there was a superior and a leader, it was Diana. Physically, she far excelled me: she was handsome; she was vigorous. In her animal spirits, there was an affluence of life, and certainty of flow, such as excited my wonder, while it baffled my comprehension. I could talk a while when the evening commenced: but the first gush of vivacity and fluency gone, I was fain to sit on a stool at Diana's feet, to rest my head on her knee, and listen alternately to her and Mary; while they sounded thoroughly the topic on which I had but touched. Diana offered to teach me German. I liked to learn of her; I saw the part of instructress pleased and suited her; that of scholar pleased and suited me no less. Our natures dovetailed: mutual affection — of the strongest kind — was the result. They discovered I could draw: their pencils and colour-boxes were immediately at my service. My skill, greater in this one point than theirs, surprised and charmed them. Mary would sit and watch me by the hour together: then she would take lessons; and a docile, intelligent, assiduous pupil, she made. Thus occupied, and mutually entertained, days passed like hours, and weeks like days.

As to Mr. St. John, the intimacy which had arisen so naturally and rapidly between me and his sisters, did not extend to him. One reason of the distance yet observed between us was, that he was comparatively seldom at home: a large proportion of his time appeared devoted to visiting the sick and poor among the scattered population of his parish.

No weather seemed to hinder him in these pastoral excursions: rain or fair, he would, when his hours of morning study were over, take his hat, and, followed by his father's old pointer, Carlo, go out on his mission of love or duty — I scarcely know in which light he regarded it. Sometimes, when the day was very unfavourable, his sisters would expostulate. He would then say, with a peculiar smile, more solemn than cheerful,—

"And if I let a gust of wind or a sprinkling of rain turn me aside from these easy tasks, what preparation would such sloth be for the future I propose to myself?"

Diana and Mary's general answer to this question was a sigh, and some minutes of apparently mournful meditation.

But besides his frequent absences, there was another barrier to friendship with him: he seemed of a reserved, an abstracted, and even of a brooding nature. Zealous in his ministerial labours, blameless in his life and habits, he yet did not appear to enjoy that mental serenity, that inward content, which should be the reward of every sincere Christian and practical philanthropist. Often, of an evening, when he sat at the window, his desk and papers before him, he would cease reading or writing, rest his chin on his hand, and deliver himself up to I know not what course of thought: but that it was perturbed and exciting might be seen in the frequent flash and changeful dilation of his eye.

I think, moreover, that Nature was not to him that treasury of delight it was to his sisters. He expressed once, and but once in my hearing, a strong sense of the rugged charm of the hills, and an inborn affection for the dark roof and hoary walls he called his home: but there was more of gloom than pleasure in the tone and words in which the sentiment was manifested; and never did he seem to roam the moors for the sake of their soothing silence — never seek out or dwell upon the thousand peaceful delights they could yield.

Incommunicative as he was, some time elapsed before I had an opportunity of gauging his mind. I first got an idea of its calibre when I heard him preach in his own church at Morton. I wish I could describe that sermon: but it is past my power. I cannot even render faithfully the effect it produced on me.

It began calm — and indeed, as far as delivery and pitch of voice went, it was calm to the end: an earnestly felt, yet strictly restrained zeal breathed soon in the distinct accents, and prompted the nervous language. This grew to force — compressed, condensed, controlled. The heart was thrilled, the mind astonished, by the power of the preacher: neither were softened. Throughout there was a strange bitterness; an absence of consolatory gentleness; stern allusions to Calvinistic doctrines — election, predestination, reprobation —

were frequent; and each reference to these points sounded like a sentence pronounced for doom. When he had done, instead of feeling better, calmer, more enlightened by his discourse, I experienced an inexpressible sadness; for it seemed to me — I know not whether equally so to others — that the eloquence to which I had been listening had sprung from a depth where lay turbid dregs of disappointment — where moved troubling impulses of insatiate yearnings and disquieting aspirations. I was sure St. John Rivers — pure-lived, conscientious, zealous as he was — had not yet found that peace of God which passeth all understanding: he had no more found it, I thought, than had I; with my concealed and racking regrets for my broken idol and lost elysium — regrets to which I have latterly avoided referring; but which possessed me and tyrannised over me ruthlessly.

Meantime a month was gone. Diana and Mary were soon to leave Moor House, and return to the far different life and scene which awaited them, as governesses in a large, fashionable, south-of-England city; where each held a situation in families, by whose wealthy and haughty members they were regarded only as humble dependants, and who neither knew nor sought one of their innate excellences, and appreciated only their acquired accomplishments as they appreciated the skill of their cook, or the taste of their waiting-woman. Mr. St. John had said nothing to me yet about the employment he had promised to obtain for me; yet it became urgent that I should have a vocation of some kind. One morning, being left alone with him a few minutes in the parlour, I ventured to approach the window-recess — which his table, chair, and desk consecrated as a kind of study — and I was going to speak; though not very well knowing in what words to frame my inquiry — for it is at all times difficult to break the ice of reserve glassing over such natures as his — when he saved me the trouble, by being the first to commence a dialogue.

Looking up as I drew near — "You have a question to ask of me?" he said.

"Yes; I wish to know whether you have heard of any service I can offer myself to undertake."

"I found or devised something for you three weeks ago; but as you seemed both useful and happy here — as my sisters had evidently become attached to you, and your society gave them unusual pleasure — I deemed it inexpedient to break in on your mutual comfort, till their approaching departure from Marsh End should render yours necessary."

"And they will go in three days now?" I said.

"Yes; and when they go, I shall return to the parsonage at Morton: Hannah will accompany me; and this old house will be shut up."

I waited a few moments, expecting he would go on with the subject first broached: but he seemed to have entered another train of reflection: his look denoted abstraction from me and my business. I was obliged to recall him to a theme which was of necessity one of close and anxious interest to me.

"What is the employment you had in view, Mr. Rivers? I hope this delay will not have increased the difficulty of securing it."

"Oh, no; since it is an employment which depends only on me to give, and you to accept."

He again paused: there seemed a reluctance to continue. I grew impatient: a restless movement or two, and an eager and exacting glance fastened on his face, conveyed the feeling to him as effectually as words could have done, and with less trouble.

"You need be in no hurry to hear," he said: "let me frankly tell you, I have nothing eligible or profitable to suggest. Before I explain, recall, if you please, my notice, clearly given, that if I helped you, it must be as the blind man would help the lame. I am poor; for I find that, when I have paid my father's debts, all the patrimony remaining to me will be this crumbling grange, the row of scathed firs behind, and the patch of moorish soil, with the yew-trees and holly-bushes in front. I am obscure: Rivers is an old name; but of the three sole descendants of the race, two earn the dependant's crust among strangers, and the third considers himself an alien from his native country — not only for life, but in death. Yes, and deems, and is bound to deem, himself honoured by the lot, and aspires but after the day when the cross of separation from fleshly ties shall be laid on his shoulders, and when the Head of that church-militant of whose humblest members he is one, shall give the word, 'Rise, follow me!'"

St. John said these words as he pronounced his sermons, with a quiet, deep voice; with an unflushed cheek, and a coruscating radiance of glance. He resumed: —

"And since I am myself poor and obscure, I can offer you but a service of poverty and obscurity. *You* may even think it degrading — for I see now your habits have been what the world calls refined: your tastes lean to the ideal; and your society has at least been amongst the educated — but *I* consider that no service degrades which can better our race. I hold that the more arid and unreclaimed the soil where the Christian labourer's task of tillage is appointed him — the scantier the meed his toil brings — the higher the honour. His, under such circumstances, is the destiny of the pioneer; and the first pioneers of the Gospel were the Apostles — their captain was Jesus, the Redeemer himself."

"Well?" I said, as he again paused —"proceed."

He looked at me before he proceeded: indeed, he seemed leisurely to read my face, as if its features and lines were characters on a page. The conclusions drawn from this scrutiny he partially expressed in his succeeding observations.

"I believe you will accept the post I offer you," said he; "and hold it for a while: not permanently, though: any more than I could permanently keep the narrow and narrowing — the tranquil, hidden office of English country incumbent: for in your nature is an alloy as detrimental to repose as that in mine; though of a different kind."

"Do explain," I urged, when he halted once more.

"I will; and you shall hear how poor the proposal is,— how trivial — how cramping. I shall not stay long at Morton, now that my father is dead, and that I am my own master. I shall leave the place probably in the course of a twelve-month: but while I do stay, I will exert myself to the utmost for its improvement. Morton, when I came to it two years ago, had no school: the children of the poor were excluded from every hope of progress. I established one for boys: I mean now to open a second school for girls. I have hired a building for the purpose, with a cottage of two rooms attached to it for the mistress's house. Her salary will be thirty pounds a year: her house is already furnished, very simply, but sufficiently, by the kindness of a lady, Miss Oliver; the only daughter of the sole rich man in my parish — Mr. Oliver, the proprietor of a needle-factory and iron-foundry in the valley. The same lady pays for the education and clothing of an orphan from the workhouse; on condition that she shall aid the mistress in such menial offices connected with her own house and the school, as her occupation of teaching will prevent her having time to discharge in person. Will you be this mistress?"

He put the question rather hurriedly; he seemed half to expect an indignant, or at least a disdainful rejection of the offer: not knowing all my thoughts and feelings, though guessing some, he could not tell in what light the lot would appear to me. In truth it was humble — but then it was sheltered, and I wanted a safe asylum: it was plodding — but then, compared with that of a governess in a rich house, it was independent; and the fear of servitude with strangers entered my soul like iron: it was not ignoble — not unworthy — not mentally degrading. I made my decision.

"I thank you for the proposal, Mr. Rivers; and I accept it with all my heart."

"But you comprehend me?" he said. "It is a village school: your scholars will be only poor girls — cottagers' children — at the best, farmers' daughters. Knitting, sewing, reading, writing, cyphering, will be all you will have to teach. What will you do with your accomplishments? What, with the largest portion of your mind — sentiments — tastes?"

"Save them till they are wanted. They will keep."

"You know what you undertake, then?"

"I do."

He now smiled: not a bitter or a sad smile; but one well pleased and deeply gratified.

"And when will you commence the exercise of your function?"

"I will go to my house to-morrow; and open the school, if you like, next week."

"Very well: so be it."

He rose and walked through the room. Standing still, he again looked at me. He shook his head.

"What do you disapprove of, Mr. Rivers?" I asked.

"You will not stay at Morton long: no, no!"

"Why! What is your reason for saying so?"

"I read it in your eye; it is not of that description which promises the maintenance of an even tenor in life."

"I am not ambitious."

He started at the word "ambitious." He repeated, "No.

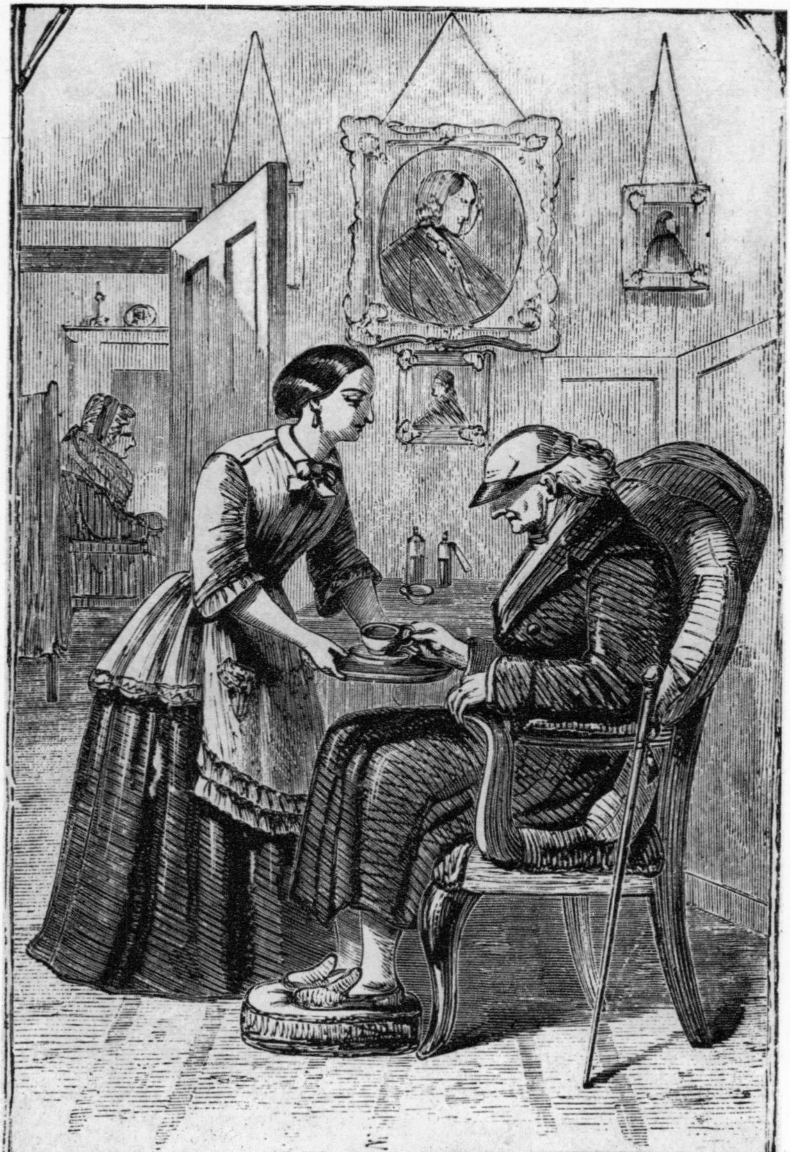

THE WORTHY DAUGHTER — CHARLOTTE BRONTË

The middle years of Charlotte Brontë's life, just before she began writing the novels which made her famous, were greatly saddened by the dissipations of her brother Branwell, her father's failing eyesight, and the fear that she might be going blind herself. This quaint old picture shows her waiting on her father in his blindness.

What made you think of ambition? Who is ambitious? I know I am: but how did you find it out?"

"I was speaking of myself."

"Well, if you are not ambitious, you are"—— He paused.

"What?"

"I was going to say impassioned: but perhaps you would have misunderstood the word, and been displeased. I mean that human affections and sympathies have a most powerful hold on you. I am sure you cannot long be content to pass your leisure in solitude, and to devote your working hours to a monotonous labour wholly void of stimulus; any more than I can be content," he added, with emphasis, "to live here buried in morass, pent in with mountains — my nature, that God gave me, contravened; my faculties, heaven-bestowed, paralysed — made useless. You hear now how I contradict myself. I, who preached contentment with a humble lot, and justified the vocation even of hewers of wood, and drawers of water, in God's service — I, his ordained minister, almost rave in my restlessness. Well, propensities and principles must be reconciled by some means."

He left the room. In this brief hour I had learnt more of him than in the whole previous month: yet still he puzzled me.

Diana and Mary Rivers became more sad and silent as the day approached for leaving their brother, and their home. They both tried to appear as usual; but the sorrow they had to struggle against was one that could not be entirely conquered or concealed. Diana intimated that this would be a different parting from any they had ever yet known. It would probably, as far as St. John was concerned, be a parting for years: it might be a parting for life.

"He will sacrifice all to his long-framed resolves," she said: "natural affection and feelings more potent still. St. John looks quiet, Jane; but he hides a fever in his vitals. You would think him gentle, yet in some things he is inexorable as death; and the worst of it is, my conscience will hardly permit me to dissuade him from his severe decision: certainly, I cannot for a moment blame him for it. It is right, noble, Christian: yet it breaks my heart." And the tears gushed to her fine eyes. Mary bent her head low over her work.

"We are now without father: we shall soon be without home and brother," she murmured.

At that moment a little accident supervened, which seemed decreed by fate, purposely to prove the truth of the adage, that "misfortunes never come singly:" and to add to their distresses the vexing one of the slip between the cup and the lip. St. John passed the window reading a letter. He entered.

"Our uncle John is dead," said he.

Both the sisters seemed struck: not shocked or appalled; the tidings appeared in their eyes rather momentous than afflicting.

"Dead?" repeated Diana.

"Yes."

She riveted a searching gaze on her brother's face. "And what then?" she demanded, in a low voice.

"What then, Die?" he replied, maintaining a marble immobility of feature. "What then? Why — nothing. Read."

He threw the letter into her lap. She glanced over it, and handed it to Mary. Mary perused it in silence, and returned it to her brother. All three looked at each other, and all three smiled — a dreary, pensive smile enough.

"Amen! We can yet live," said Diana, at last.

"At any rate, it makes us no worse off than we were before," remarked Mary.

"Only it forces rather strongly on the mind the picture of what *might have been,*" said Mr. Rivers; "and contrasts it somewhat too vividly with what *is.*"

He folded the letter, and locked it in his deck, and again went out.

For some minutes no one spoke. Diana then turned to me.

"Jane, you will wonder at us and our mysteries," she said; "and think us hard-hearted beings not to be more moved at the death of so near a relation as an uncle; but we have never seen him or known him. He was my mother's brother. My father and he quarrelled long ago. It was by his advice that my father risked most of his property in the speculation that ruined him. Mutual recrimination passed between them: they parted in anger, and were never reconciled. My uncle engaged afterwards in more prosperous undertakings: it appears he realised a fortune of twenty thousand pounds. He was never married, and had no near kindred but ourselves, and one other person, not more closely related than we. My father always cherished the idea that he would atone for his error, by leaving his possessions to us; that letter informs us that he has bequeathed every penny to the other relation; with the exception of thirty guineas, to be divided between St. John, Diana, and Mary Rivers, for the purchase of three mourning rings. He had a right, of course, to do as he pleased: and yet a momentary damp is cast on the spirits by the receipt of such news. Mary and I would have esteemed ourselves rich with a thousand pounds each; and to St. John such a sum would have been valuable, for the good it would have enabled him to do."

This explanation given, the subject was dropped, and no further reference made to it, by either Mr. Rivers or his sisters. The next day, I left Marsh End for Morton. The day after, Diana and Mary quitted it for distant B——. In a week, Mr. Rivers and Hannah repaired to the parsonage: and so the old grange was abandoned.

## CHAPTER XXXI

MY home, then,— when I at last find a home,— is a cottage: a little room with white-washed walls, and a sanded floor; containing four painted chairs and a table, a clock, a cupboard, with two or three plates and dishes, and a set of tea-things in delf. Above, a chamber of the same dimensions as the kitchen, with a deal bedstead, and chest of drawers; small, yet too large to be filled with my scanty wardrobe: though the kindness of my gentle and generous friends has increased that, by a modest stock of such things as are necessary.

It is evening. I have dismissed, with the fee of an orange, the little orphan who serves me as a handmaid. I am sitting alone on the hearth. This morning, the village school opened. I had twenty scholars. But three of the number can read: none write or cypher. Several knit, and a few sew a little. They speak with the broadest accent of the district. At present, they and I have a difficulty in understanding each other's language. Some of them are unmannered, rough, intractable, as well as ignorant; but others are docile, have a wish to learn, and evince a disposition that pleases me. I must not forget that these coarsely-clad little peasants are of flesh and blood as good as the scions of gentlest genealogy; and that the germs of native excellence, refinement, intelligence, kind feeling, are as likely to exist in their hearts as in those of the best-born. My duty will be to develop these germs: surely I shall find some happiness in discharging that office. Much enjoyment I do not expect in the life opening before me: yet it will, doubtless, if I regulate my mind, and exert my powers as I ought, yield me enough to live on from day to day.

Was I very gleeful, settled, content, during the hours I passed in yonder bare, humble school-room this morning and afternoon? Not to deceive myself, I must reply — No: I felt desolate to a degree. I felt — yes, idiot that I am — I felt degraded. I doubted I had taken a step which sank instead of raising me in the scale of social existence. I was weakly dismayed at the ignorance, the poverty, the coarseness of all I heard and saw round me. But let me not hate and despise myself too much for these feelings: I know them to be wrong — that is a great step gained; I shall strive to overcome them. To-morrow, I trust, I shall get the better of them partially; and in a few weeks, perhaps, they will be quite subdued. In a few months, it is possible, the happiness of seeing progress, and a change for the better in my scholars, may substitute gratification for disgust.

Meantime, let me ask myself one question — Which is better? — To have surrendered to temptation; listened to passion; made no painful effort — no struggle; — but to have sunk down in the silken snare; fallen asleep on the flowers covering it; wakened in a southern clime, amongst the luxuries of a pleasure villa: to have been now living in France, Mr. Rochester's mistress; delirious with his love half my time — for he would — oh, yes, he would have loved me well for a while. He *did* love me — no one will ever love me so again. I shall never more know the sweet homage given to beauty. youth, and grace — for never to any one else shall I seem to possess these charms. He was fond and proud of me — it is what no man besides will ever be.— But where am I wandering, and what am I saying; and, above all, feeling? Whether is it better, I ask, to be a slave in a fool's paradise at Marseilles — fevered with delusive bliss one hour — suffocating with the bitterest tears of remorse and shame the next — or to be a village-schoolmistress, free and honest, in a breezy mountain nook in the healthy heart of England?

Yes; I feel now that I was right when I adhered to principle and law, and scorned and crushed the insane promptings of a frenzied moment. God directed me to a correct choice: I thank His providence for the guidance!

Having brought my eventide musings to this point, I rose, went to my door, and looked at the sunset of the harvest-day, and at the quiet fields before my cottage; which, with the school, was distant half a mile from the village. The birds were singing their last strains —

"The air was mild; the dew was balm."

While I looked, I thought myself happy, and was surprised to find myself ere long weeping — and why? For the doom which had reft me from adhesion to my master: for him I was no more to see; for the desperate grief and fatal fury — consequences of my departure — which might now, perhaps, be dragging him from the path of right, too far to leave hope of ultimate restoration thither. At this thought, I turned my face aside from the lovely sky of eve and lonely vale of Morton — I say *lonely,* for in that bend of it visible to me, there was no building apparent save the church and the parsonage, half-hid in trees; and, quite at the extremity, the roof of Vale Hall, where the rich Mr. Oliver and his daughter lived. I hid my eyes, and leant my head against the stone frame of my door; but soon a slight noise near the wicket which shut in my tiny garden from the meadow beyond it, made me look up. A dog — old Carlo, Mr. Rivers' pointer, as I saw in a moment — was pushing the gate with his nose, and St. John himself leant upon it with folded arms; his brow knit, his gaze, grave almost to displeasure, fixed on me. I asked him to come in.

"No, I cannot stay; I have only brought you a little parcel my sisters left for you. I think it contains a colour-box, pencils, and paper."

I approached to take it: a welcome gift it was. He examined my face, I thought, with austerity, as I came near: the traces of tears were doubtless very visible upon it.

"Have you found your first day's work harder than you expected?" he asked.

"Oh, no! On the contrary, I think in time I shall get on with my scholars very well."

"But perhaps your accommodations — your cottage — your furniture — have disappointed your expectations? They are, in truth, scanty enough; but" — I interrupted:

"My cottage is clean and weather-proof; my furniture sufficient and commodious. All I see has made me thankful, not despondent. I am not absolutely such a fool and sensualist as to regret the absence of a carpet, a sofa, and silver plate: besides, five weeks ago I had nothing — I was an outcast, a beggar, a vagrant; now I have acquaintance, a home, a business. I wonder at the goodness of God; the generosity of my friends; the bounty of my lot. I do not repine."

"But you feel solitude an oppression? The little house there behind you is dark and empty."

"I have hardly had time yet to enjoy a sense of tranquillity, much less to grow impatient under one of loneliness."

"Very well; I hope you feel the content you express: at any rate, your good sense will tell you that it is too soon yet to yield to the vacillating fears of Lot's wife. What you had left before I saw you, of course I do not know; but I counsel you to resist, firmly, every temptation which would incline you to look back: pursue your present career steadily, for some months at least."

"It is what I mean to do," I answered. St. John continued: —

"It is hard work to control the workings of inclination, and turn the bent of nature: but that it may be done, I know from experience. God has given us, in a measure, the power to make our own fate; and when our energies seem to demand a sustenance they cannot get — when our will strains after a path we may not follow — we need neither starve from inanition, nor stand still in despair: we have but to seek another nourishment for the mind, as strong as the forbidden food it longed to taste — and perhaps purer; and to hew out for the adventurous foot a road as direct and broad as the one Fortune has blocked up against us, if rougher than it.

"A year ago, I was myself intensely miserable, because I thought I had made a mistake in entering the ministry: its uniform duties wearied me to death. I burnt for the more active life of the world — for the more exciting toils of a literary career — for the destiny of an artist, author, orator; anything rather than that of a priest: yes, the heart of a politician, of a soldier, of a votary of glory, a lover of renown, a luster after power, beat under my curate's surplice. I considered; my life was so wretched, it must be changed, or I must die. After a season of darkness and struggling, light broke and relief fell: my cramped existence all at once spread out to a plain without bounds — my powers heard a call from heaven to rise, gather their full strength, spread their wings, and mount beyond ken. God had an errand for me; to bear which afar, to deliver it well, skill and strength, courage and eloquence, the best qualifications of soldier, statesman, and orator, were all needed: for these all centre in the good missionary.

"A missionary I resolved to be. From that moment my state of mind changed; the fetters dissolved and dropped from every faculty, leaving nothing of bondage but its galling soreness — which time only can heal. My father, indeed, opposed the determination, but since his death, I have not a legitimate obstacle to contend with; some affairs settled, a successor for Morton provided, an entanglement or two of the feelings broken through or cut asunder — a last conflict with human weakness, in which I know I shall overcome, because I have vowed that I *will* overcome — and I leave Europe for the East."

He said this, in his peculiar, subdued, yet emphatic voice; looking, when he had ceased speaking, not at me, but at the setting sun, at which I looked too. Both he and I had our backs towards the path leading up the field to the wicket. We had heard no step on the grass-grown tracks; the water running in the vale was the one lulling sound of the hour and scene; we might well then start, when a gay voice, sweet as a silver bell, exclaimed: —

"Good evening, Mr. Rivers. And good evening, old Carlo. Your dog is quicker to recognise his friends than you are, sir; he pricked his ears and wagged his tail when I was at the bottom of the field, and you have your back towards me now."

It was true. Though Mr. Rivers had started at the first of those musical accents, as if a thunderbolt had split a cloud over his head, he stood yet, at the close of the sentence, in the same attitude in which the speaker had surprised him — his arm resting on the gate, his face directed towards the west. He turned at last, with measured deliberation. A vision, as it seemed to me, had risen at his side. There appeared, within three feet of him, a form clad in pure white — a youthful, graceful form: full, yet fine in contour; and when, after bending to caress Carlo, it lifted up its head, and threw back a long veil, there bloomed under his glance a face of perfect beauty. Perfect beauty is a strong expression; but I do not retract or qualify it: as sweet features as ever the temperate clime of Albion moulded; as pure hues of rose and lily as ever her humid gales and vapoury skies generated and screened, justified, in this instance, the term. No charm was wanting, no defect was perceptible; the young girl had regular and delicate lineaments; eyes shaped and coloured as we see them in lovely pictures, large, and dark, and full; the long and shadowy eyelash which encircles a fine eye with so soft a fascination; the pencilled brow which gives such clearness; the white, smooth forehead, which adds such repose to the livelier beauties of tint and ray; the cheek, oval, fresh and smooth; the lips, fresh too, ruddy, healthy, sweetly formed; the even and gleaming teeth without flaw; the small dimpled chin; the ornament of rich, plenteous tresses — all advantages, in short, which, combined, realise the ideal of beauty, were fully hers. I wondered, as I looked at this fair creature: I admired her with my whole heart. Nature had surely formed her in a partial mood; and forgetting her usual stinted step-mother dole of gifts, had endowed this, her darling, with a grandame's bounty.

What did St. John Rivers think of this earthly angel? I naturally asked myself that question as I saw him turn to her and look at her; and, as naturally, I sought the answer to the inquiry in his countenance. He had already withdrawn his eye from the Peri, and was looking at a humble tuft of daisies which grew by the wicket.

"A lovely evening, but late for you to be out alone," he said, as he crushed the snowy heads of the closed flowers with his foot.

"Oh, I only came home from S——" (she mentioned the name of a large town some twenty miles distant) "this afternoon. Papa told me you had opened your school, and that the new mistress was come; and so I put on my bonnet after tea, and ran up the valley to see her: this is she?" pointing to me.

"It is," said St. John.

"Do you think you shall like Morton?" she asked of me, with a direct and naïve simplicity of tone and manner, pleasing, if childlike.

"I hope I shall. I have many inducements to do so."

"Did you find your scholars as attentive as you expected?"

"Quite."

"Do you like your house?"

"Very much."

"Have I furnished it nicely?"

"Very nicely, indeed."

"And made a good choice of an attendant for you in Alice Wood?"

"You have, indeed. She is teachable and handy." (This, then, I thought, is Miss Oliver, the heiress; favoured, it seems, in the gifts of fortune, as well as in those of nature! What happy combination of the planets presided over her birth, I wonder?)

"I shall come up and help you to teach sometimes," she added. "It will be a change for me to visit you now and then; and I like a change. Mr. Rivers, I have been *so* gay during my stay at S——. Last night, or rather this morning, I was dancing till two o'clock.

The ——th regiment are stationed there since riots; and the officers are the most agreeable men in the world: they put all our young knife-grinders and scissor merchants to shame."

It seemed to me that Mr. St. John's under lip protruded, and his upper lip curled a moment. His mouth certainly looked a good deal compressed, and the lower part of his face unusually stern and square, as the laughing girl gave him this information. He lifted his gaze, too, from the daisies, and turned it on her. An unsmiling, a searching, a meaning gaze it was. She answered it with a second laugh, and laughter well became her youth, her roses, her dimples, her bright eyes.

As he stood, mute and grave, she again fell to caressing Carlo. "Poor Carlo loves me," said she. "*He* is not stern and distant to his friends; and if he could speak, he would not be silent."

As she patted the dog's head, bending with native grace before his young and austere master, I saw a glow rise to that master's face. I saw his solemn eye melt with sudden fire, and flicker with resistless emotion. Flushed and kindled thus, he looked nearly as beautiful for a man as she for a woman. His chest heaved once, as if his large heart, weary of despotic constriction, had expanded, despite the will, and made a vigorous bound for the attainment of liberty. But he curbed it, I think, as a resolute rider would curb a rearing steed. He responded neither by word nor movement to the gentle advances made him.

"Papa says you never come to see us now," continued Miss Oliver, looking up. "You are quite a stranger at Vale Hall. He is alone this evening, and not very well: will you return with me and visit him?"

"It is not a seasonable hour to intrude on Mr. Oliver," answered St. John.

"Not a seasonable hour! But, I declare, it is. It is just the hour when papa most wants company: when the works are closed, and he has no business to occupy him. Now, Mr. Rivers, *do* come. Why are you so very shy, and so very sombre?" She filled up the hiatus his silence left by a reply of her own.

"I forgot!" she exclaimed, shaking her beautiful curled head, as if shocked at herself. "I am so giddy and thoughtless! *Do* excuse me. It had slipped my memory that you have good reasons to be indisposed for joining in my chatter. Diana and Mary have left you, and Moor House is shut up, and you are so lonely. I am sure I pity you. Do come and see papa."

"Not to-night, Miss Rosemond, not to-night."

Mr. St. John spoke almost like an automaton: himself only knew the effort it cost him thus to refuse.

"Well, if you are so obstinate, I will leave you; for I dare not stay any longer: the dew begins to fall. Good evening!"

She held out her hand. He just touched it. "Good evening!" he repeated, in a voice low and hollow as an echo. She turned; but in a moment returned.

"Are you well?" she asked. Well might she put the question: his face was blanched as her gown.

"Quite well," he enunciated; and, with a bow, he left the gate. She went one way; he another. She turned twice to gaze after him, as she tripped fairy-like down the field; he, as he strode firmly across, never turned at all.

This spectacle of another's suffering and sacrifice rapt my thoughts from exclusive meditation on my own. Diana Rivers had designated her brother "inexorable as death." She had not exaggerated.

## CHAPTER XXXII

I CONTINUED the labours of the village-school as actively and faithfully as I could. It was truly hard work at first. Some time elapsed before, with all my efforts, I could comprehend my scholars and their nature. Wholly untaught, with faculties quite torpid, they seemed to me hopelessly dull; and, at first sight, all dull alike: but I soon found I was mistaken. There was a difference amongst them as amongst the educated; and when I got to know them, and they me, this difference rapidly developed itself. Their amazement at me, my language, my rules, and ways, once subsided, I found some of these heavy-looking, gaping rustics wake up into sharp-witted girls enough. Many showed themselves obliging, and amiable too; and I discovered amongst them not a few examples of natural politeness, and innate self-respect, as well as of excellent capacity, that won my good-will and my admiration. These soon took a pleasure in doing their work well; in keeping their persons neat; in learning their tasks regularly; in acquiring quiet and orderly manners. The rapidity of their progress, in some instances, was even surprising; and an honest and happy pride I took in it: besides, I began personally to like some of the best girls; and they liked me. I had amongst my scholars several farmers' daughters: young women grown, almost. These could already read, write, and sew; and to them I taught the elements of grammar, geography, history, and the finer kinds of needlework. I found estimable characters amongst them — characters desirous of information, and disposed for improvement — with whom I passed many a pleasant evening hour in their own homes. Their parents then (the farmer and his wife) loaded me with attentions. There was an enjoyment in accepting their simple kindness, and in repaying it by a consideration — a scrupulous regard to their feelings — to which they were not, perhaps, at all times accustomed, and which both charmed and benefited them; because, while it elevated them in their own eyes, it made them emulous to merit the deferential treatment they received.

I felt I became a favourite in the neighbourhood. Whenever I went out, I heard on all sides cordial salutations, and was welcomed with friendly smiles. To live amidst general regard, though it be but the regard of working-people, is like "sitting in sunshine, calm and sweet": serene inward feelings bud and bloom under the ray. At this period of my life, my heart far oftener swelled with thankfulness than sank with dejection: and yet, reader, to tell you all, in the midst of this calm, this useful existence — after a day passed in honourable exertion amongst my scholars, an evening spent in drawing or reading contentedly alone — I used to rush into strange dreams at night: dreams many-coloured, agitated, full of the ideal, the stirring, the stormy — dreams where, amidst unusual scenes, charged with adventure, with agitating risk and romantic chance, I still again and again met Mr. Rochester, always at some exciting crisis; and then the sense of being in his arms, hearing his voice, meeting his eye, touching his hand and cheek, loving him, being loved by him — the hope of passing a lifetime at his side, would be renewed, with all its first force and fire. Then I awoke. Then I recalled where I was, and how situated. Then I rose up on my curtainless bed, trembling and quivering; and then the still, dark night witnessed the convulsion of despair, and heard the burst of passion. By nine o'clock the next morning I was punctually opening the school; tranquil, settled, prepared for the steady duties of the day.

Rosamond Oliver kept her word in coming to visit me. Her call at the school was generally made in the course of her morning ride. She would canter up to the door on her pony, followed by a mounted livery servant. Anything more exquisite than her appearance, in her purple habit, with her Amazon's cap of black velvet placed gracefully above the long curls that kissed her cheek and floated to her shoulders, can scarcely be imagined: and it was thus she would enter the rustic building, and glide through the dazzled ranks of the village children. She generally came at the hour when Mr. Rivers was engaged in giving his daily catechising lesson. Keenly, I fear, did the eye of the visitress pierce the young pastor's heart. A sort of instinct seemed to warn him of her entrance, even when he did not see it; and when he was looking quite away from the door, if she appeared at it, his cheek would glow, and his marble-seeming features, though they refused to relax, changed indescribably; and in their very quiescence became expressive of a repressed fervour, stronger than working muscle or darting glance could indicate.

Of course, she knew her power: indeed, he did not, because he could not, conceal it from her. In spite of his Christian stoicism, when she went up and addressed him, and smiled gaily, encouragingly, even fondly in his face, his hand would tremble, and his eye burn. He seemed to say, with his sad and resolute look, if he did not say it with his lips, "I love you, and I know you prefer me. It is not despair of success that keeps me dumb. If I offered my heart, I believe you would accept it. But that heart is already laid on a sacred altar: the fire is arranged round it. It will soon be no more than a sacrifice consumed."

And then she would pout like a disappointed child; a pensive cloud would soften her radiant vivacity; she would withdraw her hand hastily from his, and turn in transient petulance from his aspect at once so heroic and so martyr-like. St. John, no doubt, would have given the world to follow, recall, retain her, when she thus left him; but he would not give one chance of Heaven; nor relinquish, for the elysium of her love, one hope of the true, eternal Paradise. Besides, he could not bound all that he had in his nature — the rover, the aspirant, the poet, the priest — in the limits of a single passion. He could not — he would not — renounce his wild field of mission warfare for the parlours and the peace of Vale Hall. I learnt so much from himself, in an inroad I once, despite his reserve, had the daring to make on his confidence.

Miss Oliver already honoured me with frequent visits to my cottage. I had learnt her whole character; which was without mystery or disguise: she was coquettish, but not heartless; exacting, but not worthlessly selfish. She had been indulged from her birth, but was not absolutely spoilt. She was hasty, but good-humoured; vain (she could not help it, when every glance in the glass showed her such a flush of loveliness), but not affected; liberal-handed; innocent of the pride of wealth; ingenuous; sufficiently intelligent; gay, lively, and unthinking: she was very charming, in short, even to a cool observer of her own sex like me; but she was not profoundly interesting or thoroughly impressive. A very different sort of mind was hers from that, for instance, of the sisters of St. John. Still, I liked her almost as I liked my pupil Adèle; except that, for a child whom we have watched over and taught, a closer affection is engendered than we can give an equally attractive adult acquaintance.

She had taken an amiable caprice to me. She said I was like Mr. Rivers (only, certainly, she allowed, "not one-tenth so handsome, though I was a nice neat little soul enough, but he was an angel"). I was, however, good, clever, composed, and firm, like him. I was a *lusus naturæ,* she affirmed, as a village schoolmistress: she was sure my previous history, if known, would make a delightful romance.

One evening, while, with her usual child-like activity, and thoughtless yet not offensive inquisitiveness, she was rummaging the cupboard and the table-drawer of my little kitchen, she discovered first two French books, a volume of Schiller, a German grammar and dictionary; and then my drawing-materials and some sketches, including a pencil-head of a pretty little cherub-like girl, one of my scholars, and sundry views from nature, taken in the Vale of Morton and on the surrounding moors. She was first transfixed with surprise, and then electrified with delight.

"Had I done these pictures? Did I know French and German? What a love—what a miracle I was! I drew better than her master in the first school in S——. Would I sketch a portrait of her, to show to papa?"

"With pleasure," I replied; and I felt a thrill of artist-delight at the idea of copying from so perfect and radiant a model. She had then on a dark-blue silk dress; her arms and her neck were bare; her only ornament was her chestnut tresses, which waved over her shoulders with all the wild grace of natural curls. I took a sheet of fine card-board, and drew a careful outline. I promised myself the pleasure of colouring it; and, as it was getting late then, I told her she must come and sit another day.

She made such a report of me to her father, that Mr. Oliver himself accompanied her next evening—a tall, massive-featured, middle-aged, and grey-headed man, at whose side his lovely daughter looked like a bright flower near a hoary turret. He appeared a taciturn, and perhaps a proud personage; but he was very kind to me. The sketch of Rosamond's portrait pleased him highly: he said I must make a finished picture of it. He insisted, too, on my coming the next day to spend the evening at Vale Hall.

I went. I found it a large, handsome residence, showing abundant evidences of wealth in the proprietor. Rosamond was full of glee and pleasure all the time I stayed. Her father was affable; and when he entered into conversation with me after tea, he expressed in strong terms his approbation of what I had done in Morton school; and said he only feared, from what he saw and heard, I was too good for the place, and would soon quit it for one more suitable.

"Indeed!" cried Rosamond, "she is clever enough to be a governess in a high family, papa."

I thought — I would far rather be where I am than in any high family in the land. Mr. Oliver spoke of Mr. Rivers — of the Rivers family — with great respect. He said it was a very old name in that neighbourhood; that the ancestors of the house were wealthy; that all Morton had once belonged to them; that even now he considered the representative of that house might, if he liked, make an alliance with the best. He accounted it a pity that so fine and talented a young man should have formed the design of going out as a missionary; it was quite throwing a valuable life away. It appeared, then, that her father would throw no obstacle in the way of Rosamond's union with St. John. Mr. Oliver evidently regarded the young clergyman's good birth, old name, and sacred profession, as sufficient compensation for the want of fortune.

It was the 5th of November, and a holiday. My little servant, after helping me to clean my house, was gone, well satisfied with the fee of a penny for her aid. All about me was spotless and bright — scoured floor, polished grate, and well rubbed chairs. I had also made myself neat, and had now the afternoon before me to spend as I would.

The translation of a few pages of German occupied an hour; then I got my palette and pencils and fell to the more soothing, because easier occupation, of completing Rosamond Oliver's miniature. The head was finished already; there was but the background to tint, and the drapery to shade off; a touch of carmine, too, to add to the ripe lips — a soft curl here and there to the tresses — a deeper tinge to the shadow of the lash under the azure eyelid. I was absorbed in the execution of these nice details, when, after one rapid tap, my door unclosed, admitting St. John Rivers.

"I am come to see how you are spending your holiday," he said. "Not, I hope, in thought? No, that is well: while you draw you will not feel lonely. You see, I mistrust you still: though you have borne up wonderfully so far. I have brought you a book for evening solace," and he laid on the table a new publication — a poem: one of those genuine productions so often vouchsafed to the fortunate public of those days — the golden age of modern literature.

Alas! the readers of our era are less favoured. But, courage! I will not pause either to accuse or repine. I know poetry is not dead, nor genius lost; nor has Mammon gained power over either, to bind or slay: they will both assert their existence, their presence, their liberty and strength again one day. Powerful angels, safe in heaven! they smile when sordid souls triumph, and feeble ones weep over their destruction. Poetry destroyed? Genius banished? No! Mediocrity, no: do not let envy prompt you to the thought. No; they not only live, but reign, and redeem: and without their divine influence spread everywhere, you would be in hell — the hell of your own meanness.

While I was eagerly glancing at the bright pages of Marmion (for Marmion it was), St. John stooped to examine my drawing. His tall figure sprang erect again with a start: he said nothing. I looked up at him: he shunned my eye. I knew his thoughts well, and could read his heart plainly; at the moment I felt calmer and cooler than he: I had then temporarily the advantage of him; and I conceived an inclination to do him some good, if I could.

"With all his firmness and self-control," thought I, "he tasks himself too far: locks every feeling and pang within — expresses, confesses, imparts nothing. I am sure it would benefit him to talk a little about this sweet Rosamond, whom he thinks he ought not to marry: I will make him talk."

I said first: "Take a chair, Mr. Rivers." But he answered, as he always did, that he could not stay. "Very well," I responded mentally, "stand if you like; but you shall not go just yet, I am determined: solitude is at least as bad for you as it is for me. I'll try if I cannot discover the secret spring of your confidence, and find an aperture in that marble breast through which I can shed one drop of the balm of sympathy.

"Is this portrait like?" I asked bluntly.

"Like! Like whom! I did not observe it closely."

"You did, Mr. Rivers."

He almost started at my sudden and strange abruptness: he looked at me astonished. "Oh, that is nothing yet," I muttered within. "I don't mean to be baffled by a little stiffness on your part; I'm prepared to go to considerable lengths." I continued, "You observed it closely and distinctly: but I have no objection to your looking at it again," and I rose and placed it in his hand.

"A well-executed picture," he said, "very soft, clear colouring; very graceful and correct drawing."

"Yes, yes; I know all that. But what of the resemblance? Who is it like?"

Mastering some hesitation, he answered, "Miss Oliver, I presume."

"Of course. And now, sir, to reward you for the accurate guess, I will promise to paint you a careful and faithful duplicate of this very picture, provided you admit that the gift would be acceptable to you. I don't wish to throw away my time and trouble on an offering you would deem worthless."

He continued to gaze at the picture: the longer he looked, the firmer he held it, the more he seemed to covet it. "It is like!" he murmured; "the eye is well managed: the colour, light, expression, are perfect. It smiles!"

"Would it comfort, or would it wound you to have a similar painting? Tell me that. When you are at Madagascar, or at the Cape, or in India, would it be a consolation to have that memento in your possession? or would the sight of it bring recollections calculated to enervate and distress?"

He now furtively raised his eyes: he glanced at me, irresolute, disturbed: he again surveyed the picture.

"That I should like to have it, is certain: whether it would be judicious or wise is another question."

Since I had ascertained that Rosamond really preferred him, and that her father was not likely to oppose the match, I — less exalted in my views than St. John — had been strongly disposed in my own heart to advocate their union. It seemed to me that, should he become the possessor of Mr. Oliver's large fortune, he might do as much good with it as if he went and laid his genius out to wither, and his strength to waste, under a tropical sun. With this persuasion I now answered: —

"As far as I can see, it would be wiser and more judicious if you were to take to yourself the original at once."

By this time he had sat down: he had laid the picture on the table before him, and with his brow supported on both hands, hung fondly over it. I discerned he was now neither angry nor shocked at my audacity. I saw even that to be thus frankly addressed on a subject he had deemed unapproachable — to hear it thus freely handled —

was beginning to be felt by him as a new pleasure — an unhoped-for relief. Reserved people often really need the frank discussion of their sentiments and griefs more than the expansive. The sternest-seeming stoic is human after all; and to "burst" with boldness and good will into "the silent sea" of their souls, is often to confer on them the first of obligations.

"She likes you, I am sure," said I, as I stood behind his chair, "and her father respects you. Moreover, she is a sweet girl — rather thoughtless; but you would have sufficient thought for both yourself and her. You ought to marry her."

"*Does* she like me?" he asked.

"Certainly; better than she likes any one else. She talks of you continually: there is no subject she enjoys so much, or touches upon so often."

"It is very pleasant to hear this," he said — "very: go on for another quarter of an hour." And he actually took out his watch and laid it upon the table to measure the time.

"But where is the use of going on," I asked, "when you are probably preparing some iron blow of contradiction, or forging a fresh chain to fetter your heart?"

"Don't imagine such hard things. Fancy me yielding and melting, as I am doing: human love rising like a freshly opened fountain in my mind and overflowing with sweet inundation all the field I have so carefully, and with such labour prepared — so assiduously sown with the seeds of good intentions, of self-denying plans. And now it is deluged with a nectarous flood — the young germs swamped — delicious poison cankering them: now I see myself stretched on an ottoman in the drawing-room at Vale Hall, at my bride Rosamond Oliver's feet: she is talking to me with her sweet voice — gazing down on me with those eyes your skilful hand has copied so well — smiling at me with these coral lips. She is mine — I am hers — this present life and passing world suffice to me. Hush! say nothing — my heart is full of delight — my senses are entranced — let the time I marked pass in peace."

I humoured him: the watch ticked on: he breathed fast and low: I stood silent. Amidst this hush the quarter sped; he replaced the watch, laid the picture down, rose, and stood on the hearth.

"Now," said he, "that little space was given to delirium and delusion. I rested my temples on the breast of temptation, and put my neck voluntarily under her yoke of flowers; I tasted her cup. The pillow was burning: there is an asp in the garland: the wine has a bitter taste: her promises are hollow — her offers false: I see and know all this."

I gazed at him in wonder.

"It is strange," pursued he, "that while I love Rosamond Oliver so wildly — with all the intensity, indeed, of a first passion, the object of which is exquisitely beautiful, graceful, and fascinating — I experience at the same time a calm, unwarped consciousness, that she would not make me a good wife; that she is not the partner suited to me; that I should discover this within a year after marriage; and that to twelve months' rapture would succeed a lifetime of regret. This I know."

"Strange, indeed!" I could not help ejaculating.

"While something in me," he went on, "is acutely sensible to her charms, something else is as deeply impressed with her defects: they are such that she could sympathise in nothing I aspired to — co-operate in nothing I undertook. Rosamond a sufferer, a labourer, a female apostle? Rosamond a missionary's wife? No!"

"But you need not be a missionary. You might relinquish that scheme."

"Relinquish! What! my vocation? My great work? My foundation laid on earth for a mansion in heaven? My hopes of being numbered in the band who have merged all ambitions in the glorious one of bettering their race — of carrying knowledge into the realms of ignorance — of substituting peace for war — freedom for bondage — religion for superstition — the hope of heaven for the fear of hell? Must I relinquish that? It is dearer than the blood in my veins. It is what I have to look forward to, and to live for."

After a considerable pause, I said,—"And Miss Oliver? Are her disappointment and sorrow of no interest to you?"

"Miss Oliver is ever surrounded by suitors and flatterers: in less than a month, my image will be effaced from her heart. She will forget me; and will marry, probably, some one who will make her far happier than I should do."

"You speak coolly enough; but you suffer in the conflict. You are wasting away."

"No. If I get a little thin, it is with anxiety about my prospects yet unsettled — my departure, continually procrastinated. Only this morning, I received intelligence that the successor, whose arrival I have been so long expecting, cannot be ready to replace me for three months to come yet; and perhaps the three months may extend to six."

"You tremble and become flushed whenever Miss Oliver enters the school-room."

Again the surprised expression crossed his face. He had not imagined that a woman would dare to speak so to a man. For me, I felt at home in this sort of discourse. I could never rest in communication with strong, discreet, and refined minds, whether male or female, till I had passed the outworks of conventional reserve, and crossed the threshold of confidence, and won a place by their heart's very hearthstone.

"You *are* original," said he, "and not timid. There is something brave in your spirit, as well as penetrating in your eye: but allow me to assure you that you partially misinterpret my emotions. You think them more profound and potent than they are. You give me a larger allowance of sympathy than I have a just claim to. When I colour, and when I shake before Miss Oliver, I do not pity myself. I scorn the weakness. I know it is ignoble; a mere fever of the flesh: not, I declare, the convulsion of the soul. *That* is just as fixed as a rock, firm set in the depths of a restless sea. Know me to be what I am — a cold, hard man."

I smiled incredulously.

"You have taken my confidence by storm," he continued: "and now it is much at your service. I am simply, in my original state — stripped of that blood-bleached robe with which Christianity covers human deformity — a cold, hard, ambitious man. Natural affection only, of all the sentiments, has permanent power over me. Reason, and not Feeling is my guide; my ambition is unlimited; my desire to rise higher, to do more than others insatiable. I honour endurance, perseverance, industry, talent; because these are the means by which men achieve great ends, and mount to lofty eminence. I watch your career with interest, because I consider you a specimen of a diligent, orderly, energetic woman: not because I deeply compassionate what you have gone through, or what you still suffer."

"You would describe yourself as a mere pagan philosopher," I said.

"No. There is this difference between me and deistic philosophers: I believe; and I believe the Gospel. You missed your epithet. I am not a pagan, but a Christian philosopher — a follower of the sect of Jesus. As his disciple I adopt his pure, his merciful, his benignant doctrines. I advocate them: I am sworn to spread them. Won in youth to religion, she has cultivated my original qualities thus: — From the minute germ, natural affection, she has developed the over-shadowing tree, philanthropy. From the wild, stringy root of human uprightness, she has reared a due sense of the Divine justice. Of the ambition to win power and renown for my wretched self, she has formed the ambition to spread my Master's kingdom; to achieve victories for the standard of the cross. So much has religion done for me; turning the original materials to the best account; pruning and training nature. But she could not eradicate nature: nor will it be eradicated 'till this mortal shall put on immortality.'"

Having said this, he took his hat, which lay on the table beside my palette. Once more he looked at the portrait.

"She *is* lovely," he murmured. "She is well named the Rose of the World, indeed!"

"And may I not paint one like it for you?"

"*Cui bono?* No."

He drew over the picture the sheet of thin paper on which I was accustomed to rest my hand in painting, to prevent the card-board from being sullied. What he suddenly saw on this blank paper, it was impossible for me to tell: but something had caught his eye. He took it up with a snatch; he looked at the edge; then shot a glance at me, inexpressibly peculiar, and quite incomprehensible: a glance that seemed to take and make note of every point in my shape, face, and dress; for it traversed all, quick, keen as lightning. His lips parted, as if to speak: but he checked the coming sentence, whatever it was.

"What is the matter?" I asked.

"Nothing in the world," was the reply: and, replacing the paper, I saw him dexterously tear a narrow slip from the margin. It disappeared in his glove; and, with one hasty nod and "good-afternoon," he vanished.

"Well!" I exclaimed, using an expression of the district; "that caps the globe, however!"

I, in my turn, scrutinised the paper; but saw nothing on it save a few dingy stains of paint where I had tried the tint in my pencil. I pondered the mystery a minute or two; but finding it insolvable, and being certain it could not be of much moment, I dismissed, and soon forgot it.

## CHAPTER XXXIII

WHEN Mr. St. John went, it was beginning to snow; the whirling storm continued all night. The next day a keen wind brought fresh and blinding falls; by twilight the valley was drifted up and almost impassable. I had closed my shutter, laid a mat to the door to prevent the snow from blowing in under it, trimmed my fire, and after sitting nearly an hour on the hearth listening to the muffled fury of the tempest, I lit a candle, took down Marmion, and beginning —

> "Day set on Norham's castled steep,
> And Tweed's fair river broad and deep,
> And Cheviot's mountains lone;
> The massive towers, the donjon keep,
> The flanking walls that round them sweep,
> In yellow lustre shone."

I soon forgot storm in music.

I heard a noise: the wind, I thought, shook the door. No; it was St. John Rivers, who, lifting the latch, came in out of the frozen hurricane — the howling darkness — and stood before me: the cloak that covered his tall figure all white as a glacier. I was almost in consternation; so little had I expected any guest from the blocked-up vale that night.

"Any ill news?" I demanded. "Has anything happened?"

"No. How very easily alarmed you are!" he answered, removing his cloak and hanging it up against the door, towards which he again coolly pushed the mat which his entrance had deranged. He stamped the snow from his boots.

"I shall sully the purity of your floor," said he, "but you must excuse me for once." Then he approached the fire: "I have had hard work to get here, I assure you," he observed, as he warmed his hands over the flame. "One drift took me up to the waist; happily the snow is quite soft yet."

"But why are you come?" I could not forbear saying.

"Rather an inhospitable question to put to a visitor; but since you ask it, I answer simply to have a little talk with you; I got tired of my mute books and empty rooms. Besides, since yesterday, I have experienced the excitement of a person to whom a tale has been half told, and who is impatient to hear the sequel."

He sat down. I recalled his singular conduct of yesterday, and really I began to fear his wits were touched. If he were insane, however, his was a very cool and collected insanity: I had never seen that handsome-featured face of his look more like chiselled marble than it did just now, as he put aside his snow-wet hair from his forehead and let the firelight shine free on his pale brow and cheek as pale, where it grieved me to discover the hollow trace of care or sorrow now so plainly graved. I waited, expecting he would say something I could at least comprehend; but his hand was now at his chin, his finger on his lip: he was thinking. It struck me that his hand looked wasted like his face. A perhaps uncalled-for gush of pity came over my heart: I was moved to say: —

"I wish Diana or Mary would come and live with you: it is too bad that you should be quite alone; and you are recklessly rash about your own health."

"Not at all," said he: "I care for myself when necessary. I am well now. What do you see amiss in me?"

This was said with a careless, abstracted indifference, which showed that my solicitude was, at least in his opinion, wholly superfluous. I was silenced.

He still slowly moved his finger over his upper lip, and still his eye dwelt dreamily on the glowing grate; thinking it urgent to say something, I asked him presently if he felt any cold draught from the door, which was behind him.

"No, no;" he responded, shortly and somewhat testily.

"Well," I reflected, "if you won't talk, you may be still; I'll let you alone now, and return to my book."

So I snuffed the candle, and resumed the perusal of Marmion. He soon stirred; my eye was instantly drawn to his movements; he only took out a morocco pocket-book, thence produced a letter, which he read in silence, folded it, put it back, relapsed into meditation. It was vain to try to read with such an inscrutable fixture before me; nor could I, in my impatience, consent to be dumb; he might rebuff me if he liked, but talk I would.

"Have you heard from Diana and Mary lately?"

"Not since the letter I showed you a week ago."

"There has not been any change made about your own arrangements? You will not be summoned to leave England sooner than you expected?"

"I fear not, indeed: such chance is too good to befall me." Baffled so far I changed my ground — I bethought myself to talk about the school and my scholars.

"Mary Garrett's mother is better, and Mary came back to the school this morning, and I shall have four new girls next week from the Foundry Close — they would have come to-day but for the snow."

"Indeed!"

"Mr. Oliver pays for two."

"Does he?"

"He means to give the whole school a treat at Christmas."

"I know."

"Was it your suggestion?"

"No."

"Whose then?"

"His daughter's, I think."

"It is like her: she is so good-natured."

"Yes."

Again came the blank of a pause: the clock struck eight strokes. It aroused him; he uncrossed his legs, sat erect, turned to me.

"Leave your book a moment, and come a little nearer the fire," he said.

Wondering, and of my wonder finding no end, I complied.

"Half an hour ago," he pursued, "I spoke of my impatience to hear the sequel of a tale: on reflection, I find the matter will be better managed by my assuming the narrator's part, and converting you into a listener. Before commencing, it is but fair to warn you that the story will sound somewhat hackneyed in your ears: but stale details often regain a degree of freshness when they pass through new lips. For the rest, whether trite or novel, it is short.

"Twenty years ago, a poor curate — never mind his name at this moment — fell in love with a rich man's daughter; she fell in love with him, and married him, against advice of all her friends; who consequently disowned her immediately after the wedding. Before two years passed, the rash pair were both dead, and laid quietly side by side under one slab. (I have seen their grave; it formed part of the pavement of a huge churchyard surrounding the grim, soot-black old cathedral of an overgrown manufacturing town in ——shire.) They left a daughter, which, at its very birth, Charity received in her lap — cold as that of the snow-drift I almost stuck fast in to-night. Charity carried the friendless thing to the house of its rich, maternal relations; it was reared by an aunt-in-law, called (I come to names now) Mrs. Reed of Gateshead — you start — did you hear a noise? I daresay it is only a rat scrambling along the rafters of the adjoining schoolroom: it was a barn before I had it repaired and altered, and barns are generally haunted by rats.— To proceed. Mrs. Reed kept the orphan ten years: whether it was happy or not with her, I cannot say, never having been told; but at the end of that time she transferred it to a place you know — being no other than Lowood School, where you so long resided yourself. It seems her career there was very honourable: from a pupil, she became a teacher, like yourself — really it strikes me there are parallel points in her history and yours — she left it to be a governess: there, again, your fates were analogous; she undertook the education of the ward of a certain Mr. Rochester."

"Mr. Rivers!" I interrupted.

"I can guess your feelings," he said, "but restrain them for a while: I have nearly finished; hear me to the end. Of Mr. Rochester's character I know nothing but the one fact that he professed to offer honourable marriage to this young girl, and that at the very altar she discovered he had a wife yet alive, though a lunatic. What his subsequent conduct and proposals were is a matter of pure conjecture; but when an event transpired which rendered inquiry after the governess necessary, it was discovered she was gone — no one could tell when, where, or how. She had left Thornfield Hall in the night; every research after her course had been vain: the country had been scoured far and wide; no vestige of information could be gathered respecting her. Yet that she should be found is become a matter of serious urgency: advertisements have been put in all the papers; I myself have received a letter from one Mr. Briggs, a solicitor, communicating the details I have just imparted. Is it not an odd tale?"

"Just tell me this," said I, "and since you know so much, you surely *can* tell it me — what of Mr. Rochester? How and where is he? What is he doing? Is he well?"

"I am ignorant of all concerning Mr. Rochester: the letter never mentions him but to narrate the fraudulent and illegal attempt I have adverted to. You should rather ask the name of the governess —the nature of the event which requires her appearance."

"Did no one go to Thornfield Hall then? Did no one see Mr. Rochester?"

"I suppose not."

"But they wrote to him?"

"Of course."

"And what did he say? Who has his letters?"

"Mr. Briggs intimates that the answer to his application was not from Mr. Rochester, but from a lady: it is signed 'Alice Fairfax.'"

I felt cold and dismayed: my worst fears then were probably true: he had in all probability left England and rushed in reckless desperation to some former haunt on the Continent. And what opiate for his severe sufferings — what object for his strong passions — had he sought there? I dared not answer the question. Oh, my poor master — once almost my husband — whom I had often called "my dear Edward!"

"He must have been a bad man," observed Mr. Rivers.

"You don't know him — don't pronounce an opinion upon him," I said, with warmth.

"Very well," he answered, quietly: "and indeed my head is otherwise occupied than with him: I have my tale to finish. Since you won't ask the governess's name, I must tell it of my own accord — stay — I have it here — it is always more satisfactory to see important points written down, fairly committed to black and white."

And the pocket-book was again deliberately produced, opened, sought through; from one of its compartments was extracted a shabby slip of paper, hastily torn off: I recognised in its texture and its stains of ultra-marine, and lake, and vermilion, the ravished margin of the portrait-cover. He got up, held it close to my eyes: and I read, traced in Indian ink, in my own hand-writing, the words "JANE EYRE"—the work doubtless of some moment of abstraction.

"Briggs wrote to me of a Jane Eyre:" he said, "the advertisements demanded a Jane Eyre: I knew a Jane Elliott.— I confess I had my suspicions, but it was only yesterday afternoon they were at once resolved into certainty. You own the name and renounce the *alias?*"

"Yes — yes — but where is Mr. Briggs? He perhaps knows more of Mr. Rochester than you do."

"Briggs is in London; I should doubt his knowing anything at all about Mr. Rochester; it is not in Mr. Rochester he is interested. Meanwhile, you forget essential points in pursuing trifles: you do not inquire why Mr. Briggs sought after you — what he wanted with you."

"Well, what did he want?"

"Merely to tell you that your uncle, Mr. Eyre of Madeira, is dead; that he has left you all his property, and that you are now rich — merely that — nothing more."

"I! rich?"

"Yes, you, rich — quite an heiress."

Silence succeeded.

"You must prove your identity of course," resumed St. John, presently: "a step which will offer no difficulties; you can then enter on immediate possession. Your fortune is vested in the English funds; Briggs has the will and the necessary documents."

Here was a new card turned up! It is a fine thing, reader, to be lifted in a moment from indigence to wealth — a very fine thing: but not a matter one can comprehend, or consequently enjoy, all at once. And then there are other chances in life far more thrilling and rapture-giving: *this* is solid, an affair of the actual world, nothing ideal about it: all its associations are solid and sober, and its manifestations are the same. One does not jump, and spring, and shout hurrah! at hearing one has got a fortune, one begins to consider responsibilities, and to ponder business; on a base of steady satisfaction rise certain grave cares — and we contain ourselves, and brood over our bliss with a solemn brow.

Besides, the words Legacy, Bequest, go side by side with the words Death, Funeral. My uncle I had heard was dead — my only relative; ever since being made aware of his existence, I had cherished the hope of one day seeing him: now, I never should. And then this money came only to me: not to me and a rejoicing family, but to my isolated self. It was a grand boon doubtless; and independence would be glorious — yes, I felt that — *that* thought swelled my heart.

"You unbend your forehead at last," said Mr. Rivers: "I thought Medusa had looked at you, and that you were turning to stone — perhaps now you will ask how much you are worth?"

"How much am I worth?"

"Oh, a trifle! Nothing of course to speak of — twenty thousand pounds, I think they say — but what is that?"

"Twenty thousand pounds?"

Here was a new stunner — I had been calculating on four or five thousand. This news actually took my breath for a moment: Mr. St. John, whom I had never heard laugh before, laughed now.

"Well," said he, "if you had committed a murder, and I had told you your crime was discovered, you could scarcely look more aghast."

"It is a large sum — don't you think there is a mistake?"

"No mistake at all."

"Perhaps you have read the figures wrong — it may be 2,000!"

"It is written in letters, not figures,— twenty thousand."

I again felt rather like an individual of but average gastronomical powers, sitting down to feast alone at a table spread with provisions for a hundred. Mr. Rivers rose now and put his cloak on.

"If it were not such a very wild night," he said, "I would send Hannah down to keep you company: you look too desperately miserable to be left alone. But Hannah, poor woman! could not stride the drifts so well as I: her legs are not quite so long: so I must e'en leave you to your sorrows. Good-night."

He was lifting the latch: a sudden thought occurred to me.

"Stop one minute!" I cried.

"Well?"

"It puzzles me to know why Mr. Briggs wrote to you about me; or how he knew you, or could fancy that you, living in such an out-of-the-way place, had the power to aid in my discovery."

"Oh! I am a clergyman," he said; "and the clergy are often appealed to about odd matters." Again the latch rattled.

"No: that does not satisfy me!" I exclaimed: and, indeed, there was something in the hasty and unexplanatory reply, which, instead of allaying, piqued my curiosity more than ever.

"It is a very strange piece of business," I added. "I must know more about it."

"Another time."

"No: to-night! — to-night!" and as he turned from the door, I placed myself between it and him. He looked rather embarrassed.

"You certainly shall not go till you have told me all!" I said.

"I would rather not, just now."

"You shall!—you must!"

"I would rather Diana or Mary informed you."

Of course these objections wrought my eagerness to a climax: gratified it must be, and that without delay; and I told him so.

"But I apprised you that I was a hard man," said he; "difficult to persuade."

"And I am a hard woman,—impossible to put off."

"And then," he pursued, "I am cold: no fervour infects me."

"Whereas I am hot, and fire dissolves ice. The blaze there has thawed all the snow from your cloak; by the same token, it has streamed on to my floor, and made it like a trampled street. As you hope ever to be forgiven, Mr. Rivers, the high crime and misdemeanor of spoiling a sanded kitchen, tell me what I wish to know."

"Well, then," he said, "I yield; if not to your earnestness, to your perseverance: as stone is worn by continual dropping. Besides, you must know some day,—as well now as later. Your name is Jane Eyre?"

"Of course: that was all settled before."

"You are not, perhaps, aware that I am your namesake?—that I was christened St. John Eyre Rivers?"

"No, indeed! I remember now seeing the letter E comprised in your initials written in books you have at different times lent me; but I never asked for what name it stood. But what then? Surely"——

I stopped: I could not trust myself to entertain, much less to express, the thought that rushed upon me—that embodied itself,—that, in a second, stood out a strong, solid probability. Circumstances knit themselves, fitted themselves, shot into order: the chain that had been lying hitherto a formless lump of links, was drawn out straight,—every ring was perfect, the connection complete. I knew, by instinct, how the matter stood, before St. John had said another word: but I cannot expect the reader to have the same intuitive perception, so I must repeat his explanation.

"My mother's name was Eyre; she had two brothers; one a clergyman, who married Miss Jane Reed, of Gateshead; the other, John Eyre, Esq., merchant, late of Funchal, Madeira. Mr. Briggs, being Mr. Eyre's solicitor, wrote to us last August to inform us of our uncle's death; and to say that he had left his property to his brother the clergyman's orphan daughter; overlooking us, in consequence of a quarrel, never forgiven, between him and my father. He wrote again a few weeks since, to intimate that the heiress was lost; and asking if we knew anything of her. A name casually written on a slip of paper has enabled me to find her out. You know the rest." Again he was going, but I set my back against the door.

"Do let me speak," I said: "let me have one moment to draw breath and reflect." I paused — he stood before me, hat in hand, looking composed enough. I resumed: —

"Your mother was my father's sister."

"Yes."

"My aunt, consequently?"

He bowed.

"My uncle John was your uncle John? You, Diana and Mary, are his sister's children; as I am his brother's child?"

"Undeniably."

"You three, then, are my cousins; half our blood on each side flows from the same source?"

"We are cousins; yes."

I surveyed him. It seemed I had found a brother: one I could be proud of, — one I could love; and two sisters, whose qualities were such, that, when I knew them but as mere strangers, they had inspired me with genuine affection and admiration. The two girls, on whom, kneeling down on the wet ground, and looking through the low, latticed window of Moor House kitchen, I had gazed with so bitter a mixture of interest and despair, were my near kinswomen; and the young and stately gentleman who had found me almost dying at his threshold, was my blood relation. Glorious discovery to a lonely wretch! This was wealth indeed — wealth to the heart! — a mine of pure, genial affections. This was a blessing, bright, vivid, and exhilarating; — not like the ponderous gift of gold: rich and welcome enough in its way, but sobering from its weight. I now clapped my hands in sudden joy — my pulse bounded, my veins thrilled.

"Oh, I am glad! — I am glad!" I exclaimed.

St. John smiled. "Did I not say you neglected essential points to pursue trifles?" he asked. "You were serious when I told you

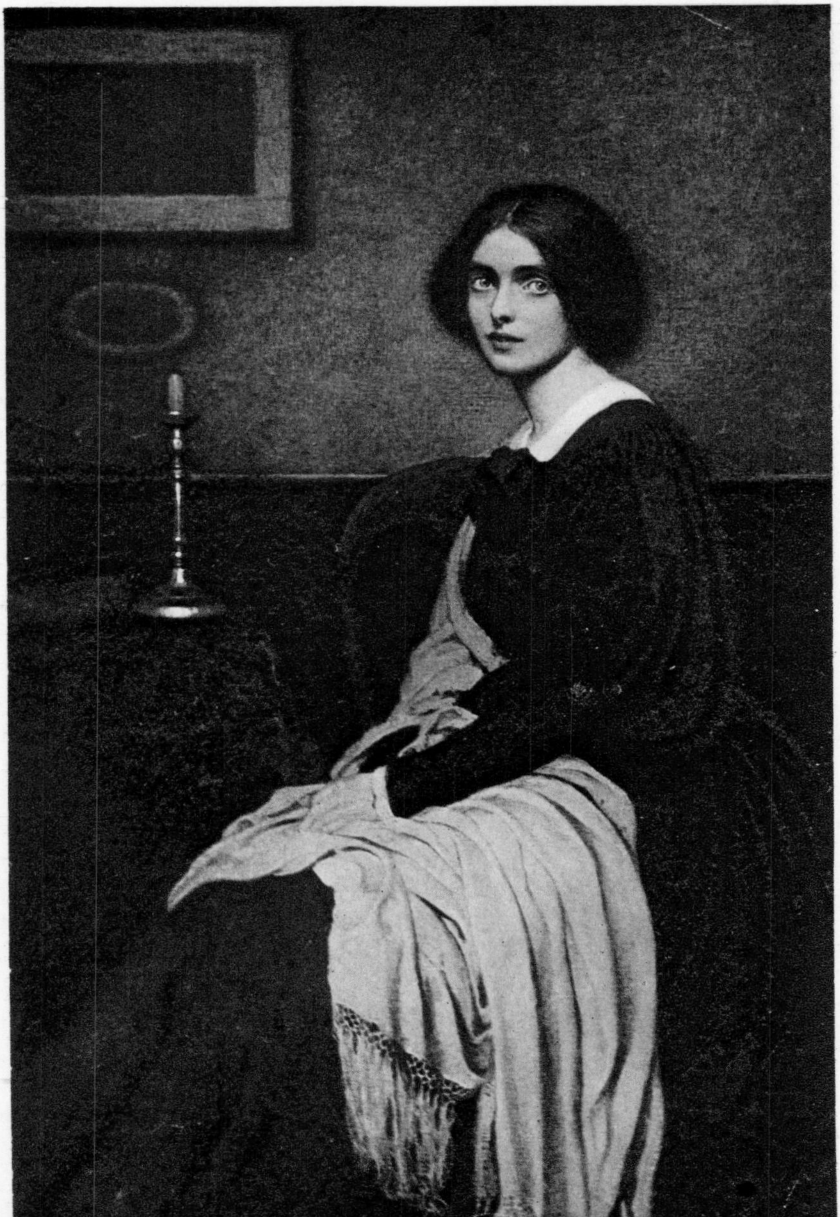

**JANE EYRE**

*From a contemporary painting by an unknown artist*

you had got a fortune; and now, for a matter of no moment, you are excited."

"What *can* you mean? It may be of no moment to you; you have sisters, and don't care for a cousin; but I had nobody; and now three relations,— or two, if you don't choose to be counted,— are born into my world full grown. I say again, I am glad!"

I walked fast through the room: I stopped, half suffocated with the thoughts that rose faster than I could receive, comprehend, settle them: — thoughts of what might, could, would, and should be, and that ere long. I looked at the blank wall: it seemed a sky, thick with ascending stars,— every one lit me to a purpose or delight. Those who had saved my life, whom, till this hour, I had loved barrenly, I could now benefit. They were under a yoke: I could free them: they were scattered,— I could reunite them — the independence, the affluence which was mine, might be theirs too. Were we not four? Twenty thousand pounds shared equally, would be five thousand each,— enough and to spare: justice would be done, —mutual happiness secured. Now the wealth did not weigh on me: now it was not a mere bequest of coin,— it was a legacy of life, hope, enjoyment.

How I looked while these ideas were taking my spirit by storm, I cannot tell; but I perceived soon that Mr. Rivers had placed a chair behind me, and was gently attempting to make me sit down on it. He also advised me to be composed: I scorned the insinuation of helplessness and distraction, shook off his hand, and began to walk about again.

"Write to Diana and Mary to-morrow," I said, "and tell them to come home directly; Diana said they would both consider themselves rich with a thousand pounds, so with five thousand, they will do very well."

"Tell me where I can get you a glass of water," said St. John; "you must really make an effort to tranquillise your feelings."

"Nonsense! and what sort of an effect will the bequest have on you? Will it keep you in England, induce you to marry Miss Oliver, and settle down like an ordinary mortal?"

"You wander: your head becomes confused, I have been too abrupt in communicating the news; it has excited you beyond your strength."

"Mr. Rivers! you quite put me out of patience; I am rational enough; it is you who misunderstand; or rather who affect to misunderstand."

"Perhaps if you explained yourself a little more fully, I should comprehend better."

"Explain! What is there to explain? You cannot fail to see that twenty thousand pounds, the sum in question, divided equally between the nephew and three nieces of our uncle, will give five thousand to each? What I want is, that you should write to your sisters and tell them of the fortune that has accrued to them."

"To you, you mean."

"I have intimated my view of the case: I am incapable of taking any other. I am not brutally selfish, blindly unjust, or fiendishly ungrateful. Besides, I am resolved I will have a home and connections. I like Moor House, and I will live at Moor House; I like Diana and Mary, and I will attach myself for life to Diana and Mary. It would please and benefit me to have five thousand pounds; it would torment and oppress me to have twenty thousand; which, moreover, could never be mine in justice, though it might in law. I abandon to you, then, what is absolutely superfluous to me. Let there be no opposition, and no discussion about it; let us agree amongst each other, and decide the point at once."

"This is acting on first impulses; you must take days to consider such a matter, ere your word can be regarded as valid."

"Oh! if all you doubt is my sincerity, I am easy: you see the justice of the case?"

"I *do* see a certain justice; but it is contrary to all custom. Besides, the entire fortune is your right: my uncle gained it by his own efforts; he was free to leave it to whom he would: he left it to you. After all, justice permits you to keep it: you may, with a clear conscience, consider it absolutely your own."

"With me," said I, "it is fully as much a matter of feeling as of conscience: I must indulge my feelings; I so seldom have had an opportunity of doing so. Were you to argue, object, and annoy me for a year, I could not forego the delicious pleasure of which I have caught a glimpse — that of repaying, in part, a mighty obligation, and winning to myself life-long friends."

"You think so now," rejoined St. John; "because you do not know what it is to possess, nor consequently to enjoy wealth: you cannot form a notion of the importance twenty thousand pounds would give you; of the place it would enable you to take in society; of the prospects it would open to you: you cannot"——

"And you," I interrupted, "cannot at all imagine the craving I have for fraternal and sisterly love. I never had a home, I never had brother or sisters; I must and will have them now: you are not reluctant to admit me and own me, are you?"

"Jane: I will be your brother — my sisters will be your sisters — without stipulating for this sacrifice of your just rights."

"Brother? Yes; at the distance of a thousand leagues! Sisters? Yes; slaving amongst strangers! I, wealthy — gorged with gold I never earned and do not merit! You, penniless! Famous equality and fraternisation! Close union! Intimate attachment!"

"But, Jane, your aspirations after family ties and domestic happiness may be realised otherwise than by the means you contemplate: you may marry."

"Nonsense, again! Marry! I don't want to marry, and never shall marry."

"That is saying too much: such hazardous affirmations are a proof of the excitement under which you labour."

"It is not saying too much: I know what I feel, and how averse are my inclinations to the bare thought of marriage. No one would take me for love; and I will not be regarded in the light of a mere money-speculation. And I do not want a stranger — unsympathising alien, different from me; I want my kindred: those with whom I have full fellow-feeling. Say again you will be my brother: when you uttered the words I was satisfied, happy; repeat them, if you can repeat them sincerely."

"I think I can. I know I have always loved my own sisters; and I know on what my affection for them is grounded,— respect for their worth, and admiration of their talents. You too have principle and mind: your tastes and habits resemble Diana's and Mary's; your presence is always agreeable to me; in your conversation I have already for some time found a salutary solace. I feel I can easily and naturally make room in my heart for you, as my third and youngest sister."

"Thank you: that contents me for to-night. Now you had better go; for if you stay longer, you will perhaps irritate me afresh by some mistrustful scruple."

"And the school, Miss Eyre? It must now be shut up, I suppose?"

"No. I will retain my post of mistress till you get a substitute."

He smiled approbation: we shook hands, and he took leave.

I need not narrate in detail the further struggle I had, and arguments I used, to get matters regarding the legacy settled as I wished. My task was a very hard one: but, as I was absolutely resolved — as my cousins saw at length that my mind was really and immutably fixed on making a just division of the property — as they must in their own hearts have felt the equity of the intention; and must, besides, have been innately conscious that in my place they would have done precisely what I wished to do — they yielded at length so far as to consent to put the affair to arbitration. The judges chosen were Mr. Oliver and an able lawyer: both coincided in my opinion: I carried my point. The instruments of transfer were drawn out: St. John, Diana, Mary, and I, each became possessed of a competency.

## CHAPTER XXXIV

IT was near Christmas by the time all was settled: the season of general holiday approached. I now closed Morton school; taking care that the parting should not be barren on my side. Good fortune opens the hand as well as the heart wonderfully; and to give somewhat when we have largely received, is but to afford a vent to the unusual ebullition of the sensations. I had long felt with pleasure that many of my rustic scholars liked me, and when we parted, that consciousness was confirmed: they manifested their affection plainly and strongly. Deep was my gratification to find I had really a place in their unsophisticated hearts: I promised them that never a week should pass in future that I did not visit them, and give them an hour's teaching in their school.

Mr. Rivers came up, as — having seen the classes, now numbering sixty girls, file out before me, and locked the door — I stood with the key in my hand, exchanging a few words of special farewell with some half-dozen of my best scholars: as decent, respectable, modest, and well-informed young women as could be found in the ranks of the British peasantry. And that is saying a great deal; for after all, the British peasantry are the best taught, best mannered, most self-respecting of any in Europe: since those days I have seen paysannes and Bäuerinnen; and the best of them seemed to me ignorant, coarse, and besotted, compared with my Morton girls.

"Do you consider you have got your reward for a season of exertion?" asked Mr. Rivers, when they were gone. "Does not the consciousness of having done some real good in your day and generation give pleasure?"

"Doubtless."

"And you have only toiled a few months! Would not a life devoted to the task of regenerating your race be well spent?"

"Yes," I said; "but I could not go on for ever so: I want to enjoy my own faculties as well as to cultivate those of other people. I must enjoy them now; don't recall either my mind or body to the school; I am out of it and disposed for full holiday."

He looked grave. "What now? What sudden eagerness is this you evince? What are you going to do?"

"To be active: as active as I can. And first I must beg you to set Hannah at liberty, and get somebody else to wait on you."

"Do you want her?"

"Yes, to go with me to Moor House: Diana and Mary will be at home in a week, and I want to have everything in order against their arrival."

"I understand: I thought you were for flying off on some excursion. It is better so: Hannah shall go with you."

"Tell her to be ready by to-morrow then; and here is the schoolroom key: I will give you the key of my cottage in the morning."

He took it. "You give it up very gleefully," said he: "I don't quite understand your light-heartedness; because I cannot tell what employment you propose to yourself as a substitute for the one you are relinquishing. What aim, what purpose, what ambition in life have you now?"

"My first aim will be to *clean down* (do you comprehend the full force of the expression?) to *clean down* Moor House from chamber to cellar; my next to rub it up with beeswax, oil, and an indefinite number of cloths, till it glitters again; my third, to arrange every chair, table, bed, carpet, with mathematical precision; afterwards I shall go near to ruin you in coals and peat to keep up good fires in every room; and lastly, the two days preceding that on which your sisters are expected, will be devoted by Hannah and me to such a beating of eggs, sorting of currants, grating of spices. compounding of Christmas cakes, chopping up of materials for mince-pies, and solemnising of other culinary rites, as words can convey but an inadequate notion of to the uninitiated like you. My purpose, in short, is to have all things in an absolutely perfect state of readiness for Diana and Mary, before next Thursday; and my ambition is to give them a beau-ideal of a welcome when they come."

St. John smiled slightly: still he was dissatisfied.

"It is all very well for the present," said he: "but seriously, I trust that when the first flush of vivacity is over, you will look a little higher than domestic endearments and household joys."

"The best things the world has!" I interrupted.

"No, Jane, no, this world is not the scene of fruition; do not attempt to make it so: nor of rest; do not turn slothful."

"I mean, on the contrary, to be busy."

"Jane, I excuse you for the present: two months' grace I allow you for the full enjoyment of your new position, and for pleasing yourself with this late-found charm of relationship; but *then,* I hope you will begin to look beyond Moor House and Morton, and sisterly society, and the selfish calm and sensual comfort of civilised affluence. I hope your energies will then once more trouble you with their strength."

I looked at him with surprise. "St. John," I said, "I think you are almost wicked to talk so. I am disposed to be as content as a queen, and you try to stir me up to restlessness! To what end?"

"To the end of turning to profit the talents which God has committed to your keeping; and of which he will surely one day demand a strict account. Jane, I shall watch you closely and anxiously—I warn you of that. And try to restrain the disproportionate fervour with which you throw yourself into commonplace home pleasures. Don't cling so tenaciously to ties of the flesh; save your constancy and ardour for an adequate cause; forbear to waste them on trite, transient objects. Do you hear, Jane?"

"Yes; just as if you were speaking Greek. I feel I have adequate cause to be happy, and I *will* be happy. Good-bye!"

Happy at Moor House I was, and hard I worked; and so did Hannah: she was charmed to see how jovial I could be amidst the bustle of a house turned topsy-turvy—how I could dust, and brush, and clean, and cook. And really after a day or two of confusion worse confounded, it was delightful, by degrees, to invoke order from the chaos ourselves had made. I had previously taken a journey to S——, to purchase some new furniture: my cousins having given me carte blanche to effect what alterations I pleased, and a sum having been set aside for that purpose. The ordinary sitting-room and bed-rooms I left much as they were: for I knew Diana and Mary would derive more pleasure from seeing again the old homely tables, and chairs, and beds, than from the spectacle of the smartest innovations. Still some novelty was necessary, to give to their return the piquancy with which I wished it to be invested. Dark handsome new carpets and curtains, an arrangement of some carefully selected antique ornaments in porcelain and bronze, new coverings, and mirrors, and dressing-cases for the toilet tables, answered the end: they looked fresh without being glaring. A spare parlour and bed-room

I refurnished entirely, with old mahogany and crimson upholstery: I laid canvas on the passage, and carpets on the stairs. When all was finished, I thought Moor House as complete a model of bright modest snugness within, as it was, at this season, a specimen of wintry waste and desert dreariness without.

The eventful Thursday at length came. They were expected about dark, and ere dusk, fires were lit upstairs and below; the kitchen was in perfect trim; Hannah and I were dressed and all was in readiness.

St. John arrived first. I had entreated him to keep quite clear of the house till everything was arranged: and, indeed, the bare idea of the commotion, at once sordid and trivial, going on within its walls sufficed to scare him to estrangement. He found me in the kitchen, watching the progress of certain cakes for tea, then baking. Approaching the hearth, he asked, "If I was at last satisfied with housemaid's work?" I answered by inviting him to accompany me on a general inspection of the result of my labours. With some difficulty, I got him to make the tour of the house. He just looked in at the doors I opened; and when he had wandered upstairs and downstairs, he said I must have gone through a great deal of fatigue and trouble to have effected such considerable changes in so short a time: but not a syllable did he utter indicating pleasure in the improved aspect of his abode.

This silence damped me. I thought perhaps the alterations had disturbed some old associations he valued. I inquired whether this was the case: no doubt in a somewhat crest-fallen tone.

"Not at all; he had, on the contrary, remarked that I had scrupulously respected every association: he feared, indeed, I must have bestowed more thought on the matter than it was worth. How many minutes, for instance, had I devoted to studying the arrangement of this very room? — By-the-by, could I tell him where such a book was?"

I showed him the volume on the shelf: he took it down, and withdrawing to his accustomed window recess, he began to read it.

Now, I did not like this, reader. St. John was a good man; but I began to feel he had spoken truth of himself, when he said he was hard and cold. The humanities and amenities of life had no attraction for him — its peaceful enjoyments no charm. Literally, he lived only to aspire — after what was good and great, certainly: but still he would never rest; nor approve of others resting round him. As I looked at his lofty forehead, still and pale as a white stone — at his fine lineaments fixed in study — I comprehended all at once that he would hardly make a good husband: that it would be a trying thing to be his wife. I understood, as by inspiration, the nature of his love for Miss Oliver; I agreed with him that it was but a love of the senses. I comprehended how he should despise himself for the feverish influence it exercised over him; how he should wish to stifle and destroy it; how he should mistrust its ever conducing permanently to his happiness, or hers. I saw he was of the material from which nature hews her heroes — Christian and Pagan — her lawgivers, her statesmen, her conquerors: a steadfast bulwark for great interests to rest upon; but, at the fireside, too often a cold, cumbrous column, gloomy and out of place.

"This parlour is not his sphere," I reflected: "the Himalayan ridge, or Caffre bush, even the plague-cursed Guinea Coast swamp, would suit him better. Well may he eschew the calm of domestic life; it is not his element: there his faculties stagnate — they cannot develop or appear to advantage. It is in scenes of strife and danger — where courage is proved, and energy exercised, and fortitude tasked — that he will speak and move, the leader and superior. A merry child would have the advantage of him on this hearth. He is right to choose a missionary's career — I see it now."

"They are coming! they are coming!" cried Hannah, throwing open the parlour door. At the same moment old Carlo barked joyfully. Out I ran. It was now dark; but a rumbling of wheels was audible. Hannah soon had a lantern lit. The vehicle had stopped at the wicket: the driver opened the door: first one well-known form, then another, stepped out. In a minute I had my face under their bonnets, in contact first with Mary's soft cheek, then with Diana's flowing curls. They laughed — kissed me — then Hannah: patted Carlo, who was half wild with delight, asked eagerly if all was well; and being assured in the affirmative, hastened into the house.

They were stiff with their long and jolting drive from Whitcross, and chilled with the frosty night air; but their pleasant countenances expanded to the cheerful firelight. While the driver and Hannah brought in the boxes, they demanded St. John. At this moment he advanced from the parlour. They both threw their arms round his neck at once. He gave each one quiet kiss, said in a low tone a few words of welcome, stood a while to be talked to, and then, intimating that he supposed they would soon rejoin him in the parlour, withdrew there as to a place of refuge.

I had lit their candles to go upstairs, but Diana had first to give hospitable orders respecting the driver; this done, both followed me. They were delighted with the renovation and decoration of their rooms; with the new drapery, and fresh carpets, and rich tinted china vases: they expressed their gratification ungrudgingly. I had the pleasure of feeling that my arrangements met their wishes exactly; and that what I had done added a vivid charm to their joyous return home.

Sweet was that evening. My cousins, full of exhilaration, were so eloquent in narrative and comment, that their fluency covered St. John's taciturnity: he was sincerely glad to see his sisters; but in their glow of fervour and flow of joy he could not sympathise. The event of the day—that is, the return of Diana and Mary—pleased him; but the accompaniments of that event, the glad tumult, the garrulous glee of reception, irked him: I saw he wished the quieter morrow was come. In the very meridian of the night's enjoyment, about an hour after tea, a rap was heard at the door. Hannah entered with the intimation that "a poor lad was come, at that unlikely time, to fetch Mr. Rivers to see his mother, who was drawing away."

"Where does she live, Hannah?"

"Clear up at Whitcross Brow, almost four miles off; and moor and moss all the way."

"Tell him I will go."

"I'm sure, sir, you had better not. It's the worst road to travel after dark that can be: there's no track at all over the bog. And then it is such a bitter night—the keenest wind you ever felt. You had better send word, sir, that you will be there in the morning."

But he was already in the passage, putting on his cloak; and without one objection, one murmur, he departed. It was then nine o'clock: he did not return till midnight. Starved and tired enough he was: but he looked happier than when he set out. He had performed an act of duty; made an exertion; felt his own strength to do and deny, and was on better terms with himself.

I am afraid the whole of the ensuing week tried his patience. It was Christmas week: we took to no settled employment, but spent it in a sort of merry domestic dissipation. The air of the moors, the freedom of home, the dawn of prosperity, acted on Diana and Mary's spirits like some life-giving elixir: they were gay from morning till noon, and from noon till night. They could always talk; and their discourse, witty, pithy, original, had such charms for me, that I preferred listening to, and sharing in it, to doing anything else. St. John did not rebuke our vivacity; but he escaped from it: he was seldom in the house; his parish was large, the population scattered, and he found daily business in visiting the sick and poor in its different districts.

One morning, at breakfast, Diana, after looking a little pensive for some minutes, asked him, "If his plans were yet unchanged?"

"Unchanged and unchangeable," was the reply. And he proceeded to inform us that his departure from England was now definitely fixed for the ensuing year.

"And Rosamond Oliver?" suggested Mary: the words seeming to escape her lips involuntarily: for no sooner had she uttered them, than she made a gesture as if wishing to recall them. St. John had a book in his hand — it was his unsocial custom to read at meals — he closed it, and looked up.

"Rosamond Oliver," said he, "is about to be married to Mr. Granby; one of the best connected and most estimable residents in S——, grandson and heir to Sir Frederic Granby: I had the intelligence from her father yesterday."

His sisters looked at each other, and at me; we all three looked at him: he was serene as glass.

"The match must have been got up hastily," said Diana: "they cannot have known each other long."

"But two months: they met in October at the county ball at S——. But where there are no obstacles to a union, as in the present case, where the connection is in every point desirable, delays are unnecessary: they will be married as soon as S—— Place, which Sir Frederic gives up to them, can be refitted for their reception."

The first time I found St. John alone after this communication, I felt tempted to inquire if the event distressed him: but he seemed so little to need sympathy, that, so far from venturing to offer him more, I experienced some shame at the recollection of what I had already hazarded. Besides, I was out of practice in talking to him: his reserve was again frozen over, and my frankness was congealed beneath it. He had not kept his promise of treating me like his sisters; he continually made little, chilling differences between us, which did not at all tend to the development of cordiality: in short, now that I was acknowledged his kinswoman, and lived under the same roof with him, I felt the distance between us to be far greater than when he had known me only as the village schoolmistress. When I remembered how far I had once been admitted to his confidence, I could hardly comprehend his present frigidity.

Such being the case, I felt not a little surprised when he raised his head suddenly from the desk over which he was stooping, and said:—

"You see, Jane, the battle is fought and the victory won."

Startled at being thus addressed, I did not immediately reply: after a moment's hesitation I answered:—

"But are you sure, you are not in the position of those conquerors whose triumphs have cost them too dear? Would not such another ruin you?"

"I think not; and if I were, it does not much signify; I shall never be called upon to contend for such another. The event of the conflict is decisive: my way is now clear; I thank God for it!" So saying, he returned to his papers and his silence.

As our mutual happiness (*i. e.* Diana's, Mary's, and mine) settled into a quieter character, and we resumed our usual habits and regular studies, St. John stayed more at home: he sat with us in the same room, sometimes for hours together. While Mary drew, Diana pursued a course of encyclopædic reading she had (to my awe and amazement) undertaken, and I fagged away at German, he pondered a mystic lore of his own: that of some Eastern tongue, the acquisition of which he thought necessary to his plans.

Thus engaged, he appeared, sitting in his own recess, quiet and absorbed enough; but that blue eye of his had a habit of leaving the outlandish-looking grammar, and wandering over, and sometimes fixing upon us, his fellow-students, with a curious intensity of observation: if caught, it would be instantly withdrawn; yet ever and anon, it returned searchingly to our table. I wondered what it meant: I wondered, too, at the punctual satisfaction he never failed to exhibit on an occasion that seemed to me of small moment, namely, —my weekly visit to Morton School; and still more was I puzzled when, if the day was unfavourable, if there was snow, or rain, or high wind, and his sisters urged me not to go, he would invariably make light of their solicitude, and encourage me to accomplish the task without regard to the elements.

"Jane is not such a weakling as you would make her," he would say: "she can bear a mountain blast, or a shower, or a few flakes of snow, as well as any of us. Her constitution is both sound and elastic: — better calculated to endure variations of climate than many more robust."

And when I returned, sometimes a good deal tired, and not a little weather-beaten, I never dared complain, because I saw that to murmur would be to vex him: on all occasions fortitude pleased him: the reverse was a special annoyance.

One afternoon, however, I got leave to stay at home, because I really had a cold. His sisters were gone to Morton in my stead: I sat reading Schiller; he, deciphering his crabbed Oriental scrolls. As I exchanged a translation for an exercise, I happened to look his way: there I found myself under the influence of the ever-watchful blue eye. How long it had been searching me through and through, and over and over, I cannot tell: so keen was it, and yet so cold, I felt for the moment superstitious — as if I were sitting in the room with something uncanny.

"Jane, what are you doing?"

"Learning German."

"I want you to give up German, and learn Hindostanee."

"You are not in earnest?"

"In such earnest that I must have it so: and I will tell you why."

He then went on to explain that Hindostanee was the language he himself was at present studying: that, as he advanced, he was apt to forget the commencement; that it would assist him greatly to have a pupil with whom he might again and again go over the elements, and so fix them thoroughly in his mind; that his choice had hovered for some time between me and his sisters; but that he had fixed on me, because he saw I could sit at a task the longest of the three. Would I do him this favour? I should not, perhaps, have to make the sacrifice long; as it wanted now barely three months to his departure.

St. John was not a man to be lightly refused: you felt that every impression made on him, either for pain or pleasure, was deep-graved and permanent. I consented. When Diana and Mary returned, the former found her scholar transferred from her to her brother: she laughed; and both she and Mary agreed that St. John should never have persuaded them to such a step. He answered, quietly:—

"I know it."

I found him a very patient, very forbearing, and yet an exacting master: he expected me to do a great deal; and when I fulfilled his expectations, he, in his own way, fully testified his approbation. By degrees, he acquired a certain influence over me that took away my liberty of mind: his praise and notice were more restraining than his indifference. I could no longer talk or laugh freely when he was by; because a tiresomely importunate instinct reminded me that vivacity (at least in me) was distasteful to him. I was so fully aware that only serious moods and occupations were acceptable, that in his presence every effort to sustain or follow any other became vain: I fell under a freezing spell. When he said "go," I went; "come," I came; "do this," I did it. But I did not love my servitude: I wished, many a time, he had continued to neglect me.

One evening, when, at bedtime, his sisters and I stood round him, bidding him good-night, he kissed each of them, as was his custom; and, as was equally his custom, he gave me his hand. Diana, who chanced to be in a frolicsome humour (*she* was not painfully controlled by his will; for hers, in another way, was as strong), exclaimed:—

"St. John! you used to call Jane your third sister, but you don't treat her as such: you should kiss her too."

She pushed me towards him. I thought Diana very provoking, and felt uncomfortably confused; and while I was thus thinking and feeling, St. John bent his head; his Greek face was brought to a level with mine, his eyes questioned my eyes piercingly — he kissed me. There are no such things as marble kisses, or ice kisses, or I should say, my ecclesiastical cousin's salute belonged to one of these classes; but there may be experiment kisses, and his was an experiment kiss. When given, he viewed me to learn the result; it was not striking: I am sure I did not blush; perhaps I might have turned a little pale, for I felt as if the kiss were a seal affixed to my fetters. He never omitted the ceremony afterwards, and the gravity and quiescence with which I underwent it, seemed to invest it for him with a certain charm.

As for me, I daily wished more to please him: but to do so, I felt daily more and more that I must disown half my nature, stifle half my faculties, wrest my tastes from their original bent, force myself to the adoption of pursuits for which I had no natural vocation. He wanted to train me to an elevation I could never reach; it racked me hourly to aspire to the standard he uplifted. The thing was as impossible as to mould my irregular features to his correct and classic pattern, to give to my changeable green eyes the sea-blue tint and solemn lustre of his own.

Not his ascendancy alone, however, held me in thrall at present. Of late it had been easy enough for me to look sad: a cankering evil sat at my heart and drained my happiness at its source — the evil of suspense.

Perhaps you think I had forgotten Mr. Rochester, reader, amidst these changes of place and fortune. Not for a moment. His idea was still with me; because it was not a vapour sunshine could disperse; nor a sand-traced effigy storms could wash away: it was a name graven on a tablet, fated to last as long as the marble it inscribed. The craving to know what had become of him followed me everywhere; when I was at Morton, I re-entered my cottage every evening to think of that; and now at Moor House, I sought my bed-room each night to brood over it.

In the course of my necessary correspondence with Mr. Briggs about the will, I had inquired if he knew anything of Mr. Rochester's present residence and state of health; but, as St. John had conjectured, he was quite ignorant of all concerning him. I then wrote to Mrs. Fairfax, entreating information on the subject. I had calculated with certainty on this step answering my end: I felt sure it would elicit an early answer. I was astonished when a fortnight passed without reply; but when two months wore away, and day after day the post arrived and brought nothing for me, I fell a prey to the keenest anxiety.

I wrote again: there was a chance of my first letter having missed. Renewed hope followed renewed effort: it shone like the former for some weeks, then, like it, faded, flickered: not a line, not a word reached me. When half a year wasted in vain expectancy my hope died out: and then I felt dark indeed.

A fine spring shone round me, which I could not enjoy. Summer approached; Diana tried to cheer me: she said I looked ill, and wished to accompany me to the sea-side. This St. John opposed; he said I did not want dissipation, I wanted employment; my present life was too purposeless, I required an aim; and, I suppose, by way of supplying deficiencies, he prolonged still further my lessons in Hindostanee, and grew more urgent in requiring their accomplishment: and I, like a fool, never thought of resisting him — I could not resist him.

One day I had come to my studies in lower spirits than usual; the ebb was occasioned by a poignantly felt disappointment: Hannah had told me in the morning there was a letter for me, and when I went down to take it, almost certain that the long looked-for tidings were vouchsafed me at last, I found only an unimportant note from Mr. Briggs on business. The bitter check had wrung from me some tears; and now as I sat poring over the crabbed characters and flourishing tropes of an Indian scribe, my eyes filled again.

St. John called me to his side to read; in attempting to do this my voice failed me: words were lost in sobs. He and I were the only occupants of the parlour: Diana was practising her music in the drawing-room, Mary was gardening — it was a very fine May-day, clear, sunny, and breezy. My companion expressed no surprise at this emotion, nor did he question me as to its cause; he only said:—

"We will wait a few minutes, Jane, till you are more composed." And while I smothered the paroxysm with all haste, he sat calm and patient, leaning on his desk and looking like a physician watching with the eye of science an expected and fully-understood crisis in a patient's malady. Having stifled my sobs, wiped my eyes, and muttered something about not being very well that morning, I resumed my task, and succeeded in completing it. St. John put away my books and his, locked his desk, and said:—

"Now, Jane, you shall take a walk; and with me."

"I will call Diana and Mary."

"No. I want only one companion this morning, and that must be you: put on your things; go out by the kitchen door: take the road towards the head of Marsh Glen: I will join you in a moment."

I know no medium: I never in my life have known any medium in my dealings with positive, hard characters, antagonistic to my own, between absolute submission and determined revolt. I have always faithfully observed the one, up to the very moment of bursting, sometimes with volcanic vehemence, into the other; and as neither present circumstances warranted, nor my present mood inclined me to mutiny, I observed careful obedience to St. John's directions; and in ten minutes I was treading the wild track of the glen, side by side with him.

The breeze was from the west: it came over the hills, sweet with scents of heath and rush; the sky was of stainless blue; the stream descending the ravine, swelled with past spring rains, poured along plentiful and clear, catching golden gleams from the sun, and sapphire tints from the firmament. As we advanced and left the track, we trod a soft turf, mossy fine and emerald green, minutely enamelled with a tiny white flower, and spangled with a star-like yellow blossom: the hills, meantime, shut us quite in; for the glen, towards its head, wound to their very core.

"Let us rest here," said St. John as we reached the first stragglers of a battalion of rocks, guarding a sort of pass, beyond which the beck rushed down a waterfall; and where, still a little further, the mountain shook off turf and flower, had only heath for raiment, and crag for gem — where it exaggerated the wild to the savage, and exchanged the fresh for the frowning — where it guarded the forlorn hope of solitude, and a last refuge for silence.

I took a seat: St. John stood near me. He looked up the pass and down the hollow; his glance wandered away with the stream, and returned to traverse the unclouded heaven which coloured it: he removed his hat, let the breeze stir his hair and kiss his brow. He seemed in communion with the genius of the haunt: with his eye he bade farewell to something.

"And I shall see it again," he said aloud, "in dreams, when I sleep by the Ganges: and again, in a more remote hour — when another slumber overcomes me—on the shore of a darker stream."

Strange words of a strange love! An austere patriot's passion for his fatherland! He sat down; for half an hour we never spoke; neither he to me nor I to him: that interval passed, he recommenced:—

"Jane, I go in six weeks: I have taken my berth in an East Indiaman which sails on the twentieth of June."

"God will protect you; for you have undertaken His work," I answered.

"Yes," said he, "there is my glory and joy. I am the servant of an infallible master. I am not going out under human guidance, subject to the defective laws and erring control of my feeble fellow-worms: my king, my lawgiver, my captain, is the All-perfect. It seems strange to me that all round me do not burn to enlist under the same banner,— to join in the same enterprise."

"All have not your powers: and it would be folly for the feeble to wish to march with the strong."

"I do not speak to the feeble, or think of them: I address only such as are worthy of the work, and competent to accomplish it."

"Those are few in number, and difficult to discover."

"You say truly: but when found, it is right to stir them up — to urge and exhort them to the effort — to show them what their gifts are, and why they were given — to speak Heaven's message in their ear,— to offer them, direct from God, a place in the ranks of His chosen."

"If they are really qualified for the task, will not their own hearts be the first to inform them of it?"

I felt as if an awful charm was framing round and gathering over me: I trembled to hear some fatal word spoken which would at once declare and rivet the spell.

"And what does *your* heart say?" demanded St. John.

"My heart is mute,— my heart is mute," I answered, struck and thrilled.

"Then I must speak for it," continued the deep, relentless voice. "Jane, come with me to India: come as my helpmeet and fellow-labourer."

The glen and sky spun round: the hills heaved! It was as if I had heard a summons from Heaven — as if a visionary messenger, like him of Macedonia, had enounced, "Come over and help us!" But I was no apostle,— I could not behold the herald,— I could not receive his call.

"Oh, St. John!" I cried, "have some mercy!"

I appealed to one who, in the discharge of what he believed his duty, knew neither mercy nor remorse. He continued:—

"God and nature intended you for a missionary's wife. It is not personal, but mental endowments they have given you: you are formed for labour, not for love. A missionary's wife you must — shall be. You shall be mine: I claim you — not for my pleasure, but for my Sovereign's service."

"I am not fit for it: I have no vocation," I said.

He had calculated on these first objections: he was not irritated by them. Indeed, as he leaned back against the crag behind him, folded his arms on his chest, and fixed his countenance, I saw he was prepared for a long and trying opposition, and had taken in a stock of patience to last him to its close — resolved, however, that that close should be conquest for him.

"Humility, Jane," said he, "is the groundwork of Christian virtues: you say right that you are not fit for the work. Who is fit for it? Or who, that ever was truly called, believed himself worthy of the summons? I, for instance, am but dust and ashes. With St. Paul, I acknowledge myself the chiefest of sinners: but I do not suffer this sense of my personal vileness to daunt me. I know my Leader: that He is just as well as mighty; and while He has chosen a feeble instrument to perform a great task, He will, from the boundless stores of His providence, supply the inadequacy of the means to the end. Think like me, Jane — trust like me. It is the Rock of Ages I ask you to lean on: do not doubt but it will bear the weight of your human weakness."

"I do not understand a missionary life: I have never studied missionary labours."

"There, I, humble as I am, can give you the aid you want: I can set your task from hour to hour; stand by you always; help you from moment to moment. This I could do in the beginning: soon (for I know your powers) you would be as strong and apt as myself, and would not require my help."

"But my powers — where are they for this undertaking? I do not feel them. Nothing speaks or stirs in me while you talk. I am sensible of no light kindling — no life quickening — no voice counselling or cheering. Oh, I wish I could make you see how much my mind is at this moment like a rayless dungeon, with one shrinking fear fettered in its depths — the fear of being persuaded by you to attempt what I cannot accomplish!"

"I have an answer for you — hear it. I have watched you ever since we first met: I have made you my study for ten months. I have proved you in that time by sundry tests: and what have I seen and elicited? In the village school I found you could perform well, punctually, uprightly, labour uncongenial to your habits and inclinations; I saw you could perform it with capacity and tact: you could win while you controlled. In the calm with which you learnt you had become suddenly rich, I read a mind clear of the vice of Demas:

— lucre had no undue power over you. In the resolute readiness with which you cut your wealth into four shares, keeping but one to yourself, and relinquishing the three others to the claim of abstract justice, I recognised a soul that revelled in the name and excitement of sacrifice. In the tractability with which, at my wish, you forsook a study in which you were interested, and adopted another because it interested me; in the untiring assiduity with which you have since persevered in it — in the unflagging energy and unshaken temper with which you have met its difficulties — I acknowledge the complement of the qualities I seek. Jane, you are docile, diligent, disinterested, faithful, constant, and courageous; very gentle, and very heroic: cease to mistrust yourself — I can trust you unreservedly. As a conductress of Indian schools, and a helper amongst Indian women, your assistance will be to me invaluable."

My iron shroud contracted round me; persuasion advanced with slow sure step. Shut my eyes as I would, these last words of his succeeded in making the way, which had seemed blocked up, comparatively clear. My work, which had appeared so vague, so hopelessly diffuse, condensed itself as he proceeded, and assumed a definite form under his shaping hand. He waited for an answer. I demanded a quarter of an hour to think, before I again hazarded a reply.

"Very willingly," he rejoined: and rising, he strode a little distance up the pass, threw himself down on a swell of heath, and there lay still.

"I *can* do what he wants me to do: I am forced to see and acknowledge that," I meditated — "That is, if life be spared me. But I feel mine is not the existence to be long protracted under an Indian sun. — What then? He does not care for that: when my time came to die he would resign me, in all serenity and sanctity, to the God who gave me. The case is very plain before me. In leaving England, I should leave a loved but empty land — Mr. Rochester is not there: and if he were, what is, what can that ever be to me? My business is to live without him now: nothing so absurd, so weak as to drag on from day to day, as if I were waiting some impossible change in circumstances, which might reunite me to him. Of course (as St. John once said) I must seek another interest in life to replace the one lost: is not the occupation he now offers me truly the most glorious man can adopt or God assign? Is it not, by its noble cares and sublime results, the one best calculated to fill the void left by uptorn affections and demolished hopes? I believe I must say, Yes — and yet I shudder. Alas! If I join St. John, I abandon half myself: if I go to India, I go to premature death. And how will the interval between leaving England for India, and India for the grave, be filled? Oh, I know well! That, too, is very clear to my vision. By straining to satisfy St. John till my sinews ache, I *shall* satisfy him — to the finest central point and farthest outward circle of his expectations. If I *do* go with him — if I *do* make the sacrifice he urges, I will make it absolutely: I will throw all on the altar — heart, vitals, the entire victim. He will never love me; but he shall approve me; I will show him energies he has not seen, resources he has never suspected. Yes: I can work as hard as he can; and with as little grudging.

"Consent, then, to his demand is possible: but for one item — one dreadful item. It is — that he asks me to be his wife, and has no more of a husband's heart for me than that frowning giant of a rock, down which the stream is foaming in yonder gorge. He prizes me as a soldier would a good weapon; and that is all. Unmarried to him, this would never grieve me; but can I let him complete his calculations — coolly put into practice his plans — go through the wedding ceremony? Can I receive from him the bridal ring, endure all the forms of love (which I doubt not he would scrupulously observe) and know that the spirit was quite absent? Can I bear the consciousness that every endearment he bestows is a sacrifice made on principle? No: such a martyrdom would be monstrous. I will never undergo it. As his sister, I might accompany him — not as his wife: I will tell him so."

I looked towards the knoll: there he lay, still as a prostrate column; his face turned to me: his eye beaming watchful and keen. He started to his feet, and approached me.

"I am ready to go to India, if I may go free."

"Your answer requires a commentary," he said; "it is not clear."

"You have hitherto been my adopted brother: I, your adopted sister; let us continue as such: you and I had better not marry."

He shook his head. "Adopted fraternity will not do in this case. If you were my real sister it would be different: I should take you, and seek no wife. But as it is, either our union must be consecrated and sealed by marriage, or it cannot exist: practical obstacles oppose themselves to any other plan. Do you not see it, Jane? Consider a moment — your strong sense will guide you."

I did consider: and still my sense, such as it was, directed me only to the fact that we did not love each other as man and wife should; and therefore it inferred we ought not to marry. I said so. "St. John," I returned, "I regard you as a brother — you, me as a sister: so let us continue."

"We cannot — we cannot," he answered, with short, sharp determination: "it would not do. You have said you will go with me to India: remember — you have said that."

"Conditionally."

"Well — well. To the main point — the departure with me from England, the co-operation with me in my future labours — you do not object. You have already as good as put your hand to the plough: you are too consistent to withdraw it. You have but one end to keep in view — how the work you have undertaken can best be done. Simplify your complicated interests, feelings, thoughts, wishes, aims; merge all considerations in one purpose: that of fulfilling with effect — with power — the mission of your great Master. To do so, you must have a coadjutor — not a brother; that is a loose tie; but a husband. I, too, do not want a sister; a sister might any day be taken from me. I want a wife: the sole helpmeet I can influence efficiently in life, and retain absolutely till death."

I shuddered as he spoke: I felt his influence in my marrow — his hold on my limbs.

"Seek one elsewhere than in me, St. John: seek one fitted to you."

"One fitted to my purpose, you mean — fitted to my vocation. Again I tell you it is not the insignificant private individual — the mere man, with the man's selfish senses — I wish to mate: it is a missionary."

"And I will give the missionary my energies — it is all he wants — but not myself: that would be only adding the husk and shell to the kernel. For them he has no use: I retain them."

"You cannot — you ought not. Do you think God will be satisfied with half an oblation? Will he accept a mutilated sacrifice? It is the cause of God I advocate: it is under his standard I enlist you. I cannot accept on His behalf a divided allegiance: it must be entire."

"Oh! I will give my heart to God," I said, "*You* do not want it."

I will not swear, reader, that there was not something of repressed sarcasm both in the tone in which I uttered this sentence, and in the feeling that accompanied it. I had silently feared St. John till now, because I had not understood him. He had held me in awe, because he had held me in doubt. How much of him was saint, how much mortal, I could not heretofore tell: but revelations were being made in this conference: the analysis of his nature was proceeding before my eyes. I saw his fallibilities: I comprehended them. I understood that, sitting there where I did, on the bank of heath, and with that handsome form before me, I sat at the feet of a man, erring as I. The veil fell from his hardness and despotism. Having felt in him the presence of these qualities, I felt his imperfection, and took courage. I was with an equal — one with whom I might argue — one whom, if I saw good, I might resist.

He was silent after I had uttered the last sentence, and I presently risked an upward glance at his countenance. His eye, bent on me, expressed at once stern surprise and keen inquiry. "Is she sarcastic, and sarcastic to *me!*" it seemed to say.

"What does this signify?"

"Do not let us forget that this is a solemn matter," he said ere long; "one of which we may neither think nor talk lightly without sin. I trust, Jane, you are in earnest when you say you will give your heart to God: it is all I want. Once wrench your heart from man, and fix it on your Maker, the advancement of that Maker's spiritual kingdom on earth will be your chief delight and endeavour; you will be ready to do at once whatever furthers that end. You will see what impetus would be given to your efforts and mine by our physical and mental union in marriage: the only union that gives a character of permanent conformity to the destinies and designs of human beings: and, passing over all minor caprices — all trivial difficulties and delicacies of feeling — all scruple about the degree, kind, strength, or tenderness of mere personal inclination — you will hasten to enter into that union at once."

"Shall I?" I said, briefly; and I looked at his features, beautiful in their harmony, but strangely formidable in their still severity; at his brow, commanding but not open; at his eyes, bright and deep, and searching, but never soft; at his tall, imposing figure; and fancied myself in idea *his wife*. Oh! it would never do! As his curate, his comrade, all would be right: I would cross oceans with him in that capacity; toil under eastern suns, in Asian deserts with him in that office; admire and emulate his courage, and devotion, and vigour; accommodate quietly to his masterhood; smile undisturbed at his ineradicable ambition; discriminate the Christian from the man; profoundly esteem the one, and freely forgive the other. I should suffer often, no doubt, attached to him only in this capacity: my body would be under rather a stringent yoke, but my heart and mind would be free. I should still have my unblighted self to turn to: my natural unenslaved feelings with which to communicate in moments of loneliness. There would be recesses in my mind which would be only mine, to which he never came; and sentiments growing there fresh and sheltered, which his austerity could never blight, nor his measured warrior-march trample down: but as his wife — at his side always, and always restrained, and always checked — forced to keep the fire of my nature continually low, to compel it to burn inwardly and never utter a cry, though the imprisoned flame consumed vital after vital — *this* would be unendurable.

"St. John!" I exclaimed, when I had got so far in my meditation.

"Well?" he answered, icily.

"I repeat: I freely consent to go with you as your fellow-missionary; but not as your wife; I cannot marry you and become part of you."

"A part of me you must become," he answered steadily; "otherwise the whole bargain is void. How can I, a man not yet thirty, take out with me to India a girl of nineteen, unless she be married to me? How can we be for ever together — sometimes in solitudes, sometimes amidst savage tribes — and unwed?"

"Very well," I said shortly; "under the circumstances, quite as well as if I were either your real sister, or a man and a clergyman like yourself."

"It is known that you are not my sister; I cannot introduce you as such: to attempt it would be to fasten injurious suspicions on us both. And for the rest, though you have a man's vigorous brain, you have a woman's heart, and — it would not do."

"It would do," I affirmed with some disdain, "perfectly well. I have a woman's heart; but not where you are concerned; for you I have only a comrade's constancy; a fellow-soldier's frankness, fidelity, fraternity, if you like; a neophyte's respect and submission to his hierophant: nothing more — don't fear."

"It is what I want," he said, speaking to himself; "it is just what I want. And there are obstacles in the way: they must be hewn down. Jane, you would not repent marrying me; be certain of that; we *must* be married. I repeat it: there is no other way; and undoubtedly enough of love would follow upon marriage to render the union right even in your eyes."

"I scorn your idea of love," I could not help saying; as I rose up and stood before him, leaning my back against the rock. "I scorn the counterfeit sentiment you offer: yes, St. John, and I scorn you when you offer it."

He looked at me fixedly: compressing his well-cut lips while he did so. Whether he was incensed or surprised, or what, it was not easy to tell: he could command his countenance thoroughly.

"I scarcely expected to hear that expression from you," he said: "I think I have done and uttered nothing to deserve scorn."

I was touched by his gentle tone, and overawed by his high calm mien.

"Forgive me the words, St. John: but it is your own fault that I have been roused to speak so unguardedly. You have introduced a topic on which our natures are at variance — a topic we should never discuss: the very name of love is an apple of discord between us — if the reality were required what should we do? How should we feel? My dear cousin, abandon your scheme of marriage — forget it."

"No," said he; "it is a long-cherished scheme, and the only one which can secure my great end: but I shall urge you no further at present. To-morrow, I leave home for Cambridge: I have many friends there to whom I should wish to say farewell. I shall be absent a fortnight — take that space of time to consider my offer: and do not forget that if you reject it, it is not me you deny, but God. Through my means, He opens to you a noble career; as my wife only can you enter upon it. Refuse to be my wife, and you limit yourself for ever to a track of selfish ease and barren obscurity. Tremble lest in that case you should be numbered with those who have denied the faith, and are worse than infidels!"

He had done. Turning from me, he once more —

"Looked to river, looked to hill:"

But this time his feelings were all pent in his heart: I was not worthy to hear them uttered. As I walked by his side homeward, I read well in his iron silence all he felt towards me: the disappointment of an austere and despotic nature, which has met resistance where it expected submission — the disapprobation of a cool, inflexible judgment, which has detected in another feelings and views in which it has no power to sympathise: in short, as a man, he would have wished to coerce me into obedience: it was only as a sincere Christian he bore so patiently with my perversity, and allowed so long a space for reflection and repentance.

That night, after he had kissed his sisters, he thought proper to forget even to shake hands with me; but left the room in silence. I — who, though I had no love, had much friendship for him — was hurt by the marked omission: so much hurt that tears started to my eyes.

"I see you and St. John have been quarrelling, Jane," said Diana, "during your walk on the moor. But go after him; he is now lingering in the passage, expecting you — he will make it up."

I have not much pride under such circumstances: I would always rather be happy than dignified; and I ran after him — he stood at the foot of the stairs.

"Good-night, St. John," said I.

"Good-night, Jane," he replied calmly.

"Then shake hands," I added.

What a cold, loose touch he impressed on my fingers! He was deeply displeased by what had occurred that day: cordiality would not warm, nor tears move him. No happy reconciliation was to be had with him — no cheering smile or generous word: but still the Christian was patient and placid; and when I asked him if he forgave me, he answered that he was not in the habit of cherishing the remembrance of vexation; that he had nothing to forgive; not having been offended.

And with that answer he left me. I would much rather he had knocked me down.

## CHAPTER XXXV

HE did not leave for Cambridge the next day, as he had said he would. He deferred his departure a whole week; and during that time he made me feel what severe punishment, a good, yet stern, a conscientious, yet implacable man can inflict on one who has offended him. Without one overt act of hostility, one upbraiding word, he contrived to impress me momently with the conviction that I was put beyond the pale of his favour.

Not that St. John harboured a spirit of unchristian vindictiveness — not that he would have injured a hair of my head, if it had been fully in his power to do so. Both by nature and principle, he was superior to the mean gratification of vengeance: he had forgiven me for saying I scorned him and his love, but he had not forgotten the words; and as long as he and I lived he never would forget them. I saw by his look, when he turned to me, that they were always written on the air between me and him; whenever I spoke, they sounded in my voice to his ear; and their echo toned every answer he gave me.

He did not abstain from conversing with me: he even called me as usual each morning to join him at his desk; and I fear the corrupt man within him had a pleasure unimparted to, and unshared by, the pure Christian, in evincing with what skill he could, while acting and speaking apparently just as usual, extract from every deed and every phrase the spirit of interest and approval which had formerly communicated a certain austere charm to his language and manner. To me, he was in reality become no longer flesh, but marble; his eye was a cold, bright, blue gem; his tongue, a speaking instrument — nothing more.

All this was torture to me — refined, lingering torture. It kept up a slow fire of indignation, and a trembling trouble of grief, which harassed and crushed me altogether. I felt how — if I were his wife, this good man, pure as the deep sunless source, could soon kill me: without drawing from my veins a single drop of blood, or receiving on his own crystal conscience the faintest stain of crime. Especially I felt this, when I made any attempt to propitiate him.

No ruth met my ruth. *He* experienced no suffering from estrangement — no yearning after reconciliation; and though, more than once, my fast falling tears blistered the page over which we both bent, they produced no more effect on him than if his heart had been really a matter of stone or metal. To his sisters, meantime, he was somewhat kinder than usual: as if afraid that mere coldness would not sufficiently convince me how completely I was banished and banned, he added the force of contrast: and this I am sure he did, not by malice, but on principle.

The night before he left home, happening to see him walking in the garden about sunset, and remembering, as I looked at him, that this man, alienated as he now was, had once saved my life, and that we were near relations, I was moved to make a last attempt to regain his friendship. I went out and approached him, as he stood leaning over the little gate: I spoke to the point at once.

"St. John, I am unhappy, because you are still angry with me. Let us be friends."

"I hope we are friends," was the unmoved reply; while he still watched the rising of the moon, which he had been contemplating as I approached.

"No, St. John, we are not friends as we were. You know that."

"Are we not? That is wrong. For my part, I wish you no ill and all good."

"I believe you, St. John; for I am sure you are incapable of wishing any one ill: but, as I am your kinswoman, I should desire somewhat more of affection than that sort of general philanthropy you extend to mere strangers."

"Of course," he said. "Your wish is reasonable; and I am far from regarding you as a stranger."

This, spoken in a cool, tranquil tone, was mortifying and baffling enough. Had I attended to the suggestions of pride and ire, I should immediately have left him: but something worked within me more strongly than those feelings could. I deeply venerated my cousin's talent and principle. His friendship was of value to me: to lose it tried me severely. I would not so soon relinquish the attempt to reconquer it.

"Must we part in this way, St. John? And when you go to India, will you leave me so, without a kinder word than you have yet spoken?"

He now turned quite from the moon, and faced me.

"When I go to India, Jane, will I leave you? What! do you not go to India?"

"You said I could not, unless I married you."

"And you will not marry me? You adhere to that resolution?"

Reader, do you know, as I do, what terror those cold people can put into the ice of their questions? How much of the fall of the avalanche is in their anger? of the breaking up of the frozen sea in their displeasure?

"No, St. John, I will not marry you. I adhere to my resolution."

The avalanche had shaken and slid a little forward; but it did not yet crash down.

"Once more, why this refusal?" he asked.

"Formerly," I answered, "because you did not love me; now, I reply, because you almost hate me. If I were to marry you, you would kill me. You are killing me now."

His lips and cheeks turned white — quite white.

"*I should kill you — I am killing you?* Your words are such as ought not to be used: violent, unfeminine, and untrue. They betray an unfortunate state of mind: they merit severe reproof: they would seem inexcusable; but that it is the duty of man to forgive his fellow, even until seventy-and-seven times."

I had finished the business now. While earnestly wishing to erase from his mind the trace of my former offence, I had stamped on that tenacious surface, another and far deeper impression: I had burnt it in.

"Now, you will indeed hate me," I said. "It is useless to attempt to conciliate you: I see I have made an eternal enemy of you."

A fresh wrong did these words inflict: the worse, because they touched on the truth. That bloodless lip quivered to a temporary spasm. I knew the steely ire I had whetted. I was heart-wrung.

"You utterly misinterpret my words," I said, at once seizing his hand: "I have no intention to grieve or pain you — indeed, I have not."

Most bitterly he smiled — most decidedly he withdrew his hand from mine. "And now you recall your promise, and will not go to India at all, I presume?" said he, after a considerable pause.

"Yes I will, as your assistant," I answered.

A very long silence succeeded. What struggle there was in him between Nature and Grace in this interval, I cannot tell: only singular gleams scintillated in his eyes, and strange shadows passed over his face. He spoke at last.

"I before proved to you the absurdity of a single woman of your age proposing to accompany abroad a single man of mine. I proved it to you in such terms as, I should have thought, would have prevented your ever again alluding to the plan. That you have done so, I regret — for your sake."

I interrupted him. Anything like a tangible reproach gave me courage at once. "Keep to common sense, St. John: you are verging on nonsense. You pretend to be shocked by what I have said. You are not really shocked; for, with your superior mind, you cannot be either so dull or so conceited as to misunderstand my meaning. I say again, I will be your curate, if you like, but never your wife."

Again he turned lividly pale; but, as before, controlled his passion perfectly. He answered emphatically, but calmly:—

"A female curate, who is not my wife, would never suit me. With me, then, it seems, you cannot go: but if you are sincere in your offer, I will, while in town, speak to a married missionary, whose wife needs a coadjutor. Your own fortune will make you independent of the Society's aid; and thus you may still be spared the dishonour of breaking your promise, and deserting the band you engaged to join."

Now I never had, as the reader knows, either given any formal promise, or entered into any engagement; and this language was all much too hard, and much too despotic for the occasion. I replied: —

"There is no dishonour; no breach of promise; no desertion in the case. I am not under the slightest obligation to go to India: especially with strangers. With you I would have ventured much; because I admire, confide in, and, as a sister, I love you: but I am convinced that, go when and with whom I would, I should not live long in that climate."

"Ah! you are afraid of yourself," he said, curling his lip.

"I am. God did not give me my life to throw away; and to do as you wish me would, I begin to think, be almost equivalent to committing suicide. Moreover, before I definitely resolve on quitting

England, I will know for certain, whether I cannot be of greater use by remaining in it than by leaving it."

"What do you mean?"

"It would be fruitless to attempt to explain: but there is a point on which I have long endured painful doubt; and I can go nowhere till by some means that doubt is removed."

"I know where your heart turns, and to what it clings. The interest you cherish is lawless and unconsecrated. Long since you ought to have crushed it: now you should blush to allude to it. You think of Mr. Rochester?"

It was true. I confessed it by silence.

"Are you going to seek Mr. Rochester?"

"I must find out what has become of him."

"It remains for me, then," he said, "to remember you in my prayers; and to entreat God for you, in all earnestness, that you may not indeed become a castaway. I had thought I recognised in you one of the chosen. But God sees not as man sees: *His* will be done."

He opened the gate, passed through it, and strayed away down the glen. He was soon out of sight.

On re-entering the parlour, I found Diana standing at the window, looking very thoughtful. Diana was a great deal taller than I: she put her hand on my shoulder, and, stooping, examined my face.

"Jane," she said, "you are always agitated and pale now. I am sure there is something the matter. Tell me what business St. John and you have on hands. I have watched you this half hour from the window: you must forgive my being such a spy, but for a long time I have fancied I hardly know what. St. John is a strange being"——

She paused — I did not speak: soon she resumed:—

"That brother of mine cherishes peculiar views of some sort respecting you, I am sure: he has long distinguished you by a notice and interest he never showed to any one else — to what end? I wish he loved you — does he, Jane?"

I put her cool hand to my hot forehead: "No, Die, not one whit."

"Then why does he follow you so with his eyes — and get you so frequently alone with him, and keep you so continually at his side? Mary and I had both concluded he wished you to marry him."

"He does — he has asked me to be his wife."

Diana clapped her hands. "That is just what we hoped and thought! And you will marry him, Jane, won't you? And then he will stay in England."

"Far from that, Diana; his sole idea in proposing to me is to procure a fitting fellow-labourer in his Indian toils."

"What! He wishes you to go to India?"

"Yes."

"Madness!" she exclaimed. "You would not live three months there, I am certain. You never shall go: you have not consented — have you, Jane?"

"I have refused to marry him" ——

"And have consequently displeased him?" she suggested.

"Deeply: he will never forgive me, I fear: yet I offered to accompany him as his sister."

"It was frantic folly to do so, Jane. Think of the task you undertook — one of incessant fatigue: where fatigue kills even the strong; and you are weak. St. John — you know him — would urge you to impossibilities — with him there would be no permission to rest during the hot hours; and unfortunately, I have noticed, whatever he exacts, you force yourself to perform. I am astonished you found courage to refuse his hand. You do not love him then, Jane?"

"Not as a husband."

"Yet he is a handsome fellow."

"And I am so plain you see, Die. We should never suit."

"Plain! You? Not at all. You are much too pretty, as well as too good, to be grilled alive in Calcutta." And again she earnestly conjured me to give up all thoughts of going out with her brother.

"I must, indeed," I said: "for when just now I repeated the offer of serving him for a deacon, he expressed himself shocked at my want of decency. He seemed to think I had committed an impropriety in proposing to accompany him unmarried: as if I had not from the first hoped to find in him a brother; and habitually regarded him as such."

"What makes you say he does not love you, Jane?"

"You should hear himself on the subject. He has again and again explained that it is not himself, but his office he wishes to mate. He has told me I am formed for labour — not for love: which is true, no doubt. But, in my opinion, if I am not formed for love,

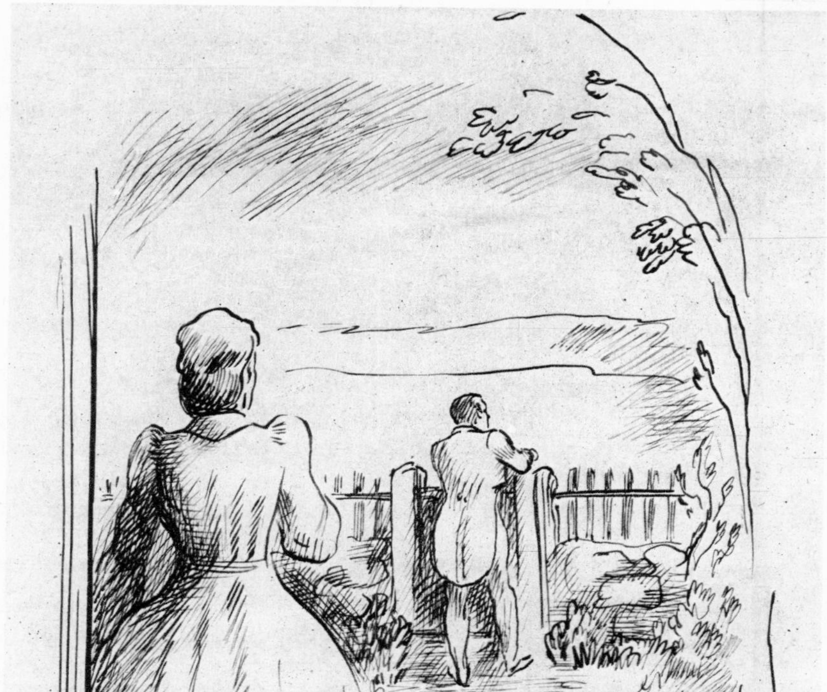

I went out and approached him, as he stood leaning over the little gate

it follows that I am not formed for marriage. Would it not be strange, Die, to be chained for life to a man who regarded one but as a useful tool?"

"Insupportable — unnatural — out of the question!"

"And then," I continued, "though I have only sisterly affection for him now, yet, if forced to be his wife, I can imagine the possibility of conceiving an inevitable, strange, torturing kind of love for him: because he is so talented; and there is often a certain heroic grandeur in his look, manner, and conversation. In that case, my lot would become unspeakably wretched. He would not want me to love him; and if I showed the feeling, he would make me sensible that it was a superfluity unrequired by him, unbecoming in me. I know he would."

"And yet, St. John is a good man," said Diana.

"He is a good and a great man: but he forgets, pitilessly, the feelings and claims of little people, in pursuing his own large views. It is better, therefore, for the insignificant to keep out of his way; lest, in his progress, he should trample them down. Here he comes! I will leave you, Diana." And I hastened upstairs, as I saw him entering the garden.

But I was forced to meet him again at supper. During that meal he appeared just as composed as usual. I had thought he would hardly speak to me, and I was certain he had given up the pursuit of his matrimonial scheme: the sequel showed I was mistaken on both points. He addressed me precisely in his ordinary manner; or what had, of late, been his ordinary manner; one scrupulously polite. No doubt he had invoked the help of the Holy Spirit to subdue the anger I had roused in him, and now believed he had forgiven me once more.

For the evening reading before prayers, he selected the twenty-first chapter of Revelation. It was at all times pleasant to listen, while from his lips fell the words of the Bible: never did his fine voice sound at once so sweet and full — never did his manner become so impressive in its noble simplicity, as when he delivered the oracles of God: and to-night that voice took a more solemn tone — that manner a more thrilling meaning — as he sat in the midst of his household circle (the May moon shining in through the uncurtained window, and rendering almost unnecessary the light of the candle on the table): as he sat there, bending over the great old Bible, and described from its page the vision of the new heaven and the new earth — told how God would come to dwell with men, how he would wipe away all tears from their eyes, and promised that there should be no more death, neither sorrow nor crying, nor any more pain, because the former things were passed away.

The succeeding words thrilled me strangely as he spoke them: especially as I felt, by the slight, indescribable alteration in sound, that in uttering them, his eye had turned on me.

"He that overcometh shall inherit all things; and I will be his God, and he shall be my son. But," was slowly, distinctly read, "the fearful, the unbelieving, etc., shall have their part in the lake which burneth with fire and brimstone, which is the second death."

Henceforward, I knew what fate St. John feared for me.

A calm, subdued triumph, blent with a longing earnestness, marked his enunciation of the last glorious verses of that chapter. The reader believed his name was already written in the Lamb's book of life, and he yearned after the hour which should admit him to the city to which the kings of the earth bring their glory and honour; which has no need of sun or moon to shine in it, because the glory of God lightens it, and the Lamb is the light thereof.

In the prayer following the chapter, all his energy gathered — all his stern zeal woke: he was in deep earnest, wrestling with God, and resolved on a conquest. He supplicated strength for the weak-hearted; guidance for wanderers from the fold: a return, even at the eleventh hour, for those whom the temptations of the world and the flesh were luring from the narrow path. He asked, he urged, he claimed the boon of a brand snatched from the burning. Earnestness is ever deeply solemn: first, as I listened to that prayer, I wondered at his; then, when it continued and rose, I was touched by it, and at last awed. He felt the greatness and goodness of his purpose so sincerely: others who heard him plead for it, could not but feel it too.

The prayer over, we took leave of him: he was to go at a very early hour in the morning. Diana and Mary having kissed him, left the room — in compliance, I think, with a whispered hint from him: I tendered my hand, and wished him a pleasant journey.

"Thank you, Jane. As I said, I shall return from Cambridge in a fortnight: that space, then, is yet left you for reflection. If I listened to human pride, I should say no more to you of marriage with me; but I listen to my duty, and keep steadily in view my first aim — to do all things to the glory of God. My Master was long-suffering: so will I be. I cannot give you up to perdition as a vessel of wrath: repent — resolve; while there is yet time. Remember, we are bid to work while it is day — warned that 'the night cometh when no man shall work.' Remember the fate of Dives, who had his good things in this life. God give you strength to choose that better part which shall not be taken from you!"

He laid his hand on my head as he uttered the last words. He had spoken earnestly, mildly: his look was not, indeed, that of a lover beholding his mistress; but it was that of a pastor recalling his wandering sheep — or better, of a guardian angel watching the soul for which he is responsible. All men of talent, whether they be men of feeling or not; whether they be zealots, or aspirants, or despots — provided only they be sincere — have their sublime moments: when they subdue and rule. I felt veneration for St. John — veneration so strong that its impetus thrust me at once to the point I had so long shunned. I was tempted to cease struggling with him — to rush down the torrent of his will into the gulf of his existence, and there lose my own. I was almost as hard beset by him now as I had been once before, in a different way, by another. I was a fool both times. To have yielded then would have been an error of principle; to have yielded now would have been an error of judgment. So I think at this hour, when I look back to the crisis through the quiet medium of time: I was unconscious of folly at the instant.

I stood motionless under my hierophant's touch. My refusals were forgotten — my fears overcome — my wrestlings paralysed. The Impossible — *i. e.* my marriage with St. John — was fast becoming the Possible. All was changing utterly, with a sudden sweep. Religion called — Angels beckoned — God commanded — life rolled together like a scroll — death's gates opening, showed eternity beyond: it seemed, that for safety and bliss there, all here might be sacrificed in a second. The dim room was full of visions.

"Could you decide now?" asked the missionary. The inquiry was put in gentle tones: he drew me to him gently. Oh, that gentleness! how far more potent is it than force! I could resist St. John's wrath: I grew pliant as a reed under his kindness. Yet I knew all the time, if I yielded now, I should not the less be made to repent, some day, of my former rebellion. His nature was not changed by one hour of solemn prayer: it was only elevated.

"I could decide if I were but certain," I answered: "were I but convinced that it is God's will I should marry you, I could vow to marry you here and now — come afterwards what would!"

"My prayers are heard!" ejaculated St. John. He pressed his hand firmer on my head, as if he claimed me: he surrounded me with his arm, *almost* as if he loved me (I say *almost* — I knew the difference — for I had felt what it was to be loved; but, like him, I had now put love out of the question, and thought only of duty): I contended with my inward dimness of vision, before which clouds yet rolled. I sincerely, deeply, fervently longed to do what was right; and only that. "Show me, show me the path!" I entreated of Heaven. I was excited more than I had ever been; and whether what followed was the effect of excitement, the reader shall judge.

All the house was still; for I believe all, except St. John and myself, were now retired to rest. The one candle was dying out: the room was full of moonlight. My heart beat fast and thick: I heard its throb. Suddenly it stood still to an inexpressible feeling that thrilled it through, and passed at once to my head and extremities. The feeling was not like an electric shock; but it was quite as sharp, as strange, as startling: it acted on my senses as if their utmost activity hitherto had been but torpor; from which they were now summoned, and forced to wake. They rose expectant: eye and ear waited, while the flesh quivered on my bones.

"What have you heard? What do you see?" asked St. John. I saw nothing: but I heard a voice somewhere cry —

"Jane! Jane! Jane!" nothing more.

"Oh God! what is it?" I gasped.

I might have said, "Where is it?" for it did not seem in the room — nor in the house — nor in the garden: it did not come out of the air — nor from under the earth — nor from overhead. I had heard it — where, or whence, for ever impossible to know! And it was the voice of a human being — a known, loved, well-remembered voice — that of Edward Fairfax Rochester; and it spoke in pain and woe wildly, eerily, urgently.

"I am coming!" I cried. "Wait for me! Oh, I will come!" I flew to the door, and looked into the passage: it was dark. I ran out into the garden: it was void.

"Where are you?" I exclaimed.

The hills beyond Marsh Glen sent the answer faintly back —

"Where are you?" I listened. The wind sighed low in the firs: all was moorland loneliness and midnight hush.

"Down, superstition!" I commented, as that spectre rose up black by the black yew at the gate. "This is not thy deception, not thy witchcraft: it is the work of nature. She was roused, and did — no miracle — but her best."

I broke from St. John; who had followed, and would have detained me. It was *my* time to assume ascendancy. *My* powers were in play, and in force. I told him to forbear question or remark; I desired him to leave me: I must, and would be alone. He obeyed at once. Where there is energy to command well enough, obedience never fails. I mounted to my chamber; locked myself in; fell on my knees; and prayed in my way — a different way to St. John's, but effective in its own fashion. I seemed to penetrate very near a Mighty Spirit; and my soul rushed out in gratitude at His feet. I rose from the thanksgiving — took a resolve — and lay down, unscared, enlightened — eager but for the daylight.

## CHAPTER XXXVI

THE daylight came. I rose at dawn. I busied myself for an hour or two with arranging my things in my chamber, drawers and wardrobe, in the order wherein I should wish to leave them during a brief absence. Meantime, I heard St. John quit his room. He stopped at my door: I feared he would knock — no, but a slip of paper was passed under the door. I took it up. It bore these words —

"You left me too suddenly last night. Had you stayed but a little longer, you would have laid your hand on the Christian's cross and the angel's crown. I shall expect your clear decision when I return this day fortnight. Meantime, watch and pray that yon enter not into temptation: the spirit, I trust, is willing, but the flesh, I see, is weak. I shall pray for you hourly,— Yours, St. John."

"My spirit," I answered, mentally, "is willing to do what is right; and my flesh, I hope, is strong enough to accomplish the will of Heaven, when once that will is distinctly known to me. At any rate, it shall be strong enough to search — inquire — to grope an outlet from this crowd of doubt, and find the open day of certainty."

It was the first of June; yet the morning was overcast and chilly: rain beat fast on my casement. I heard the front-door open, and St. John pass out. Looking through the window, I saw him traverse the garden. He took the way over the misty moors in the direction of Whitcross — there he would meet the coach.

"In a few more hours I shall succeed you in that track, cousin," thought I: "I too have a coach to meet at Whitcross. I too have some to see and ask after in England, before I depart for ever."

It wanted yet two hours of breakfast-time. I filled the interval in walking softly about my room, and pondering the visitation which had given my plans their present bent. I recalled that inward sensation I had experienced: for I could recall it, with all its unspeakable strangeness. I recalled the voice I had heard; again I questioned whence it came, as vainly as before: it seemed in *me* — not in the external world. I asked, was it a mere nervous impression

— a delusion? I could not conceive or believe: it was more like an inspiration. The wondrous shock of feeling had come like the earthquake which shook the foundations of Paul and Silas's prison; it had opened the doors of the soul's cell, and loosed its bands — it had wakened it out of its sleep, whence it sprang trembling, listening aghast; then vibrated thrice a cry on my startled ear, and in my quaking heart, and through my spirit; which neither feared nor shook, but exulted as if in joy over the success of one effort it had been privileged to make, independent of the cumbrous body.

"Ere many days," I said, as I terminated my musings, "I will know something of him whose voice seemed last night to summon me. Letters have proved of no avail — personal inquiry shall replace them."

At breakfast I announced to Diana and Mary that I was going a journey, and should be absent at least four days.

"Alone, Jane?" they asked.

"Yes; it was to see, or hear news of, a friend about whom I had for some time been uneasy."

They might have said, as I have no doubt they thought, that they had believed me to be without any friends save them: for, indeed, I had often said so; but with their true natural delicacy, they abstained from comment: except that Diana asked me if I was sure I was well enough to travel. I looked very pale, she observed. I replied, that nothing ailed me save anxiety of mind, which I hoped soon to alleviate.

It was easy to make my further arrangements; for I was troubled with no inquiries — no surmises. Having once explained to them that I could not now be explicit about my plans, they kindly and wisely acquiesced in the silence with which I pursued them; according to me the privilege of free action I should, under similar circumstances, have accorded them.

I left Moor House at three o'clock P. M., and soon after four, I stood at the foot of the sign-post of Whitcross, waiting the arrival of the coach which was to take me to distant Thornfield. Amidst the silence of those solitary roads and desert hills, I heard it approach from a great distance. It was the same vehicle whence, a year ago, I had alighted one summer evening on this very spot — how desolate, and hopeless, and objectless! It stopped as I beckoned. I entered — not now obliged to part with my whole fortune as the price of its accommodation. Once more on the road to Thornfield, I felt like the messenger-pigeon flying home.

It was a journey of six and thirty hours. I had set out from Whitcross on a Tuesday afternoon, and early on the succeeding Thursday morning the coach stopped to water the horses at a wayside inn, situated in the midst of scenery whose green hedges and large fields, and low pastoral hills (how mild of feature and verdant of hue compared with the stern north-midland moors of Morton!) met my eye like the lineaments of a once familiar face. Yes, I knew the character of this landscape: I was sure we were near my bourne.

"How far is Thornfield Hall from here?" I asked of the ostler.

"Just two miles, ma'am, across the fields."

"My journey is closed," I thought to myself. I got out of the coach, gave a box I had into the ostler's charge, to be kept till I called for it; paid my fare; satisfied the coachman, and was going: the brightening day gleamed on the sign of the inn, and I read in gilt letters, "The Rochester Arms." My heart leapt up: I was already on my master's very lands. It fell again: the thought struck it:—

"Your Master himself may be beyond the British Channel, for aught you know: and then, if he is at Thornfield Hall, towards which you hasten, who besides him is there? His lunatic wife: and you have nothing to do with him: you dare not speak to him or seek his presence. You have lost your labour—you had better go no farther," urged the monitor. "Ask information of the people at the inn; they can give you all you seek: they can solve your doubts at once. Go up to that man, and inquire if Mr. Rochester be at home."

The suggestion was sensible; and yet I could not force myself to act on it. I so dreaded a reply that would crush me with despair. To prolong doubt was to prolong hope. I might yet once more see the Hall under the ray of her star. There was the stile before me—the very fields through which I had hurried, blind, deaf, distracted, with a revengeful fury tracking and scourging me, on the morning I fled from Thornfield: ere I well knew what course I had resolved to take, I was in the midst of them. How fast I walked! How I ran sometimes! How I looked forward to catch the first view of the well-known woods! With what feelings I welcomed single trees I knew, and familiar glimpses of meadow and hill between them!

At last the woods rose; the rookery clustered dark; a loud cawing

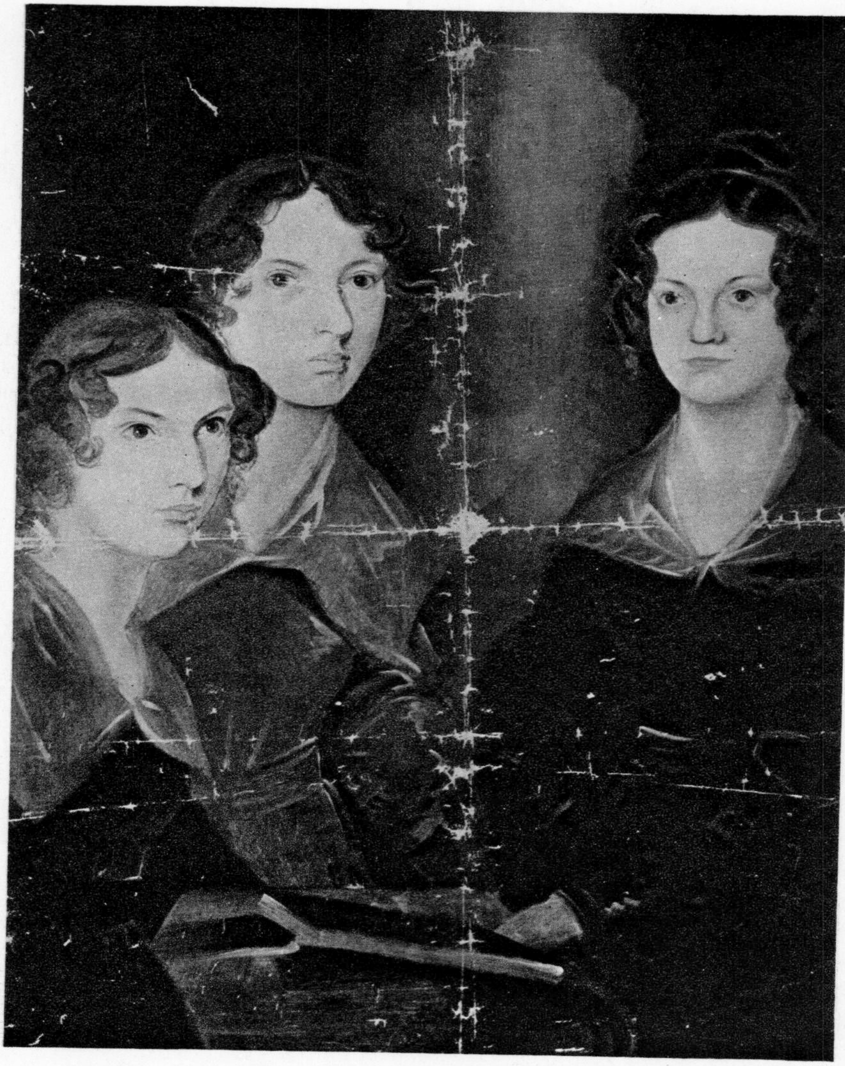

A FAMILY GROUP OF THE BRONTËS, PAINTED BY CHARLOTTE'S BROTHER BRANWELL

Branwell studied briefly at the Royal Academy, and hoped to become a portrait painter. This aim was less difficult to achieve, and less ambitious, than it is now, for before the invention of photography many towns had takers of likenesses who were not expected to have much artistic ability. Branwell, however, received no commissions, and came back to live at home, where he ruined himself by his addiction to drink and drugs.

broke the morning stillness. Strange delight inspired me: on I hastened. Another field crossed — a lane threaded — and there were the courtyard walls — the back offices: the house itself, the rookery still hid. "My first view of it shall be in front," I determined, "where its bold battlements will strike the eye nobly at once, and where I can single out my master's very window: perhaps he will be standing at it — he rises early: perhaps he is now walking in the orchard, or on the pavement in front. Could I but see him! — but a moment! Surely, in that case, I should not be so mad as to run to him? I cannot tell — I am not certain. And if I did — what then? God bless him! What then? Who would be hurt by my once more tasting the life his glance can give me — I rave: perhaps at this moment he is watching the sun rise over the Pyrenees, or on the tideless sea of the south."

I had coasted along the lower wall of the orchard — turned its angle: there was a gate just there, opening into the meadow, between two stone pillars, crowned by stone balls. From behind one pillar, I could peep round quietly at the full front of the mansion. I advanced my head with precaution, desirous to ascertain if any bedroom window-blinds were yet drawn up: battlements, windows, long front — all from this sheltered station were at my command.

The crows sailing overhead perhaps watched me while I took this survey. I wonder what they thought: they must have considered I was very careful and timid at first, and then gradually I grew very bold and reckless. A peep, and then a long start; and then a departure from my niche and a straying out into the meadow; and a sudden stop full in front of the great mansion, and a protracted, hardy gaze towards it. "What affectation of diffidence was this at first?" they might have demanded, "What stupid regardlessness now?"

Hear an illustration, reader.

A lover finds his mistress asleep on a mossy bank; he wishes to catch a glimpse of her fair face without waking her. He steals softly over the grass, careful to make no sound; he pauses — fancying she has stirred: he withdraws; not for worlds would he be seen. All is still: he again advances: he bends above her; a light veil rests on her features: he lifts it, bends lower; now his eyes anticipate the vision of beauty — warm, and blooming, and lovely, in rest. How hurried was their first glance! But how they fix! How he starts! How he suddenly and vehemently clasps in both arms the form he dared not, a moment since, touch with his finger! How he calls aloud a name, and drops his burden, and gazes on it wildly! He thus grasps and cries, and gazes, because he no longer fears to waken by any sound he can utter — by any movement he can make. He thought his love slept sweetly: he finds she is stone-dead.

I looked with timorous joy towards a stately house: I saw a blackened ruin.

No need to cower behind a gate-post, indeed! — to peep up at chamber lattices, fearing life was astir behind them! No need to listen for doors opening — to fancy steps on the pavement or the gravel-walk! The lawn, the grounds were trodden and waste: the portal yawned void. The front was, as I had once seen it in a dream, but a shell-like wall, very high and very fragile looking, perforated with paneless windows: no roof, no battlements, no chimneys — all had crashed in.

And there was the silence of death about it: the solitude of a lonesome wild. No wonder that letters addressed to people here had never received an answer: as well despatch epistles to a vault in a church aisle. The grim blackness of the stones told by what fate the Hall had fallen — by conflagration: but how kindled? What story belonged to this disaster? What loss, besides mortar and marble, and woodwork, had followed upon it? Had life been wrecked, as well as property? If so, whose? Dreadful question: there was no one here to answer it — not even dumb sign, mute token.

In wandering round the shattered walls and through the devastated interior. I gathered evidence that the calamity was not of late occurrence. Winter snows, I thought. had drifted through that void arch; winter rains beaten in at those hollow casements; for. amidst the drenched piles of rubbish, spring had cherished vegetation: grass and weed grew here and there between the stones and fallen rafters. And oh! where, meantime, was the hapless owner of this wreck? In what land? Under what auspices? My eye involuntarily wandered to the grey church tower near the gates, and I asked. "Is he with Damer de Rochester, sharing the shelter of his narrow marble house?"

Some answer must be had to these questions. I could find it nowhere but at the inn, and thither, ere long, I returned. The host himself brought my breakfast into the parlour. I requested him to shut the door and sit down: I had some questions to ask him. But when he complied, I scarcely knew how to begin; such horror had I of possible answers. And yet the spectacle of desolation I had just left, prepared me in a measure for a tale of misery. The host was a respectable-looking, middle-aged man.

"You know Thornfield Hall, of course?" I managed to say at last.

"Yes, ma'am; I lived there once."

"Did you?" Not in my time, I thought; you are a stranger to me.

"I was the late Mr. Rochester's butler," he added.

The late! I seemed to have received with full force, the blow I had been trying to evade.

"The late!" I gasped. "Is he dead?"

"I mean the present gentleman, Mr. Edward's father," he explained. I breathed again: my blood resumed its flow. Fully assured by these words that Mr. Edward — *my* Mr. Rochester (God bless him, wherever he was!) was at least alive: was, in short, "the present gentleman." Gladdening words! It seemed I could hear all that was to come — whatever the disclosures might be — with comparative tranquillity. Since he was not in the grave, I could bear, I thought, to learn that he was at the Antipodes.

"Is Mr. Rochester living at Thornfield Hall now?" I asked, knowing, of course, what the answer would be, but yet desirous of deferring the direct question as to where he really was.

"No, ma'am — oh, no! No one is living there. I suppose you are a stranger in these parts, or you would have heard what happened last autumn,— Thornfield Hall is suite a ruin: it was burnt down just about harvest time. A dreadful calamity! such an immense quantity of valuable property destroyed: hardly any of the furniture could be saved. The fire broke out at dead of night, and before the engines arrived from Millcote, the buildings was one mass of flame. It was a terrible spectacle: I witnessed it myself."

"At dead of night!" I muttered. Yes, that was ever the hour of fatality at Thornfield. "Was it known how it originated?" I demanded.

"They guessed, ma'am: they guessed. Indeed, I should say it

was ascertained beyond a doubt. You are not perhaps aware," he continued, edging his chair a little nearer the table, and speaking low, "that there was a lady,— a — a lunatic, kept in the house?"

"I have heard something of it."

"She was kept in very close confinement, ma'am; people even for years was not absolutely certain of her existence. No one saw her; they only knew by rumour that such a person was at the Hall; and who or what she was it was difficult to conjecture. They said Mr. Edward had brought her from abroad; and some believed she had been his mistress. But a queer thing happened a year since — a very queer thing."

I feared now to hear my own story. I endeavoured to recall him to the main fact.

"And this lady?"

"This lady, ma'am," he answered, "turned out to be Mr. Rochester's wife! The discovery was brought about in the strangest way. There was a young lady, a governess at the Hall, that Mr. Rochester fell in"——

"But the fire," I suggested.

"I'm coming to that, ma'am — that Mr. Edward fell in love with. The servants say they never saw anybody so much in love as he was: he was after her continually. They used to watch him — servants will, you know, ma'am — and he set store on her past everything: for all, nobody, but him thought her so very handsome. She was a little small thing, they say, almost like a child. I never saw her myself; but I've heard Leah, the housemaid, tell of her. Leah liked her well enough. Mr. Rochester was about forty, and this governess not twenty; and you see, when gentlemen of his age fall in love with girls, they are often like as if they were bewitched: well, he would marry her."

"You shall tell me this part of the story another time," I said; "but now I have a particular reason for wishing to hear all about the fire. Was it suspected that this lunatic, Mrs. Rochester, had any hand in it?"

"You've hit it, ma'am: it's quite certain that it was her and nobody but her, that set it going. She had a woman to take care of her called Mrs. Poole — an able woman in her line, and very trustworthy, but for one fault — a fault common to a deal of them nurses and matrons — *she kept a private bottle of gin by her,* and now and then took a drop over much. It is excusable, for she had a hard life of it: but still it was dangerous; for when Mrs. Poole was fast asleep, after the gin and water, the mad lady, who was as cunning as a witch, would take the keys out of her pocket, let herself out of her chamber, and go roaming about the house, doing any wild mischief that came into her head. They say she had nearly burnt her husband in his bed once: but I don't know about that. However, on this night, she set fire first to the hangings of the room next to her own; and then she got down to a lower story, and made her way to the chamber that had had been the governess's — (she was like as if she knew somehow how matters had gone on, and had a spite at her) — and she kindled the bed there; but there was nobody sleeping in it fortunately. The governess had run away two months before; and for all Mr. Rochester sought her as if she had been the most precious thing he had in the world, he never could hear a word of her; and he grew savage — quite savage in his disappointment; he never was a wild man, but he got dangerous after he lost her. He would be alone, too. He sent Mrs. Fairfax, the housekeeper, away to her friends at a distance; but he did it handsomely, for he settled an annuity on her for life: and she deserved it — she was a very good woman. Miss Adèle, a ward he had, was put to school. He broke off acquaintance with all the gentry, and shut himself up, like a hermit, at the Hall."

"What! did he not leave England?"

"Leave England? Bless you, no! He would not cross the door-stones of the house; except at night, when he walked just like a ghost about the grounds and in the orchard as if he had lost his senses — which it is my opinion he had; for a more spirited, bolder, keener gentleman than he was before that midge of a governess crossed him, you never saw, ma'am. He was not a man given to wine, or cards, or racing, as some are, and he was not so very handsome; but he had a courage and a will of his own, if ever a man had. I knew him from a boy, you see: and for my part I have often wished that Miss Eyre had been sunk in the sea before she came to Thornfield Hall."

"Then Mr. Rochester was at home when the fire broke out?"

"Yes, indeed was he; and he went up to the attics when all was burning above and below, and got the servants out of their beds and helped them down himself — and went back to get his mad wife out of her cell. And then they called out to him that she was on the roof; where she was standing, waving her arms, above the battlements, and shouting out till they could hear her a mile off: I saw and heard her with my own eyes. She was a big woman, and had long, black hair: we could see it streaming against the flames as she stood. I witnessed, and several more witnessed Mr. Rochester ascend through the skylight on to the roof: we heard him call 'Bertha!' We saw him approach her; and then, ma'am, she yelled, and gave a spring, and the next minute she lay smashed on the pavement."

"Dead?"

"Dead? Ay, dead as the stones on which her brains and blood were scattered."

"Good God!"

"You may well say so, ma'am: it was frightful!"

He shuddered.

"And afterwards?" I urged.

"Well, ma'am, afterwards the house was burnt to the ground: there are only some bits of walls standing now."

"Were there any other lives lost?"

"No — perhaps it would have been better if there had."

"What do you mean?"

"Poor Mr. Edward!" he ejaculated, "I little thought ever to have seen it! Some say it was a just judgment on him for keeping his first marriage secret, and wanting to take another wife while he had one living: but I pity him, for my part."

"You said he was alive?" I exclaimed.

"Yes, yes: he is alive; but many think he had better be dead."

"Why? How?" My blood was again running cold. "Where is he?" I demanded. "Is he in England?"

"Ay — ay — he's in England; he can't get out of England, I fancy — he's a fixture now."

What agony was this! And the man seemed resolved to protract it.

"He is stone-blind," he said at last. "Yes — he is stone-blind — is Mr. Edward."

I had dreaded worse. I had dreaded he was mad. I summoned strength to ask what had caused this calamity.

"It was all his own courage, and a body may say, his kindness, in a way, ma'am: he wouldn't leave the house till every one else was out before him. As he came down the great staircase at last, after

Mrs. Rochester had flung herself from the battlements, there was a great crash — all fell. He was taken out from under the ruins, alive, but sadly hurt: a beam had fallen in such a way as to protect him partly; but one eye was knocked out, and one hand so crushed that Mr. Carter, the surgeon, had to amputate it directly. The other eye inflamed: he lost the sight of that also. He is now helpless, indeed — blind and a cripple."

"Where is he? Where does he now live?"

"At Ferndean, a manor-house on a farm he has, about thirty miles off: quite a desolate spot."

"Who is with him?"

"Old John and his wife: he would have none else. He is quite broken down, they say."

"Have you any sort of conveyance?"

"We have a chaise, ma'am, a very handsome chaise."

"Let it be got ready instantly; and if your post-boy can drive me to Ferndean before dark this day, I'll pay both you and him twice the hire you usually demand."

# CHAPTER XXXVII

THE manor-house of Ferndean was a building of considerable antiquity, moderate size, and no architectural pretensions, deep buried in a wood. I had heard of it before. Mr. Rochester often spoke of it, and sometimes went there. His father had purchased the estate for the sake of the game covers. He would have let the house: but could find no tenant, in consequence of its ineligible and insalubrious site. Ferndean then remained uninhabited and unfurnished; with the exception of some two or three rooms fitted up for the accommodation of the squire when he went there in the season to shoot.

To this house I came, just ere dark, on an evening marked by the characteristics of sad sky, cold gale, and continued small penetrating rain. The last mile I performed on foot, having dismissed the chaise and driver with the double remuneration I had promised. Even when within a very short distance of the manor-house, you could see nothing of it; so thick and dark grew the timber of the gloomy wood about it. Iron gates between granite pillars showed me where to enter, and passing through them, I found myself at once in the twilight of close-ranked trees. There was a grass-grown track descending the forest aisle, between hoar and knotty shafts and under branched arches. I followed it, expecting soon to reach the dwelling; but it stretched on and on, it wound far and farther: no sign of habitation or grounds was visible.

I thought I had taken a wrong direction and lost my way. The darkness of natural as well as of sylvan dusk gathered over me. I looked round in search of another road. There was none: all was interwoven stem, columnar trunk, dense summer foliage — no opening anywhere.

I proceeded: at last my way opened, the trees thinned a little; presently I beheld a railing, then the house — scarce, by this dim light, distinguishable from the trees, so dank and green were its decaying walls. Entering a portal, fastened only by a latch, I stood amidst a space of enclosed ground, from which the wood swept away in a semicircle. There were no flowers, no garden-beds; only a broad gravel-walk girdling a grass-plat, and this set in the heavy frame of the forest. The house presented two pointed gables in its front: the windows were latticed and narrow: the front-door was narrow too, one step led up to it. The whole looked, as the host of the Rochester Arms had said, "quite a desolate spot." It was as still as a church on a week-day: the pattering rain on the forest leaves was the only sound audible in its vicinage.

"Can there be life here?" I asked.

Yes: life of some kind there was; for I heard a movement — that narrow front-door was unclosing, and some shape was about to issue from the grange.

It opened slowly; a figure came out into the twilight and stood on the step; a man without a hat: he stretched forth his hand as if to feel whether it rained. Dusk as it was, I had recognized him — it was my master, Edward Fairfax Rochester, and no other.

I stayed my step, almost my breath, and stood to watch him — to examine him, myself unseen, and alas! to him invisible. It was a sudden meeting, and one in which rapture was kept well in check by pain. I had no difficulty in restraining my voice from exclamation, my step from hasty advance.

His form was of the same strong and stalwart contour as ever: his port was still erect, his hair was still raven-black; nor were his features altered or sunk: nor in one year's space, by any sorrow, could his athletic strength be quelled, or his vigorous prime blighted. But in his countenance, I saw a change: that looked desperate and brooding — that reminded me of some wronged and fettered wild beast or bird, dangerous to approach in his sullen woe. The caged eagle whose gold-ringed eyes cruelty has extinguished, might look as looked that sightless Samson.

And, reader, do you think I feared him in his blind ferocity? — if you do, you little know me. A soft hope blent with my sorrow that soon I should dare to drop a kiss on that brow of rock, and on those lips so sternly sealed beneath it: but not yet. I would not accost him yet.

He descended the one step, and advanced slowly and gropingly towards the grass plat. Where was his daring stride now? Then he paused, as if he knew not which way to turn. He lifted his hand and opened his eyelids; gazed blank, and with a straining effort, on the sky, and towards the amphitheatre of trees: one saw that all to him was void darkness. He stretched his right hand (the left arm, the mutilated one, he kept hidden in his bosom) ; he seemed to wish by touch to gain an idea of what lay around him: he met but vacancy still; for the trees were some yards off where he stood. He relinquished the endeavour, folded his arms, and stood quiet and mute in the rain, now falling fast on his uncovered head. At this moment John approached him from some quarter.

"Will you take my arm, sir?" he said; "there is a heavy shower coming on: had you not better go in?"

"Let me alone," was the answer.

John withdrew, without having observed me. Mr. Rochester now tried to walk about: vainly,—all was too uncertain. He groped his way back to the house, and, re-entering it, closed the door.

I now drew near and knocked: John's wife opened for me. "Mary," I said, "how are you?"

She started as if she had seen a ghost: I calmed her. To her hurried "Is it really you, miss, come at this late hour to this 'only place?" I answered by taking her hand; and then I followed her into the kitchen, where John now sat by a good fire. I explained to them, in a few words, that I had heard all which had happened since I left Thornfield, and that I was come to see Mr. Rochester. I asked John to go down to the turnpike-house, where I had dismissed the chaise, and bring my trunk, which I had left there: and then while I removed my bonnet and shawl, I questioned Mary as to whether I could be accommodated at the Manor House for the night; and finding that arrangement to that effect, though difficult, would not be impossible, I informed her I should stay. Just at this moment the parlour-bell rang.

"When you go in," said I, "tell your master that a person wishes to speak to him, but do not give my name."

"I don't think he will see you," she answered; "he refuses everybody."

When she returned, I inquired what he had said.

"You are to send in your name and your business," she replied. She then proceeded to fill a glass with water, and place it on a tray, together with candles.

"Is that what he rang for?" I asked.

"Yes: he always has candles brought in at dark, though he is blind."

"Give the tray to me, I will carry it in."

I took it from her hand: she pointed me out the parlour door. The tray shook as I held it; the water spilt from the glass; my heart struck my ribs loud and fast. Mary opened the door for me, and shut it behind me.

This parlour looked gloomy: a neglected handful of fire burnt low in the grate; and, leaning over, it with his head supported against the high, old-fashioned mantelpiece, appeared the blind tenant of the room. His old dog, Pilot, lay on one side, removed out of the way, and coiled up as if afraid of being inadvertently trodden upon. Pilot pricked up his ears when I came in: then he jumped up with a yelp and a whine, and bounded towards me: he almost knocked the tray from my hands. I set it on the table; then patted him, and said softly, "Lie down!" Mr. Rochester turned mechanically to *see* what the commotion was: but as he *saw* nothing, he returned and sighed.

"Give me the water, Mary," he said.

I approached him with now only half-filled glass. Pilot followed me, still excited.

"What is the matter?" he inquired.

"Down, Pilot!" I again said. He checked the water on its way to his lips, and seemed to listen: he drank, and put the glass down. "This is you, Mary, is it not?"

"Mary is in the kitchen," I answered.

He put out his hand with a quick gesture, but not seeing where I stood, he did not touch me. "Who is this? Who is this?" he demanded, trying, as it seemed, to *see* with those sightless eyes — unavailing and distressing attempt! "Answer me — speak again!" he ordered, imperiously and aloud.

"Will you have a little more water, sir? I spilt half of what was in the glass," I said.

"*Who* is it? *What* is it? Who speaks?"

"Pilot knows me, and John and Mary know I am here. I came only this evening," I answered.

"Great God! — what delusion has come over me? What sweet madness has seized me?"

"No delusion — no madness: your mind, sir, is too strong for delusion, your health too sound for frenzy."

"And where is the speaker? Is it only a voice? Oh! I *cannot* see, but I must feel, or my heart will stop and my brain burst. Whatever — whoever you are — be perceptible to the touch or I cannot live!"

He groped; I arrested his wandering hand, and prisoned it in both mine.

"Her very fingers!" he cried; "her small, slight fingers! If so, there must be more of her."

The muscular hand broke from my custody; my arm was seized, my shoulder — neck — waist — I was entwined and gathered to him.

"It is Jane? *What* is it? This is her shape — this is her size" —

"And this her voice," I added. "She is all here: her heart, too. God bless you, sir! I am glad to be so near you again."

"Jane Eyre! — Jane Eyre," was all he said.

"My dear master," I answered, "I am Jane Eyre: I have found you out — I am come back to you."

"In truth? — in the flesh? My living Jane?"

"You touch me, sir, — you hold me, and fast enough: I am not like a corpse, nor vacant like air, am I?"

"My living darling! These are certainly her limbs, and these her features; but I cannot be so blest, after all my misery. It is a dream; such dreams as I have had at night when I have clasped her once more to my heart, as I do now; and kissed her, as thus — and felt that she loved me, and trusted that she would not leave me."

"Which I never will, sir, from this day."

"Never will, says the vision? But I always woke and found it an empty mockery; and I was desolate and abandoned — my life dark, lonely, hopeless — my soul athirst and forbidden to drink — my heart famished and never to be fed. Gentle, soft dream, nestling in my arms now, you will fly, too, as your sisters have all fled before you: but kiss me before you go — embrace me, Jane."

"There, sir — and there!"

I pressed my lips to his once brilliant and now rayless eyes — I swept his hair from his brow, and kissed that too. He suddenly seemed to arouse himself: the conviction of the reality of all this seized him.

"It is you — is it, Jane? You are come back to me, then?"

"I am."

"And you do not lie dead in some ditch under some stream? And you are not a pining outcast amongst strangers?"

"No, sir, I am an independent woman now."

"Independent! What do you mean, Jane?"

"My uncle in Madeira is dead, and he left me five thousand pounds."

"Ah, this is practical — this is real!" he cried: "I should never dream that. Besides, there is that peculiar voice of hers, so animating and piquant, as well as soft: it cheers my withered heart; it puts life into it.— What, Janet! Are you an independent woman? A rich woman?"

"Quite rich, sir. If you won't let me live with you, I can build a house of my own close up to your door, and you may come and sit in my parlour when you want company of an evening."

"But as you are rich, Jane, you have now, no doubt, friends who will look after you, and not suffer you to devote yourself to a blind lamenter like me?"

"I told you I am independent, sir, as well as rich: I am my own mistress."

"And you will stay with me?"

"Certainly — unless you object. I will be your neighbour, your nurse, your housekeeper. I find you lonely: I will be your companion — to read to you, to walk with you, to sit with you, to wait on you, to be eyes and hands to you. Cease to look so melancholy, my dear master; you shall not be left desolate, so long as I live."

He replied not: he seemed serious — abstracted; he sighed; he half-opened his lips as if to speak: he closed them again. I felt a little embarrassed. Perhaps I had too rashly overleaped conventionalities; and he, like St. John, saw impropriety in my inconsiderateness. I had indeed made my proposal from the idea that he wished and would ask me to be his wife: an expectation, not the less certain because unexpressed, had buoyed me up, that he would claim me at once as his own. But no hint to that effect escaping him and his countenance becoming more overcast, I suddenly remembered that I might have been all wrong, and was perhaps playing the fool unwittingly: and I began gently to withdraw myself from his arms — but he eagerly snatched me closer.

"No — no — Jane; you must not go. No — I have touched you, heard you, felt the comfort of your presence — the sweetness of your consolation: I cannot give up these joys. I have little left in myself — I must have you. The world may laugh — may call me absurd, selfish — but it does not signify. My very soul demands you: it will be satisfied: or it will take deadly vengeance on its frame."

"Well, sir, I will stay with you: I have said so."

"Yes — but you understand one thing by staying with me: and I understand another. You, perhaps, could make up your mind to be about my hand and chair — to wait on me as a kind of little nurse (for you have an affectionate heart and a generous spirit, which prompt you to make sacrifices for those you pity), and that ought to suffice for me no doubt. I suppose I should now entertain none but fatherly feeling for you: do you think so? Come — tell me."

"I will think what you like, sir: I am content to be only your nurse, if you think it better."

"But you cannot always be my nurse, Janet: you are young — you must marry one day."

"I don't care about being married."

"You should care, Janet: if I were what I once was, I would try to make you care — but — a sightless block!"

He relapsed again into gloom. I, on the contrary, became more cheerful, and took fresh courage: these last words gave me an insight as to where the difficulty lay; and as it was no difficulty with me, I felt quite relieved from my previous embarrassment. I resumed a livelier vein of conversation.

"It is time some one undertook to rehumanise you," said I, parting his thick and long uncut locks; "for I see you are being metamorphosed into a lion, or something of that sort. You have a 'faux air' of Nebuchadnezzar in the fields about you, that is certain: your hair reminds me of eagles' feathers; whether your nails are grown like birds' claws or not, I have not yet noticed."

"On this arm, I have neither hand nor nails," he said, drawing the mutilated limb from his breast, and showing it to me. "It is a mere stump — a ghastly sight! Don't you think so, Jane?"

"It is a pity to see it; and a pity to see your eyes — and the scar of fire on your forehead: and the worst of it is, one is in danger of loving you too well for all this; and making too much of you."

"I thought you would be revolted, Jane, when you saw my arm, and my cicatrised visage."

"Did you? Don't tell me so — lest I should say something disparaging to your judgment. Now, let me leave you an instant, to make a better fire, and have the hearth swept up. Can you tell when there is a good fire?"

"Yes; with the right eye I see a glow — a ruddy haze."

"And you see the candles?"

"Very dimly — each is a luminous cloud."

"Can you see me?"

"No, my fairy: but I am only too thankful to hear and feel you."

"When do you take supper?"

"I never take supper."

"But you shall have some to-night. I am hungry: so are you, I daresay, only you forget."

Summoning Mary, I soon had the room in more cheerful order: I prepared him, likewise, a comfortable repast. My spirits were excited, and with pleasure and ease I talked to him during supper, and for a long time after. There was no harassing restraint, no repressing of glee and vivacity with him; for with him I was at perfect ease, because I knew I suited him: all I said or did seemed either to console or revive him. Delightful consciousness! It brought to life and light my whole nature: in his presence I thoroughly lived; and he lived in mine. Blind as he was smiles played over his face, joy dawned on his forehead: his lineaments softened and warmed.

After supper, he began to ask me many questions, of where I had been, what I had been doing, how I had found him out; but I gave him only very partial replies: it was too late to enter into particulars that night. Besides, I wished to touch no deep-thrilling chord — to open no fresh well of emotion in his heart: my sole present aim was to cheer him. Cheered, as I have said, he was: and yet but by fits. If a moment's silence broke the conversation, he would turn restless, touch me, then say, "Jane."

"You are altogether a human being, Jane? You are certain of that?"

"I conscientiously believe so, Mr. Rochester."

"Yet how, on this dark and doleful evening, could you so suddenly rise on my lone hearth? I stretched my hand to take a glass of water from a hireling, and it was given me by you: I asked a question, expecting John's wife to answer me, and your voice spoke in my ear."

"Because I had come in, in Mary's stead, with the tray."

"And there is enchantment in the very hour I am now spending with you. Who can tell what a dark, dreary, hopeless life I have dragged on for months past? Doing nothing, expecting nothing; merging night in day; feeling but the sensation of cold when I let the fire go out, of hunger when I forgot to eat: and then a ceaseless sorrow, and, at times, a very delirium of desire to behold my Jane again. Yes: for her restoration I longed, far more than for that of my lost sight. How can it be that Jane is with me, and says she loves me? Will she not depart as suddenly as she came? To-morrow, I fear I shall find her no more."

A commonplace, practical reply, out of the train of his own disturbed ideas, was I was sure, the best and most reassuring for him in this frame of mind. I passed my finger over his eyebrows, and remarked that they were scorched, and that I would apply something which should make them grow as broad and black as ever.

"Where is the use of doing me good in any way, beneficent spirit, when, at some fatal moment, you will again desert me — passing like a shadow, whither and how to me unknown; and for me, remaining afterwards undiscoverable?"

"Have you a pocket-comb about you, sir?"

"What for, Jane?"

"Just to comb out this shaggy black mane. I find you rather alarming, when I examine you close at hand: you talk of my being a fairy; but I am sure, you are more like a brownie."

"Am I hideous, Jane?"

"Very, sir: you always were, you know."

"Humph! The wickedness has not been taken out of you, wherever you have sojourned."

"Yet I have been with good people; far better than you: a hundred times better people; possessed of ideas and views you never entertained in your life: quite more refined and exalted."

"Who the deuce have you been with?"

"If you twist in that way you will make me pull the hair out of your head; and then I think you will cease to entertain doubts of my substantiality."

"Who have you been with, Jane?"

"You shall not get it out of me to-night, sir; you must wait till to-morrow; to leave my tale half-told, will, you know, be a sort of security that I shall appear at your breakfast-table to finish it. By-the-by, I must mind not to rise on your hearth with only a glass of water, then: I must bring an egg at the least, to say nothing of fried ham."

"You mocking changeling — fairy-born and human-bred! You make me feel as I have not felt these twelve months. If Saul could have had you for his David, the evil spirit would have been exorcised without the aid of the harp."

"There, sir, you are redd up and made decent. Now I'll leave you: I have been travelling these last three days, and I believe I am tired. Good-night."

"Just one word, Jane: were there only ladies in the house where you have been?"

I laughed and made my escape, still laughing as I ran upstairs. "A good idea!" I thought, with glee. "I see I have the means of fretting him out of his melancholy for some time to come."

Very early the next morning, I heard him up and astir, wandering from one room to another. As soon as Mary came down I heard the question: "Is Miss Eyre here?" Then: "Which room did you put her into? Was it dry? Is she up? Go and ask if she wants anything; and when she will come down."

I came down as soon as I thought there was a prospect of breakfast. Entering the room very softly, I had a view of him before he discovered my presence. It was mournful, indeed, to witness the subjugation of that vigorous spirit to a corporeal infirmity. He sat in his chair,— still, but not at rest: expectant evidently; the lines of now habitual sadness marking his strong features. His countenance reminded one of a lamp quenched, waiting to be relit — and alas! it was not himself that could kindle the lustre of animated expression: he was dependent on another for that office! I had meant to be gay and careless but the powerlessness of the strong man touched my heart to the quick: still I accosted him with what vivacity I could: —

"It is a bright, sunny morning, sir," I said. "The rain is over and gone, and there is a tender shining after it: you shall have a walk soon."

I had wakened the glow: his features beamed.

"Oh, you are indeed there, my skylark! Come to me. You are not gone: not vanished? I heard one of your kind an hour ago, singing high over the wood: but its song had no music for me, any more than the rising sun had rays. All the melody on earth is concentrated in my Jane's tongue to my ear (I am glad it is not naturally a silent one): all the sunshine I can feel is in her presence."

The water stood in my eyes to hear this avowal of his dependence: just as if a royal eagle, chained to a perch, should be forced to entreat a sparrow to become its purveyor. But I would not be lachrymose: I dashed off the salt drops, and busied myself with preparing breakfast.

Most of the morning was spent in the open air. I led him out of the wet and wild wood into some cheerful fields: I described to him how brilliantly green they were; how the flowers and hedges looked refreshed; how sparkling blue was the sky. I sought a seat for him in a hidden and lovely spot: a dry stump of a tree; nor did I refuse to let him, when seated, place me on his knee: why should I, when both he and I were happier near than apart? Pilot lay beside us: all was quiet. He broke out suddenly while clasping me in his arms: —

"Cruel, cruel deserter! Oh, Jane, what did I feel when I discovered you had fled from Thornfield, and when I could nowhere find you; and, after examining your apartment, ascertained that you had taken no money, nor anything which could serve as an equivalent! A pearl necklace I had given you lay untouched in its little casket; your trunks were left corded and locked as they had been prepared for the bridal tour. What could my darling do, I asked, left destitute and penniless? And what did she do? Let me hear now."

Thus urged, I began the narrative of my experience for the last year. I softened considerably what related to the three days of wandering and starvation, because to have told him all would have been to inflict unnecessary pain: the little I did say lacerated his faithful heart deeper than I wished.

I should not have left him thus, he said, without any means of making my way: I should have told him my intention. I should have confided in him: he would never have forced me to be his mistress. Violent as he had seemed in his despair, he, in truth, loved me far too well and too tenderly to constitute himself my tyrant: he would have given me half his fortune, without demanding so much as a kiss in return, rather than I should have flung myself friendless on the wide world. I had endured, he was certain, more than I had confessed to him.

"Well, whatever my sufferings had been, they were very short," I answered: and then I proceeded to tell him how I had been received at Moor House; how I had obtained the office of schoolmistress, etc. The accession of fortune, the discovery of my relations, followed in due order. Of course, St. John Rivers' name came in frequently in the progress of my tale. When I had done, that name was immediately taken up.

"This St. John, then, is your cousin?"

"Yes."

"You have spoken of him often: did you like him?"

"He was a very good man, sir; I could not help liking him."

"A good man? Does that mean a respectable, well-conducted man of fifty? Or what does it mean?"

"St. John was only twenty-nine, sir."

"'*Jeune encore,*' as the French say. Is he a person of low stature, phlegmatic, and plain? A person whose goodness consists rather in his guiltlessness of vice, than in his prowess in virtue?"

"He is untiringly active. Great and exalted deeds are what he lives to perform."

"But his brain? That is probably rather soft? He means well: but you shrug your shoulders to hear him talk?"

"He talks little, sir: what he does say is ever to the point. His brain is first-rate, I should think not impressible, but vigorous."

"Is he an able man, then?"

"Truly able."

"A thoroughly educated man?"

"St. John is an accomplished and profound scholar."

"His manners, I think you said, are not to your taste? — priggish and parsonic?"

"I never mentioned his manners; but, unless I had a very bad taste, they must suit it; they are polished, calm, and gentlemanlike."

"His appearance,— I forget what description you gave of his appearance;— a sort of raw curate, half strangled with his white neckcloth, and stilted up on his thick-soled highlows, eh?"

"St. John dresses well. He is a handsome man: tall, fair with blue eyes, and a Grecian profile."

(*Aside.*) "Damn him!"—(*To me.*) "Did you like him, Jane?"

"Yes, Mr. Rochester, I liked him: but you asked me that before."

I perceived, of course, the drift of my interlocutor. Jealousy had got hold of him: she stung him; but the sting was salutary: it gave him respite from the gnawing fang of melancholy. I would not, therefore, immediately charm the snake.

"Perhaps you would rather not sit any longer on my knee, Miss Eyre?" was the next somewhat unexpected observation.

"Why not, Mr. Rochester?"

"The picture you have just drawn is suggestive of a rather too overwhelming contrast. Your words have delineated very prettily a graceful Apollo: he is present to your imagination,—tall, fair, blue-eyed, and with a Grecian profile. Your eyes dwell on a Vulcan,—a real blacksmith, brown, broad-shouldered; and blind and lame into the bargain."

"I never thought of it, before; but you certainly are rather like Vulcan, sir."

"Well,—you can leave me, ma'am: but before you go" (and he retained me by a firmer grasp than ever), "you will be pleased just to answer me a question or two." He paused.

"What questions, Mr. Rochester?"

Then followed this cross-examination.

"St. John made you schoolmistress of Morton before he knew you were his cousin?"

"Yes."

"You would often see him? He would visit the school sometimes?"

"Daily."

"He would approve of your plans, Jane? I know they would be clever, for you are a talented creature."

"He approved of them—yes."

"He would discover many things in you he could not have expected to find? Some of your accomplishments are not ordinary."

"I don't know about that."

"You had a little cottage near the school, you say: did he ever come there to see you?"

"Now and then?"

"Of an evening?"

"Once or twice."

A pause.

"How long did you reside with him and his sisters after the cousinship was discovered?"

"Five months."

"Did Rivers spend much time with the ladies of his family?"

"Yes; the back parlour was both his study and ours: he sat near the window, and we by the table."

"Did he study much?"

"A good deal."

"What?"

"Hindostanee."

"And what did you do meantime?"

"I learnt German, at first."

"Did he teach you?"

"He did not understand German."

"Did he teach you nothing?"

"A little Hindostanee."

"Rivers taught you Hindostanee?"

"Yes, sir."

"And his sisters also?"

"No."

"Only you?"

"Only me."

"Did you ask to learn?"

"No."

"He wished to teach you?"

"Yes."

A second pause.

"Why did he wish it? Of what use could Hindostanee be to you?"

"He intended me to go with him to India."

"Ah! here I reach the root of the matter. He wanted you to marry him?"

"He asked me to marry him."

"That is a fiction — an impudent invention to vex me."

"I beg your pardon, it is the literal truth: he asked me more than once, and was as stiff about urging his point as ever you could be."

"Miss Eyre, I repeat it, you can leave me. How often am I to say the same thing? Why do you remain pertinaciously perched on my knee, when I have given you notice to quit?"

"Because I am comfortable there."

"No, Jane, you are not comfortable there, because your heart is not with me: it is with this cousin — this St. John. Oh, till this moment, I thought my little Jane was all mine! I had a belief she loved me even when she left me: that was an atom of sweet in much bitter. Long as we have been parted, hot tears as I have wept over our separation, I never thought that while I was mourning her, she was loving another! But it is useless grieving. Jane, leave me: go and marry Rivers."

"Shake me off, then, sir,— push me away, for I'll not leave you of my own accord."

"Jane, I ever like your tone of voice: it still renews hope, it sounds so truthful. When I hear it, it carries me back a year. I forget that you have formed a new tie. But I am not a fool — go"——

"Where must I go, sir?"

"Your own way — with the husband you have chosen."

"Who is that?"

"You know — this St. John Rivers."

"He is not my husband, nor ever will be. He does not love me: I do not love him. He loves (as he *can* love, and that is not as you love) a beautiful young lady called Rosamond. He wanted to marry me only because he thought I should make a suitable missionary's wife, which she would not have done. He is good and great, but severe; and, for me, cold as an iceberg. He is not like you, sir: I am not happy at his side, nor near him, nor with him. He has no indulgence for me — no fondness. He sees nothing attractive in me; not even youth — only a few useful mental points.— Then I must leave you, sir, to go to him?"

I shuddered involuntarily, and clung instinctively closer to my blind but beloved master. He smiled.

"What, Jane! Is this true? Is such really the state of matters between you and Rivers?"

"Absolutely, sir. Oh, you need not be jealous! I wanted to tease you a little to make you less sad: I thought anger would be better than grief. But if you wish me to love you, could you but see how much I *do* love you, you would be proud and content. All my heart is yours, sir: it belongs to you; and with you it would remain, were fate to exile the rest of me from your presence for ever."

Again, as he kissed me, painful thoughts darkened his aspect.

"My seared vision! My crippled strength!" he murmured regretfully.

I caressed, in order to soothe him. I knew of what he was thinking, and wanted to speak for him; but dared not. As he turned aside his face a minute, I saw a tear slide from under the sealed eyelid and trickle down the manly cheek. My heart swelled.

"I am no better than the old lightning-struck chestnut-tree in Thornfield orchard," he remarked, ere long. "And what right would that ruin have to bid a budding woodbine cover its decay with freshness?"

"You are no ruin, sir — no lightning-struck tree: you are green and vigorous. Plants will grow about your roots, whether you ask them or not, because they take delight in your bountiful shadow; and as they grow they will lean towards you, and wind round you, because your strength offers them so safe a prop."

Again he smiled: I gave him comfort.

"You speak of friends, Jane?" he asked.

"Yes; of friends," I answered, rather hesitatingly: for I knew I meant more than friends, but could not tell what other word to employ. He helped me!

"Ah! Jane. But I want a wife."

"Do you, sir?"

"Yes: is it news to you?"

"Of course: you said nothing about it before."

"Is it unwelcome news?"

"That depends on circumstances, sir — on your choice."

"Which you shall make for me, Jane. I will abide by your decision."

"Choose then, sir — *her who loves you best.*"

"I will at least choose — *her I love best.* Jane, will you marry me?"

"Yes, sir."

"A poor blind man, whom you will have to lead about by the hand?"

"Yes, sir."

"A crippled man, twenty years older than you, whom you will have to wait on?"

"Yes, sir."

"Truly, Jane?"

"Most truly, sir."

"Oh! my darling! God bless you and reward you!"

"Mr. Rochester, if ever I did a good deed in my life — if ever I thought a good thought — if ever I prayed a sincere and blameless prayer — if ever I wished a righteous wish,— I am rewarded now. To be your wife is, for me, to be as happy as I can be on earth."

"Because you delight in sacrifice."

"Sacrifice! What do I sacrifice? Famine for food, expectation for content. To be privileged to put my arms round what I value — to press my lips to what I love — to repose on what I trust: is that to make a sacrifice? If so, then certainly I delight in sacrifice."

"And to bear with my infirmities, Jane: to overlook my deficiencies."

"Which are none, sir, to me. I love you better now, when I can really be useful to you, than I did in your state of proud independence, when you disdained every part but that of the giver and protector."

"Hitherto I have hated to be helped — to be led: henceforth, I feel, I shall hate it no more. I did not like to put my hand into a hireling's, but it is pleasant to feel it circled by Jane's little fingers. I preferred utter loneliness to the constant attendance of servants; but Jane's soft ministry will be a perpetual joy. Jane suits me: do I suit her?"

"To the finest fibre of my nature, sir."

"The case being so, we have nothing in the world to wait for: we must be married instantly."

He looked and spoke with eagerness: his old impetuosity was rising.

"We must become one flesh without any delay, Jane: there is but the licence to get — then we marry."

"Mr. Rochester, I have just discovered the sun is far declined from its meridian, and Pilot is actually gone home to his dinner. Let me look at your watch."

"Fasten it into your girdle, Janet, and keep it henceforward: I have no use for it."

"It is nearly four o'clock in the afternoon, sir. Don't you feel hungry?"

"The third day from this must be our wedding-day, Jane. Never mind fine clothes and jewels, now: all that is not worth a fillip."

"The sun has dried up all the rain-drops, sir. The breeze is still: it is quite hot."

"Do you know, Jane, I have your little pearl necklace at this moment fastened round my bronze scrag under my cravat? I have worn it since the day I lost my only treasure: as a memento of her."

"We will go home through the wood: that will be the shadiest way."

He pursued his own thought without heeding me.

"Jane! you think me, I daresay, an irreligious dog: but my heart swells with gratitude to the beneficent God of this earth just now. He sees not as man sees, but far clearer: judges not as man judges, but far more wisely. I did wrong: I would have sullied my innocent flower — breathed guilt on its purity: the Omnipotent snatched it from me. I, in my stiff-necked rebellion, almost cursed the dispensation: instead of bending to the decree, I defied it. Divine justice pursued its course; disasters came thick on me: I was forced to pass through the valley of the shadow of death. *His* chastisements are mighty; and one smote me which has humbled me forever. You know I was proud of my strength: but what is it now, when I must give it over to foreign guidance, as a child does its weakness? Of late, Jane — only — only of late — I began to see and acknowledge the hand of God in my doom. I began to experience remorse, repentance; the wish for reconcilement to my Maker. I began sometimes to pray: very brief prayers they were, but very sincere.

"Some days since: nay, I can number them — four; it was last Monday night, a singular mood came over me: one in which grief replaced frenzy — sorrow, sullenness. I had long had the impression that since I could nowhere find you, you must be dead. Late that night — perhaps it might be between eleven and twelve o'clock — ere I retired to my dreary rest, I supplicated God, that, if it seemed good to Him, I might soon be taken from this life, and admitted to that world to come, where there was still hope of rejoining Jane.

"I was in my own room, and sitting by the window, which was open: it soothed me to feel the balmy night-air; though I could see no stars, and only by a vague, luminous haze, knew the presence of a moon. I longed for thee, Jane! Oh, I longed for thee both soul and flesh! I asked of God, at once in anguish and humility, if I had not been long enough desolate, afflicted, tormented; and might not soon taste bliss and peace once more. That I merited all I endured, I acknowledged — that I could scarcely endure more, I pleaded; and the alpha and omega of my heart's wishes broke involuntarily from my lips in the words — 'Jane! Jane! Jane!'"

"Did you speak these words aloud?"

"I did, Jane. If any listener heard me, he would have thought me mad: I pronounced them with such frantic energy."

"And it was last Monday night: somewhere near midnight?"

"Yes; but the time is of no consequence: what followed is the strange point. You will think me superstitious,— some superstition I have in my blood, and always had: nevertheless, this is true — true at least it is that I heard what I now relate.

"As I exclaimed 'Jane! Jane! Jane!' a voice — I cannot tell whence the voice came, but I know whose voice it was — replied, 'I am coming: wait for me;' and a moment after, went whispering on the wind, the words — 'Where are you?'

"I'll tell you, if I can, the idea, the picture these words opened to my mind: yet it is difficult to express what I want to express. Ferndean is buried, as you see, in a heavy wood, where sound falls dull, and dies unreverberating. 'Where are you?' seemed spoken amongst mountains; for I heard a hill-sent echo repeat the words. Cooler and fresher at the moment the gale seemed to visit my brow: I could have deemed that in some wild, lone scene, I and Jane were meeting. In spirit, I believe we must have met. You no doubt were, at that hour, in unconscious sleep, Jane: perhaps your soul wandered from its cell to comfort mine: for those were your accents — as certain as I live — they were yours!"

Reader, it was on Monday night — near midnight — that I too had received the mysterious summons: those were the very words by which I replied to it. I listened to Mr. Rochester's narrative; but made no disclosure in return. The coincidence struck me as too awful and inexplicable to be communicated or discussed. If I told anything, my tale would be such as must necessarily make a profound impression on the mind of my hearer: and that mind, yet from its sufferings too prone to gloom, needed not the deeper shade of the supernatural. I kept these things then, and pondered them in my heart.

"You cannot now wonder," continued my master, "that when you rose upon me so unexpectedly last night, I had difficulty in believing you any other than a mere voice and vision: something that would melt to silence and annihilation, as the midnight whisper and mountain echo had melted before. Now, I thank God! I knew it to be otherwise. Yes, I thank God!"

He put me off his knee, rose, and reverently lifting his hat from his brow, and bending his sightless eyes to the earth, he stood in mute devotion. Only the last words of the worship were audible.

"I thank my Maker, that in the midst of judgment he has remembered mercy. I humbly entreat my Redeemer to give me strength to lead henceforth a purer life than I have done hiterto!"

Then he stretched out his hand to be led, I took that dear hand, held it a moment to my lips, then let it pass around my shoulder: being so much lower in stature than he, I served both for his prop and guide. We entered the wood, and wended homeward.

# CHAPTER XXXVIII

## CONCLUSION

READER, I married him. A quiet wedding we had: he and I, the parson and clerk, were alone present. When we got back from church, I went into the kitchen of the manor-house, where Mary was cooking the dinner, and John cleaning the knives, and I said:—

"Mary, I have been married to Mr. Rochester this morning." The housekeeper and her husband were both of that decent phlegmatic order of people, to whom one may at any time safely communicate a remarkable piece of news without incurring the danger of having one's ears pierced by some shrill ejaculation, and subsequently stunned by a torrent of wordy wonderment. Mary did look up, and she did stare at me: the ladle with which she was basting a pair of chickens roasting at the fire, did for some three minutes hang suspended in the air; and for the same space of time John's knives also had a rest from the polishing process: but Mary, bending again over the roast, said only—

"Have you, Miss? Well, for sure!"

A short time after she pursued: "I seed you go out with the master, but I didn't know you were gone to church to be wed;" and she basted away. John, when I turned to him, was grinning from ear to ear.

"I telled Mary how it would be," he said: "I knew what Mr. Edward" (John was an old servant, and had known his master when he was the cadet of the house, therefore, he often gave him his Christian name)—"I knew what Mr. Edward would do; and I was certain he would not wait long neither: and he's done right, for aught I know. I wish you joy, Miss!" and he politely pulled his forelock.

"Thank you, John. Mr. Rochester told me to give you and Mary this." I put into his hand a five-pound note. Without waiting to hear more, I left the kitchen. In passing the door of the sanctum some time after, I caught the words,—

"She'll happen do better for him nor ony o' t' grand ladies." And again, "If she ben't one o' th' handsomest, she's noan faâl and varry good-natured; and i' his een she's fairly beautiful, onybody may see that."

I wrote to Moor House and to Cambridge immediately, to say what I had done: fully explaining also why I had thus acted. Diana and Mary approved the step unreservedly. Diana announced that she would just give me time to get over the honey-moon, and then she would come and see me.

"She had better not wait till then, Jane," said Mr. Rochester, when I read her letter to him; "if she does, she will be too late, for our honey-moon will outshine our life-long: its beams will only fade over your grave or mine."

How St. John received the news, I don't know; he never answered the letter in which I communicated it; yet six months after he wrote to me; without, however, mentioning Mr. Rochester's name, or alluding to my marriage. His letter was then calm; and, though very serious, kind. He has maintained a regular, though not frequent correspondence ever since; he hopes I am happy, and trusts I am not of those who live without God in the world, and only mind earthly things.

You have not quite forgotten little Adèle, have you, reader? I had not; I soon asked and obtained leave of Mr. Rochester, to go and see her at the school where he had placed her. Her frantic joy at beholding me again moved me much. She looked pale and thin; she said she was not happy. I found the rules of the establishment were too strict, its course of study too severe, for a child of her age: I took her home with me. I meant to become her governess once more; but I soon found this impracticable; my time and cares were now required by another — my husband needed them all. So I sought out a school conducted on a more indulgent system; and near enough to permit of my visiting her often, and bringing her home sometimes. I took care she should never want for anything that could contribute to her comfort; she soon settled in her new abode, became very happy there, and made fair progress in her studies. As she grew up, a sound English education corrected in a great measure her French defects; and when she left school, I found her a pleasing and obliging companion: docile, good-tempered, and well-principled. By her grateful attention to me and mine, she has long since well repaid any little kindness I ever had it in my power to offer her.

My tale draws to its close: one word respecting my experience of married life, and one brief glance at the fortunes of those whose names have most frequently recurred in this narrative, and I have done.

I have now been married ten years. I know what it is to live entirely for and with what I love best on earth. I hold myself supremely blest — blest beyond what language can express; because I am my husband's life as fully as he is mine. No woman was ever nearer to her mate than I am: ever more absolutely bone of his bone, flesh of his flesh. I know no weariness of my Edward's society: he knows none of mine, any more than we each do of the pulsation of the heart that beats in our separate bosoms; consequently, we are ever together. To be together is for us to be at once as free as in solitude, as gay as in company. We talk, I believe, all day long; to talk to each other is but a more animated and an audible thinking. All my confidence is bestowed on him, all his confidence is devoted to me; we are precisely suited in character — perfect concord is the result.

Mr. Rochester continued blind the first two years of our union: perhaps it was that circumstance that drew us so very near — that knit us so very close! for I was then his vision, as I am still his right hand. Literally, I was (what he often called me) the apple of his eye. He saw nature — he saw books through me; and never did I weary of gazing for his behalf, and of putting into words the effect of field, tree, town, river, cloud, sunbeam — of the landscape before us; of the weather round us — and impressing by sound on his ear what light could no longer stamp on his eye. Never did I weary of reading to him; never did I weary of conducting him where he wished to go: of doing for him what he wished to be done. And there was a pleasure in my services, most full, most exquisite, even though sad — because he claimed these services without painful shame or damping humiliation. He loved me so truly, that he knew no reluctance in profiting by my attendance: he felt that I loved him so fondly, that to yield that attendance was to indulge my sweetest wishes.

One morning at the end of the two years, as I was writing a letter to his dictation, he came and bent over me and said —

"Jane, have you a glittering ornament round your neck?"

I had a gold watch-chain: I answered "Yes."

"And have you a pale blue dress on?"

I had. He informed me then, that for some time he had fancied the obscurity clouding one eye was becoming less dense; and that now he was sure of it.

He and I went up to London. He had the advice of an eminent oculist: and he eventually recovered the sight of that one eye. He cannot now see very distinctly: he cannot read or write much; but he can find his way without being led by the hand; the sky is no longer a blank to him — the earth no longer a void. When his first-born was put into his arms, he could see that the boy had inherited his own eyes, as they once were — large, brilliant, and black. On that occasion, he again, with a full heart, acknowledged that God had tempered judgment with mercy.

My Edward and I, then, are happy: and the more so, because those we most love are happy likewise. Diana and Mary Rivers are both married: alternately, once every year, they come to see us, and we go to see them. Diana's husband is a captain in the navy; a gallant officer and a good man. Mary's is a clergyman; a college friend of her brother's; and, from his attainments and principles, worthy of the connection. Both Captain Fitzjames and Mr. Wharton love their wives, and are loved by them.

As to St. John Rivers, he left England: he went to India. He entered on the path he had marked for himself; he pursues it still. A more resolute, indefatigable pioneer never wrought amidst rocks and dangers. Firm, faithful, and devoted; full of energy, and zeal, and truth, he labours for his race: he clears their painful way to improvement: he hews down like a giant the prejudices of creed and caste that encumber it. He may be stern; he may be exacting; he may be ambitious yet; but his is the sternness of the warrior Great-Heart, who guards his pilgrim convoy from the onslaught of Apollyon. His is the exaction of the apostle, who speaks but for Christ, when he says —"Whosoever will come after me, let him deny himself, and take up his cross and follow me." His is the ambition of the high master-spirit, which aims to fill a place in the first rank of those who are redeemed from the earth — who stand without fault before the throne of God; who share the last mighty victories of the Lamb; who are called, and chosen, and faithful.

St. John is unmarried: he never will marry now. Himself has hitherto sufficed to the toil; and the toil draws near its close: his glorious sun hastens to its setting. The last letter I received from him drew from my eyes human tears, and yet filled my heart with Divine joy: he anticipated his sure reward, his incorruptible crown. I know that a stranger's hand will write me next, to say that the good and faithful servant has been called at length into the joy of his Lord. And why weep for this? No fear of death will darken St. John's last hour: his mind will be unclouded: his heart will be undaunted: his hope will be sure; his faith stedfast. His own words are a pledge of this:—

"My Master," he says, "has forewarned me. Daily he announces more distinctly,—'Surely I come, quickly!' and hourly I more eagerly respond,—'Amen; even so come, Lord Jesus!'"

**THE END**